Carnegie Learning Advanced Algebra

Student Edition

Volume 1

Carnegie Learning

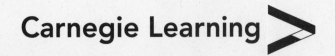

Carnegie Learning

437 Grant St., Suite 918
Pittsburgh, PA 15219
Phone 412.690.2442
Customer Service Phone 877.401.2527
Fax 412.690.2444

www.carnegielearning.com

Chapter 1 © iStockphoto.com/marekuliasz;
Chapter 2 © iStockphoto.com/Cristian Baitg;
Chapter 3 © David Rivera/Aquarium of the Pacific;
Chapter 4 © istockphoto.com/Alistair Forrester Shankie;
Chapter 5 © istockphoto.com/Steve Maehl;
Chapter 6 © istockphoto.com/Carolina K. Smith, M.D.;
Chapter 7 © istockphoto.com/Ryan Kelly;
Chapter 8 © istockphoto.com/Florin Tirlea;

ISBN: 978-1-60972-246-3
Student Edition, Advanced Algebra, Volume 1

Printed in the United States of America
1-12/2013 B&B

Dear Student,

You are about to begin an exciting endeavor using mathematics! To be successful, you will need the right tools. This book is one of the most important tools you will use this year. Throughout this book there is space for note-taking, sketching, and calculating. You will be given opportunities to think and reason about various mathematical concepts and use tools such as tables, graphs, and graphing calculators.

This year you will face many new challenges both in and outside of the classroom. While some challenges may seem difficult, it is important to remember that effort matters. You must realize that it may take hard work and perseverance to succeed—and your hard work will pay off!

Connections in mathematics are important. Throughout this text, you will build new knowledge based upon your prior knowledge. It is our goal that you see mathematics as relevant because it provides a common and useful language for discussing and solving real-world problems.

I bet the folks at home would like to know what we're going to do this year!

Don't worry—you will not be working alone. Working with others is a skill that you will need throughout your life. When you begin your career, you will most likely work with all sorts of people, from shy to outgoing, from leaders to supporters, from innovators to problem solvers—and many more types of people! Throughout this book, you will have many opportunities to work with your classmates. You will be able to discuss your ideas and predictions to different problem situations; present your calculations and solutions to questions; and analyze, critique and suggest, or support your classmates' answers to problem situations.

Today's workplace demands teamwork and self-confidence. At Carnegie Learning, our goal is to provide you with opportunities to be successful in your math course. Enjoy the year and have fun Learning by Doing™!

—The Carnegie Learning Curriculum Development Team

Acknowledgments

Carnegie Learning Authoring Team

- Sandy Bartle
  Senior Academic Officer
- David Dengler
  Sr. Director, Curriculum Development
- Michael Amick
  Math Editor
- Joshua Fisher
  Math Editor
- Allison Dockter
  Math Editor
- John Fitsioris
  Curriculum Developer
- Danielle Kandrack
  Math Editor
- Beth Karambelkar
  Curriculum Developer
- David "Augie" Rivera
  Math Editor
- Lezlee Ross
  Curriculum Developer

Contributing Author

- Dr. Mary Lou Metz
- Jaclyn Snyder

Vendors

- Cenveo Publisher Services
- Mathematical Expressions
- Bookmasters, Inc.
- Hess Print Solutions
- Bradford & Bigelow
- Mind Over Media
- Lapiz
- eInstruction

Special Thanks

- Carnegie Learning Managers of School Partnerships for their content review.
- Teacher reviewers and students for their input and review of lesson content.
- Carnegie Learning Software Development Team for their contributions to research and content.
- William S. Hadley for being a mentor to the development team, his leadership, and his pedagogical pioneering in mathematics education.
- Amy Jones Lewis for her review of content.
- Colleen Wolfe for project management.

Table of Contents

5 Polynomial Functions 313

6 Polynomial Expressions and Equations 423

Table of Contents

The Crew

The Crew is here to help you throughout the text. Sometimes they will remind you about things you have already learned. Sometimes they will ask you questions to help you think about different strategies. Sometimes they will share fun facts. They are members of your group—someone you can rely on!

Teacher aides will guide you along your way. They will help you make connections and remind you to think about the details.

Mathematical Representations

Introduction

During this course, you will solve problems and work with many different representations of mathematical concepts, ideas, and processes to better understand the world. Each lesson will provide you with opportunities to discuss your ideas, work within groups, and share your solutions and methods with your class. These process icons are placed throughout the text.

Discuss to Understand

- Read the problem carefully.
- What is the context of the problem? Do we understand it?
- What is the question that we are being asked? Does it make sense?
- Is this problem similar to some other problem we know?

Think for Yourself

- Do I need any additional information to answer the question?
- Is this problem similar to some other problem that I know?
- How can I represent the problem using a picture, a diagram, symbols, or some other representation?

Work with Your Partner

- How did you do the problem?
- Show me your representation.
- This is the way I thought about the problem—how did you think about it?
- What else do we need to solve the problem?
- Does our reasoning and our answer make sense to each other?
- How will we explain our solution to the class?

Share with the Class

- Here is our solution and the methods we used.
- Are we communicating our strategies clearly?
- We could only get this far with our solution. How can we finish?
- Could we have used a different strategy to solve the problem?

Academic Glossary

Key Terms of the Course

There are important terms you will encounter throughout this book. It is important that you have an understanding of these words as you get started through the mathematical concepts. Knowing what is meant by these terms and using these terms will help you think, reason, and communicate your ideas. The Graphic Organizers shown display a definition for a key term, related words, sample questions, and examples.

You will see these terms throughout each lesson.

Definition

To study or look closely for patterns.

Analyzing can involve examining or breaking a concept down into smaller parts to gain a better understanding of it.

Related Words

- examine
- evaluate
- determine
- observe
- consider
- investigate
- what do you notice?
- what do you think?
- sort and match
- identify

Ask Yourself

- Do I see any patterns?
- Have I seen something like this before?
- What happens if the shape, representation, or numbers change?
- What is the question asking me to accomplish?
- What is the context?
- What does the solution mean in terms of this problem situation?

Analyze

Example

PROBLEM 1 Feeling a Little Congested

City planners consider building a new stadium on several acres of land close to the downtown of a large city. They monitored the number of cars entering and exiting downtown from a major highway between 1:00 PM and 7:00 PM to determine current traffic conditions.

1. Analyze the table of values that represent the average number of cars entering and exiting downtown during the given hours of a typical weekday. The value for time represents the start-time for the full hour over which the vehicles were monitored.

Time (PM)	Average Number of Vehicles on a Typical Weekday (thousands)
1:00	7.0
2:00	10.8
3:00	14.5
4:00	21.1
5:00	23.9
6:00	19.0
7:00	10.0

When entering the data into your calculator, enter 1:00 as 1, 2:00 as 2, 3:00 as 3, etc.

a. Describe any patterns you notice. Explain the patterns in the context of this problem situation.

The number of cars increase, reach a maximum at 5:00 PM, and then decrease again. This pattern makes sense in the context of this problem because rush hour occurs around 5:00 PM.

b. Predict the type of polynomial that best fits the data. Explain your reasoning.

Answers will vary.

The data increases and then decreases. The curve appears to be quadratic.

Academic Glossary

Definition

To give details or describe how to determine an answer or solution.

Explaining your reasoning helps justify conclusions.

Related Words

- show your work
- explain your calculation
- justify
- why or why not?

Ask Yourself

- How should I organize my thoughts?
- Is my explanation logical?
- Does my reasoning make sense?
- How can I justify my answer to others?
- Did I use complete sentences in my answer?

Don't forget to check your answers!

Explain Your Reasoning

Academic Glossary

Example

12. Circle the function(s) shown that could describe the given graph. Explain your reasoning.

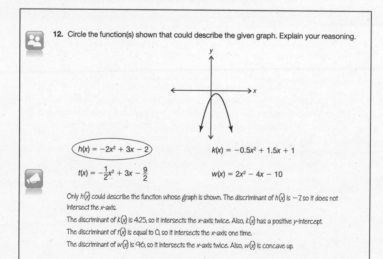

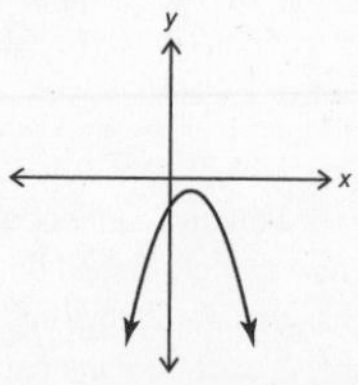
y
x

$h(x) = -2x^2 + 3x - 2$ (circled)

$k(x) = -0.5x^2 + 1.5x + 1$

$t(x) = -\frac{1}{2}x^2 + 3x - \frac{9}{2}$

$w(x) = 2x^2 - 4x - 10$

Only $h(x)$ could describe the function whose graph is shown. The discriminant of $h(x)$ is -7, so it does not intersect the x-axis.

The discriminant of $k(x)$ is 4.25, so it intersects the x-axis twice. Also, $k(x)$ has a positive y-intercept.

The discriminant of $t(x)$ is equal to 0, so it intersects the x-axis one time.

The discriminant of $w(x)$ is 96, so it intersects the x-axis twice. Also, $w(x)$ is concave up.

Definition

To display information in various ways.

Representing mathematics can be done using words, tables, graphs, or symbols.

Related Words

- show
- sketch
- draw
- create
- plot
- graph
- write an equation
- complete the table

Ask Yourself

- How should I organize my thoughts?
- How do I use this model to show a concept or idea?
- What does this representation tell me?
- Is my representation accurate?
- What units or labels should I include?
- Are there other ways to model this concept?

Represent

Example

PROBLEM 4 Just Another Day at the Circus

Write a quadratic function to represent each situation using the given information. Be sure to define your variables.

1. The Amazing Larry is a human cannonball. He would like to reach a maximum height of 30 feet during his next launch. Based on Amazing Larry's previous launches, his assistant DaJuan has estimated that this will occur when he is 40 feet from the cannon. When Amazing Larry is shot from the cannon, he is 10 feet above the ground. Write a function to represent Amazing Larry's height in terms of his distance.

   Let $h(d)$ represent Amazing Larry's height in terms of his distance, d.

   $h(d) = a(d - 40)^2 + 30$

   $10 = a(0 - 40)^2 + 30$

   $10 = 1600a + 30$

   $-20 = 1600a$

   $-\frac{1}{80} = a$

   $h(d) = -\frac{1}{80}(d - 40)^2 + 30$

Academic Glossary

Definition

To declare or tell in advance based on the analysis of given data.

Predicting first helps inform reasoning.

Related Words

- estimate
- approximate
- expect
- about how much?

Ask Yourself

- What do I know about this problem situation?
- What predictions can I make from this problem situation?
- Does my reasoning make sense?
- Is my solution close to my estimation?

Predict

Example

In the problem, *You're So Square*, you added the functions $w(n)$ and $g(n)$ algebraically to create a new function $t(n)$. Manipulating algebraic representations is a common method for building new functions. However, you can also build new functions graphically. Let's consider two graphs of functions on a coordinate plane and what happens when you add, subtract, or multiply the output values of each.

1. Analyze the graphs of $f(x)$ and $g(x)$.

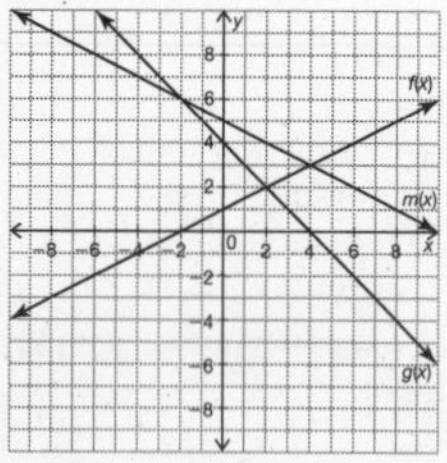

a. Predict the function family of $m(x)$ if $m(x) = f(x) + g(x)$. Explain your reasoning.

The function $m(x)$ will belong to the linear function family.
I know this because $f(x)$ and $g(x)$ are both linear.

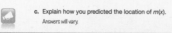

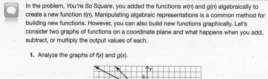

You are just predicting right now, so mistakes are OK. You will return to this graph at the end of this problem.

b. Predict and sketch the graph of $m(x)$.

See graph.

c. Explain how you predicted the location of $m(x)$.

Answers will vary.

Academic Glossary

Definition

To represent or give an account of in words.

Describing communicates mathematical ideas to others.

Related Words

- demonstrate
- label
- display
- compare
- define
- determine
- what are the advantages?
- what are the disadvantages?
- what is similar?
- what is different?

Ask Yourself

- How should I organize my thoughts?
- Is my explanation logical?
- Did I consider the context of this situation?
- Does my reasoning make sense?
- Did I use complete sentences in my answer?
- Did I include appropriate units and labels?
- Will my classmates understand my reasoning?

Describe

Example

2. Analyze the graphs of the functions shown. Describe why each function is not a polynomial function.

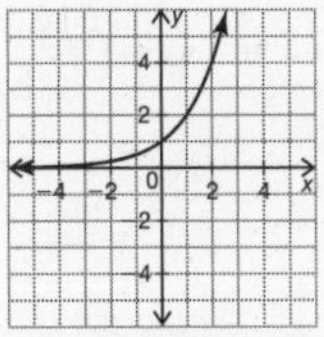

As *x* approaches negative infinity, *f*(*x*) approaches 0, therefore not positive or negative infinity.

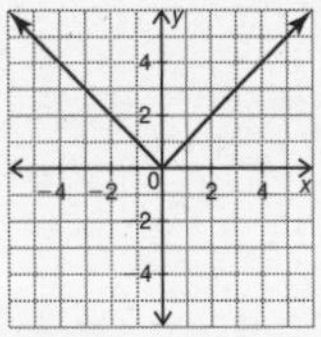

The graph is not a smooth curve. A linear function is the only polynomial that is a straight line and this function is not linear.

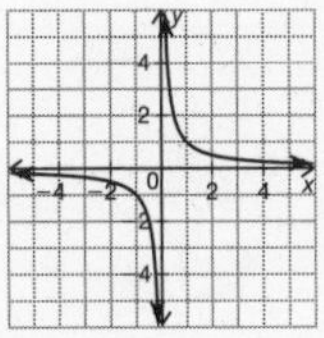

The graph is not continuous.

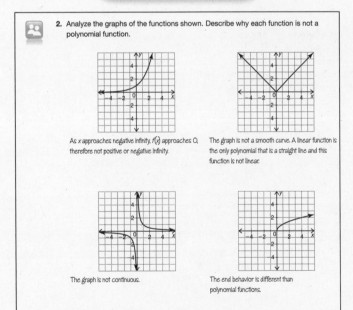

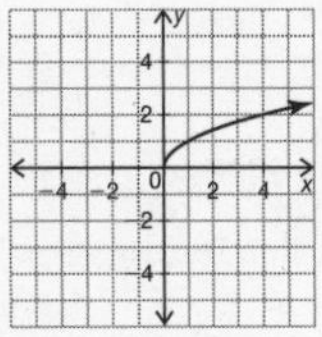

The end behavior is different than polynomial functions.

Problem Types You Will See

Worked Example

WHEN YOU SEE A WORKED EXAMPLE

- Take your time to read through it,
- Question your own understanding, and
- Think about the connections between steps.

ASK YOURSELF

- What is the main idea?
- How would this work if I changed the numbers?
- Have I used these strategies before?

You can use reference points to graph the function $d(x) = f\left(\frac{1}{3}x\right)$ when $f(x) = x^2$.

From $d(x)$ you know that $C = 0$, $D = 0$, and $B = \frac{1}{3}$. The vertex for $d(x)$ is (0, 0).

Notice $0 < |B| < 1$ so the graph will horizontally stretch by a factor of $\frac{1}{\frac{1}{3}}$ or 3.

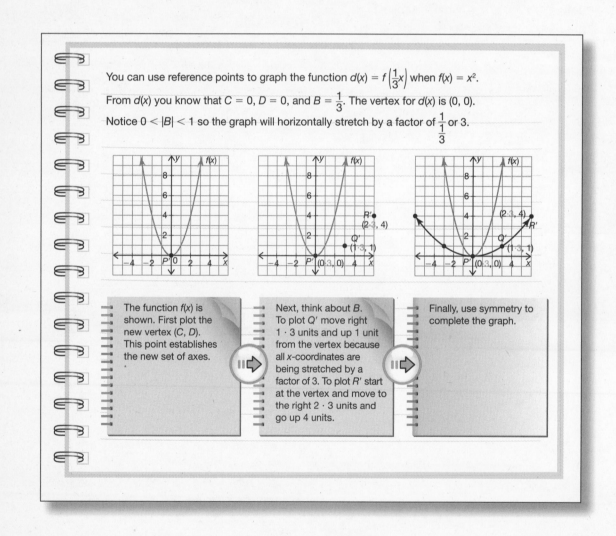

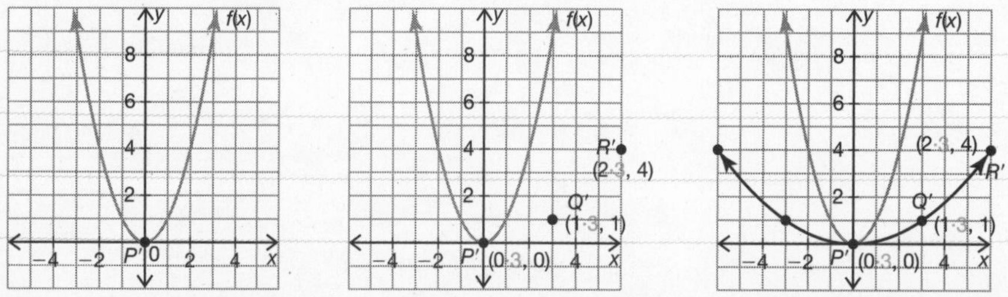

The function $f(x)$ is shown. First plot the new vertex (C, D). This point establishes the new set of axes.

Next, think about B. To plot Q' move right $1 \cdot 3$ units and up 1 unit from the vertex because all x-coordinates are being stretched by a factor of 3. To plot R' start at the vertex and move to the right $2 \cdot 3$ units and go up 4 units.

Finally, use symmetry to complete the graph.

Thumbs Down

WHEN YOU SEE A THUMBS DOWN ICON

- Take your time to read through the *incorrect* solution.
- Think about what error was made.

ASK YOURSELF

- Where is the error?
- Why is it an error?
- How can I correct it?

5. Emily makes an observation about the number of imaginary zeros a cubic function may have.

> **Emily**
>
> A cubic function must have three zeros. I know this from the Fundamental Theorem. However, the number of real and imaginary zeros can vary. The function may have 0, 1, 2, or 3 imaginary zeros.

Explain the error in Emily's reasoning.

If a cubic function has imaginary roots, those imaginary roots come from the quadratic function that builds the cubic function. The imaginary roots will appear only in pairs when the quadratic function never intersects the x-axis. Therefore, the number of imaginary zeros a cubic function may have is 0 or 2 imaginary roots.

Problem Types

Thumbs Up

WHEN YOU SEE A THUMBS UP ICON

- Take your time to read through the *correct* solution.
- Think about the connections between steps.

ASK YOURSELF

- Why is this method correct?
- Have I used this method before?

4. Christine and Kate were asked to determine the vertex of two different quadratic functions each written in different forms. Analyze their calculations.

Christine

$f(x) = 2x^2 + 12x + 10$

The quadratic function is in standard form. So I know the axis of symmetry is $x = \frac{-b}{2a}$.

$x = \frac{-12}{2(2)}$

$= -3.$

Now that I know the axis of symmetry, I can substitute that value into the function to determine the y-coordinate of the vertex.

$f(-3) = 2(-3)^2 + 12(-3) + 10$

$= 2(9) - 36 + 10$

$= 18 - 36 + 10$

$= 8$

Therefore, the vertex is (3, 8).

Kate

$g(x) = \frac{1}{2}(x + 3)(x - 7)$

The form of the function tells me the x-intercepts are −3 and 7. I also know the x-coordinate of the vertex will be directly in the middle of the x-intercepts. So, all I have to do is calculate the average.

$x = \frac{-3 + 7}{2}$

$= \frac{4}{2} = 2$

Now that I know the x-coordinate of the vertex, I can substitute that value into the function to determine the y-coordinate.

$g(2) = \frac{1}{2}(2 + 3)(2 - 7)$

$= \frac{1}{2}(5)(-5)$

$= -12.5$

Therefore, the vertex is (2, −12.5).

a. How are these methods similar? How are they different?

Both methods require that you determine the axis of symmetry, and then substitute that value into the function to determine the *y*-coordinate of the vertex.

The methods are different in the ways the axis of symmetry was determined. Christine used $x = \frac{-b}{2a}$ and Kate used $x = \frac{r_1 + r_2}{2}$.

b. What must Kate do to use Christine's method?

Kate knows the *a*-value from the form of her quadratic equation. She must multiply the terms together and combine like terms. She would then have a quadratic function in standard form to determine the *b*-value.

c. What must Christine do to use Kate's method?

Christine must factor the quadratic function or use the quadratic formula to determine the *x*-intercepts. Once she determines the *x*-intercepts, she can use the same method as Kate.

Who's Correct?

WHEN YOU SEE A WHO'S CORRECT? ICON

- Take your time to read through the situation.
- Question the strategy or reason given.
- Determine which solution is correct and which is not correct.

ASK YOURSELF

- Does the reasoning make sense?
- If the reasoning makes sense, what is the justification?
- If the reasoning does not make sense, what error was made?

7. Tonya and Alex came up with different expressions to represent the number of gray tiles in each pattern. Their expressions are shown.

Tonya	Alex
$4n^2 + (2n + 1)(2n + 1)$	$(4n + 1)^2 - 4n(2n + 1)$

Tonya claims that they are the same expression written different ways. Alex says, "One expression has addition and the other has subtraction. There is no way they are equivalent!"

Who is correct? Justify your reasoning using algebraic and graphical representations.

Tonya is correct.

Tonya's expression

$4n^2 + (2n + 1)(2n + 1)$

$4n^2 + 4n^2 + 4n + 1$

$8n^2 + 4n + 1$

Alex's expression

$(4n + 1)^2 - 4n(2n + 1)$

$16n^2 + 8n + 1 - 4n^2 - 4n$

$8n^2 + 4n + 1$

Both expressions are equivalent to $8n^2 + 4n + 1$.

When I graph both expressions as equations, they produce the same graph which guarantees equivalence.

Problem Types

The Standards for Mathematical Practice

Effective communication and collaboration are essential skills of a successful learner. With practice, you can develop the habits of mind of a productive mathematical thinker.

Make sense of problems and persevere in solving them.

I can:

- explain what a problem "means" in my own words.
- analyze and organize information.
- keep track of my plan and change it if necessary
- always ask myself, "does this make sense?"

Attend to precision.

I can:

- calculate accurately and efficiently.
- use clear definitions when I talk with my classmates, my teacher, and others.
- specify units of measure and label diagrams and other figures appropriately to clarify the meaning of different representations.

Reasoning and Explaining

Reason abstractly and quantitatively.

I can:

- create an understandable representation of a problem situation.
- consider the units of measure involved in a problem.
- understand and use properties of operations.

Construct viable arguments and critique the reasoning of others.

I can:

- use definitions and previously established results in constructing arguments.
- communicate and defend my own mathematical reasoning using examples, drawings, or diagrams.
- distinguish correct reasoning from reasoning that is flawed.
- listen to or read the conclusions of others and decide whether they make sense.
- ask useful questions in an attempt to understand other ideas and conclusions.

Modeling and Using Tools

Model with mathematics.

I can:

- identify important relationships in a problem situation and represent them using tools such as, diagrams, tables, graphs, and formulas.
- apply mathematics to solve problems that occur in everyday life.
- interpret mathematical results in the contexts of a variety of problem situations.
- reflect on whether my results make sense, improving the model I used if it is not appropriate for the situation.

Use appropriate tools strategically.

I can:

- use a variety of different tools that I have to solve problems.
- use a graphing calculator to explore mathematical concepts.
- recognize when a tool that I have to solve problems might be helpful and also when it has limitations.

Seeing Structure and Generalizing

Look for and make use of structure.

I can:

- look closely to see a pattern or a structure in a mathematical argument.
- can see complicated things as single objects or as being composed of several objects.
- can step back for an overview and can shift my perspective.

Look for and express regularity in repeated reasoning.

I can:

- notice if calculations are repeated.
- look for general methods and more efficient methods to solve problems.
- evaluate the reasonableness of intermediate results.
- make generalizations based on results.

Each lesson provides opportunities for you to think, reason, and communicate mathematical understanding. Here are a few examples of how you will develop expertise using the Standards for Mathematical Practice throughout this text.

PROBLEM 1 Business Is Growing

The Plant-A-Seed Planter Company produces planter boxes. To make the boxes, a square is cut from each corner of a rectangular copper sheet. The sides are bent to form a rectangular prism without a top. Cutting different sized squares from the corners results in different sized planter boxes. Plant-A-Seed takes sales orders from customers who request a sized planter box.

Reason abstractly and quantitatively. You will move from a real-life context to the mathematics and back to the context throughout problems.

Each rectangular copper sheet is 12 inches by 18 inches. In the diagram, the solid lines indicate where the square corners are cut and the dotted lines represent where the sides are bent for each planter box.

It may help to create a model of the planter by cutting squares out of the corners of a sheet of paper and folding.

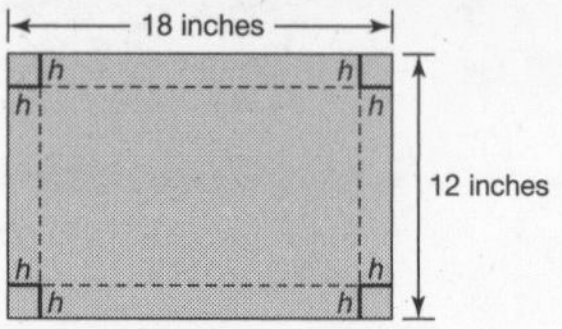

1. Organize the information about each sized planter box made from a 12 inch by 18 inch copper sheet.

   a. Complete the table. Include an expression for each planter box's height, width, length, and volume for a square corner side of length h.

Model with mathematics. You will identify relationships and represent them using diagrams, tables, graphs, and formulas.

Recall the volume formula $V = lwh$.

Square Corner Side Length (inches)	Height (inches)	Width (inches)	Length (inches)	Volume (cubic inches)
0				
1				
2				
3				
4				
5				
6				
7				
h				

Look for and make use of structure. You will look for patterns in your calculations and use those to write formal expressions and equations.

Habits of Mind

b. What patterns do you notice in the table?

Attend to precision.
You will specify units of measure and express answers with a degree of precision appropriate for the problem context.

2. Analyze the relationship between the height, length, and width of each planter box.

   a. What is the largest sized square corner that can be cut to make a planter box? Explain your reasoning.

   b. What is the relationship between the size of the corner square and the length and width of each planter box?

   c. Write a function $V(h)$ to represent the volume of the planter box in terms of the corner side of length h.

Model with mathematics.
You will identify important quantities and map their relationships using functions.

Construct viable arguments and critique the reasoning of others.
You will share your answers with your classmates and listen to their responses to decide whether they make sense.

Interpreting Data in Normal Distributions

1

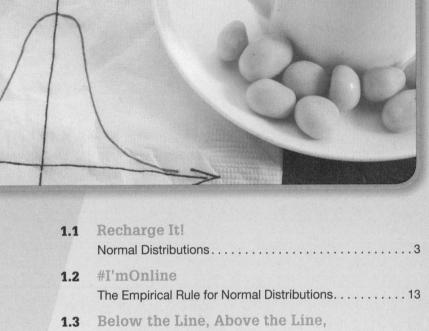

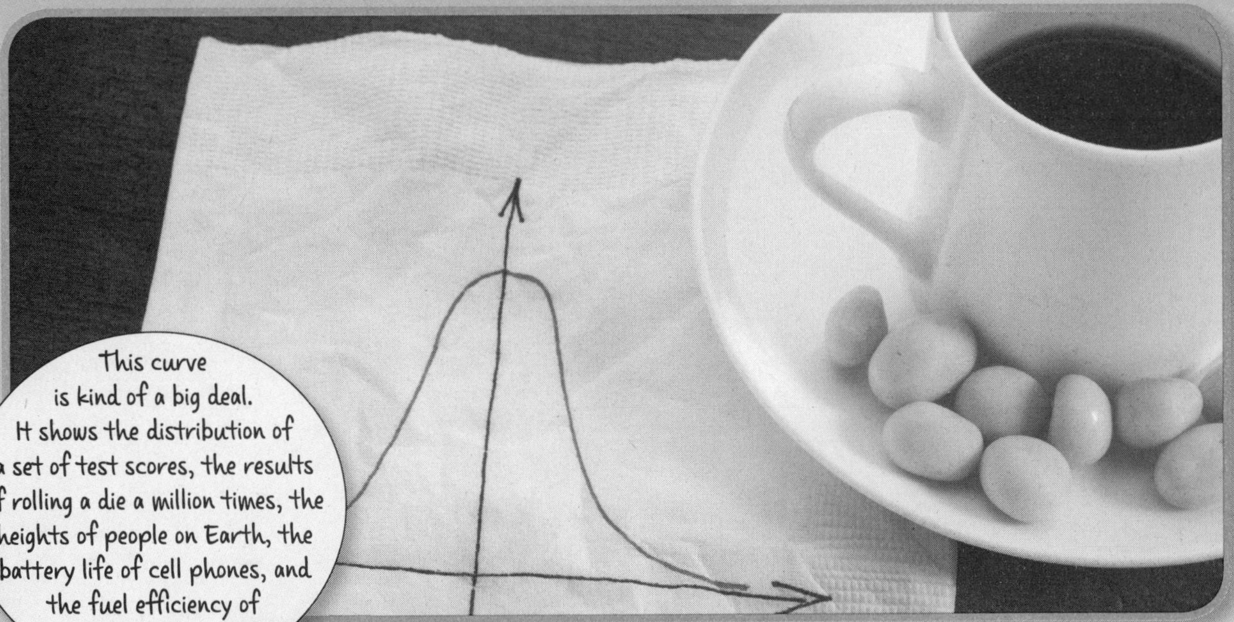

This curve is kind of a big deal. It shows the distribution of a set of test scores, the results of rolling a die a million times, the heights of people on Earth, the battery life of cell phones, and the fuel efficiency of hybrid cars.

1.1

Recharge It!
Normal Distributions

LEARNING GOALS

In this lesson, you will:

- Differentiate between discrete data and continuous data.
- Draw distributions for continuous data.
- Recognize the difference between normal distributions and non-normal distributions.
- Recognize and interpret properties of a normal curve and a normal distribution.
- Describe the effect of changing the mean and standard deviation on a normal curve.

KEY TERMS

- discrete data
- continuous data
- sample
- population
- normal curve
- normal distribution
- mean (μ)
- standard deviation (σ)

Imagine carrying around a cell phone that weighed 80 pounds, provided 30 minutes of talk time on a 100% charged battery, needed 10 hours to fully recharge the battery, and worked in only one assigned local calling area! That's a snapshot of a cell phone in the 1950s.

Cell phones have come a long way since then. Today's cell phone users send and receive texts, emails, photos and videos, they surf the web, play games, use GPS, listen to music, and much more—all on a device that fits in the palm of your hand.

1

PROBLEM 1 Low Battery

Recall that a discrete graph is a graph of isolated points and a continuous graph is a graph of points that are connected by a line or smooth curve on the graph. Data can also be discrete or continuous.

Discrete data are data whose possible values are countable and often finite. The scores of baseball games are examples of discrete data, because a team's score must be a positive whole number or zero.

Continuous data are data which can take any numerical value within a range. Heights of students, times required to complete a test, and distances between cities are examples of continuous data.

Suppose that two cell phone companies, E-Phone and Unlimited, claim that the cell phones of two of their comparable models have a mean battery life of 10 hours.

1. Are the durations of the cell phone batteries examples of discrete data or continuous data? Explain your reasoning.

2. If the mean battery life is 10 hours, does that indicate that all of E-Phone's phones and all of Unlimited's phones have a 10-hour battery life? Explain your reasoning.

One way to display continuous data is by using a relative frequency table. The relative frequency tables shown display the battery lives of a *sample* of 100 E-Phone cell phones and 100 Unlimited cell phones.

A **sample** is a subset of data selected from a *population*. A **population** represents all the possible data that are of interest in a study or survey.

The battery lives are divided into intervals. Each interval includes the first value but does not include the second value. For example, the interval 8.0–8.5 includes phones with battery lives greater than or equal to 8 hours and less than 8.5 hours.

Recall that relative frequency is the ratio of occurrences within an interval to the total number of occurrences.

3. Complete the tables by calculating the relative frequency of phones in each interval. Explain how you determined the relative frequencies.

E-Phone		
Battery Life (hours)	**Number of Phones**	**Relative Frequency**
8.0–8.5	1	
8.5–9.0	2	
9.0–9.5	17	
9.5–10.0	30	
10.0–10.5	32	
10.5–11.0	15	
11.0–11.5	3	
11.5–12.0	0	

Unlimited		
Battery Life (hours)	**Number of Phones**	**Relative Frequency**
8.0–8.5	0	
8.5–9.0	1	
9.0–9.5	14	
9.5–10.0	37	
10.0–10.5	36	
10.5–11.0	11	
11.0–11.5	0	
11.5–12.0	1	

For continuous data, a relative frequency histogram displays continuous intervals on the horizontal axis and relative frequency on the vertical axis.

4. Create a relative frequency histogram to represent the battery lives of the 100 cell phones in each sample.

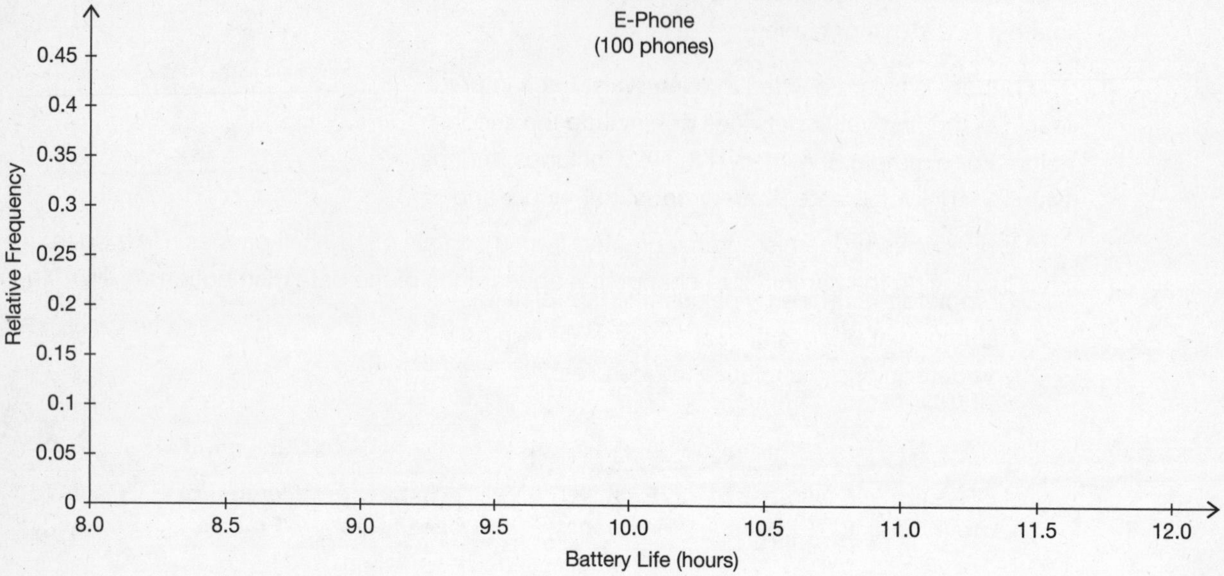

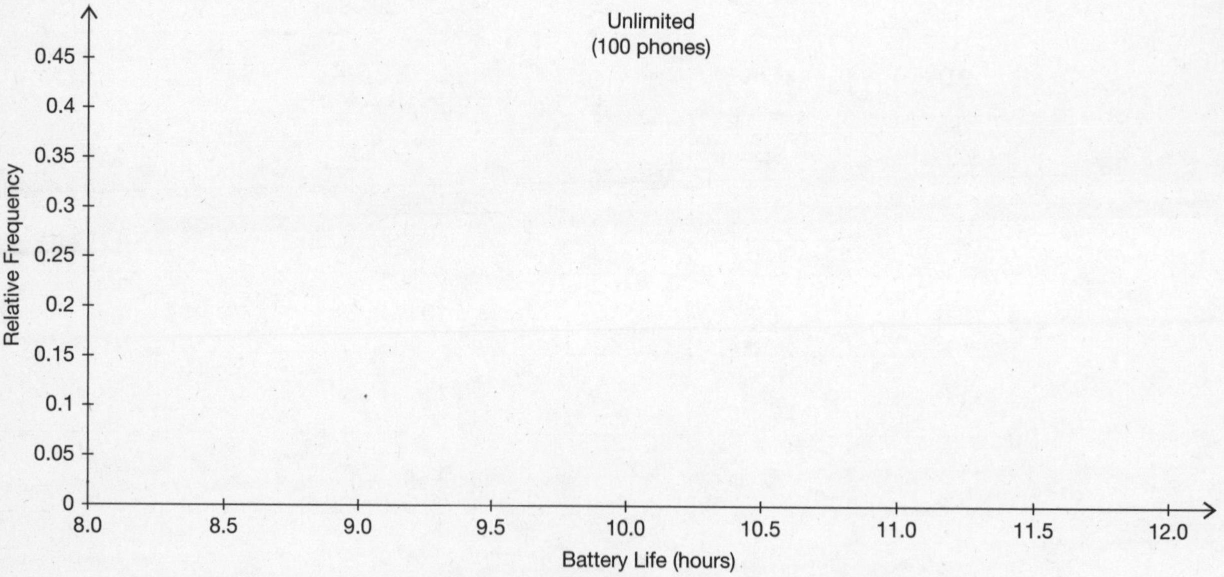

Recall that the shape of a data distribution can reveal information about the data. Data can be widely spread out or packed closer together. Data distributions can also be skewed or symmetric.

5. Describe the shape and spread of the histograms. What might these characteristics reveal about the data for each company?

6. The relative frequency histograms shown represent samples of 10,000 phones from each of the two companies. Compare the histograms created from a sample of 10,000 cell phones to the histograms created from a sample of 100 cell phones. How does increasing the sample size change the appearance of the data distributions?

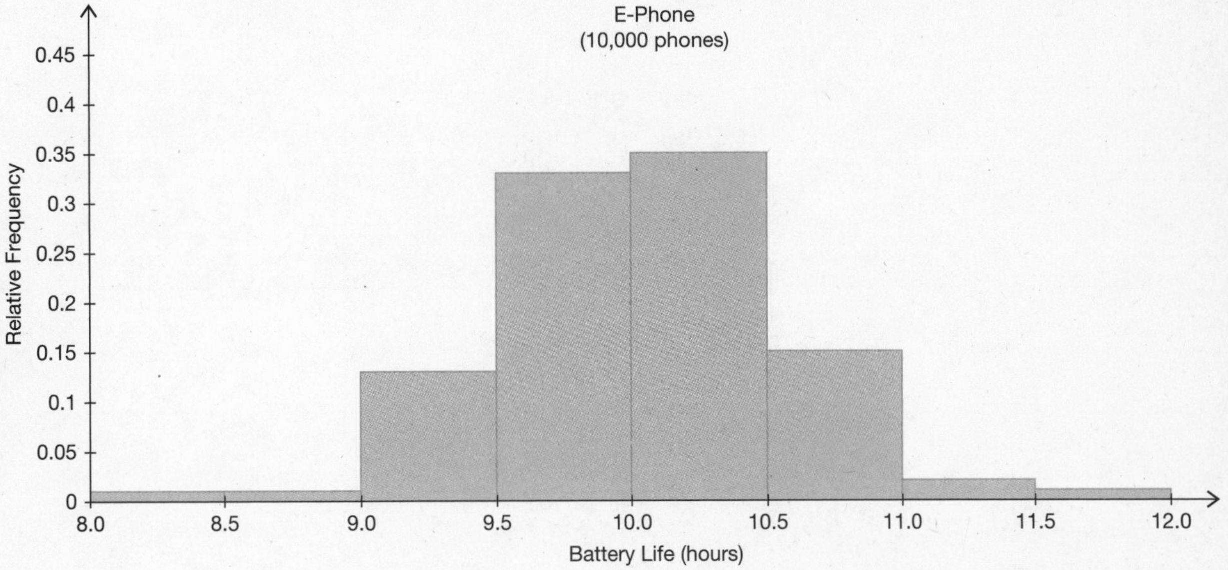

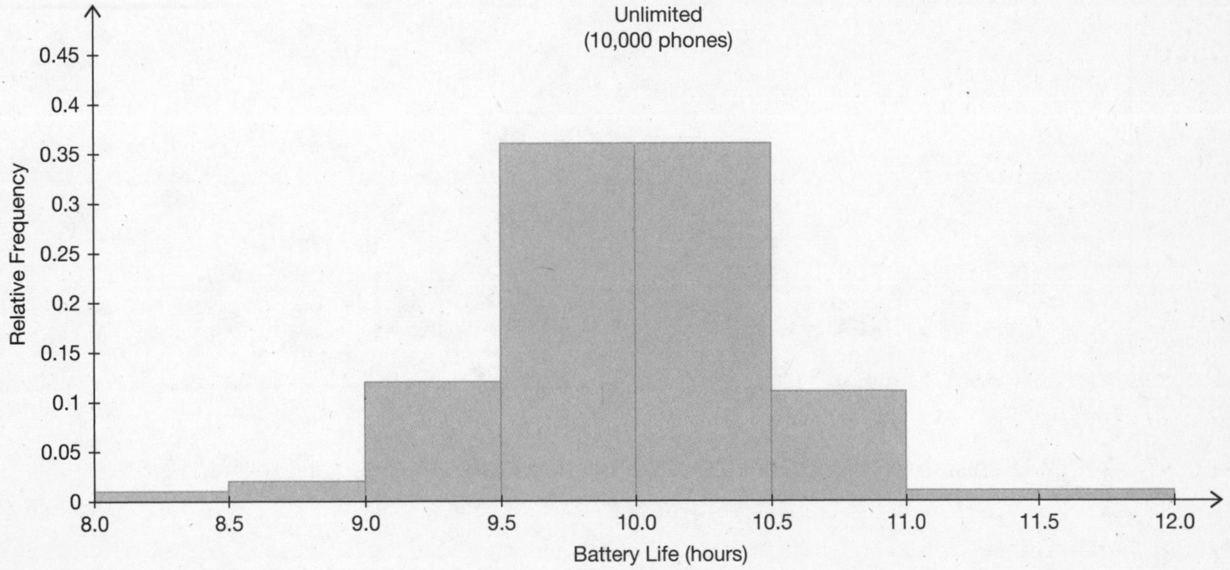

7. The histograms shown represent the same samples of 10,000 phones, but now the data have been divided into intervals of 0.1 hour instead of 0.5 hour. Compare these histograms with the histograms from the previous question. How does decreasing the interval size change the appearance of the data distributions?

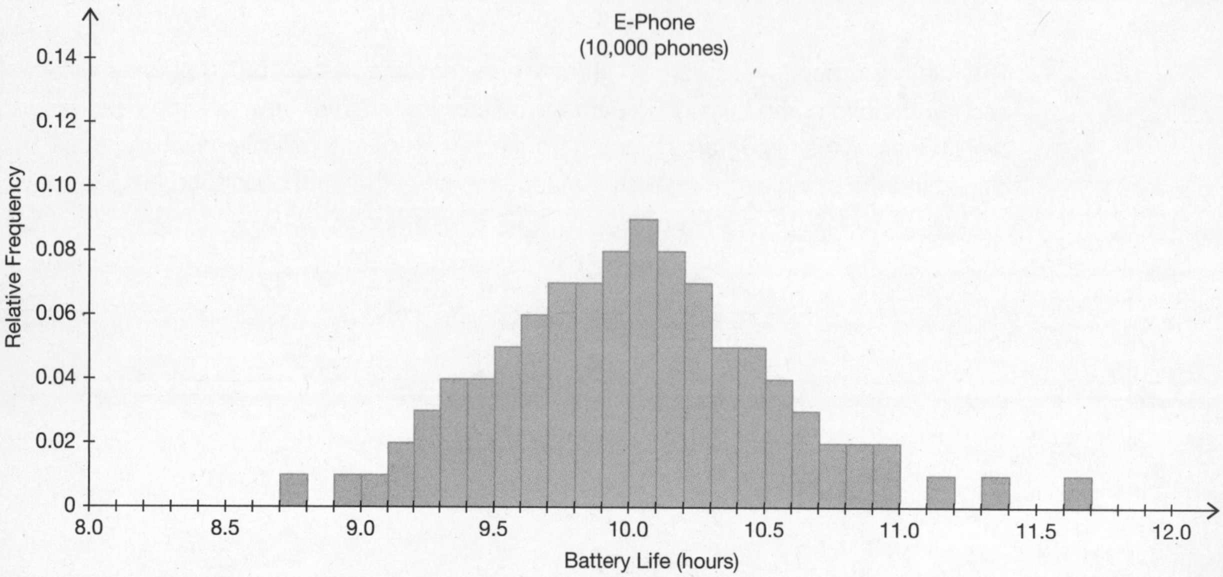

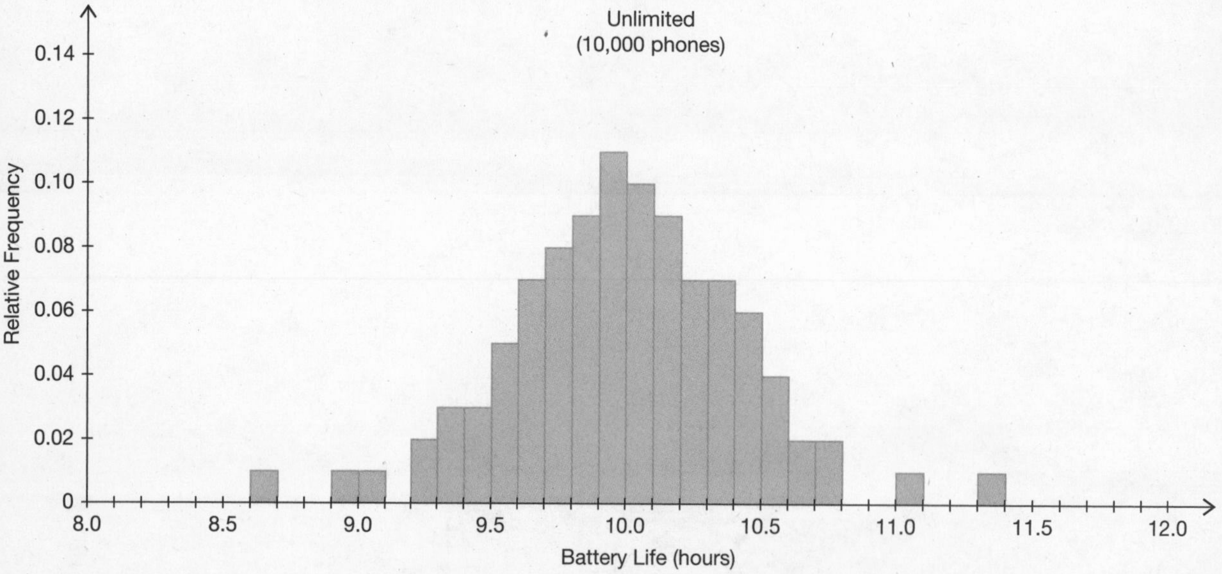

8. Explain why the scale of the y-axis changed when the interval size increased.

As the sample size continues to increase and the interval size continues to decrease, the shape of each relative frequency histogram will likely start to resemble a *normal curve*. A **normal curve** is a bell-shaped curve that is symmetric about the mean of the data.

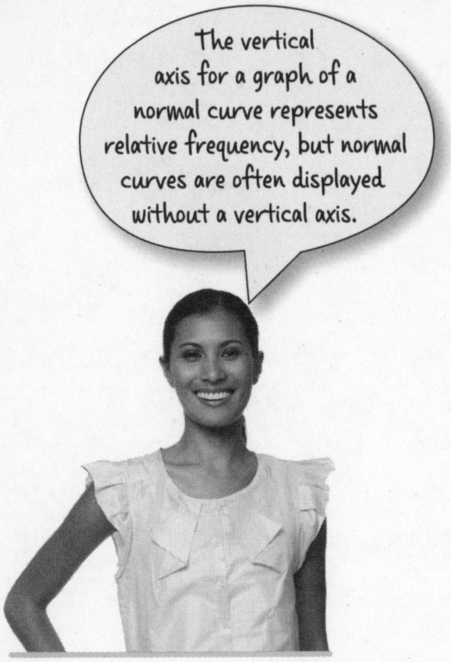
The vertical axis for a graph of a normal curve represents relative frequency, but normal curves are often displayed without a vertical axis.

A normal curve models a theoretical data set that is said to have a **normal distribution**.

The normal curves for the E-Phone and Unlimited cell phone battery lives are shown. In order to display normal curves for each data set, different intervals were used on the horizontal axis in each graph.

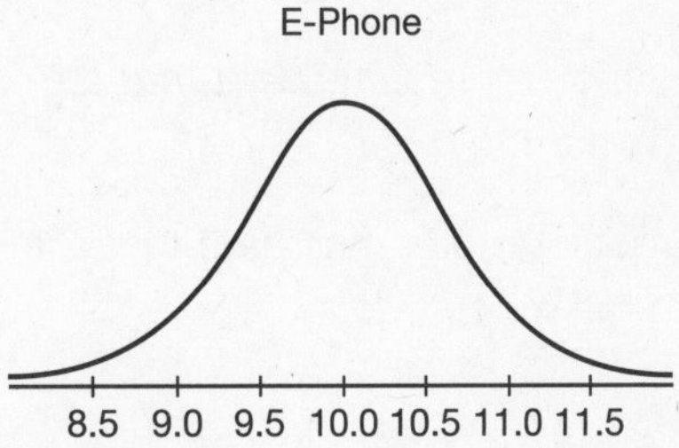
E-Phone
8.5 9.0 9.5 10.0 10.5 11.0 11.5

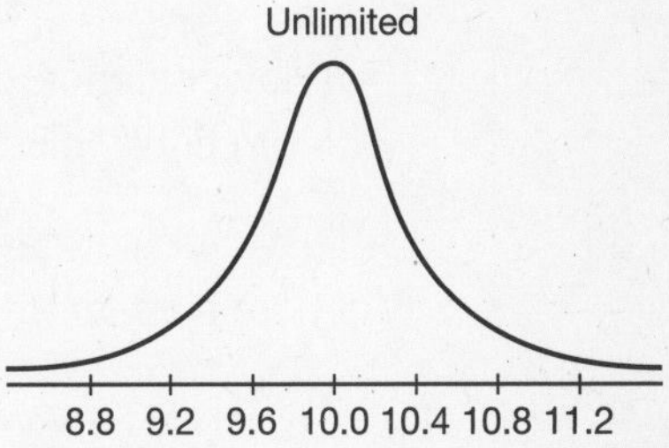
Unlimited
8.8 9.2 9.6 10.0 10.4 10.8 11.2

Although normal curves can be narrow or wide, all normal curves are symmetrical about the mean of the data.

Normal Distributions

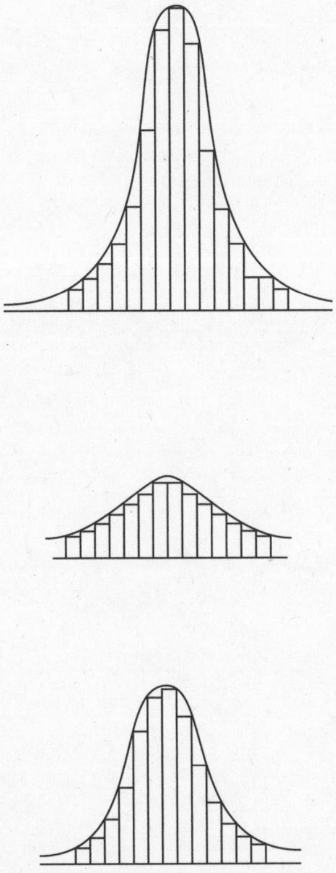

Not Normal Distributions

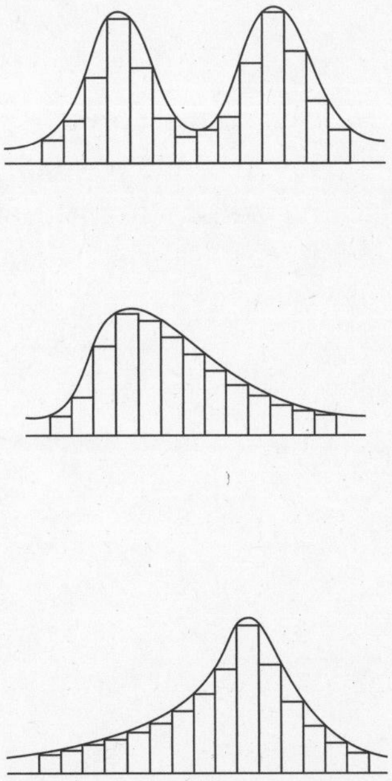

PROBLEM 2 Deviating Slightly

You already know a lot about the mean. With normal curves, the **mean** of a population is represented with the symbol μ. The mean of a sample is represented with the symbol $\bar{x}$. The **standard deviation** of data is a measure of how spread out the data are from the mean. The symbol used for the standard deviation of a population is the sigma symbol (σ). The standard deviation of a sample is represented with the variable s. When interpreting the standard deviation of data:

- A lower standard deviation represents data that are more tightly clustered near the mean.
- A higher standard deviation represents data that are more spread out from the mean.

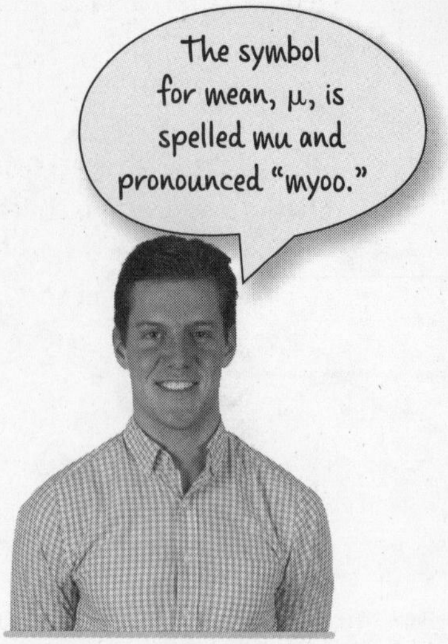

The symbol for mean, μ, is spelled mu and pronounced "myoo."

1. Normal curves *A*, *B*, and *C* represent the battery lives of a population of cell phones of comparable models from three different companies.

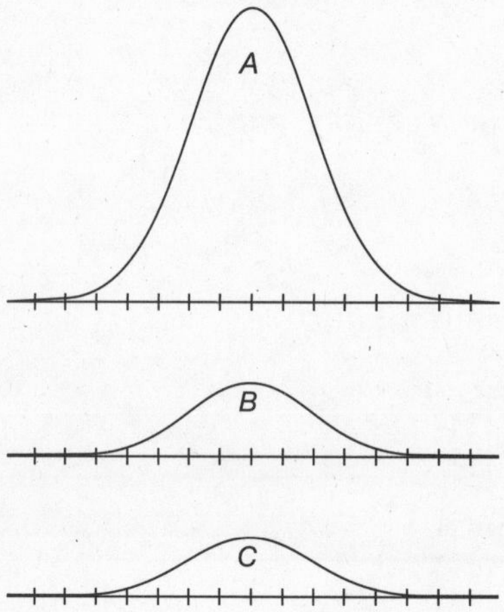

The normal curves represent distributions with standard deviations of $\sigma = 0.1$, $\sigma = 0.4$, and $\sigma = 0.5$. Match each standard deviation value with one of the normal curves and explain your reasoning.

2. Normal curves *A*, *B*, and *C* represent the battery lives of cell phones from three different companies.

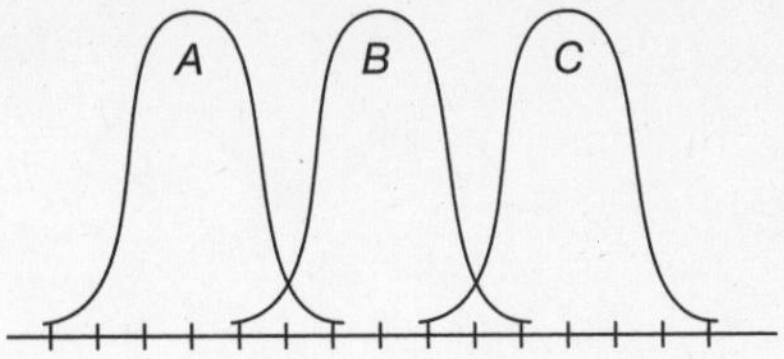

a. Compare the mean of each company.

b. Compare the standard deviation of each distribution.

 Be prepared to share your solutions and methods.

© Carnegie Learning

1.2

#I'mOnline

The Empirical Rule for Normal Distributions

LEARNING GOALS

In this lesson, you will:

- Recognize the connection between normal curves, relative frequency histograms, and the Empirical Rule for Normal Distributions.
- Use the Empirical Rule for Normal Distributions to determine the percent of data in a given interval.

KEY TERMS

- standard normal distribution
- Empirical Rule for Normal Distributions

On October 19, 1987, stock markets around the world fell into sharp decline. In the United States, the Dow Jones Industrial Average dropped 508 points—a 22% loss in value. Black Monday, as the day came to be called, represented at the time the largest one-day decline in the stock market ever.

According to some economic models, the crash that occurred on Black Monday represented an event that was 20 standard deviations away from the normal behavior of the market. Mathematically, the odds of a Black Monday–type event occurring were 1 in 10^{50}.

PROBLEM 1 Count 'em Up

Let's investigate what the standard deviation can tell us about a normal distribution.

The relative frequency histograms for the battery lives of E-Phone and Unlimited cell phones are shown. The normal curves for each data set are mapped on top of the histogram.

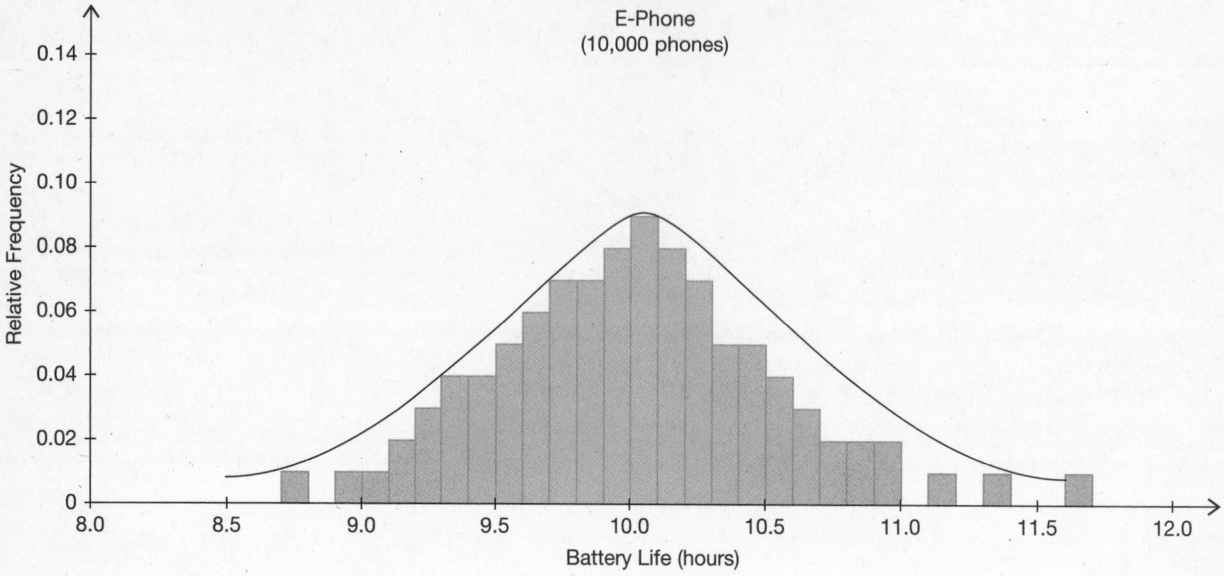

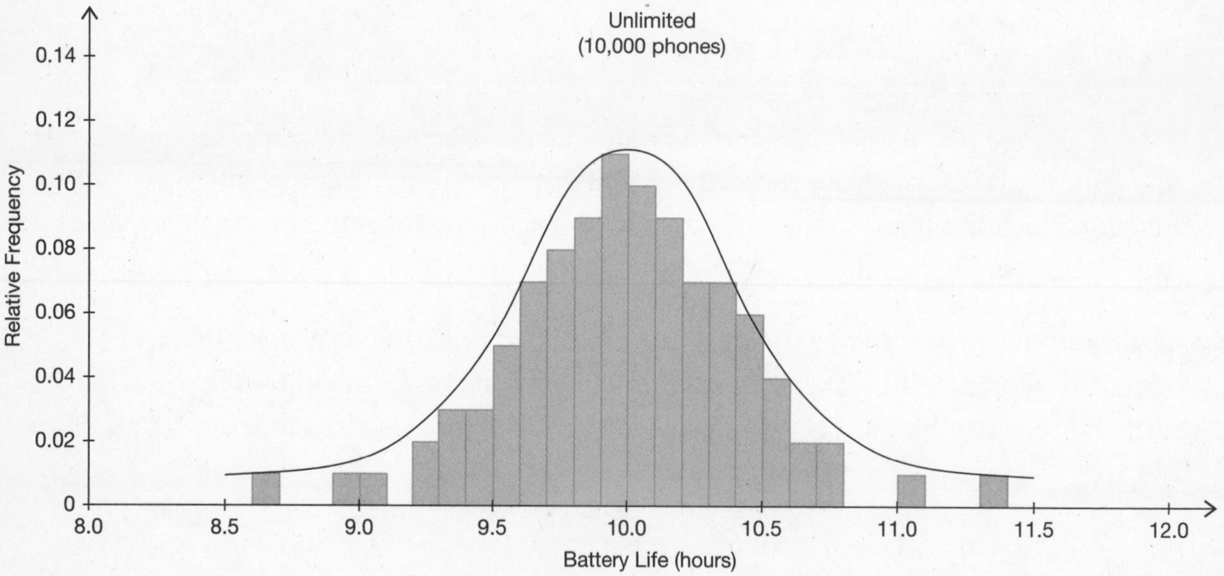

Normal curves can be graphed with units of standard deviation on the horizontal axis. The normal curve for the E-Phone sample has a standard deviation of 0.5 hour ($s = 0.5$), and the normal curve for the Unlimited sample has a standard deviation of 0.4 hour ($s = 0.4$). The mean of each sample is $\bar{x} = 10.0$ hours.

1. Study the graphs shown.

   a. For each graph, label each standard deviation unit with its corresponding battery life.

   Notice that different symbols are used to represent the mean and standard deviation of a sample as opposed to a population.

   b. What value is represented at $s = 0$ for both graphs?

2. Use the histograms on the previous page to estimate the percent of data within each standard deviation. Write each percent in the appropriate space below the horizontal axis.

E-Phone

$-3s \quad -2s \quad -1s \quad 0 \quad 1s \quad 2s \quad 3s$

Unlimited

$-3s \quad -2s \quad -1s \quad 0 \quad 1s \quad 2s \quad 3s$

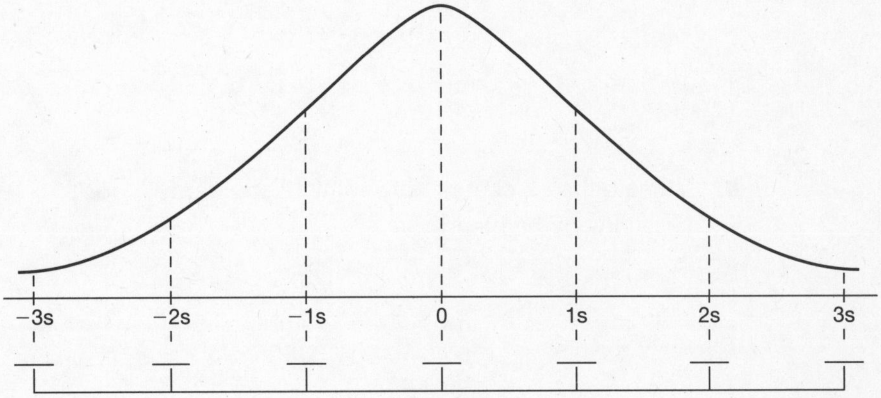

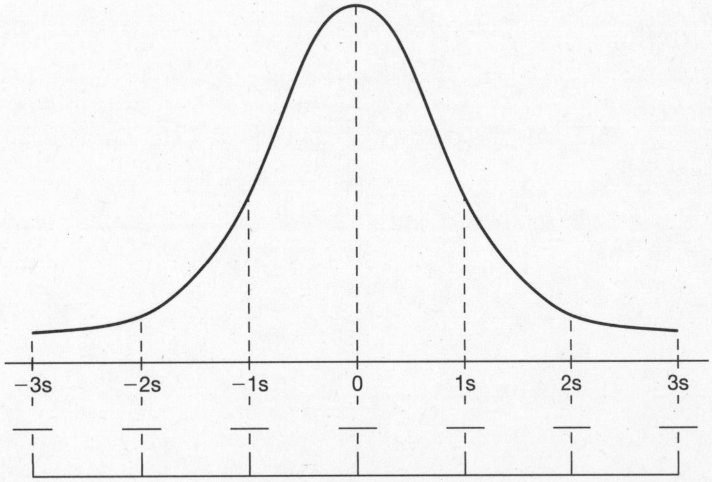

3. Compare the percents in each standard deviation interval for E-Phone with the percents in each standard deviation interval for Unlimited. What do you notice?

4. Use your results to answer each question. Explain your reasoning.

"Within one standard deviation" means between −1s and 1s, or between −1σ and 1σ.

a. Estimate the percent of data within 1 standard deviation of the mean.

b. Estimate the percent of data within 2 standard deviations of the mean.

c. Estimate the percent of data within 3 standard deviations of the mean.

The **standard normal distribution** is a normal distribution with a mean value of 0 and a standard deviation of 1σ or $1s$. In a standard normal distribution, 0 represents the mean. Positive integers represent standard deviations greater than the mean. Negative integers represent standard deviations less than the mean.

The Empirical Rule for Normal Distributions is often summarized using a standard normal distribution curve because it can be generalized for any normal distribution curve.

The **Empirical Rule for Normal Distributions** states:

- Approximately 68% of the data in a normal distribution for a population is within 1 standard deviation of the mean.

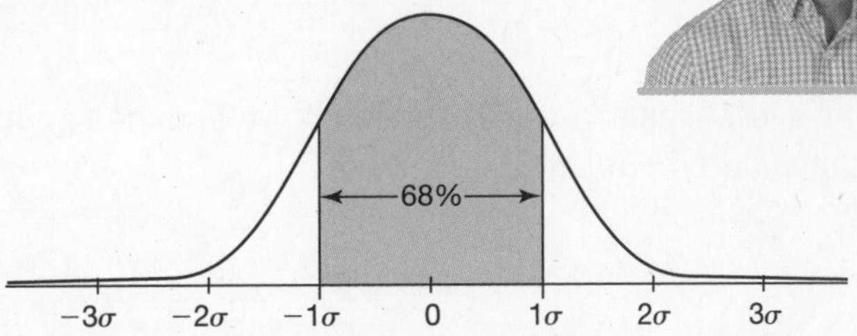

- Approximately 95% of the data in a normal distribution for a population is within 2 standard deviations of the mean.

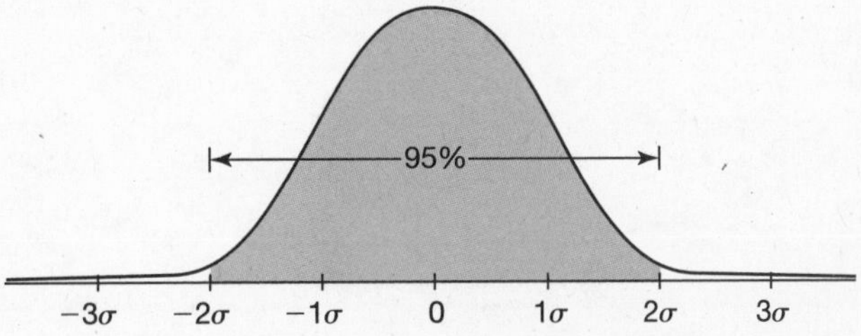

- Approximately 99.7% of the data in a normal distribution for a population is within 3 standard deviations of the mean.

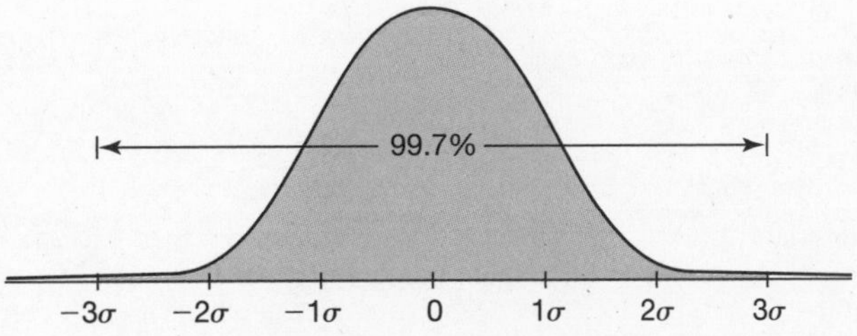

The Empirical Rule applies most accurately to population data rather than sample data. However, the Empirical Rule is often applied to data in large samples.

Recall that a box-and-whisker plot is a graph that organizes, summarizes, and displays data based on quartiles that each contains 25% of the data values.

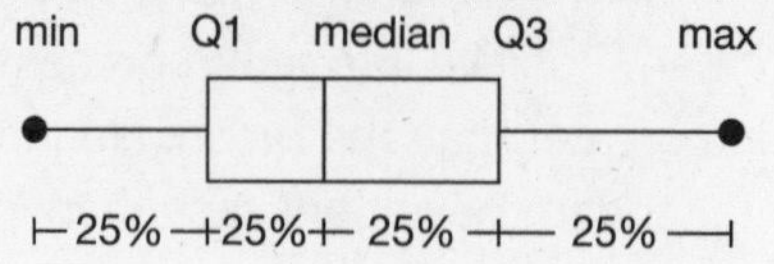

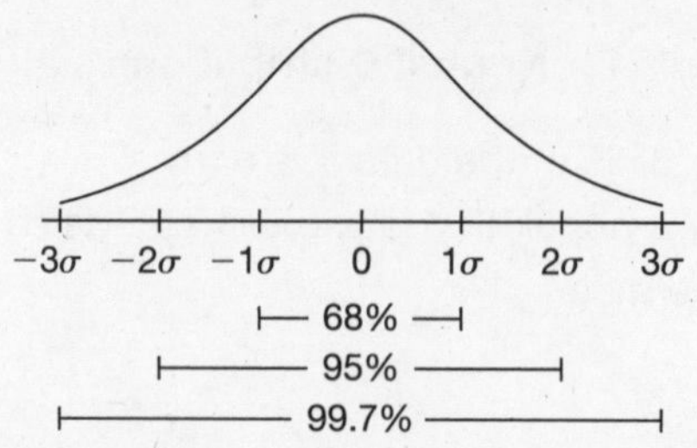

5. What similarities and/or differences do you notice about the box-and-whisker plot and the standard normal distribution?

PROBLEM 2 Interval Training

You can use the Empirical Rule for Normal Distributions to estimate the percent of data within specific intervals of a normal distribution.

1. Determine each percent and explain your reasoning. Shade the corresponding region under each normal curve. Then tell whether the distribution represents population data or sample data.

   a. What percent of the data is greater than the mean?

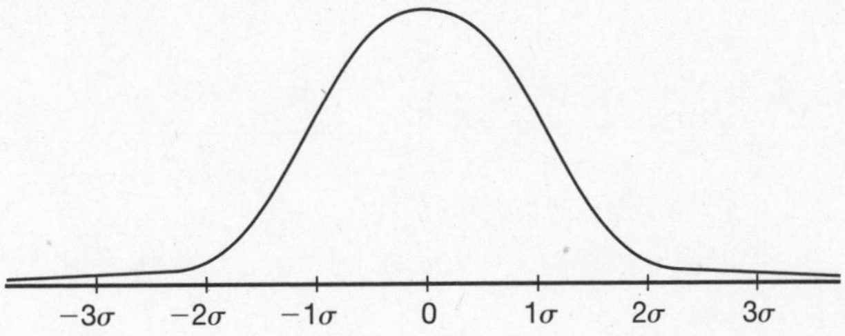

   b. What percent of the data is between the mean and 2 standard deviations below the mean?

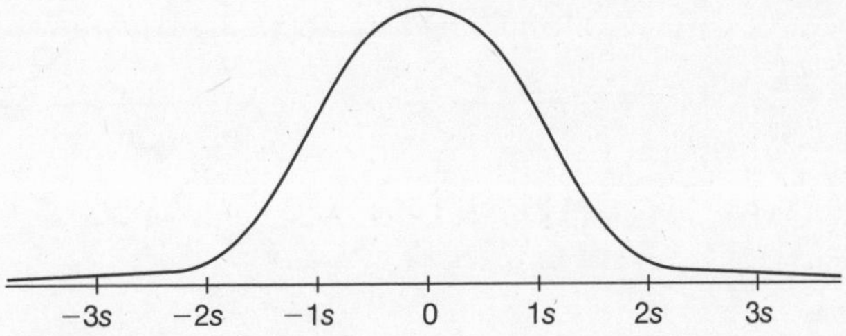

1

c. What percent of the data is between 1 and 2 standard deviations above the mean?

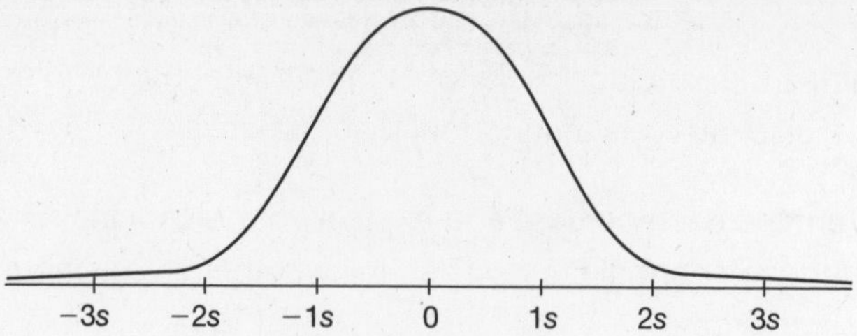

d. What percent of the data is more than 2 standard deviations below the mean?

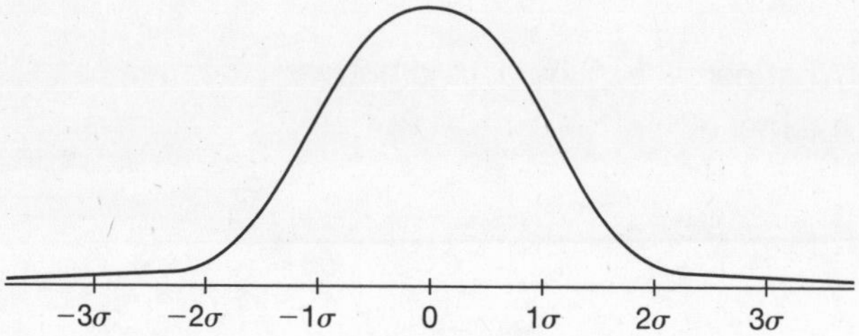

2. Use the normal curve to answer each question and explain your reasoning. Shade the region under each normal curve to represent your answer. Then tell whether the distribution represents population data or sample data.

a. What percent of adult males have a height between 62 inches and 74 inches?

| 58 | 62 | 66 | 70 | 74 | 78 | 84 |
| -3σ | -2σ | -1σ | μ | 1σ | 2σ | 3σ |

Heights of Adult Males

Keep in mind that 1σ corresponds to a data value that is one standard deviation greater than the population mean and -1σ corresponds to a data value that is one standard deviation less than the mean.

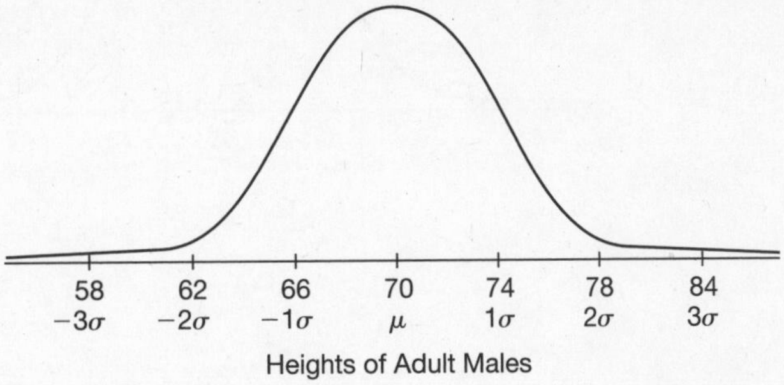

b. What percent of adult females are taller than 68.5 inches?

| 54.5 | 58 | 61.5 | 65 | 68.5 | 72 | 75.5 |
| -3σ | -2σ | -1σ | μ | 1σ | 2σ | 3σ |

Heights of Adult Females

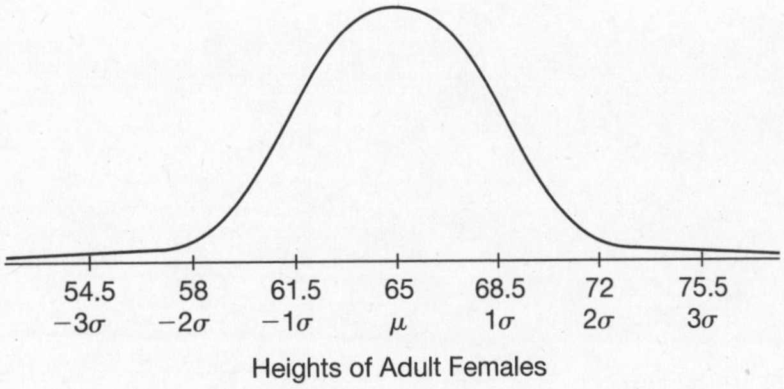

1

c. What percent of history test scores are between 63 points and 70 points?

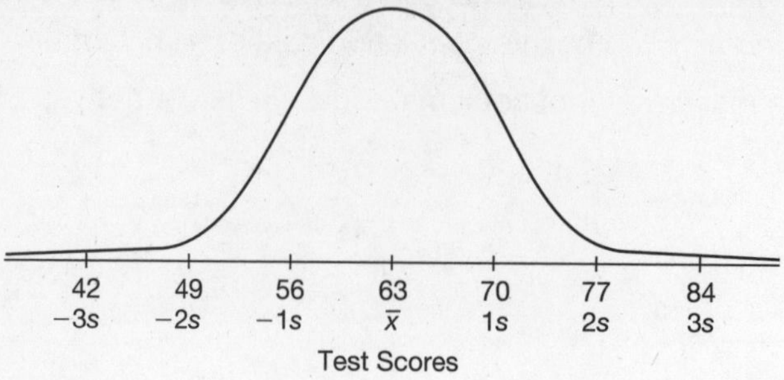

Be prepared to share your solutions and methods.

Below the Line, Above the Line, and Between the Lines

1.3

Z-Scores and Percentiles

LEARNING GOALS

In this lesson, you will:

- Use a *z*-score table to calculate the percent of data below any given data value, above any given data value, and between any two given data values in a normal distribution.
- Use a graphing calculator to calculate the percent of data below any given data value, above any given data, and between any two given data values in a normal distribution.
- Use a *z*-score table to determine the data value that represents a given percentile.
- Use a graphing calculator to determine the data value that represents a given percentile.

KEY TERMS

- *z*-score
- percentile

In 2013, the labels on new vehicles sold in the U.S. got a little different. Instead of just showing how many miles per gallon the vehicle gets, the label also shows the number of gallons per mile it gets.

Why is that important? The reason can be seen on this graph.

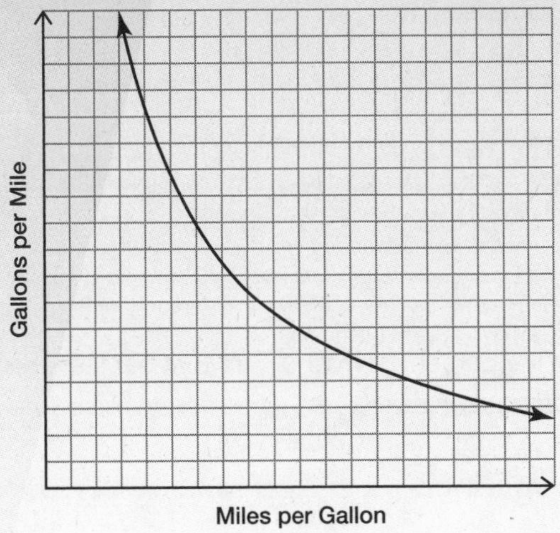

When a car gets a low number of miles per gallon (say, 12 mpg), switching to a slightly higher number (say, 15 mpg) represents a large decrease in the number of gallons per mile, which is a big savings–even bigger than switching from 30 mpg to 50 mpg!

How many gallons per mile does your car get?

PROBLEM 1 Off the Mark

1. The fuel efficiency of a sample of hybrid cars is normally distributed with a mean of 54 miles per gallon (mpg) and a standard deviation of 6 miles per gallon.

   a. Use the mean and standard deviation to label the intervals on the horizontal axis of the normal curve in miles per gallon.

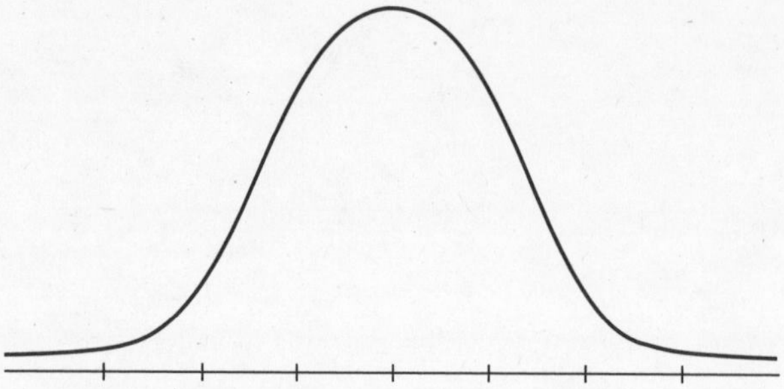

   b. Determine the percent of hybrid cars that get less than 60 miles per gallon. Explain your reasoning.

   c. Determine the percent of hybrid cars that get less than 66 miles per gallon. Explain your reasoning.

   d. Determine the percent of hybrid cars that get less than 72 miles per gallon. Explain your reasoning.

When data values are aligned with integer multiples of the standard deviation from the mean, you can use the Empirical Rule for Normal Distributions to calculate the percent of data values less than that value. But what if a data value does not align with the standard deviations?

2. Let's consider the fuel efficiency of hybrid cars again. The mean is 54 miles per gallon and 1 standard deviation is 6 miles per gallon. What percent of cars get less than 57 miles per gallon?

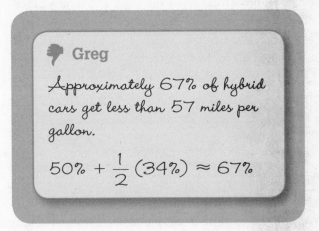

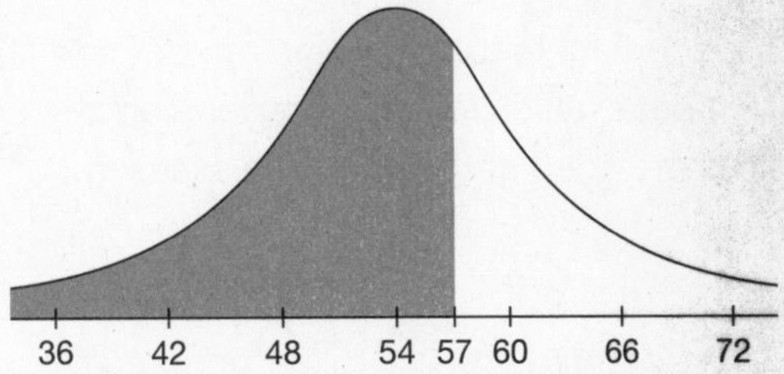

a. How many standard deviations from the mean is 57 miles per gallon? Explain how you determined your answer.

b. Greg incorrectly estimated the percent of hybrid cars that get less than 57 miles per gallon.

> **Greg**
>
> Approximately 67% of hybrid cars get less than 57 miles per gallon.
>
> $50\% + \frac{1}{2}(34\%) \approx 67\%$

Explain why Greg's reasoning is incorrect.

The number you calculated in Question 2 is a *z-score*. A ***z*-score** is a number that describes a specific data value's distance from the mean in terms of standard deviation units.

For a population, a *z*-score is determined by the equation

$$z = \frac{(x - \mu)}{\sigma},$$

where *x* represents a value from the data.

You can use a *z*-score table to determine the percent of data less than a given data value with a corresponding *z*-score. A *z*-score table is provided at the end of this lesson.

So a z-score is just how many standard deviations the data value is from the mean.

To determine the percent of hybrid cars that get less than 57 miles per gallon with a *z*-score table, first calculate the *z*-score for 57 miles per gallon. In Question 2, you calculated the score for 57 miles per gallon as 0.5.

z	0.0	0.01	0.02	0.03	0.04	0.05
0.0	0.5000	0.5040	0.5080	0.5120	0.5160	0.5199
0.1	0.5398	0.5433	0.5478	0.5517	0.5557	0.5596
0.2	0.5793	0.5832	0.5871	0.5910	0.5948	0.5987
0.3	0.6179	0.6217	0.6255	0.6293	0.6331	0.6368
0.4	0.6554	0.6591	0.6628	0.6664	0.6700	0.6736
0.5	0.6915	0.6950	0.6985	0.7019	0.7054	0.7088

Next, locate the row that represents the ones and tenths place of the *z*-score. For a *z*-score of 0.5, this is the row labeled 0.5. Also locate the column that represents the hundredths place of the *z*-score. For a *z*-score of 0.5, this is the column labeled 0.0. Note that the table represents *z*-scores only to the hundredths place.

Finally, locate the cell that is the intersection of the row and column. The numbers in each cell represent the percent of data values below each *z*-score. For a *z*-score of 0.5, the corresponding cell reads 0.6915.

This means that 69.15% of hybrid cars get less than 57 miles per gallon.

3. What would a negative *z*-score indicate? Explain your reasoning.

A graphing calculator can determine a percent of data below a *z*-score. This function is called the normal cumulative density function (normalcdf). The function determines the percent of data values within an interval of a normal distribution.

You can also use a graphing calculator to determine the percent of data below a given z-score.

Step 1: Press **2nd** and then **VARS**. Select **2:normalcdf(**

Step 2: Enter the lower bound of the interval, the upper bound of the interval, the mean, and the standard deviation, including commas between each number.

Step 3: Press **ENTER**. Calculator results will vary from results obtained using a z-score table.

In this problem, the lower bound is negative infinity, the upper bound is 57, the mean is 54, and the standard deviation is 6. Most calculators do not have an infinity button. You can use -1×10^{99}, a very small number, for the lower bound.

4. Use a graphing calculator to determine the approximate percent of hybrid cars that get less than 57 miles per gallon.

5. How does this answer compare to the answer you got by using the *z*-score table?

6. Juan and Michael used a graphing calculator to determine that the percent of hybrid cars that get less than 57 miles per gallon is approximately 69.15%. Juan entered values in standard deviation units, and Michael entered values in terms of miles per gallon.

Juan

```
normalcdf(-9,0.5,
0,1)
     .6914624678
```

Michael

```
normalcdf(0,57,
54,6)
     .6914624678
```

a. Explain why Juan and Carlos used different values but still got the same result.

b. Explain why Michael used 0 for the lower bound of the interval. Explain why Juan used -9 for the lower bound of the interval.

1

7. Josh calculated the percent of hybrid cars that get less than 56 miles per gallon using the *z*-score table and a graphing calculator.

z	0.0	0.01	0.02	0.03
0.0	0.5000	0.5040	0.5080	0.5120
0.1	0.5398	0.5438	0.5478	0.5517
0.2	0.5793	0.5832	0.5871	0.5910
0.3	0.6179	0.6217	0.6255	0.6293

Josh

```
normalcdf(-1E99,
56,54,6)
                .6305585963
```

Explain why Josh received different results from the *z*-score table and the graphing calculator.

PROBLEM 2 More or Less . . .

1. Calculate the percent of hybrid cars that get less than 50 miles per gallon.

2. Use your answer to Question 1 to calculate the percent of hybrid cars that get more than 50 miles per gallon. Explain your reasoning.

3. Calculate the percent of hybrid cars that get less than 50 miles per gallon and the percent of hybrid cars that get less than 60 miles per gallon.

4. Use your answer to Question 3 to calculate the percent of hybrid cars that get between 50 and 60 miles per gallon. Explain your reasoning.

PROBLEM 3 Top Texters

You may have heard someone say, "My baby's weight is in the 90th percentile" or, "My student scored in the 80th percentile in math." What do these phrases mean?

A **percentile** is a data value for which a certain percentage of the data is below the data value in a normal distribution. For example, 90% of the data in a set is below the value at the 90th percentile, and 80% of the data is below the value at the 80th percentile.

The number of text messages teens send and receive every day can be represented as a normal distribution with a mean of 100 text messages per day and a standard deviation of 25 texts per day.

1. Calculate the 50th percentile for this data set. Explain your reasoning.

2. Would a teen in the 90th percentile send and receive more or fewer than 100 text messages per day? Explain your reasoning.

3. Would a teen in the 10th percentile send and receive more or fewer than 100 text messages per day? Explain your reasoning.

1

z	0.0	0.01	0.02	0.03	0.04	0.05	0.06	0.07	0.08	0.09
0.0	0.5000	0.5040	0.5080	0.5120	0.5160	0.5199	0.5239	0.5279	0.5319	0.5359
0.1	0.5398	0.5438	0.5478	0.5517	0.5557	0.5596	0.5636	0.5875	0.5714	0.5753
0.2	0.5793	0.5832	0.5871	0.5910	0.5948	0.5967	0.6026	0.6064	0.6103	0.6141
0.3	0.6179	0.6217	0.6255	0.6293	0.6331	0.6368	0.6406	0.6443	0.6480	0.6517
0.4	0.6554	0.6591	0.6628	0.6664	0.6700	0.6736	0.6772	0.6808	0.6844	0.6879
0.5	0.6915	0.6950	0.6985	0.7019	0.7054	0.7068	0.7123	0.7157	0.7190	0.7224
0.6	0.7257	0.7291	0.7324	0.7357	0.7389	0.7422	0.7454	0.7486	0.7517	0.7549
0.7	0.7580	0.7611	0.7642	0.7673	0.7704	0.7734	0.7764	0.7794	0.7823	0.7852
0.8	0.7881	0.7910	0.7939	0.7967	0.7995	0.8023	0.8051	0.8078	0.8106	0.8133
0.9	0.8159	0.8186	0.8212	0.8238	0.8264	0.8269	0.8315	0.8340	0.8365	0.8389
1.0	0.8413	0.8438	0.8461	0.8485	0.8508	0.8531	0.8554	0.8577	0.8599	0.8621
1.1	0.8643	0.8665	0.8686	0.8708	0.8729	0.8749	0.8770	0.8790	0.8810	0.8830
1.2	0.8849	0.8869	0.8888	0.8907	0.8925	0.8944	0.8962	0.8960	0.8997	0.9015
1.3	0.9032	0.9049	0.9066	0.9082	0.9099	0.9115	0.9131	0.9147	0.9162	0.9177
1.4	0.9192	0.9207	0.9222	0.9236	0.9251	0.9265	0.9279	0.9292	0.9306	0.9319
1.5	0.9332	0.9345	0.9357	0.9370	0.9382	0.9394	0.9406	0.9418	0.9429	0.9441
1.6	0.9452	0.9463	0.9474	0.9484	0.9495	0.9505	0.9515	0.9525	0.9535	0.9545
1.7	0.9554	0.9564	0.9573	0.9582	0.9591	0.9599	0.9608	0.9616	0.9625	0.9633
1.8	0.9641	0.9649	0.9656	0.9664	0.9671	0.9678	0.9666	0.9693	0.9699	0.9706
1.9	0.9713	0.9719	0.9726	0.9732	0.9738	0.9744	0.9750	0.9756	0.9761	0.9767
2.0	0.9772	0.9778	0.9783	0.9788	0.9793	0.9798	0.9803	0.9808	0.9812	0.9817
2.1	0.9821	0.9826	0.9830	0.9834	0.9838	0.9842	0.9846	0.9850	0.9854	0.9857
2.2	0.9861	0.9864	0.9868	0.9871	0.9875	0.9878	0.9881	0.9884	0.9887	0.9890
2.3	0.9893	0.9896	0.9898	0.9901	0.9904	0.9906	0.9909	0.9911	0.9913	0.9916
2.4	0.9918	0.9920	0.9922	0.9925	0.9927	0.9929	0.9931	0.9932	0.9934	0.9936
2.5	0.9938	0.9940	0.9941	0.9943	0.9945	0.9946	0.9948	0.9949	0.9951	0.9952
2.6	0.9953	0.9955	0.9956	0.9957	0.9959	0.9960	0.9961	0.9962	0.9963	0.9964
2.7	0.9965	0.9966	0.9967	0.9968	0.9969	0.9970	0.9971	0.9972	0.9973	0.9974
2.8	0.9974	0.9975	0.9976	0.9977	0.9977	0.9978	0.9979	0.9979	0.9980	0.9981
2.9	0.9981	0.9982	0.9982	09983	0.9984	0.9984	0.9985	0.9985	0.9986	0.9986
3.0	0.9987	0.9987	0.9987	0.9988	0.9988	0.9989	0.9989	0.9989	0.9990	0.9990
3.1	0.9990	0.9991	0.9991	0.9991	0.9992	0.9992	0.9992	0.9992	0.9993	0.9993
3.2	0.9993	0.9993	0.9994	0.9994	0.9994	0.9994	0.9994	0.9995	0.9995	0.9995
3.3	0.9995	0.9995	0.9995	0.9996	0.9996	0.9996	0.9996	0.9996	0.9996	0.9997
3.4	0.9997	0.9997	0.9997	0.9997	0.9997	0.9997	0.9997	0.9997	0.9997	0.9998

1.4

You Make the Call

Normal Distributions and Probability

LEARNING GOALS

In this lesson, you will:

- Interpret a normal curve in terms of probability.
- Use normal distributions to determine probabilities.
- Use normal distributions and probabilities to make decisions.

You can grow both tomatoes and potatoes easily in a home garden—separately—but what about a plant that can grow both vegetables (or is it a fruit and a vegetable?) at the same time?

A company based in the United Kingdom created just that—a hybrid plant that produces both tomatoes above the ground and potatoes below. This remarkable plant was not created through genetic engineering, but rather by grafting the two types of plants together at the stem.

Now for the important question: What would you call this hybrid plant?

PROBLEM 1 Teens and Texting

So far, you have explored the percent of data values that fall within specified intervals. However, you can also interpret a normal distribution in terms of probabilities.

Based on a survey, the number of text messages that teens send and receive every day is a normal distribution with a mean of 100 text messages per day and a standard deviation of 25 text messages per day.

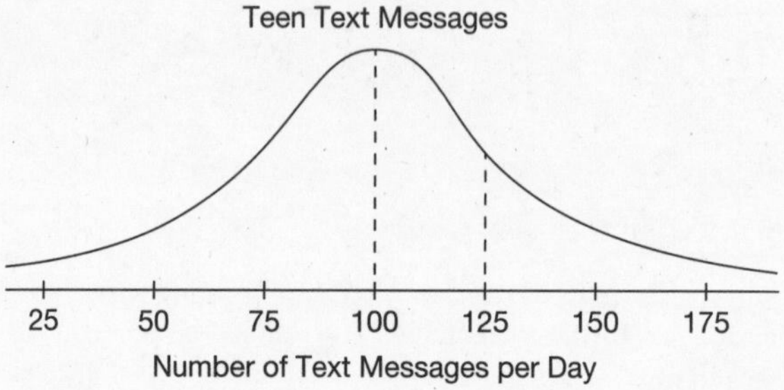

You randomly select a teen from the survey. Calculate each probability.

1. Determine the probability that the randomly selected teen sends and receives between 100 and 125 text messages per day.

2. Determine the probability that the randomly selected teen sends and receives fewer than 75 text messages per day.

3. Determine the probability that the randomly selected teen sends and receives more than 140 text messages per day.

PROBLEM 2 Pizza Anyone?

You have collected data on the delivery times for two local pizza shops, Antonio's Pizza and Wood Fire Pizza. Based on your data, Antonio's Pizza has a mean delivery time of 30 minutes and a standard deviation of 3 minutes. Wood Fired Pizza has a mean delivery time of 25 minutes and a standard deviation of 8 minutes.

1. What factors could influence the delivery time of an order from either pizza shop?

2. What can you conclude based only on the mean and standard deviation for each pizza shop?

3. A friend of yours is planning a party. She needs the pizza for the party delivered in 35 minutes or less or the party will be a complete disaster! Which pizza shop has a greater probability of delivering the order within 35 minutes?

1

PROBLEM 3 You Say Tomato, I Say Prize-Winning Tomato!

1. Brad and Toby both plan to enter the county tomato growing competition. Each person who enters the competition must submit a basket of tomatoes. The judges randomly select a tomato from each contestant's basket. According to the rules of the competition, a "golden" tomato has a diameter between 4 inches and 4.5 inches.

   The diameters of tomatoes in Brad's basket are normally distributed with a mean diameter of 3.6 inches and a standard deviation of 1 inch. The diameters of tomatoes in Toby's basket are also normally distributed with a mean diameter of 3.8 inches and a standard deviation of 0.2 inches.

   When the judges randomly select a tomato from Brad's and Toby's basket, whose is more likely to result in a "golden" tomato?

Be prepared to share your solutions and methods.

Chapter 1 Summary

KEY TERMS

- discrete data (1.1)
- continuous data (1.1)
- sample (1.1)
- population (1.1)
- normal curve (1.1)
- normal distribution (1.1)
- mean (μ) (1.1)
- standard deviation (σ) (1.1)
- standard normal distribution (1.2)
- Empirical Rule for Normal Distributions (1.2)
- *z*-score (1.3)
- percentile (1.3)

1.1 Differentiating Between Discrete Data and Continuous Data

Discrete data are data whose possible values are countable and often finite. The scores of baseball games are examples of discrete data, because a term's score must be a positive whole number or zero.

Continuous data are data which can take any numerical value within a range. Heights of students, times required to complete a test, and distances between cities are examples of continuous data.

Example

The heights of basketball players are examples of continuous data.

1.1 Drawing Distributions for Continuous Data

For continuous data, a relative frequency histogram displays continuous intervals on the horizontal axis and relative frequency on the vertical axis.

Example

Weights of Chicken Eggs (ounces)	Relative Frequency
0.0–0.5	0.05
0.5–1.0	0.23
1.0–1.5	0.44
1.5–2.0	0.22
2.0–2.4	0.06

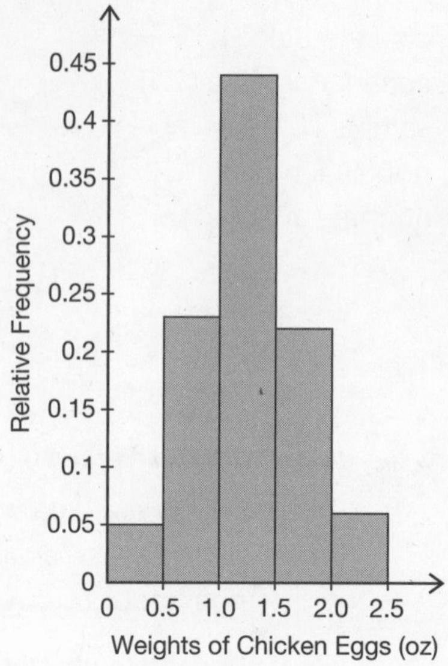

1.1 Recognizing the Difference Between Normal Distributions and Non-normal Distributions

A normal distribution is bell-shaped and symmetrical, and a non-normal distribution is neither bell-shaped nor symmetrical.

Example

The graph does not represent a normal distribution. It is neither bell-shaped nor symmetric, it is skewed.

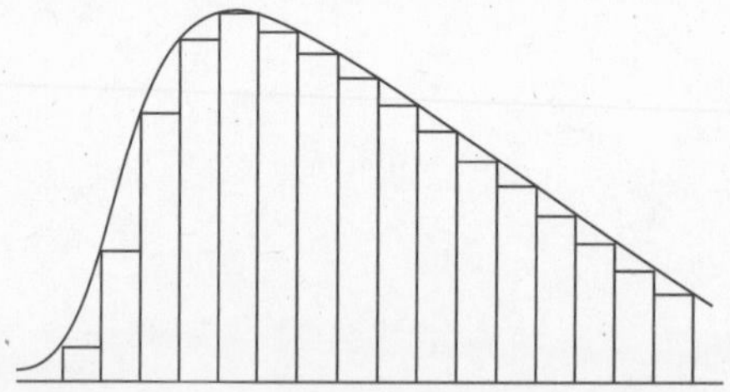

1.1 Recognizing and Interpreting Properties of a Normal Curve and a Normal Distribution

The mean of a normal curve is at the center of the curve. The standard deviation of a normal distribution describes how spread out the data are.

The symbol for the population mean is μ, and the symbol for the sample mean is $\bar{x}$. The standard deviation of a sample is represented with the variable s. The standard deviation of a population is represented with the symbol σ.

Example

The mean is 2.6 and the standard deviation is 0.4.

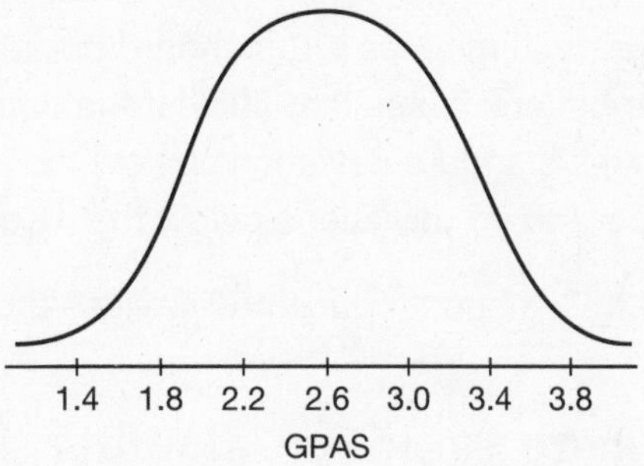

1.2 Recognizing the Connection Between Normal Curves, Relative Frequency Histograms, and the Empirical Rule for Normal Distributions

The standard normal distribution is a normal distribution with a mean value of zero and a standard deviation of 1. The Empirical Rule states that approximately 68% of the data in a normal distribution is within 1 standard deviation of the mean, 95% is within two standard deviations of the mean, and 99.7% is within three standard deviations of the mean.

Example

The percent of data that is more than 2 standard deviations above the mean for the standard normal curve is shaded.

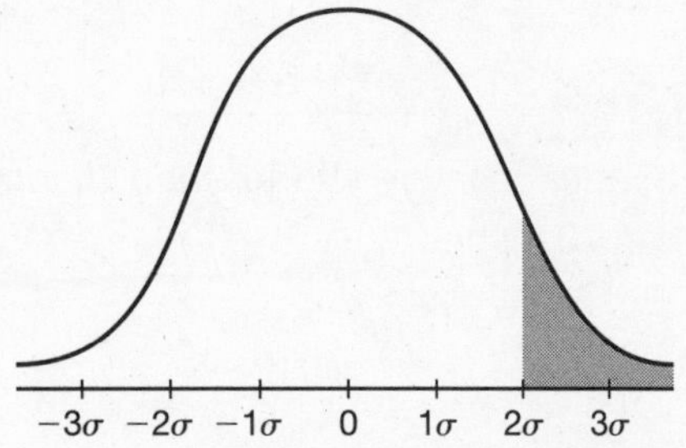

1

1.2 Using the Empirical Rule for Normal Distributions to Determine the Percent of Data in a Given Interval

The Empirical Rule for Normal Distributions states that approximately 68% of the data in a normal distribution is within one standard deviation of the mean, 95% is within two standard deviations of the mean, and 99.7% is within three standard deviations of the mean. The percent of data for any normal distribution can be determined using the Empirical Rule.

Example

Determine the percent of commute times less than 36 minutes for a certain city, given that the commute times are normally distributed and the mean commute is 41 minutes with a standard deviation of 2.5 minutes.

A commute time of 36 minutes is 2 standard deviations below the mean. The Empirical Rule for Normal Distributions states that 50% of the data is below the mean and that 47.5% of the data is within 2 standard deviations below the mean. So, 50% – 47.5% or 2.5% of the data is below 2 standard deviations below the mean.

Approximately 2.5% of commute times are less than 36 minutes.

1.3 Using a *z*-score Table to Calculate the Percent of Data Below any Given Data Value, Above any Given Data Value, and Between any Two Given Data Values in a Normal Distribution

Data points can be converted into *z*-scores which represent the number of standard deviations the data value is from the mean. It is positive if above the mean and negative if below the mean. A *z*-score table can then be used to determine the percent of data you are looking for based on the *z*-scores.

Example

You can calculate the percent of adult men taller than 70 inches, given that adult men's heights are normally distributed and the mean height is 69.3 inches with a standard deviation of 2.8 inches.

$$z = \frac{70 - 69.3}{2.8}$$
$$= \frac{0.7}{2.8}$$
$$= 0.25$$

About 59.87% of adult men are shorter than 70 inches, so 100 − 59.87, or 40.13% of adult men are taller than 70 inches.

1.3 Using a Graphing Calculator to Calculate The Percent of Data Below any Given Data Value, Above any Given Data Value, and Between any Two Given Data Values in a Normal Distribution

To determine the percent of data between two scores on a normal curve, a graphing calculator can be used. The function and its arguments are entered as normalcdf(lower bound of the interval, upper bound of the interval, the mean, the standard deviation).

Example

You can determine the percent of adults with IQ scores between 102 and 132, given that IQ scores are normally distributed and the mean IQ score for adults is a 100 with a standard deviation is 15.

Normalcdf (102, 132, 100, 15)

Approximately 43.05% of adults have IQ scores between 102 and 132.

1.3 Using a *Z*-score Table to Determine The Data Value That Represents a Given Percentile

A percentile is the data value for which a certain percentage of the data is below the data value in a normal distribution. A *z*-score can be used to determine the data value. First, the percent value in the table closest to the percentage you are looking for should be found. Then the *z*-score for the percentile can be found from the table. This can be converted back to the original data value by using the formula for a *z*-score and solving for the *x*.

Example

You can determine the 80th percentile for SAT scores, given that SAT scores are normally distributed and the mean is 1500 with a standard deviation of 280.

The percent value in the *z*-score table that is closest to 80% is 0.0793. The *z*-score for this percent value is -1.41.

$$-1.41 = \frac{x - 1500}{280}$$

$$-394.8 = x - 1500$$

$$1105.2 \approx x$$

The SAT score that represents the 80th percentile is approximately 1105.2.

1.3 Using a Graphing Calculator to Determine The Data Value That Represents a Given Percentile

To determine a percentile on a normal curve, a graphing calculator can be used. The function and its arguments are entered as invNorm(percentile in decimal form, the mean, the standard deviation).

Example

You can determine the 45th percentile for the length of time of a dance studio's recitals, given that the times are normally distributed and the mean is 145 minutes with a standard deviation of 7 minutes.

Invnorm (0.45, 145, 7) $\approx$ 144.12

The length of time that represents the 45th percentile is approximately 144.12 minutes.

1.4 Interpreting a Normal Curve in Terms of Probability

The percent of data values that fall within specified intervals on a normal distribution can also be interpreted as probabilities.

Example

You can calculate the probability that a randomly selected annual precipitation amount in a city is more than 340 inches, given that the amounts are normally distributed with a mean of 320 inches and a standard deviation of 20 inches.

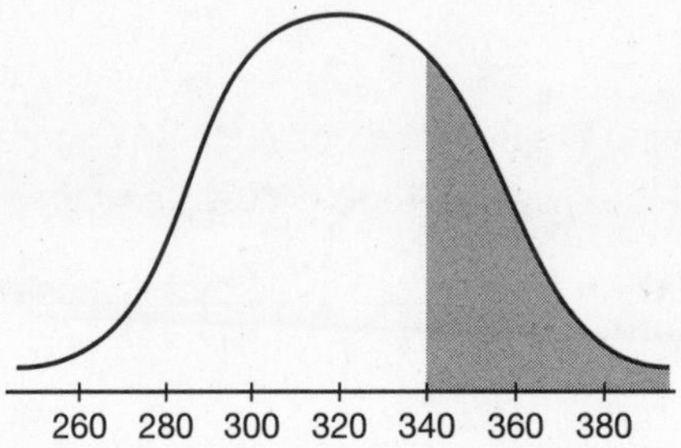

The probability that the randomly selected precipitation amount in a city is more than 340 inches is 16%.

The mean is 320 and one standard deviation above the mean is 340. I know that 34% of the data is between the mean and one standard deviation above the mean. I also know that 50% of the data is above the mean. So, 50 − 34, or 16% of the data is more than one standard deviation above the mean.

1

1.4 Using Normal Distributions to Determine Probabilities

A normal distribution can be used to determine probabilities. The percent of data between specified intervals represents probabilities. The *z*-score table or a graphing calculator can be used to find the percents.

Example

You can determine the probability that a randomly selected student will score between a 74 and an 80 on an exam, if the exam scores are normally distributed and the mean is 82 with a standard deviation of 2.8

The probability that a randomly selected student will score between a 74 and an 80 is approximately 23.54%.

Normalcdf(74,80,82,2.8) ≈ 0.2354.

1.4 Using Normal Distributions And Probabilities to Make Decisions

Determining probabilities of events occurring by using percentages from a normal distribution can help to make decisions about different products or situations.

Example

You can determine the factory that should be used to fill an order if it is needed in between 25 and 30 minutes, if Factory A has a mean order time of 27.5 minutes with a standard deviation of 0.8 minutes and Factory B has a mean order time of 28.2 minutes with a standard deviation of 1.2 minutes. Assume both order times can be represented by a normal distribution.

Factory A should be used because it has the best chance of filling an order between 25 and 30 minutes. The probability Factory A will fill the order between 25 and 30 minutes is 99.82%, while the probability that Factory B will fill the order between 25 and 30 minutes is only 92.94%.

Factory A: normalcdf(25, 30, 27.5, 0.8) ≈ 0.9982

Factory B: normalcdf(25, 30, 28.2, 1.2) ≈ 0.9294

Making Inferences and Justifying Conclusions

2

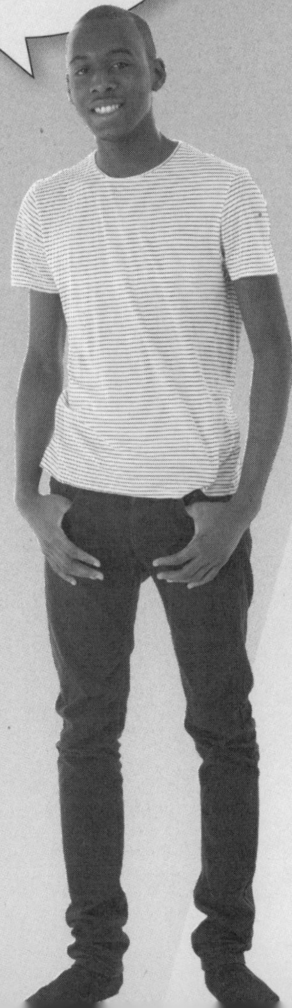
Every 2, 4, and 6 years, Americans head to the polls to select the women and men who will represent them in the Congress and the White House. And more often than that, these Americans will be polled about their choices. Although election polls can be remarkably accurate, there is always some margin for error.

For Real?

Sample Surveys, Observational Studies, and Experiments

LEARNING GOALS

In this lesson, you will:

- Identify characteristics of sample surveys, observational studies, and experiments.
- Differentiate between sample surveys, observational studies, and experiments.
- Identify possible confounds in the design of experiments.

KEY TERMS

- characteristic of interest
- sample survey
- random sample
- biased sample
- observational study
- experiment
- treatment
- experimental unit
- confounding

Have you taken medicine to treat an illness? Imagine that the medicine you took was not really medicine, but just a sugar pill. In medical studies, people who have unknowingly taken a sugar pill—called a placebo—have reported that the pill has had an effect similar to medicine, even though there was no medicine in the pill at all. This is an example of what is called the placebo effect.

Researchers must always be on the lookout for placebo effects. They may be to blame for successful or unsuccessful outcomes to experiments.

PROBLEM 1 Survey Says

You can use data to help answer questions about the world. The specific question that you are trying to answer or the specific information that you are trying to gather is called a **characteristic of interest**.

For example, you can use data to help determine which drug is most effective, teenagers' favorite television program, or how often doctors wash their hands.

One way of collecting data is by using a *sample survey*. A **sample survey** poses one or more questions of interest to obtain sample data from a population. Recall, a population represents all the possible data that are of interest in a survey, and a sample is a subset of data that is selected from the population.

I see how samples are especially useful when collecting data for large populations. Imaging trying to survey every young person in the U.S.!

A researcher wants to design a sample survey to determine the amount of time that U.S. teenagers between the ages of 16 to 18 spend online each day.

1. Identify the characteristic of interest in the sample survey.

2. Identify the population that the researcher is trying to measure by using a sample survey.

3. Augie and Sandy were discussing the population of the survey.

Augie

The population is all 16- to 18-year-olds in the United States.

Sandy

The population is all teenagers in the United States.

Who is correct? Explain your reasoning.

4. Write a survey question or questions that the researcher could use to collect data from the participants in the survey.

2

When sample data are collected in order to describe a characteristic of interest, it is important that such a sample be as representative of the population as possible. One way to collect a representative sample is by using a *random sample*. A **random sample** is a sample that is selected from the population in such a way that every member of the population has the same chance of being selected. A **biased sample** is a sample that is collected in a way that makes it unrepresentative of the population.

5. Joanie and Richie were discussing strategies the researcher could use to select a representative sample of 16- to 18-year-olds.

Joanie

The sample should include 16- to 18-year-olds from various states.

Richie

Include 16- to 18-year-olds who live in various types of communities, like urban, suburban, and rural.

List some additional strategies the researcher should consider when selecting the sample.

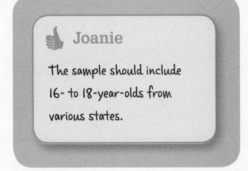

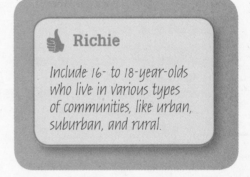

6. Cherese suggested that the researcher could post the survey online and then distribute the link to the survey to students after school on Friday as they are leaving the building.

   Will this method result in a biased sample? Explain your reasoning.

2

PROBLEM 2 Confound It All!

In an **observational study,** data are gathered about a characteristic of the population by simply observing and describing events in their natural settings. Recording the number of children who use the swings at a local park would be an example of a simple observational study.

The results of an observational study state that approximately 70% of in-house day care centers in one U.S. state show as much as 2.5 hours of television to the children per day. The observational study examined 132 day care centers in one state.

1. Identify the population, the sample, and the characteristic of interest in the observational study.

2. List some similarities and differences between an observational study and a sample survey.

An **experiment** gathers data on the effect of one or more **treatments**, or experimental conditions, on the characteristic of interest. Members of a sample, also known as **experimental units**, are randomly assigned to a treatment group.

A placebo treatment is a treatment that is assumed to have no real effect on the characteristic of interest.

Researchers conducted an experiment to test the effectiveness of a new asthma drug. They collected data from a sample of 200 asthma patients. One hundred of the patients received a placebo treatment along with an inhaler. The other one hundred patients received the new drug along with an inhaler. Monthly blood and breathing tests were performed on all 200 patients to determine if the new drug was effective.

3. Identify the population, the sample, and the characteristic of interest in the experiment.

4. What are the treatments in the experiment?

5. What are some ways the researchers could choose a biased sample for this experiment?

Confounding occurs when there are other possible reasons, called confounds, for the results to have occurred that were not identified prior to the study.

6. Suppose one of the treatment groups was given the new drug with an inhaler and the other group was given a placebo with no inhaler. Describe how this design of the experiment introduces a confound.

Talk the Talk

Classify each scenario as a sample survey, an observational study, or an experiment, and explain your reasoning. Then, identify the population, the sample, and the characteristic of interest.

1. To determine whether there is a link between high-voltage power lines and illnesses in children who live in the county, researchers examined the illness rate for 100 children that live within $\frac{1}{4}$ of a mile from power lines and the illness rate for 100 children that live more than $\frac{1}{4}$ of a mile from power lines.

2. Seventy of the school's calculus students are randomly divided into two classes. One class uses a graphing calculator all the time, and the other class never uses graphing calculators. The math department team leader wants to determine whether there is a link between graphing calculator use and students' calculus grades.

3. A medical researcher wants to learn whether or not there is a link between the amount of TV children watch each day and childhood obesity in a particular school district. She gathers data from the records of 15 local pediatricians.

4. In a particular school district, a researcher wants to learn whether or not there is a link between a child's daily amount of physical activity and their overall energy level. During lunch at a school, she distributed a short questionnaire to students in the cafeteria.

Online Time Study, Part I

To design a sample survey, observational study, or experiment, consider these steps:

- Identify the characteristic of interest.
- Identify the population.
- Identify methods to collect the sample so that the sample is not biased.
- Ensure that participants are randomly assigned to a treatment.
- Eliminate elements of the design that may introduce confounding.

1. Design a data collection plan to learn how much time students in your school spend online each day.

   a. Identify the population and the characteristic of interest.

You will revisit this Online Time Study in each lesson of the chapter.

   b. Is the most efficient method for collecting the data a sample survey, an observational study, or an experiment? Explain your reasoning.

   c. Explain how you can gather data from a representative, unbiased sample of students in your school.

Be prepared to share your solutions and methods.

2.2

Circle Up

Sampling Methods and Randomization

LEARNING GOALS

In this lesson, you will:

- Use a variety of sampling methods to collect data.
- Identify factors of sampling methods that could contribute to gathering biased data.
- Explore, identify, and interpret the role of randomization in sampling.
- Use data from samples to estimate population mean.

KEY TERMS

- convenience sample
- subjective sample
- volunteer sample
- simple random sample
- stratified random sample
- cluster sample
- cluster
- systematic sample
- parameter
- statistic

What English word is missing below?

______ ______ ______ ______ ______ ______

When you play word games like this, where you guess the letters until you figure out the word, you think about samples and populations.

For example, you know that the missing word is a sample of the population of words in the English language. Since "e" is a frequently used letter and "z" is used infrequently in words, you would probably guess "e" before you guessed "z".

It is useful in statistics, too, to assume that the characteristics of a sample match those of a population—as long as that sample is chosen wisely!

PROBLEM 1 You Gotta Mix It Up

When you use statistics, you are often measuring the values of a population by focusing on the measurements of a sample of that population. A population does not have to refer to people. It can be any complete group of data—like the areas of 100 circles.

2

The end of this lesson includes 100 circles and a table. The table lists an identification number, the diameter, and the area for each circle. Suppose you want to determine the mean area of all 100 circles. Calculating the areas of all of the circles would be time-consuming. Instead, you can use different samples of this population of circles to estimate the mean area of the entire population.

1. Without looking at the circles, Mauricia decided to use Circles 1–5 for her sample. Is it likely that those 5 circle areas are representative of all 100 circles? Explain your reasoning.

2. Analyze the circles. Select a sample of 5 circles that you think best represents the entire set of circles.

The sample of circles Mauricia chose is called a *convenience sample*. A **convenience sample** is a sample whose data is based on what is convenient for the person choosing the sample.

The sample of circles you chose in Question 2 is called a *subjective sample*. A **subjective sample** is a sample drawn by making a judgment about which data items to select.

Another type of sample is a *volunteer sample*. A **volunteer sample** is a sample whose data consists of those who volunteer to be part of a sample.

Okay, circles can't really volunteer to be in a sample. But people can!

3. Olivia and Ricky discussed whether a convenience sample or a subjective sample is more likely to be representative of the population of circle areas.

> **Olivia**
>
> I think a subjective sample is more likely to be representative of the 100 circles than the convenience sample.

> **Ricky**
>
> The subjective sample and the convenience sample are equally likely to be representative of the 100 circles.

Who is correct? Explain your reasoning.

4. Olivia shared her conclusion about convenience samples, subjective samples, and volunteer samples.

It's the sampling method that leads to the bias. It's not that an individual sample is biased or not.

> **Olivia**
>
> Even though one method may be better than another in a specific situation, collecting data using a convenience sample, subjective sample, or volunteer sample will likely result in a biased sample.

Explain why Olivia's statement is correct.

2

PROBLEM 2 Equal Opportunity for All

A **simple random sample** is a sample composed of data elements that were equally likely to have been chosen from the population.

1. Explain how convenience samples, subjective samples, and volunteer samples do not include data elements that were equally likely to have been chosen from the population.

Using a random digit table is one option for selecting a simple random sample. To use the table, begin at any digit and follow the numbers in a systematic way, such as moving across a row until it ends and then moving to the beginning of the next row.

Random Digit Table										
Line 1	65285	97198	12138	53010	94601	15838	16805	61004	43516	17020
Line 2	17264	57327	38224	29301	31381	38109	34976	65692	98566	29550
Line 3	95639	99754	31199	92558	68368	04985	51092	37780	40261	14479
Line 4	61555	76404	86210	11808	12841	45147	97438	60022	12645	62000
Line 5	78137	98768	04689	87130	79225	08153	84967	64539	79493	74917
Line 6	62490	99215	84987	28759	19177	14733	24550	28067	68894	38490
Line 7	24216	63444	21283	07044	92729	37284	13211	37485	10415	36457
Line 8	16975	95428	33226	55903	31605	43817	22250	03918	46999	98501
Line 9	59138	39542	71168	57609	91510	77904	74244	50940	31553	62562
Line 10	29478	59652	50414	31966	87912	87154	12944	49862	96566	48825
Line 11	96155	95009	27429	72918	08457	78134	48407	26061	58754	05326
Line 12	29621	66583	62966	12468	20245	14015	04014	35713	03980	03024
Line 13	12639	75291	71020	17265	41598	64074	64629	63293	53307	48766
Line 14	14544	37134	54714	02401	63228	26831	19386	15457	17999	18306
Line 15	83403	88827	09834	11333	68431	31706	26652	04711	34593	22561
Line 16	67642	05204	30697	44806	96989	68403	85621	45556	35434	09532
Line 17	64041	99011	14610	40273	09482	62864	01573	82274	81446	32477
Line 18	17048	94523	97444	59904	16936	39384	97551	09620	63932	03091
Line 19	93039	89416	52795	10631	09728	68202	20963	02477	55494	39563
Line 20	82244	34392	96607	17220	51984	10753	76272	50985	97593	34320

You can use two digits at a time to choose a sample of 5 circles.

If the same two-digit number comes up more than once, I'll skip it each time it is repeated and go to the next number.

2. Select a simple random sample of 5 circles using the random digit table. Pick any row of the table. Use the first two digits to represent the first circle of the sample, the next two digits to represent the second circle of the sample, and so on. List the identification numbers of the 5 circles.

You can also use a graphing calculator to generate a random list of numbers.

> You can use a graphing calculator to generate a random list of numbers and select a simple random sample of 5 circles.
>
> **Step 1:** Press **MATH**. Scroll to the **PRB** menu. Select **5:randInt(**
>
> **Step 2:** Enter a lower bound for the random number, an upper bound for the random number, and how many random numbers to generate. Use commas between values as you enter them.
>
> **Step 3:** Press **ENTER**.

The lower bound is 0, the upper bound is 99, and the number of random numbers to generate is 5.

3. Use a graphing calculator to generate a random sample of 5 circles.

4. Calculate the mean area of the circles in your simple random sample.

5. Compare your simple random sample with your classmates' samples. What do you notice?

There are several other types of random samples, including *stratified random samples, cluster samples*, and *systematic samples*.

A **stratified random sample** is a random sample obtained by dividing a population into different groups, or strata, according to a characteristic and randomly selecting data from each group.

You can collect a stratified random sample of circles by first dividing the circles into groups.

Define groups of circles based on the lengths of their diameters.

- Small circles: diameter $\le \frac{1}{4}$ in.
- Medium circles: $\frac{1}{4}$ in. $<$ diameter $\le 1\frac{1}{2}$ in.
- Large circles: diameter $> 1\frac{1}{2}$ in.

Small Circles (46)	Medium Circles (39)	Large Circles (15)
1, 4, 6, 13, 14, 16, 17, 19, 22, 24, 26, 28, 30, 33, 34, 37, 39, 42, 45, 46, 47, 51, 53, 56, 57, 58, 59, 62, 63, 67, 68, 72, 74, 78, 79, 82, 85, 87, 88, 89, 93, 94, 95, 97, 98, 99	0, 2, 3, 8, 9, 10, 11, 12, 21, 23, 25, 29, 31, 35, 36, 40, 41, 43, 49, 50, 52, 61, 64, 65, 66, 69, 71, 73, 75, 76, 77, 80, 81, 83, 84, 86, 90, 91, 96	5, 7, 15, 18, 20, 27, 32, 38, 44, 48, 54, 55, 60, 70, 92

There are about an equal number of small and medium circles and about a third as many small circles. To maintain this ratio in your stratified random sample, you can choose 3 small circles, 3 medium circles, and 1 small circle.

Select random circles from each group using a random digit table or a graphing calculator.

Another option is to randomly select 2 large circles, 6 medium circles, and 6 small circles. This keeps the ratios the same.

6. Collect a stratified random sample of circles. List the sample and explain your method.

7. Calculate the mean of the circle areas in your stratified random sample.

A **cluster sample** is a random sample that is obtained by creating *clusters*. Then, one cluster is randomly selected for the sample. Each **cluster** contains the characteristics of a population.

8. Use the page that contains the circles at the end of this lesson to answer each question.

Here we have to assume that each rectangle contains a representative cluster of circles.

   a. Draw 4 horizontal lines and 2 vertical lines so that the page is divided into 12 congruent rectangles. Each rectangle represents a cluster of circles. Number each cluster from 1 to 12.

   b. Use a graphing calculator or the random digit table to randomly select one of the clusters. List the cluster sample.

   c. Calculate the mean of the circle areas included in your cluster sample.

A **systematic sample** is a random sample obtained by selecting every *n*th data value in a population.

9. Select a systematic sample by choosing every 20th circle. First, randomly choose a number from 0 to 20 to start at and then choose every 20th circle after that.

10. Calculate the mean of the circle areas included in your systematic sample.

2

11. Faheem and Calvin shared their thoughts about random sampling.

Faheem

Simple random sampling, stratified random sampling, and cluster sampling will always produce a representative, unbiased sample.

Calvin

Simple random sampling, stratified random sampling, or cluster sampling does not guarantee a representative, unbiased sample.

Who is correct? Explain your reasoning.

The mean of a sample, $\bar{x}$, can be used to estimate the population mean, μ. The population mean is an example of a **parameter**, because it is a value that refers to a population. The sample mean is an example of a **statistic**, because it is a value that refers to a sample.

The population mean for the 100 circles is $\mu = 0.58\pi$ square inches, or approximately 1.82 square inches.

2

12. Carla collected three simple random samples from the population of 100 circles and calculated the mean of each sample.

> *Carla*
>
> *I didn't expect the sample of 5 circles to have a mean closest to the mean of the population. I must have done something wrong when collecting the samples.*
>
> *Mean of 5 circles $\approx 0.55\pi$ square inches*
>
> *Mean of 15 circles $\approx 0.49\pi$ square inches*
>
> *Mean of 30 circles $\approx 0.65\pi$ square inches*

Is Carla's statement correct? Explain your reasoning.

Online Time Study, Part II

In the first lesson of this chapter, you designed a plan to learn about the amount of time students in your school are online each day.

1. Which sampling method would be best to select the data? Explain your reasoning.

How can you apply your new knowledge of sampling to the Online Time Study?

Be prepared to share your results and methods.

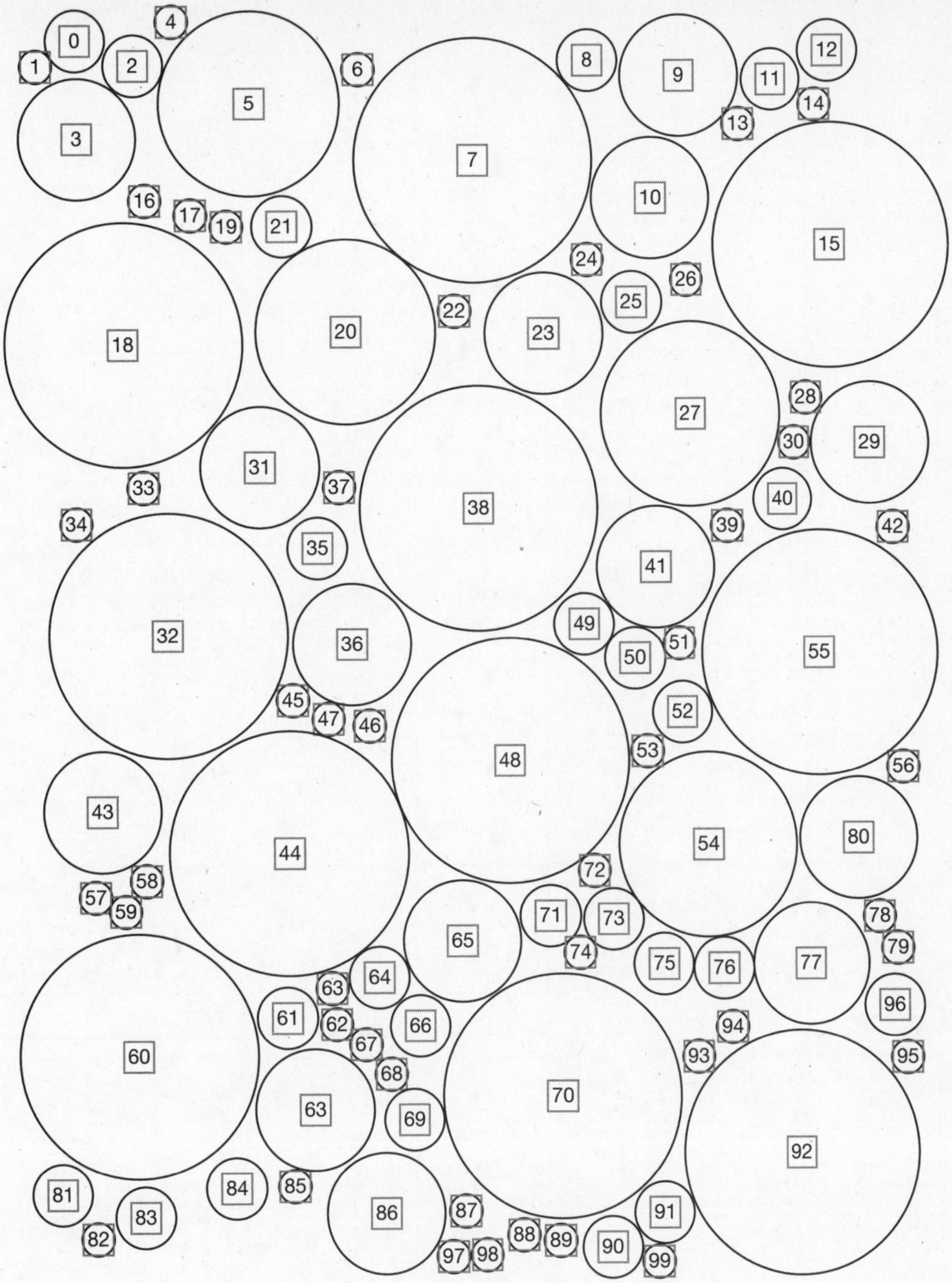
0
1
2
3
4
5
6
7
8
9
10
11
12
13
14
15
16
17
18
19
20
21
22
23
24
25
26
27
28
29
30
31
32
33
34
35
36
37
38
39
40
41
42
43
44
45
46
47
48
49
50
51
52
53
54
55
56
57
58
59
60
61
62
63
63
64
65
66
67
68
69
70
71
72
73
74
75
76
77
78
79
80
81
82
83
84
85
86
87
88
89
90
91
92
93
94
95
96
97
98
99

2

Circle Number	Diameter (in.)	Area (in.^{2})	Circle Number	Diameter (in.)	Area (in.^{2})	Circle Number	Diameter (in.)	Area (in.^{2})
0	$\frac{1}{2}$	$\frac{1}{16}\pi$	18	2	π	36	1	$\frac{1}{4}\pi$
1	$\frac{1}{4}$	$\frac{1}{64}\pi$	19	$\frac{1}{4}$	$\frac{1}{64}\pi$	37	$\frac{1}{4}$	$\frac{1}{64}\pi$
2	$\frac{1}{2}$	$\frac{1}{16}\pi$	20	$1\frac{1}{2}$	$\frac{9}{16}\pi$	38	2	π
3	1	$\frac{1}{4}\pi$	21	$\frac{1}{2}$	$\frac{1}{16}\pi$	39	$\frac{1}{4}$	$\frac{1}{64}\pi$
4	$\frac{1}{4}$	$\frac{1}{64}\pi$	22	$\frac{1}{4}$	$\frac{1}{64}\pi$	40	$\frac{1}{2}$	$\frac{1}{16}\pi$
5	$1\frac{1}{2}$	$\frac{9}{16}\pi$	23	1	$\frac{1}{4}\pi$	41	1	$\frac{1}{4}\pi$
6	$\frac{1}{4}$	$\frac{1}{64}\pi$	24	$\frac{1}{4}$	$\frac{1}{64}\pi$	42	$\frac{1}{4}$	$\frac{1}{64}\pi$
7	2	π	25	$\frac{1}{2}$	$\frac{1}{4}\pi$	43	1	$\frac{1}{4}\pi$
8	$\frac{1}{2}$	$\frac{1}{16}\pi$	26	$\frac{1}{4}$	$\frac{1}{64}\pi$	44	2	π
9	1	$\frac{1}{4}\pi$	27	$1\frac{1}{2}$	$\frac{9}{16}\pi$	45	$\frac{1}{4}$	$\frac{1}{64}\pi$
10	1	$\frac{1}{4}\pi$	28	$\frac{1}{4}$	$\frac{1}{64}\pi$	46	$\frac{1}{4}$	$\frac{1}{64}\pi$
11	$\frac{1}{2}$	$\frac{1}{16}\pi$	29	1	$\frac{1}{4}\pi$	47	$\frac{1}{4}$	$\frac{1}{64}\pi$
12	$\frac{1}{2}$	$\frac{1}{16}\pi$	30	$\frac{1}{4}$	$\frac{1}{64}\pi$	48	2	π
13	$\frac{1}{4}$	$\frac{1}{64}\pi$	31	1	$\frac{1}{4}\pi$	49	$\frac{1}{2}$	$\frac{1}{16}\pi$
14	$\frac{1}{4}$	$\frac{1}{64}\pi$	32	2	π	50	$\frac{1}{2}$	$\frac{1}{16}\pi$
15	2	π	33	$\frac{1}{4}$	$\frac{1}{64}\pi$	51	$\frac{1}{4}$	$\frac{1}{64}\pi$
16	$\frac{1}{4}$	$\frac{1}{64}\pi$	34	$\frac{1}{4}$	$\frac{1}{64}\pi$	52	$\frac{1}{2}$	$\frac{1}{64}\pi$
17	$\frac{1}{4}$	$\frac{1}{64}\pi$	35	$\frac{1}{2}$	$\frac{1}{16}\pi$	53	$\frac{1}{4}$	$\frac{1}{64}\pi$

Circle Number	Diameter (in.)	Area (in.^{2})	Circle Number	Diameter (in.)	Area (in.^{2})	Circle Number	Diameter (in.)	Area (in.^{2})
54	$1\frac{1}{2}$	$\frac{9}{16}\pi$	72	$\frac{1}{4}$	$\frac{1}{64}\pi$	90	$\frac{1}{2}$	$\frac{1}{16}\pi$
55	2	π	73	$\frac{1}{2}$	$\frac{1}{16}\pi$	91	$\frac{1}{2}$	$\frac{1}{16}\pi$
56	$\frac{1}{4}$	$\frac{1}{64}\pi$	74	$\frac{1}{4}$	$\frac{1}{64}\pi$	92	2	π
57	$\frac{1}{4}$	$\frac{1}{64}\pi$	75	$\frac{1}{2}$	$\frac{1}{16}\pi$	93	$\frac{1}{4}$	$\frac{1}{64}\pi$
58	$\frac{1}{4}$	$\frac{1}{64}\pi$	76	$\frac{1}{2}$	$\frac{1}{16}\pi$	94	$\frac{1}{4}$	$\frac{1}{64}\pi$
59	$\frac{1}{4}$	$\frac{1}{64}\pi$	77	1	$\frac{1}{4}\pi$	95	$\frac{1}{4}$	$\frac{1}{64}\pi$
60	2	π	78	$\frac{1}{4}$	$\frac{1}{64}\pi$	96	$\frac{1}{2}$	$\frac{1}{16}\pi$
61	$\frac{1}{2}$	$\frac{1}{16}\pi$	79	$\frac{1}{4}$	$\frac{1}{64}\pi$	97	$\frac{1}{4}$	$\frac{1}{64}\pi$
62	$\frac{1}{4}$	$\frac{1}{64}\pi$	80	1	$\frac{1}{4}\pi$	98	$\frac{1}{4}$	$\frac{1}{64}\pi$
63	$\frac{1}{4}$	$\frac{1}{64}\pi$	81	$\frac{1}{2}$	$\frac{1}{16}\pi$	99	$\frac{1}{4}$	$\frac{1}{64}\pi$
64	$\frac{1}{2}$	$\frac{1}{16}\pi$	82	$\frac{1}{4}$	$\frac{1}{64}\pi$			
65	1	$\frac{1}{4}\pi$	83	$\frac{1}{2}$	$\frac{1}{16}\pi$			
66	$\frac{1}{2}$	$\frac{1}{16}\pi$	84	$\frac{1}{2}$	$\frac{1}{16}\pi$			
67	$\frac{1}{4}$	$\frac{1}{64}\pi$	85	$\frac{1}{4}$	$\frac{1}{64}\pi$			
68	$\frac{1}{4}$	$\frac{1}{64}\pi$	86	1	$\frac{1}{4}\pi$			
69	$\frac{1}{2}$	$\frac{1}{16}\pi$	87	$\frac{1}{4}$	$\frac{1}{64}\pi$			
70	2	π	88	$\frac{1}{4}$	$\frac{1}{64}\pi$			
71	$\frac{1}{2}$	$\frac{1}{16}\pi$	89	$\frac{1}{4}$	$\frac{1}{64}\pi$			

2

2.3

Sleep Tight

Using Confidence Intervals to Estimate Unknown Population Means

LEARNING GOALS

In this lesson, you will:

- Interpret the margin of error for estimating a population proportion.
- Interpret the margin of error for estimating a population mean.
- Recognize the difference between a sample and a sampling distribution.
- Recognize that data from samples are used to estimate population proportions and population means.
- Use confidence intervals to determine the margin of error of a population proportion estimate.
- Use confidence intervals to determine the margin of error of a population mean estimate.

KEY TERMS

- population proportion
- sample proportion
- sampling distribution
- confidence interval

Why do we have dreams? Scientists still don't really have the answer to that question, but there have been many theories.

Some suggest that dreaming is the brain's way of discarding memories you have gathered during the day but no longer need, and studies have shown that dreaming increases as a result of learning. Another theory suggests that your brain is simply constantly churning out thoughts and images and that this doesn't stop when the rest of your body is asleep.

Some scientists are looking to evolution to provide some clues about why we dream—especially since humans don't seem to be the only animals that dream.

Why do you think some animals dream?

PROBLEM 1 Every Vote Counts: Exploring Categorical Data

In a poll of 1100 registered voters before an upcoming mayoral election, 594 people, or 54%, said they would vote to re-elect the current mayor, while the remaining voters said they would not vote for the mayor. The margin of error for the poll was ±3 percent, which means that the poll predicts that somewhere between 51% (54% − 3%) and 57% (54% + 3%) of people will actually vote to re-elect the mayor.

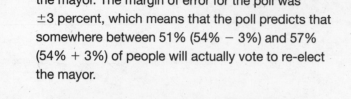

The poll results are categorical data because there are two categories: those who will vote for the mayor and those who won't.

1. Does the poll represent a sample survey, an observational study, or an experiment?

2. Based on the poll, can you conclude that the current mayor will be re-elected? Explain your reasoning.

3. Is it possible for fewer than 50% of respondents in a new sample to respond that they will vote for the mayor in the election? Is it likely? Explain your reasoning.

4. With your classmates, conduct a simulation to represent polling a new sample of 1100 voters.

   a. Divide 1100 by the number of students in your class to determine the size of each student's sample.

   b. Generate an amount of random numbers equal to the sample size in part (a) to represent responses to the polling question. Generate random numbers between 1 and 100, with numbers from 1 to 54 representing support for re-electing the mayor and the numbers 55 to 100 representing support for not re-electing the mayor. Tally the results of your simulation, and then list the total number of tallies for each category.

Here we assume that an average of 54% will vote to re-elect the mayor.

Number of People Who Respond that They Will Vote to Re-elect the Mayor	Number of People Who Respond that They Will Not Vote to Re-elect the Mayor

2

c. Calculate the percent of people who state that they will vote to re-elect the mayor and the percent of people who state that they will vote to not re-elect the mayor based on your simulation.

2

d. Complete the simulation for the 1100 voters by combining the data from your classmates. List the percent of votes for each category.

Percent of People Who Respond that They Will Vote to Re-elect the Mayor	Percent of People Who Respond that They Will Vote to Not Re-elect the Mayor

e. Are the results of the simulation different from the results of the original poll? Explain.

f. If you conducted the simulation over and over, would you expect to get the same results or different results each time? Explain your reasoning.

The percent of voters who actually vote for the mayor in the election is the **population proportion**. The percent of voters in the sample who respond that they will vote for the mayor is the **sample proportion**. The population proportion and sample proportion are measures used for discrete, or categorical, data. For continuous data, these are called the population mean and sample mean.

For continuous data, it's called the population or sample mean. For categorical data, it's called the population or sample proportion.

2

When you and your classmates generated random numbers to simulate multiple samples of the 1100 voters, you came up with different sample proportions. The set of all of your classmates' sample proportions is part of a *sampling distribution*.

A **sampling distribution** is the set of sample proportions for all possible equal-sized samples. A sampling distribution will be close to a normal distribution, and the center of a sampling distribution is a good estimate of a population proportion—in this case, the percent of people who will actually vote to re-elect the mayor.

You can learn the details of deriving the formula for the standard deviation of the sampling distribution, $\sqrt{\frac{\hat{p}(1-\hat{p})}{n}}$, in a statistics course.

But rather than collecting a very large number of samples, a more practical method for estimating a population proportion is to use the sample proportion of a single sample to estimate the standard deviation of the sampling distribution. The standard deviation of a sampling distribution can give you a range in which the population proportion is likely to fall, relative to the sample proportion.

For example, to estimate the standard deviation of the sampling distribution for the sample of 1100 voters, you can use the formula $\sqrt{\frac{\hat{p}(1-\hat{p})}{n}}$, where $(\hat{p})$ is the sample proportion and n is the sample size.

The sample proportion from the original poll is 54%, or 0.54. This is the percent of the 1100 people in the poll who said they would vote to re-elect the mayor.

The standard deviation of the sampling distribution for this poll is

$$\sqrt{\frac{\hat{p}(1-\hat{p})}{n}} = \sqrt{\frac{0.54(1-0.54)}{1100}}$$
$$\approx 0.0150$$

This means that 1 standard deviation below the sample proportion of 54% is 54% − 1.5%, or 52.5%. And 1 standard deviation above the sample proportion of 54% is 54% + 1.5%, or 55.5%.

5. Use the sample proportion and standard deviation of the sampling distribution to label the horizontal axis of the normal curve.

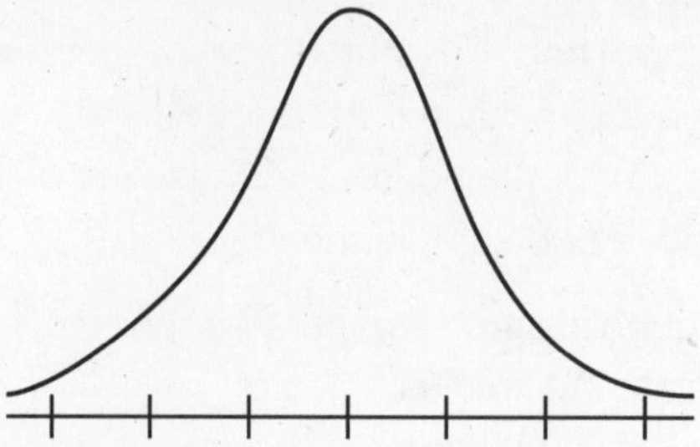

Percent Voting for Mayor's Re-election

6. Bobbie made an observation about the standard deviation of a sampling distribution.

> Bobbie
>
> The standard deviation of a sampling distribution gets smaller and smaller as the size of the sample gets larger and larger.

Is Bobbie's statement correct? Explain why or why not.

An estimated range of values that will likely include the population proportion or population mean is called a **confidence interval**. When stating the margin of error, a 95% confidence interval is typically used. However, other confidence intervals may also be used.

For example, the standard deviation of the sampling distribution for the election sample is 0.015, or 1.5%. Two standard deviations is 3%, so the margin of error is reported as ±3%.

Confidence intervals for a population proportion are calculated using the sample proportion of a sample and the standard deviation of the sampling distribution.

- The lower bound of a 68% confidence interval ranges from 1 standard deviation below the sample proportion to 1 standard deviation above the sample proportion.
- The lower bound of a 95% confidence interval ranges from 2 standard deviations below the sample proportion to 2 standard deviations above the sample proportion.
- The lower bound of a 99.7% confidence interval ranges from 3 standard deviations below the sample proportion to 3 standard deviations above the sample proportion.

2

7. Determine each confidence interval for the election poll.

a. 68%

b. 95%

c. 99.7%

8. Explain the similarities and differences between each confidence interval for the election poll.

9. The result of the original poll was 54% with 3% margin of error. What confidence interval does 3% represent? Explain your reasoning.

10. Use a 95% confidence interval to determine a margin of error and a range of values for each population proportion.

a. A survey of 1500 teenagers shows that 83% do not like waking up early in the morning.

b. A survey of 200 licensed high school students shows that 16% own their own car.

c. A survey of 500 high school students shows that 90% say math is their favorite class.

PROBLEM 2 Sweet Dreams: Exploring Continuous Data

2

A sample of 50 students at High Marks High School responded to a survey about their amount of sleep during an average night. The sample mean was 7.7 hours and the sample standard deviation was 0.8 hour.

Let's determine an estimate for the population mean sleep time for all High Marks High School students.

Notice that 'sample mean' is used instead of 'sample proportion.' This is because the data are continuous.

1. If you gathered data from many new samples, would you expect the samples to have equal means or different means? Explain your reasoning.

Collecting additional samples of 50 students and plotting the sample mean of each sample will result in a sampling distribution. The sampling distribution will be approximately normal, and the mean of the sampling distribution is a good estimate of the population mean.

Just like with the categorical data, a more practical method for estimating the population mean amount of sleep for High Marks High School students is to use the sample mean to calculate an estimate for the standard deviation of the sampling distribution. The formula for the standard deviation of a sampling distribution for continuous data is $\frac{s}{\sqrt{n}}$, where s is the standard deviation of the original sample and n is the sample size.

2. Use the standard deviation from the original sample to determine the standard deviation for the sampling distribution. Explain your work.

3. Use the standard deviation of the sampling distribution to determine a 95% confidence interval for the population mean. Explain your work.

4. Write the 95% confidence interval in terms of the population mean plus or minus a margin of error.

5. Use a 95% confidence interval to determine a range of values for each population mean.

   a. A sample of 75 students responded to a survey about the amount of time spent online each day. The sample mean was 3.2 hours, and the standard deviation of the sampling distribution was 0.9 hour.

   b. A sample of 1000 teachers responded to a survey about the amount of time they spend preparing for class outside of school hours. The sample mean was 2.5 hours, and the standard deviation of the sampling distribution was 0.5 hour.

   c. A sample of 400 adults responded to a survey about the distance from their home to work. The sample mean was 7.8 miles, and the standard deviation of the sampling distribution was 1.6 miles.

Talk the Talk

1. What is the difference between a sample and a sampling distribution?

2. What is the difference between a sample proportion and a sample mean?

Online Time Study, Part III

To summarize data from a sample survey, observational study, or experiment:

- Calculate measures of center.
- Calculate measures of spread.
- Select the most appropriate method(s) to display the data (dot plot, histogram, stem-and-leaf plot, box-and-whisker plot, normal curve).
- Describe the characteristics of the graphical display.

How can you apply your new knowledge from this lesson to analyze data in the Online Time Study?

To analyze data from a sample survey, observational study, or experiment:

- Use confidence intervals to determine a range of values for the population mean(s) or proportion(s).

Recall the study described in previous lessons about the amount of time students in your school are online each day.

1. Will your study involve estimating a population mean or a population proportion? Explain your reasoning.

2. Use a 95% confidence interval to determine a range of values for the population mean, given a random sample of 60 students with a sample mean of 3.5 hours and a standard deviation of 1.1.

3. Use the sample mean and standard deviation of the sampling distribution to label the horizontal axis of the normal curve.

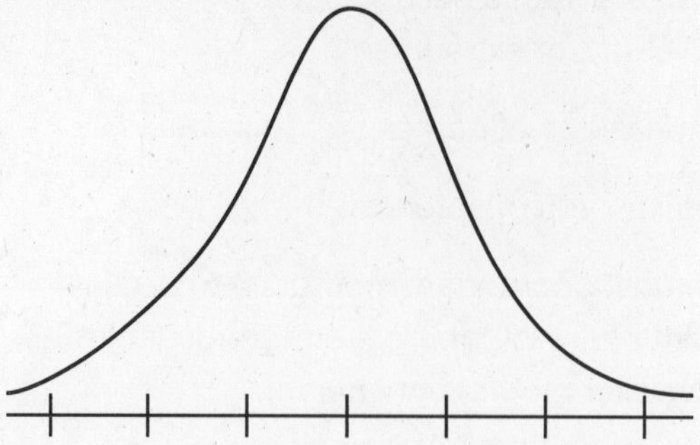

Average Time Spent Online

Be prepared to share your results and methods.

How Much Different?

2.4

Using Statistical Significance to Make Inferences About Populations

LEARNING GOALS

In this lesson, you will:

- Use sample proportions to determine whether differences in population proportions are statistically significant.
- Use sample means to determine whether differences in population means are statistically significant.

KEY TERM

- statistically significant

A person's blood pressure is typically measured using two numbers. One number represents the pressure in the arteries when the heart beats. This is the systolic pressure. The other number represents the pressure in the arteries between heartbeats. This is the diastolic pressure. For example, $\frac{118}{74}$ represents a systolic pressure of 118 and a diastolic pressure of 74.

PROBLEM 1 Whatta Water: Exploring Categorical Data

Commercials on a local TV station claim that Whatta Water tastes better than tap water, but a local news anchor does not believe the claim. She sets up an experiment at a local grocery store to test the claim. A representative, unbiased sample of 120 shoppers participate in the tasting survey using unmarked cups. Out of the 120 people, 64 said Whatta Water tastes better than tap water.

2

1. If shoppers had to choose one or the other and there was no difference in the tastes of the two waters, what proportion of shoppers would you expect to say that Whatta Water tastes better? Explain your reasoning.

2. What is the sample proportion of shoppers who stated that Whatta Water tastes better?

3. Based on your answers to Questions 1 and 2, what reason(s) can you give to doubt Whatta Water's claim? Explain your reasoning.

The term **statistically significant** is used to indicate that a result is very unlikely to have occurred by chance. Typically, a result that is more than 2 standard deviations from the mean, or outside a 95% confidence interval, is considered statistically significant.

Two standard deviations from the mean seems to come up a lot!

4. Use a 95% confidence interval to determine a range of values for the population proportion of people who prefer the taste of Whatta Water. Explain your work.

5. Use the sample proportion and standard deviation of the sampling distribution to label the horizontal axis of the normal curve.

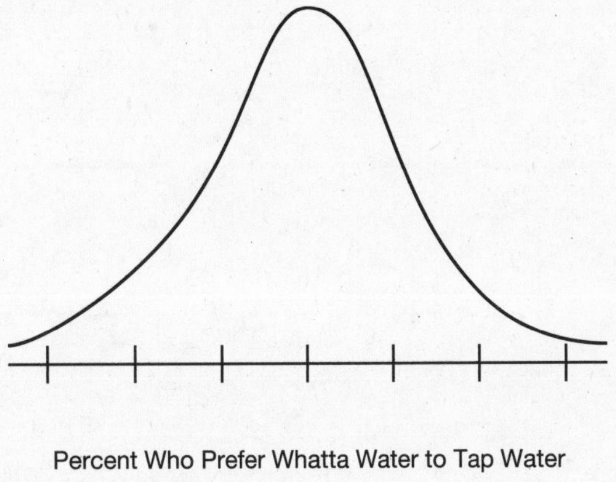
Percent Who Prefer Whatta Water to Tap Water

6. Based on the range of values of the 95% confidence interval, what conclusion can you make about Whatta Water's claim that their water tastes better than tap water?

7. The local water company also conducted a survey of 120 people which they said showed that people prefer tap water over Whatta Water. Forty-one of the respondents said Whatta Water tastes better.

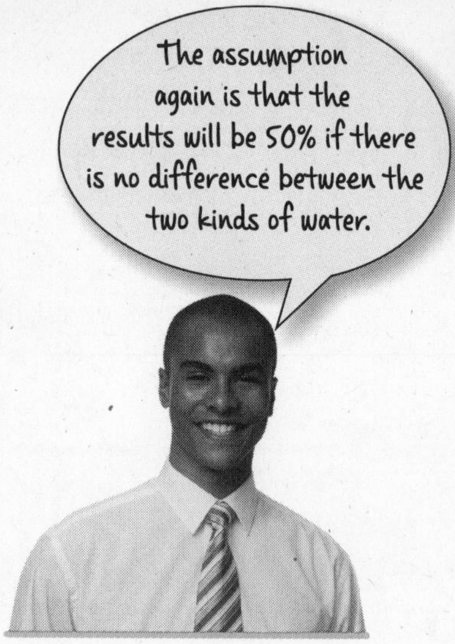
The assumption again is that the results will be 50% if there is no difference between the two kinds of water.

a. Use a 95% confidence interval to determine a range of values for the population proportion of people who prefer Whatta Water. Explain your work.

b. Use the sample proportion and standard deviation of the sampling distribution to label the horizontal axis of the normal curve.

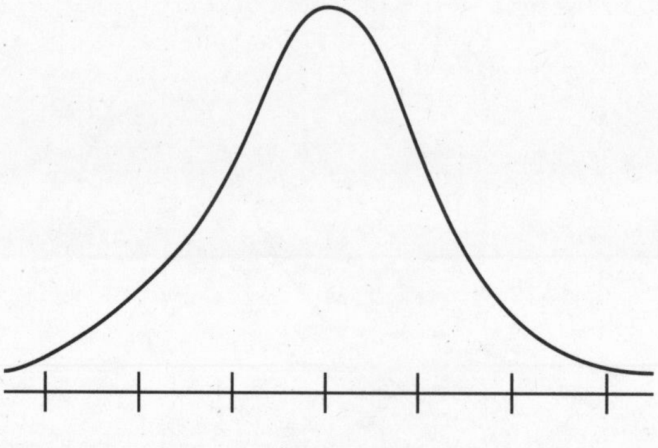

Percent Preferring Whatta Water

c. Based on the range of values of the 95% confidence interval, what conclusion can you draw about the local water company's claim that tap water tastes better than Whatta Water?

8. Use a random number generator to conduct a simulation of the local water company's survey, for a new sample of 120 people. Generate a random number between 1 and 100, with numbers from 1 to 34 representing that Whatta Water tastes better and numbers from 35 to 100 representing that tap water tastes better. List the results in the table.

Percent of People in Simulation Who Said Whatta Water Tastes Better	Percent of People in Simulation Who Said Tap Water Tastes Better

9. On the normal curve in Question 7 part (b), locate and mark the sample proportion of your simulation. Describe the location of the sample proportion on the normal curve.

10. Compare the results of your simulation with the water company's study and with Whatta Water's study. Are your results significantly different? Explain your reasoning.

PROBLEM 2 Nonstop Homework: Exploring Continuous Data

A sample of 40 students at High Marks High School responded to a survey about the average amount of time spent on homework each day. The sample mean was 2.9 hours and the sample standard deviation was 0.8 hour.

This problem is similar to the last problem, only using continuous data instead of discrete data.

1. Use a 95% confidence interval to determine a range of values for the population mean. Explain your work.

2. Label the horizontal axis of the normal curve that represents the sampling distribution.

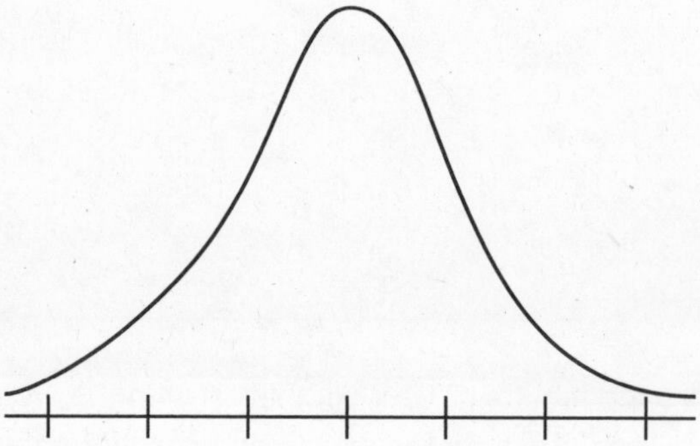

Mean Hours Spent on Homework

3. A new sample of 40 students was taken and the resulting sample mean was 2.70 hours.
   a. On the normal curve in Question 2, locate and mark the sample mean of the new sample. Describe the location of the sample mean on the normal curve.

b. Are the results of the new sample statistically significant? Explain your reasoning.

2

4. What sample mean values are statistically significant? Explain your reasoning.

5. Mary shared a comment about the time she spends on homework.

> *Mary*
>
> *I spend an average of 3.5 hours on homework every night. Compared to the sample mean, the average amount of time I spend on homework every night is statistically significant.*

Is Mary's reasoning valid? Explain why or why not.

PROBLEM 3 Read Between the Lines: Comparing Categorical Data

Two hometown newspapers conducted a poll about whether residents are for or against a tax to provide funding for school renovations in the district. Today's News polled 75 residents and 53 stated that they are in favor of the tax increase. Local Time polled 100 residents and 54 stated they are in favor of the tax increase.

1. Calculate the sample proportion for each poll.

2. Use the results from each poll to estimate a range of values for the population proportion using a 95% confidence interval. Explain your work.

3. The Reporter newspaper published a survey of 90 residents and 38 stated that they are in favor of the tax increase. Use a 95% confidence interval to determine a range of values for the population proportion. Explain your work.

2

If two confidence intervals overlap, then the difference between the population proportions or population means is not statistically significant. If the intervals do not overlap then the difference between the population proportions or population means is statistically significant.

4. Compare the population proportion estimates and determine whether their differences are statistically significant. Explain your reasoning.

   a. The Reporter and Local Times

   b. The Reporter and Today's News

PROBLEM 4 Pressure Situation: Comparing Continuous Data

2

A researcher conducted a randomized experiment to see whether there was a link between a new supplement and blood pressure. She collected data from a representative, unbiased sample of 200 people who had high blood pressure. One hundred of the people were randomly selected to take the supplement and the other 100 people were given a placebo. Recall that a placebo is a treatment that is assumed to have no real effect on the characteristic of interest.

This experiment has two treatments: taking the supplement and taking the placebo.

The participants' blood pressures were recorded at the beginning and at the end of the 12-week experiment, and the difference (end − beginning) was calculated.

1. For the 100-person treatment that took the placebo, what value would you expect for the difference of sample means at the beginning of the experiment and at the end of the experiment. Explain your reasoning.

2. For the 100-person treatment that took the supplement, what value would you expect for the difference of sample means at the beginning of the experiment and at the end of the experiment. Explain your reasoning.

Suppose that the mean difference in blood pressure of the group who took the supplement was -15 with a standard deviation of 3.2, and the mean difference in blood pressure of the group who took the placebo was 1.7 with a standard deviation of 0.3.

3. Interpret and explain the meaning of a negative mean difference for the treatment that took the supplement and a positive mean difference for the treatment that took the placebo.

4. Use a 95% confidence interval to determine a range of values for the population mean of each treatment. Explain your work.

2

5. What conclusion can you make about whether or not the supplement effectively lowers high blood pressure? Explain your reasoning.

The results of an experiment may indicate a correlation but not a causation. Do you remember the difference?

2

PROBLEM 5 Decisions, Decisions . . .

1. A manufacturing company has a policy that states that if significantly more than 2% of computer parts are defective during an 8-hour shift, then the parts from that shift will not be shipped. During an 8 hour shift, 1020 parts were produced and 22 were defective. Should the parts be shipped? Explain your reasoning.

2. The mean grade point average (GPA) of a random sample of 50 High Mark High School students who had a part-time job during the previous grading period is 3.15 with a standard deviation of 0.44. The mean GPA of a random sample of 50 High Mark High School students who did not have a part-time job during the previous grading period is 2.77 with a standard deviation of 0.35. Does that data suggest a possible link between High Mark High School students' part-time job status and their GPA?

PROBLEM 6 The End of the Line

Recall the problem from the previous lesson about part-time job status and grade point average (GPA).

The population mean interval for the GPA of High Mark High School students who have a part-time job, 3.03 to 3.27, does not overlap with population mean interval for the GPA of High Mark High School students who do not have a part-time job, 2.67 to 2.87.

2

1. Carmen shared a conclusion about part-time job status and GPA.

> *Carmen*
>
> *Because the results of the statistical analysis are statistically significant, I can conclude that holding a part-time job will result in a higher GPA.*

Is Carmen's statement correct? Explain why or why not.

The interval for the estimate of the population mean for the GPA of neighboring Great Beginnings High School students who do not have a part-time job is 3.18 to 3.39.

2. Is the GPA of students who do not have a part-time job statistically different at High Mark High and Great Beginnings High School? Explain your reasoning.

3. The estimate for the population mean for the math GPA of Great Beginnings High School students using a sample of the math club is 3.27 to 3.54. The estimate for the population mean for the math GPA of Great Beginnings High School students using a sample of the government club is 3.11 to 3.40.

> *Max*
>
> *The results of the statistical analysis are not statistically significant because the population mean intervals for math GPA overlap.*

Is Max's statement correct? Explain why or why not.

2

Online Time Study, Part IV

To analyze data from a sample survey, observational study, or experiment, you can use statistical significance to make inferences about populations.

Recall the study you have been planning about the amount of time students in your school are online each day.

How can you use statistical significance to make inferences in the Online Time Study?

2

Suppose two samples of data were collected. One sample of 40 students in your school has a sample mean of 2.3 hours and a standard deviation of 0.7 hour. Another sample of 40 students in your school has a sample mean of 3.7 hours and a standard deviation of 1.1 hours.

1. Use a 95% confidence interval to determine whether the estimate of the population means using each sample is statistically significant. Explain your work.

Be prepared to share your results and methods.

2.5

DIY

Designing a Study and Analyzing the Results

LEARNING GOALS

In this lesson, you will:

- Analyze the validity of conclusions based on statistical analysis of data.
- Design a sample survey, observational study, or experiment to answer a question.
- Conduct a sample survey, observational study, or experiment to collect data.
- Summarize the data of your sample survey, observational study, or experiment.
- Analyze the data of your sample survey, observational study, or experiment.
- Summarize the results and justify conclusions of your sample survey, observational study, or experiment.

DIY stands for "do it yourself." So, why not? Try to write an interesting opener yourself for this lesson. Use these hints to help you get started:

- Make your opener related to something about the lesson or the whole chapter.
- Write about something you think other students would be interested in reading.
- Be creative!

Share your opener with your classmates. Which one did you like best?

PROBLEM 1 Do It Yourself!

Use the following guidelines to design and conduct a sample survey, observational study, or experiment, summarize and analyze the data, and draw conclusions. You can use this page as a checklist while planning and conducting your study.

I. Design a sample survey, observational study, or experiment.	
• Select a characteristic of interest to learn about from a sample survey, observational study, or experiment.	
• Select a question that can be answered by collecting quantitative data.	
• Identify the population.	
• Identify the characteristic being studied.	
• Describe the method for choosing a random sample.	
• Address potential sources of bias.	
II. Conduct the sample survey, observational study, or experiment.	
• Use the sampling method to collect data for your sample survey, observational study, or experiment.	
III. Summarize the data of the sample survey, observational study, or experiment.	
• Calculate measures of center.	
• Calculate measures of spread.	
• Select the most appropriate method(s) to display the data (dot plot, histogram, stem-and-leaf plot, box-and-whisker plot, normal curve).	
• Describe the characteristics of the graphical display.	
IV. Analyze the data of the sample survey, observational study, or experiment.	
• Use confidence intervals to determine a range of values for the population mean(s) or proportion(s).	
• Using statistical significance to make inferences about populations.	
V. Draw conclusions based on the results of the sample survey, observational study, or experiment.	
• Write a conclusion that answers the question of interest of your sample survey, observational study, or experiment. Use the data and data analysis to justify your conclusion.	

Be prepared to share your results and methods.

Chapter 2 Summary

KEY TERMS

- characteristic of interest (2.1)
- sample survey (2.1)
- random sample (2.1)
- biased sample (2.1)
- observational study (2.1)
- experiment (2.1)
- treatment (2.1)
- experimental unit (2.1)
- confounding (2.1)
- convenience sample (2.2)
- subjective sample (2.2)
- volunteer sample (2.2)
- simple random sample (2.2)
- stratified random sample (2.2)
- cluster sample (2.2)
- cluster (2.2)
- systematic sample (2.2)
- parameter (2.2)
- statistic (2.2)
- population proportion (2.3)
- sample proportion (2.3)
- sampling distribution (2.3)
- confidence interval (2.3)
- statistically significant (2.4)

2.1 Identifying Characteristics of Sample Surveys, Observational Studies, and Experiments

The characteristic of interest is the specific question to be answered or the specific information to be gathered for sample surveys, observational studies, and experiments. The entire set of items from which data can be selected is the population. A subset of the population that is selected is a sample.

Example

Fifty-five deer are randomly selected from a park in the township. They are anesthetized, weighed, and then released back into the park.

The population is all of the deer in the park. The sample is the 55 deer selected. The characteristic of interest is the mean weight of the deer.

2

2.1 Differentiating Between Sample Surveys, Observational Studies, and Experiments

A sample survey poses a question of interest to a sample of the targeted population. An observational study gathers data about a characteristic of the population without trying to influence the data. An experiment gathers data on the effect of one or more treatments on the characteristic of interest.

Example

A study states that approximately 78% of planes arrived on time during a 3 hour period at an airport.

This is an observational study since the study only gathered data about the number of planes that arrived on time and did not try to influence the data.

2.2 Using a Variety of Sampling Methods to Collect Data

Sampling methods could include convenience sampling, volunteer sampling, simple random sampling, stratified random sampling, cluster sampling, and systematic sampling.

Example

The data set below shows the number of late student arrivals at four elementary schools each week for five weeks.

Number of Late Arrivals				
Week 1	**Week 2**	**Week 3**	**Week 4**	**Week 5**
49	37	45	44	43
47	41	45	46	48
39	43	38	44	42
43	47	39	39	42
52	55	50	54	55

You can create a stratified random sample with 5 data values to describe the number of late arrivals by randomly choosing one school from each of the 5 weeks and recording the number of late arrivals: {39, 37, 50, 46, 42}.

2.2 Identifying Factors of Sampling Methods that could Contribute to Gathering Biased Data

Some sampling methods introduces bias, which reduces the likelihood of a representative, unbiased sample.

Example

A cereal company conducts taste tests for a new cereal on a random sample of its employees.

There is bias in this study because the taste test is only conducted on the company's employees. It is possible that the employees will prefer the cereal of the company that employs them for other reasons than taste.

2

2.2 Exploring, Identifying, and Interpreting the Role of Randomization in Sampling

You can use random sampling by using a random digit table or a graphing calculator to create unbiased samples.

Example

For the data set, you can use a calculator to generate four random numbers between 1 and 10. Then you can use the numbers generated to create a random sample of four from the data set.

The 25-meter freestyle times, in seconds, of ten young swimmers are shown.

Swimmer	1	2	3	4	5	6	7	8	9	10
Time	21.2	19.3	18.7	20.6	20.5	18.4	22.9	23.5	18.2	17.9

Possible random numbers: 19.3, 18.7, 22.9, 17.9.

2.3 Recognizing that Data from Samples are Used to Estimate Population Proportions and Population Means

Data from samples are used to calculate confidence intervals that estimate population proportions and population means.

Example

2

A sample of 250 women responded to a survey about the amount of money they spend on cosmetics each month. The sample mean was \$45.50 and the sample standard deviation was \$10.75.

The interval from \$44.14 to \$46.86 represents a 95% confidence interval for the population mean.

$$\frac{s}{\sqrt{n}} = \frac{10.75}{\sqrt{250}} \approx 0.68$$

2.4 Using Sample Proportions to Determine Whether Differences in Population Proportions are Statistically Significant

To determine the sample proportions that would be statistically significant, use the normal curve and label it based on the standard deviation from the sample.

Example

Use the sample proportion and standard deviation of the sampling distribution to label the horizontal axis of the normal curve. Then, determine what sample proportions would be statistically significant.

A sample proportion of families that own dogs is 74%, and the standard deviation is 0.017.

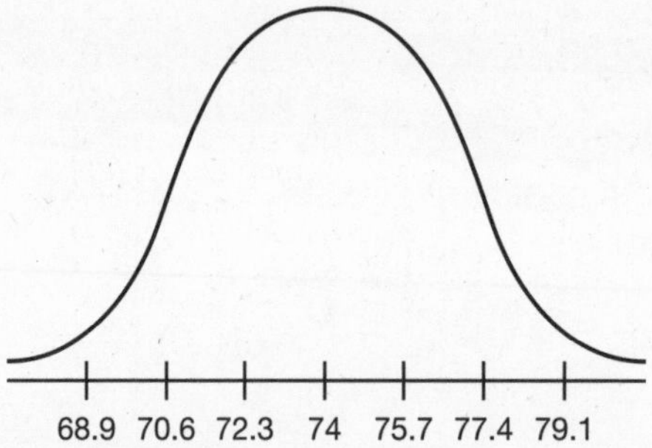

Sample proportion values less than 70.6% and greater than 77.4% are statistically significant because those values are outside of the 95% confidence interval.

2.4 Using Sample Means to Determine Whether Differences in Population Means are Statistically Significant

Use the sample mean and standard deviation to determine the margin of error for the confidence interval. The margin of error is 2 times the standard deviation.

Example

Use a 95% confidence interval to determine a range of values for the population mean. Explain your work.

A sample of 80 doctors took a stress test. The sample mean was 44.5 and the sample standard deviation was 14.8.

The interval from 41.2 to 44.5 represents a 95% confidence interval for the population mean.

The margin of error is approximately ± 3.30.

$$\frac{s}{\sqrt{n}} = \frac{14.8}{\sqrt{80}} \approx 1.65$$

$2(1.65) = 3.30$

2.5 Conducting a Sample Survey, Observational Study, or Experiment to Answer a Question

You can determine what type of sample technique would be most appropriate to answer a question for a sample survey, observational study, or experiment.

Example

Suppose you want to estimate the number of senior citizens in a town that are on public assistance.

You can assign all the senior citizens in the town an ID number and use a computer to randomly generate a sample of senior citizens. This technique provides a random sample of the population of the senior citizens in the town, and random sampling is typically representative of a population.

2

Searching for Patterns

3

The Aquarium of the Pacific's Watershed Exhibit shows the intricacies of the Los Angeles flood channel system. Originally, many of the channels were small streams, but were converted to concrete flood channels. The impacts of this change help create what the City of Angels is today.

Patterns: They're Grrrrrowing!

Exploring and Analyzing Patterns

3.1

LEARNING GOALS

In this lesson, you will:

- Identify multiple patterns within a sequence.
- Use patterns to solve problems.

You can find patterns everywhere! Sometimes you can describe them in terms of color, shape, size or texture. Other times, a pattern's beauty isn't evident until you describe it using mathematics.

Let's consider a pattern found in nature—the family tree of a male drone bee. Female bees have two parents, a male and a female whereas male bees have just one parent, a female. In this family tree the parents appear below the original male drone bee.

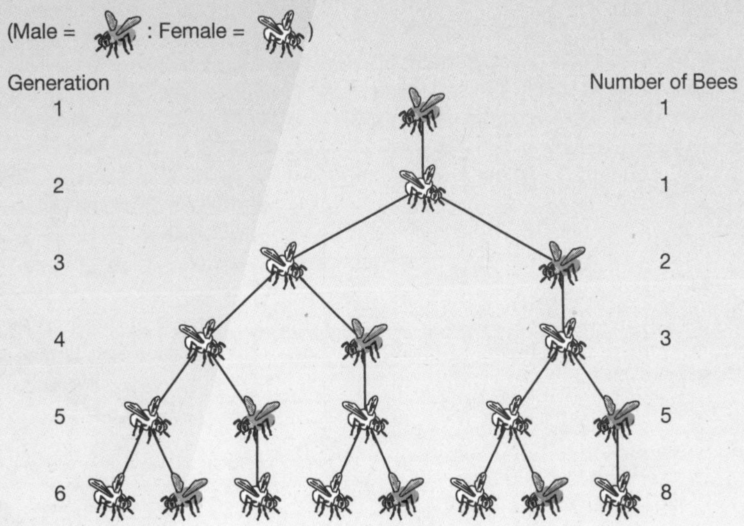

The total number of bees in each generation follows the pattern:

$$1, 1, 2, 3, 5, 8, \ldots$$

What makes this particular pattern fascinating is that it seems to appear everywhere! This pattern is called the Fibonacci Sequence and you can find it in flowers, seashells, pineapples, art, architecture, and even in your DNA!

Do you see the pattern? If so, name the next three terms.

PROBLEM 1 There's More Than One Way to Tile a Floor

Terrance owns a flooring company. His latest job involves tiling a square room. Terrance's customer, Mr. Rivera, requests a tile pattern of alternating black, white, and gray tiles as shown. Each tile is one square foot.

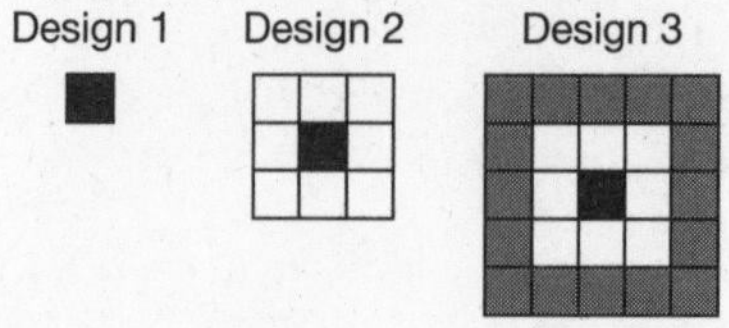
Design 1
Design 2
Design 3

1. Analyze Terrance's design of a tile pattern for a square floor. Describe as many patterns as you can.

2. Sketch the design for a square floor that is 9 feet by 9 feet.

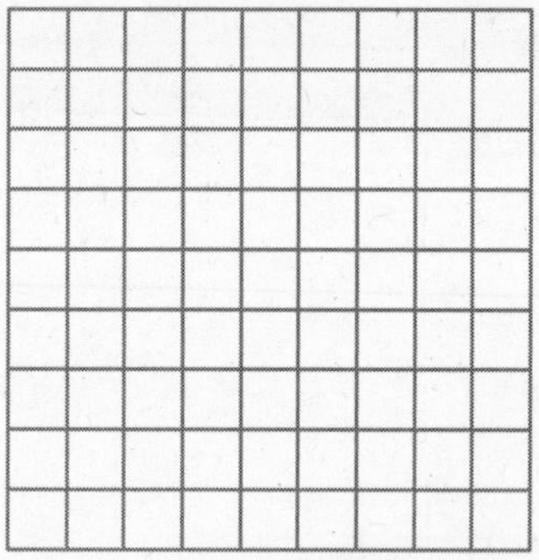

Remember, each tile is one square foot.

3. Describe the key features of Design 8 of a square floor. Write as many key features as you can.

A table might help you organize the various patterns you noticed in Question 1.

Design	1	2	3	4	5	6	7	8
Square Dimensions								
Edge Color								
Number of Black Tiles								
Number of White Tiles								
Number of Gray Tiles								
Total Tiles								

4. A hotel manager wants Terrance to tile their lobby using the same design he created for Mr. Rivera. The lobby measures 45 feet by 45 feet. He wants the outer edge to be the same color as the center tile. Will this occur? Justify your answer.

Think about how you can work backwards to get to this answer efficiently.

3

5. Very picky Paula Perkins requests a tile floor from Terrance. She also wants the alternating black, white, and gray tile pattern; however, she wants the outer edge of the tile to match her wall color. The room is 101 feet by 101 feet and the wall color is white. What color must the center tile be to ensure the outer edge is white? Show or explain your work.

How can you predict what will happen without doing all of the calculations?

PROBLEM 2 Can You Keep a Secret?

The class president, vice president, and treasurer of a high school count the ballots for the homecoming king election. The election result is generally kept a secret until the pep rally, when the winner is announced in front of the entire senior class. Unfortunately, this year's ballot counters are not very good at keeping a secret. The very next day, each ballot counter tells two of their friends in the senior class the election result, but makes each friend vow not to spread the result. However, each of the ballot counter's friends cannot keep a secret either. The following day each friend of each ballot counter shares the election result with two of their friends in the senior class. This pattern continues for the entire week leading up to the pep rally.

Let's assume that no student is told the result of the election twice.

1. Create a visual model to represent this problem situation. Describe the patterns you observe.

2. How many new seniors will know the winner of the homecoming king election on the fourth day? Explain your reasoning.

3. The total number of students in the senior class is 250. If the ballot counters knew the election result on Monday, will every senior already know the winner of the election when the result is announced at the pep rally 6 days later? Explain your reasoning.

PROBLEM 3 How Large Is Your Yard?

Maureen and Matthew are designing their backyard patio. There will be an entrance and exit off the front and back of the patio. The sequence shown represents different designs depending on the size of the patio.

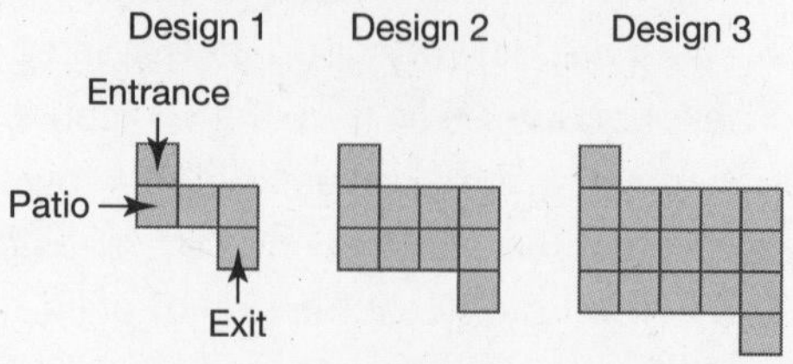

1. Analyze each design in the sequence. Describe as many patterns as you can.

2. Sketch Design 6 of the sequence.

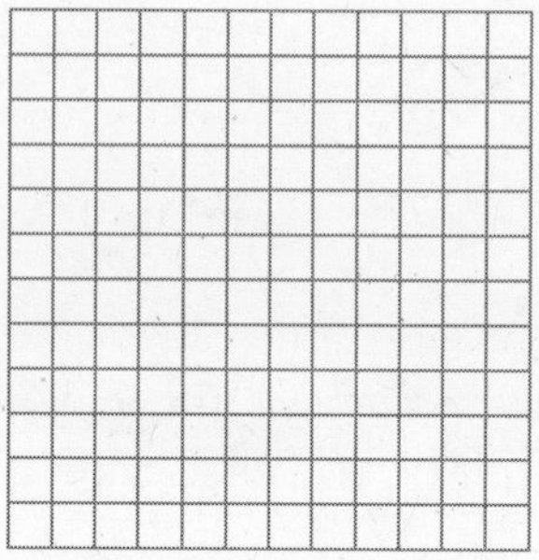

3. Matthew has 180 tiles he can use for this project. Identify the largest patio design that he can make. Show or explain your reasoning.

Be prepared to share your solutions and methods.

Are They Saying the Same Thing?

3.2

Using Patterns to Generate Algebraic Expressions

LEARNING GOALS

In this lesson, you will:

- Generate algebraic expressions using geometric patterns.
- Represent algebraic expressions in different forms.
- Determine whether expressions are equivalent.
- Identify patterns as linear, exponential, or quadratic using a visual model, a table of values, or a graph.

Are natural habits hard to break? The answer for most grocery stores would be, "Why in the world would we break these habits?" This is the reason why many grocery stores have followed a tried-and-true way for laying out their items in the aisles. Studies have shown that most Americans tend to prefer to shop in a counter-clockwise pattern; thus, most grocery stores have their produce at the front and to the right of the entrance which then leads (in a counter-clockwise manner) toward the bakery. And more cleverly, the bakery is toward the middle or the back of the store. From here, many stores lead you to the meat section and then the dairy section. So, why are the bakery, meat, and dairy sections toward the back of the store? Once again, grocery stores embrace people's natural tendencies. For most families, the most needed items are meats, breads, and milk. So, when these items are toward the back of the store, it provides more chances for customers to make "impulse" purchases along the way—buying things that weren't on the original grocery list!

While scientists don't know what causes this impulse (moving in a counter-clockwise manner, or buying items that aren't necessarily needed), it is extremely strong.

This impulse to move in a counter-clockwise direction can be thought of as a pattern similar to animal migrations. Is this the only way to get to where you are going? Of course not, but for some reason, it seems to be a more comfortable path. When problem solving in mathematics there are often many ways for you to approach a problem, but usually you choose a familiar method. Do you usually find one way to do something and then stick with it, or do you look for different methods?

PROBLEM 1 Floors by Terrance

Terrance's flooring business from the problem, *There's More Than One Way to Tile a Floor*, was booming! He decides to hire several employees to help lay out his tile designs. It will be necessary for Terrance to describe his tile designs in a clear manner so that all of the employees can create them correctly. Recall that Terrance's square floor design uses alternating black, white, and gray tiles.

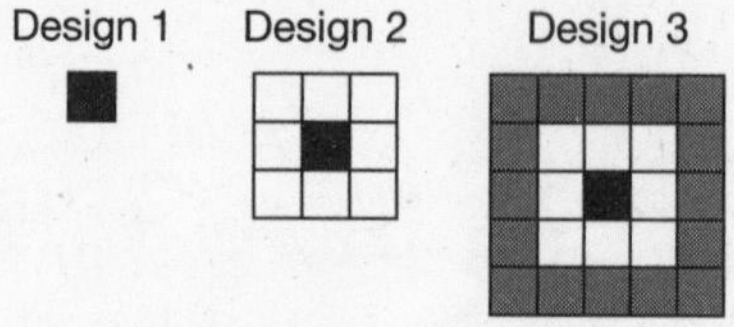

1. Describe the pattern in terms of the number of new tiles that must be added to each new square floor design.

2. Write an expression to represent the number of new tiles that must be added to an n by n square floor design. Let n represent the number of tiles along each edge of the square.

3. Describe which values for n make sense in this problem situation?

4. Ramone determined an expression to represent this pattern. His expression and explanation are shown.

Ramone

Design	1	2	3
New Tiles	0	8	16

The expression $8(n - 1)$ represents Terrance's square floor pattern. I noticed that the number of new tiles is increasing by 8 in each new design.

Explain why Ramone's expression is incorrect.

3

5. Describe the pattern as new tiles are added as linear, quadratic, exponential, or none of these. Explain your reasoning.

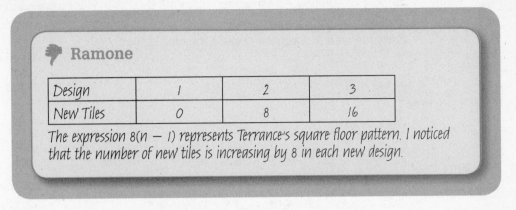

6. Terrance asks his employees to determine the number of new tiles added to Design 2 to create Design 3. Each employee describes a unique method to determine the number of additional tiles needed to create Design 3. Represent each of his employee's explanations with an algebraic expression that describes how many new tiles must be added to an $n \times n$ square to build the next design.

Wilma

I must add 3 tiles to each of the four sides of the white square, which is $4 \cdot 3$ tiles. Then I must add 1 tile at each corner. So the number of additional tiles added to a Design 2 square floor design is $4 \cdot 3 + 4$.

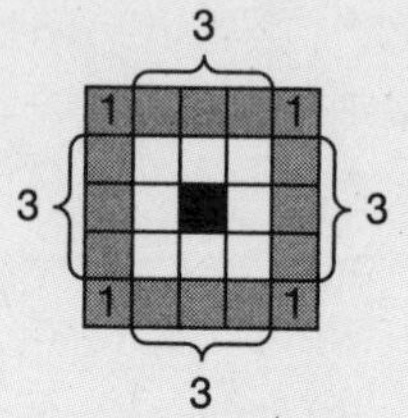

Expression: ____________________

Howard

I must add 5 tiles to two of the sides and 3 tiles to the other two sides. The number of additional tiles added to Design 2 square floor design is $2(3 + 2) + 2 \cdot 3$.

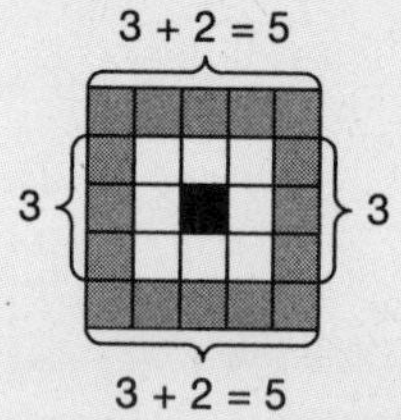

Expression: ____________________

Tyler

I need to add 3 tiles four times and then add the four corner tiles. The number of additional tiles added to Design 2 square floor design is 3 + 3 + 3 + 3 + 4.

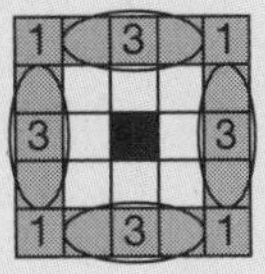

Expression: ______________________________

Tamara

The way I look at it, I really have two squares. The original square for Design 2 has 3 · 3 tiles. The newly formed Design 3 square has 5 · 5 tiles. So, the number of additional tiles added to the Design 2 square floor design is 5 · 5 − 3 · 3.

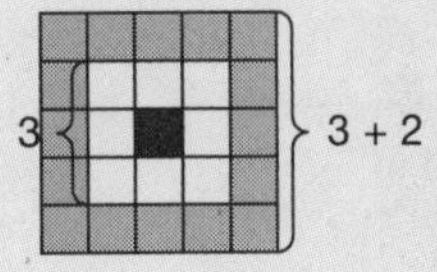

Expression: ______________________________

7. Which expression do you think Terrance should use? Explain your reasoning.

Does the expression you determined match one of the expressions Terrance's employees determined?

3

8. Michael and Louise analyze the expressions they wrote for each student. They both determined that the expression to represent Tamara's method is $(n + 2)^2 - n^2$. Michael claims that this expression is quadratic because of the n^2 term. Louise disagrees and says the expression is linear because the pattern is linear.
Who is correct? Explain your reasoning.

9. Use each expression you determined in Question 6 to calculate the number of tiles that must be added to squares with side lengths of 135 tiles to create the next design.

Wilma's expression:

Tyler's expression:

Howard's expression:

Tamara's expression:

10. Wilma tells Terrance that since all of the expressions resulted in the same solution, any of the expressions can be used to determine the number of additional tiles needed to make more $n \times n$ designs. Terrance thinks that the employees need to use more values in the expressions than just one to make this conclusion.
Who is correct? Explain your reasoning.

Recall that two or more algebraic expressions are equivalent if they produce the same output for all input values. You can verify that two expressions are equivalent by using properties to rewrite the two expressions as the same expression.

11. Show that Wilma, Howard, Tyler, and Tamara's expressions are equivalent. Justify your reasoning.

3

Let's revisit the problem, *Can You Keep a Secret?* about the homecoming king election. The visual model shown represents the number of new seniors who learn about the election result each day that passes.

Day 1

Day 2

Day 3

1. Analyze the pattern.

    a. Complete the table to summarize the number of new seniors who learn about the election result each day. Then write an expression to represent the number of new seniors who learn about the election result on the *n*th day. Finally, describe how each part of your expression relates to the visual model.

Number of Days That Pass	Number of Seniors Who Hear the Results That Day
1	
2	
3	
4	
5	
6	
n	

b. Create a graph of the data from your table on the coordinate plane shown. Then draw a smooth curve to model the relationship between the number of days that pass and the number of seniors who hear the senior election results.

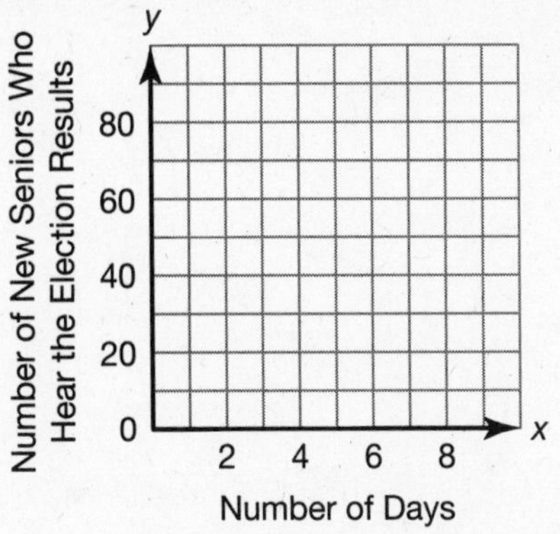

2. Do all the points on the smooth curve make sense in terms of this problem situation? Why or why not?

When you model a relationship on a coordinate plane with a smooth curve, it is up to you to consider the situation and interpret the meaning of the data values shown.

3. Describe this pattern as linear, exponential, quadratic, or none of these. Then write the corresponding equation. How does each representation support your answer?

4. Describe the key characteristics of your graph. Explain each characteristic algebraically and in terms of this problem situation.

5. After how many days will 500 new seniors learn about the election results?

6. Determine the number of seniors who hear the election results on the twelfth day. Does your answer make sense in the context of this problem? Explain your reasoning.

PROBLEM 3 Several Spreading Sequences of Squares

Let's revisit the problem, *How Large Is Your Yard?* about backyard patio designs. The model shown represents the first three designs Maureen and Matthew could use. Each square represents 1 square foot.

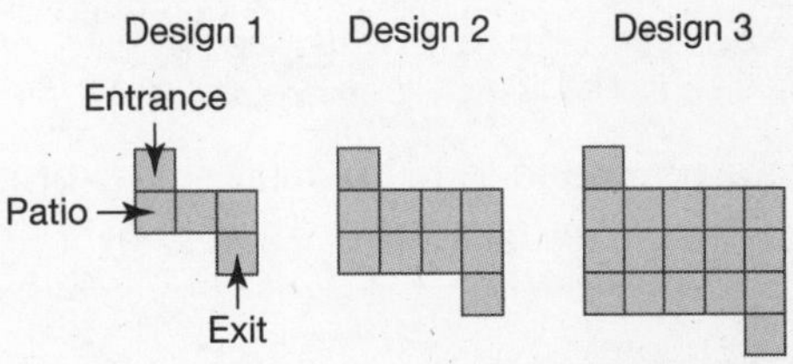

1. Determine the number of squares in the next two patio designs of the pattern.

2. Write an expression to determine the total number of squares in patio Design n. Describe how each part of your expression relates to the visual model.

3. Maureen and Matthew each write different expressions to represent the patio designs.

a.

Maureen

$(n + 2)^2 - 2(n + 1)$

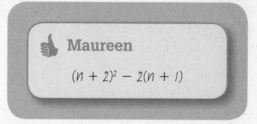

Maureen's expression uses subtraction. How can she take away tiles if the number of tiles in each term is increasing?

Describe how each term in Maureen's expression represents the visual model.

3

b.

Matthew

$n^2 + 2n + 2$

Use a graphing calculator to graph each expression. Is Matthew's expression correct? Explain your reasoning in terms of the graph.

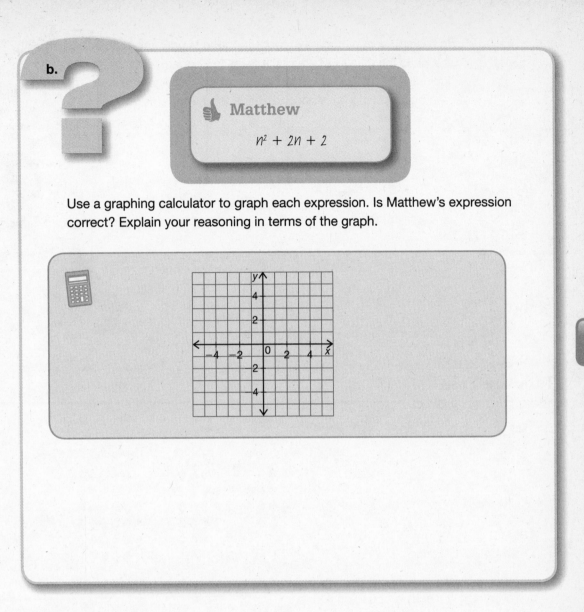

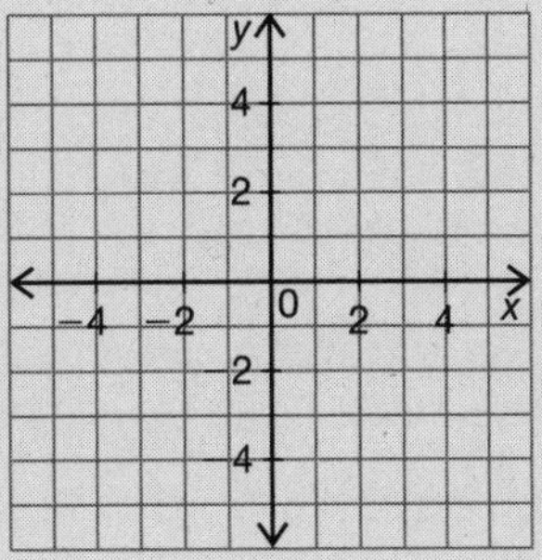

4. Identify the parts of the graph that represent this problem situation.

3

5. In order to accommodate outdoor furniture, a grill, and a shed, the patio must have an area of at least 125 square feet (not including the walkways). What is the smallest design Matthew can build and still have enough space for these items?

How is the number of tiles in each design related to the one that came before it?

Talk the Talk

1. Analyze the pattern shown.

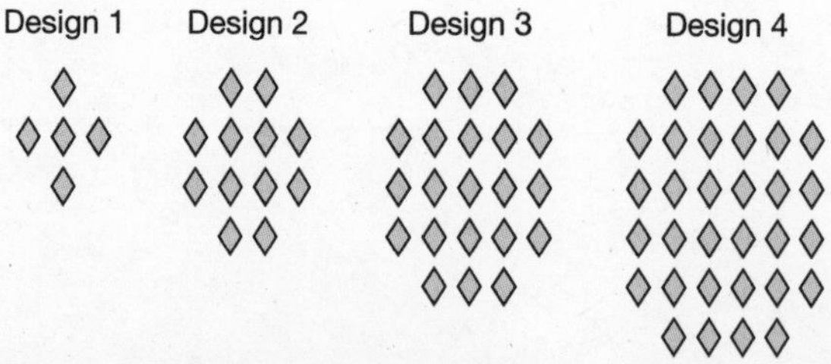

   a. Identify two expressions that represent the total number of diamonds used to construct Design n.

   b. Describe how your expressions relate to the visual model.

c. Algebraically prove your expressions are equivalent.

d. Graphically show that your expressions are equivalent.

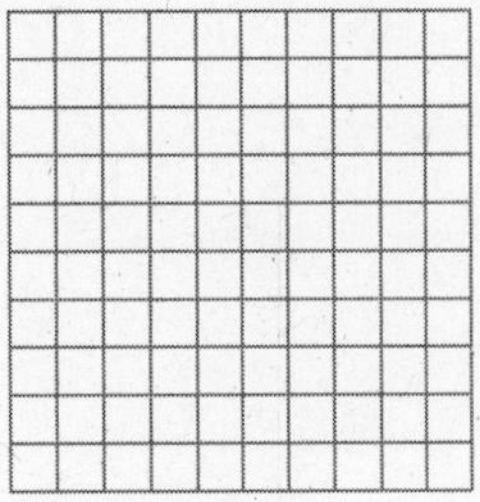

2. Describe the ways you can prove any two expressions are equivalent.

Be prepared to share your solutions and methods.

3

Are All Functions Created Equal?

3.3

Comparing Multiple Representations of Functions

LEARNING GOALS

In this lesson, you will:

- Identify equivalent forms of functions in various representations.
- Model situations using tables, graphs, and equations.
- Use functions to make predictions.
- Determine whether two forms of a function are equivalent.

KEY TERMS

- relation
- function
- function notation

Every year during the first full week in August, the residents of Twinsburg, Ohio literally see double! That's because Twinsburg hosts the annual Twin Day Festival. It is the largest gathering of twins in the world, with thousands of twins, triplets, and multiple-birth families converging on the town for a weekend of games and activities. Although twins develop their own unique personalities, they often stand out in a crowd. It might be an interesting experience for twins and non-twins alike to be in a town completely filled with groups of people who look the same. *Not* having a person who looks just like you might actually make you stand out in the crowd.

Twins only account for about 1% of the pregnancies in the world, but the number of twin births actually varies depending on where you live. For example, the rate of twin births in Massachusetts is much higher than the rate in New Mexico. The highest rates in the world are found in central Africa while the lowest rates are found in Asia.

What do you think might account for differences throughout the world in the rate of twin births? Have you ever known twins? Would you like to have a twin brother or sister?

PROBLEM 1 You Aren't Looking Like Yourself Today

Understanding patterns not only gives insight into the world around you, it provides you with a powerful tool for predicting the future. Pictures, words, graphs, tables, and equations can describe the exact same pattern, but in different ways.

A relation is a mapping between a set of input values and a set of output values. In the problem, *The Cat's Out of the Bag*, you used a visual model, graph, table, and context to describe the relation between the number of ballot counters, and the total number of seniors that learned the result of the homecoming king election. In relations such as this one, there is only one output for each input. This type of relation is called a *function.* A **function** is a relation such that for each element of the domain there exists exactly one element in the range. **Function notation** is a way to represent functions algebraically. The function $f(x)$ is read as "f of x" and indicates that x is the input and $f(x)$ is the output.

Remember that the domain is the set of all the input values and the range is the set of all the output values.

3

Directions: Cut out the relations provided on the following pages. You will encounter graphs, tables, equations, and contexts. Analyze and then sort the relations into groups of equivalent representations. All relations will have at least one match.

Attach your groupings on the blank pages that follow the cut-out pages. Then provide a brief rationale for how you grouped each set of relations.

Be careful—all groupings do not necessarily have the same number of representations. Also, remember that equations can be written in different forms and still be equivalent.

A

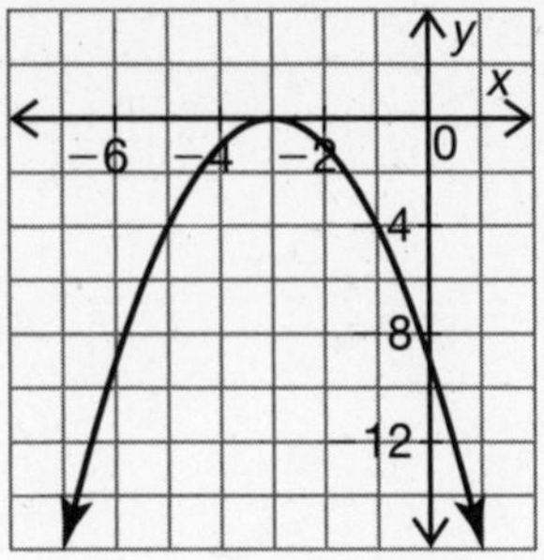

B

$f(x) = x^2 + 2x + 5$

C

x	y
1	2
2	4
3	6
4	8
5	10

D

$f(x) = x^2 + 6x + 5$

E

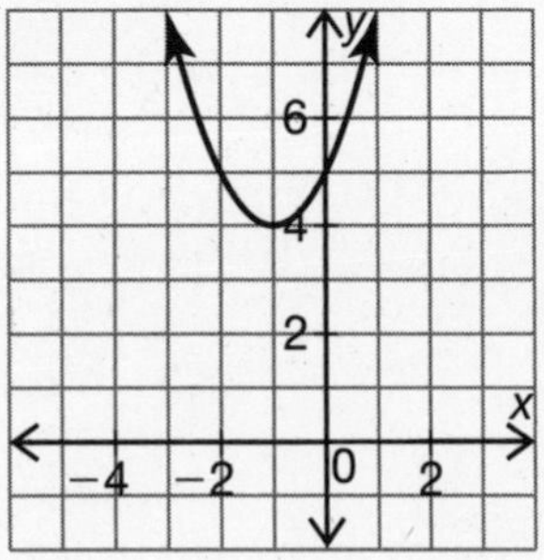

F

$f(x) = -(x^2 + 6x + 9)$

3

3

G

$f(x) = 2x$

H

$f(x) = (x + 5)(x + 1)$

I

$f(x) = -(x + 3)(x + 3)$

J

A relation with a line of symmetry at $x = -3$, a vertex that is a maximum value, and a graph that opens down.

K

Louise heard a rumor. She tells the rumor to two people the next day. The two people that she told then tell two more people the following day, who each then go on to tell two more new people the rumor the following day. The relationship between the days that have passed and the number of new people who hear the rumor that day.

L

x	y
−3	8
−2	5
−1	4
0	5
1	8

3

3

M

x	y
−4	−1
−3	0
−2	−1
−1	−4
0	−9

N

$y = 2^x$

O

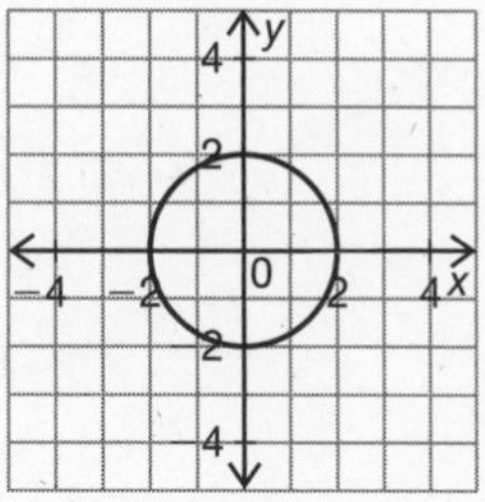

P

$y = (x + 3)^2 - 4$

Q

x	y
0	1
1	2
2	4
3	8
4	16

R

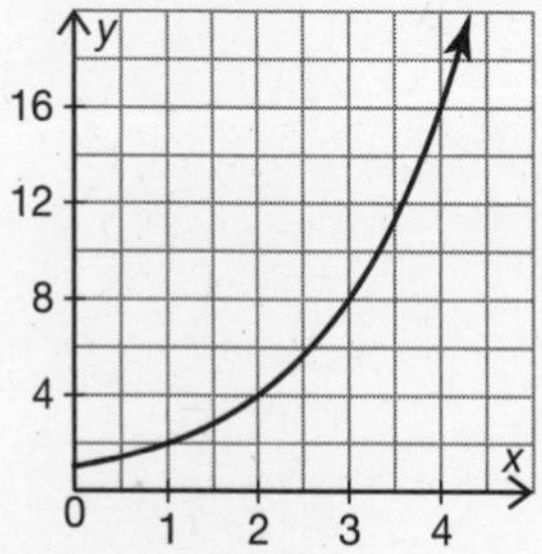

3

3

S

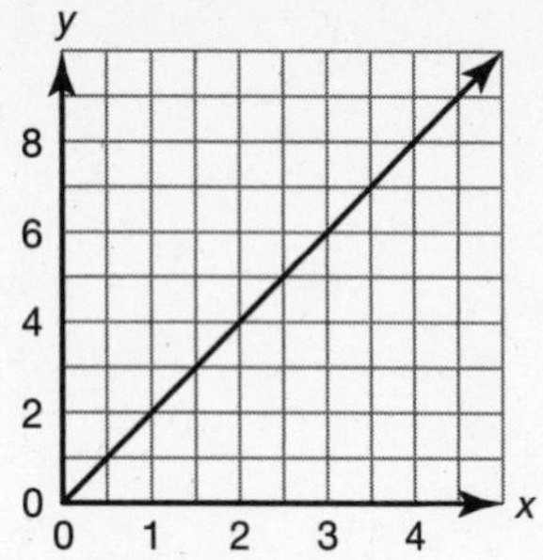

T

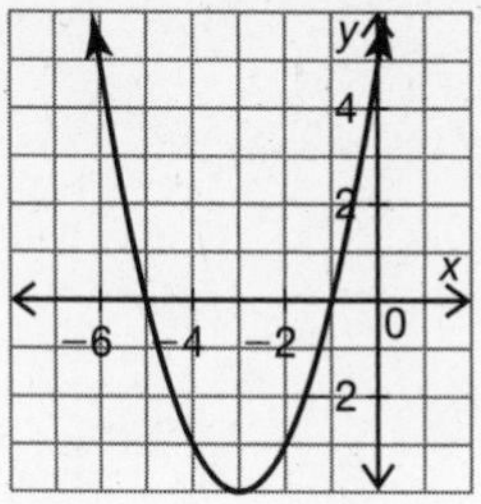

U

Erika is worried that her secret got out. On the first day she and her best friend were the only people who knew about the secret. But now, two new people are finding out the secret every day. The relationship between the number of days that have passed and the total number of people who know about her secret.

V

$x^2 + y^2 = 4$

W

x	y
−5	0
−4	−3
0	5
1	12
2	21

X

x	y
−1	1.73
−1	−1.73
0	2
0	−2
1	1.73
1	−1.73

3

3

3

3

3

3

© Carnegie Learning

1. What strategies did you use to sort the representations into your groups?

Did you come up with more than one way to show that different representations are equivalent?

2. How do you know which relations are functions and which are not functions? Explain your reasoning in terms of the graph, table, and equation.

3. Identify the function family associated with each grouping. How can you determine the function family from the graph, table, context, and the equation?

PROBLEM 2 Why Are You So Square?

A ceramic tile company creates a new line of decorative kitchen and bathroom tiles. The company will sell larger tiles that are created from combinations of small gray and white square tiles. The designs follow the pattern shown.

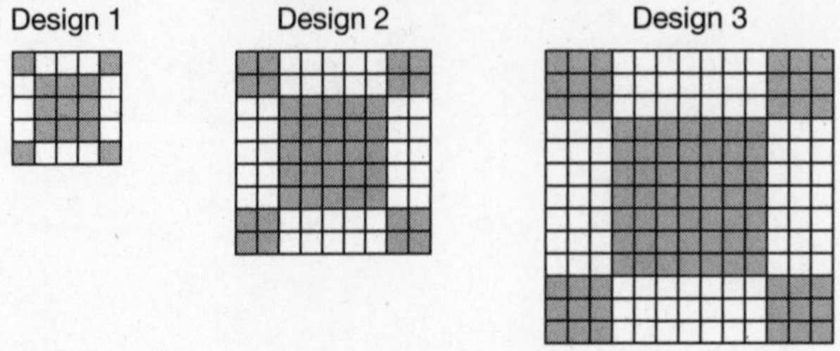

1. Analyze the tile designs. Describe all of the various patterns that you notice.

2. Numerically organize the pattern.

Design Number	1	2	3	4	7	10	
Number of White Tiles, $w(n)$							
Number of Gray Tiles, $g(n)$							
Total Number of Tiles, $t(n)$							

3. What new patterns do you notice?

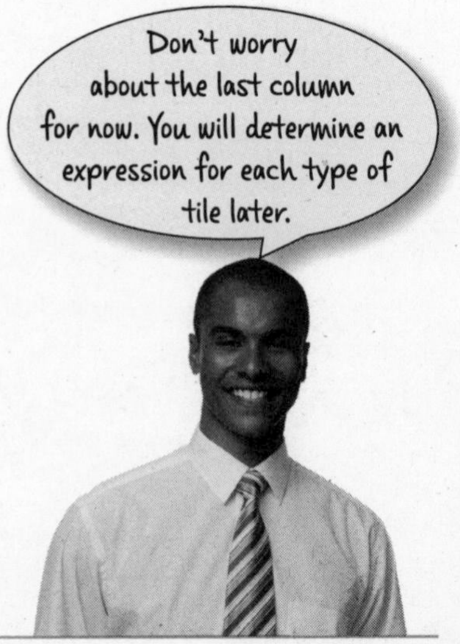

Don't worry about the last column for now. You will determine an expression for each type of tile later.

4. How many total tiles are in Design 7? How many of the tiles are white? How many are gray? Explain your reasoning.

5. A hotel would like to order the largest design possible. They have enough money in their budget to order a design made up of 1700 total gray and white tiles. Which design can they afford? How many tiles in the design will be white? How many will be gray? Explain your reasoning.

3

6. Complete the last column of the table in Question 2 by writing an expression to describe the number of white tiles, gray tiles, and total tiles for Design n.

7. Tonya and Alex came up with different expressions to represent the number of gray tiles in each pattern. Their expressions are shown.

Tonya	Alex
$4n^2 + (2n + 1)(2n + 1)$	$(4n + 1)^2 - 4n(2n + 1)$

Tonya claims that they are the same expression written different ways. Alex says, "One expression has addition and the other has subtraction. There is no way they are equivalent!"

Who is correct? Justify your reasoning using algebraic and graphical representations.

3

You may have noticed several patterns in this sequence. An obvious pattern is that the sum of the white tiles and gray tiles is equal to the total number of tiles. This pattern is clear when analyzing the values in the table. However, adding $w(n)$ and $g(n)$ creates a brand new function that looks very different from the function $t(n)$.

In order to prove that the sum of the white tiles and gray tiles is equal to the total number of tiles, you must show that the expressions are equivalent.

$w(n) + g(n)$	$t(n)$
$4n(2n + 1) + (2n + 1)^2 + 4n^2$	$(4n + 1)^2$
$(8n^2 + 4n) + (4n^2 + 4n + 1) + 4n^2$	$(4n + 1)(4n + 1)$
$16n^2 + 8n + 1$	$16n^2 + 8n + 1$

8. Analyze the context, table, and expressions in this problem.

   a. Identify the function family that describes the pattern for the number of white tiles. Explain your reasoning.

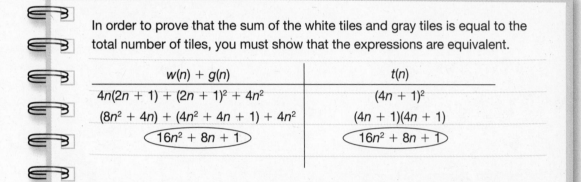

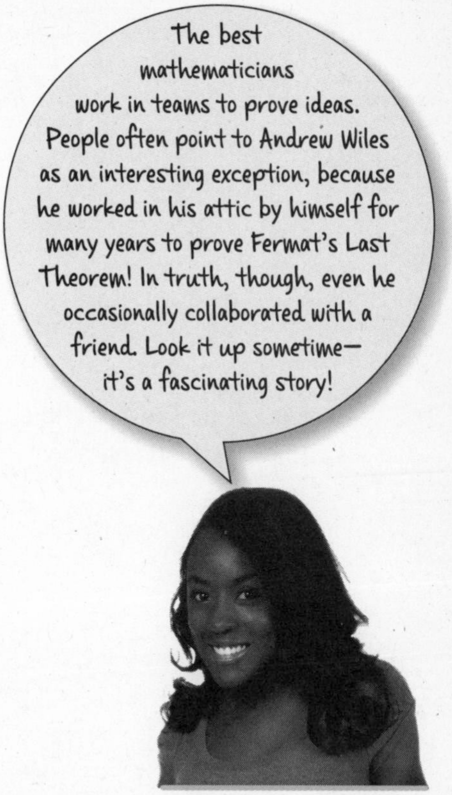
The best mathematicians work in teams to prove ideas. People often point to Andrew Wiles as an interesting exception, because he worked in his attic by himself for many years to prove Fermat's Last Theorem! In truth, though, even he occasionally collaborated with a friend. Look it up sometime—it's a fascinating story!

   b. Identify the function family that describes the pattern for the number of gray tiles. Explain your reasoning.

   c. When you add the functions that represent the number of gray tiles and white tiles, does the new function belong to the same function family? Explain your reasoning.

9. Describe the relationship between the number of white tiles and gray tiles in each design. Prove that this relationship exists.

There are many ways to prove something. Mathematical proofs consist of equations, written arguments, pictures, and flow charts. Use correct terminology to describe mathematically why you know something is true.

10. Analyze the tile patterns.

   a. Prove that the number of white tiles is always an even number.

   b. Prove that the total number of tiles is always an odd number.

Talk the Talk

Choose a word that makes each statement true. Explain your reasoning.

always	sometimes	never

You can use a word more than once, or not at all. Choose wisely!

1. Two functions are __________________ equivalent if their algebraic representations are the same.

2. Two functions are __________________ equivalent if they produce the same output for a specific input value.

3. Two functions are __________________ equivalent if their graphical representations are the same.

Be prepared to share your solutions and methods.

3

3.4

Water Under the Bridge

Modeling with Functions

LEARNING GOALS

In this lesson, you will:

- Use multiple representations of functions to model and solve problems.
- Use multiple representations of functions to analyze problems.

"It's just water under the bridge" is more than a saying for some hydrologists. To them, it's their career. Some hydrologists specialize in the design of city drainage systems.

So, you might be asking: how important is a city's drainage system? The key function to any drainage system is to channel rain water out of the area at the maximum speed possible. In the early part of the 20th century, the Los Angeles River routinely jumped its banks causing some areas of the city to flood. Outraged citizens demanded a better means of draining water after torrential rains. Hydrologists at the time decided to convert the Los Angeles River from a natural river to a massive storm drain. By pouring concrete and building up the sides of the drain, the city no longer flooded. However, the water that rushes through the drain can reach speeds of 45 miles per hour. These speeds are obviously very dangerous for anyone who might be in the storm drain system at the time of the storm. So while the drain has helped save the city from destruction caused by flooding, many lives have been lost as a result of citizens and rescuers being swept away in the drain system during a storm.

Do you think the city should raise the height of the drain so fewer people fall in? Would that affect how quickly the water flows through the drain?

PROBLEM 1 The Water's Five Feet High and Rising

A nearby town hired a civil engineer to rebuild their storm drainage system. The drains in this town are open at the top to allow water to flow directly into them. While designing the drains, the engineer must keep in mind the height and the width of the drain. She needs to consider the height because the water cannot rise above the drain or it will flood the town and cause major destruction. However the drain must also be wide enough that it will not get clogged by debris.

The civil engineer will use rectangular sheets of metal to build the drains. These sheets are bent up on both sides to represent the height of the drain. An end view of the drain is shown.

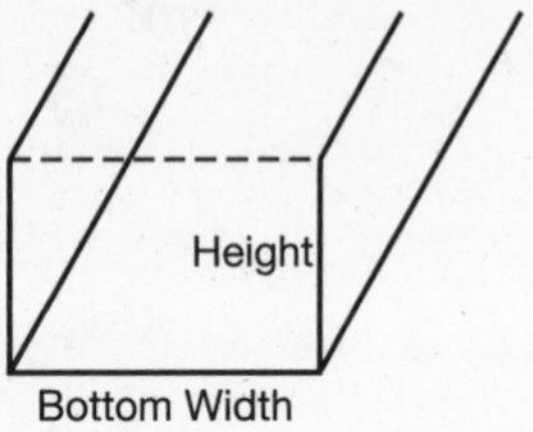

1. Use a sheet of paper to model a drain.

   a. Compare your model of a drain to your classmate's models. Identify similarities and differences between your models.

   b. How does folding the sides of the drain affect the bottom width of the drain?

   c. Describe the drain that you think best fits the needs of the town. Explain your reasoning.

The sheets of metal being used to create the drain are 8.5 feet wide. The engineer wants to identify possible heights and bottom width measurements she could use to construct the drains.

2. Determine the bottom width for each given height. Then complete the table by choosing different heights and calculating the bottom widths for those heights. If necessary, construct models of each drain.

Height of the Drain (feet)	Bottom Width of the Drain (feet)
0	
1.5	
3	

Which height values make sense for this situation?

3. Describe how to calculate the bottom width for any height.

4. Define a function $w(h)$ for the bottom width given a height of h feet.

5. The engineer needs to identify the measurements that allow the most water to flow through the drain. What does the engineer need to calculate? What does she need to consider?

In order to determine the drain dimensions that allows the most water to flow through, the engineer must calculate the cross-sectional area. The cross-sectional area of a drain is shown.

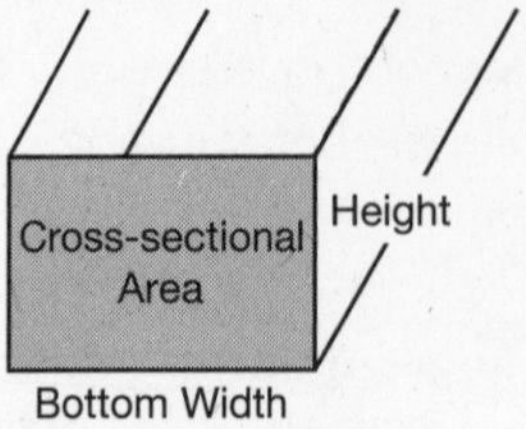
Cross-sectional Area
Height
Bottom Width

Do I just use w for width? Didn't I already write a formula to determine width? Hmmmm maybe I should look back . . .

6. Describe how to determine the cross-sectional area of any drain.

7. Predict and describe the drain with the maximum cross-sectional area.

8. Define a function $A(h)$ for the cross-sectional area of the drain with a height of h feet.

9. Use a graphing calculator to graph the function $A(h)$. Label your axes.

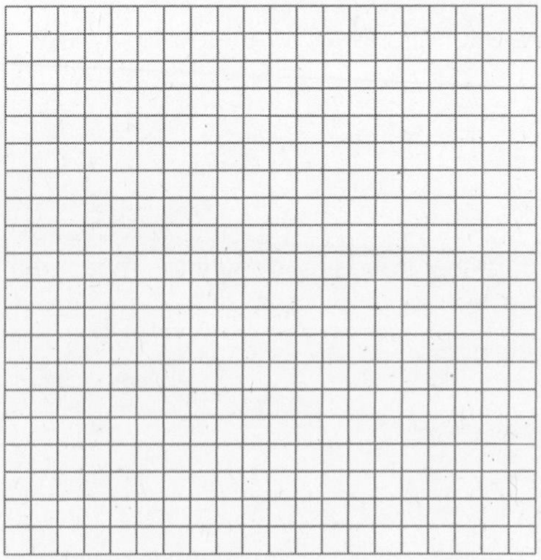

10. Analyze your graph.

a. What is the maximum cross-sectional area for the drain pipe? Explain your reasoning.

b. Identify the intercepts of $A(h)$. What does each mean in terms of this problem situation? Label each intercept on the graph.

3

c. Identify the equation of the axis of symmetry. Then label the axis of symmetry on the graph. Finally, describe the relationship between the axis of symmetry and the maximum cross-sectional area.

11. Draw and label the drain with the greatest cross-sectional area.

Is there a way to determine the maximum cross-sectional area using the x-intercepts?

12. In this problem you built a new function $A(h) = h(8.5 - 2h)$ using two existing functions.

a. What is the first factor in this function? What does it represent in terms of this problem situation?

b. What is the second factor in this function? What does it represent in terms of this problem situation?

3

c. Identify the function families represented by each factor.

d. When these factors are multiplied together what type of function is created? Why does this happen?

PROBLEM 2 Determine the Best Design

A civil engineering company is hired to design a new drainage system for your town. To construct one of the storm drains, a sheet of metal that is 15.25 feet wide is folded on both sides.

Describe the drain that has the maximum cross-sectional area. Include at least two different representations in your description. Show all work and explain your reasoning.

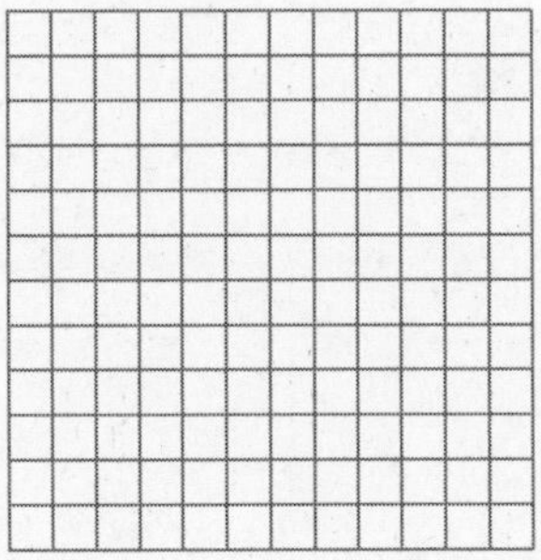

Be prepared to share your solutions and methods.

3

I've Created a Monster, $m(x)$

3.5

Analyzing Graphs to Build New Functions

LEARNING GOALS

In this lesson, you will:

- Model operations on functions graphically.
- Sketch the graph of the sum, difference, and product of two functions on a coordinate plane.
- Predict and verify the graphical behavior of functions.
- Build functions graphically.
- Predict and verify the behavior of functions using a table of values.
- Build functions using a table of values.

KEY TERM

- Zero Product Property
- polynomial
- degree

In 1818 Mary Shelley wrote the science fiction novel *Frankenstein*. It is the tale of Dr. Victor Frankenstein, a scientist who dreams of creating life. He accomplishes this dream by using old body parts and electricity. Unfortunately, he creates a monster! Horrified and filled with regret, Victor decides that he must end the life that he created. His monster has other plans, though. He is lonely and wants Victor to create a woman to keep him company in this cruel world! Crime, drama, and vengeance follow as the creator struggles with his creation.

Frankenstein laid the foundation for many of the horror and science fiction movies that you see today. While Mary Shelley's novel is a literary classic for how it tackles deep issues such as the meaning of life and the ethics of creation, it is also good old-fashioned, scary fun. Do you enjoy scary movies? If so, do you think any of your favorites may have been influenced by this classic tale?

PROBLEM 1 It's Moving . . . It's Alive!

In the problem, *You're So Square*, you added the functions $w(n)$ and $g(n)$ algebraically to create a new function $t(n)$. Manipulating algebraic representations is a common method for building new functions. However, you can also build new functions graphically. Let's consider two graphs of functions on a coordinate plane and what happens when you add, subtract, or multiply the output values of each.

1. Analyze the graphs of $f(x)$ and $g(x)$.

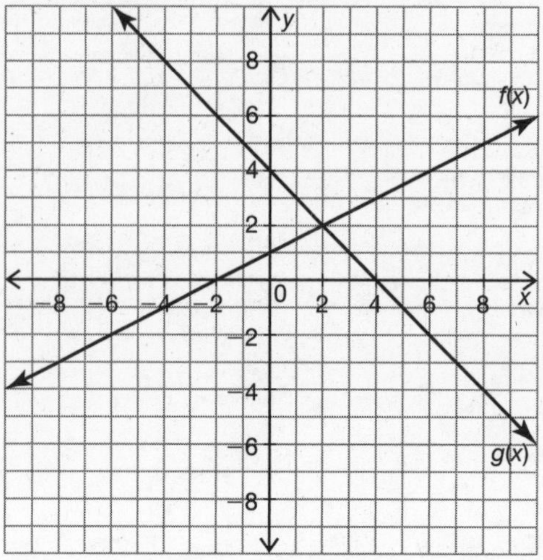

a. Predict the function family of $m(x)$ if $m(x) = f(x) + g(x)$. Explain your reasoning.

You are just predicting right now, so mistakes are OK. You will return to this graph at the end of this problem.

b. Predict and sketch the graph of $m(x)$.

c. Explain how you predicted the location of $m(x)$.

A graph of a function is a set of an infinite number of points. When you add two functions you are adding the output values for each input value. Given two functions, $f(x)$ and $g(x)$, on a coordinate plane, you can graphically add these functions to produce a new function, $m(x)$. To get started, let's consider what happens when you add $f(x)$ and $g(x)$ at a single point.

Let's add the output values for $f(x)$ and $g(x)$ at $x = 6$ to determine $(6, m(6))$.

$m(6) = f(6) + g(6)$
$m(6) = 4 + -2$
$m(6) = 2$

The point on the new function $m(x)$ is $(6, 2)$.

Other points on the graph of $m(x)$ can be determined in a similar way.

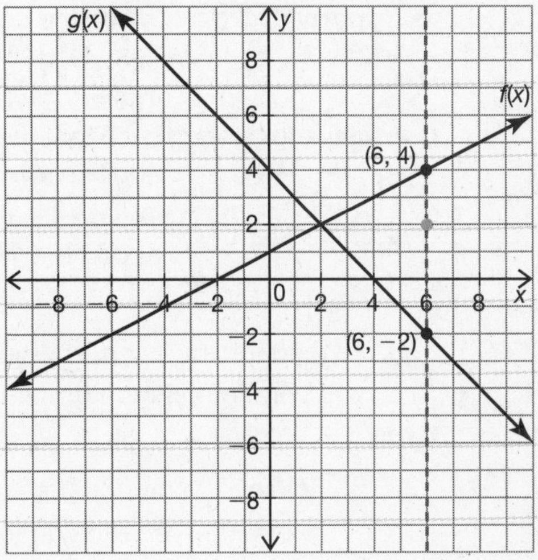

2. Analyze the addition of the output values for the input value $x = 6$ in the worked example.

a. How is this process similar to adding integers on a number line?

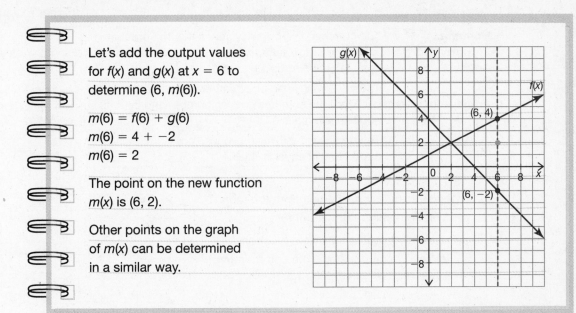

Drawing a vertical line can help you determine the two output values for a given input. Notice the x-values are the same in these points.

b. Why is the point $(6, m(6))$ closer to $f(x)$ than $g(x)$?

c. Why did the input value of 6 stay the same while the output values changed?

d. Choose a different input value. Add the output values for $f(x)$ and $g(x)$ to determine a new point on the graph of $m(x)$.

Now, let's consider what happens when you add $f(x)$ and $g(x)$ at a few other points. The properties you use in integer operations also extend to operations on the graphs of functions. Recall the integer properties shown in the table.

Property	Definition	Integer Example
Commutative Property over Addition	The commutative property states that the order in which the terms are added does not change the sum. In other words $a + b = b + a$.	$35 + 43 = 43 + 35$
Additive Inverse	The additive inverse of a number is the number such that the sum of the given number and its additive inverse is 0.	The numbers -5 and 5 are additive inverses because $-5 + 5 = 0$.
Additive Identity	The additive identity is 0 because any number added to 0 is equal to itself.	$5 + 0 = 5$

3

3. Extend the integer properties from the table to operations on the graphs of functions.

a. Use two output values from functions $f(x)$ and $g(x)$ to demonstrate the commutative property over addition for functions.

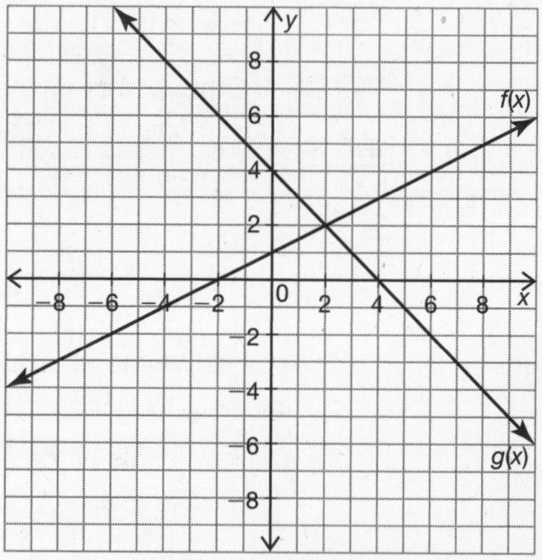

b. Determine output values for $f(x)$ and $g(x)$ that demonstrate the Additive Inverse Property. Show that they are additive inverses algebraically and graphically.

c. Determine output values for $f(x)$ and $g(x)$ that demonstrate the Additive Identity Property. Show that they are additive identities algebraically and graphically.

4. Ari and Will disagree over the location of $(2, m(2))$ when the output values of the functions $f(x)$ and $g(x)$ are added.

Ari	Will
$g(2) + f(2) = (2, m(2))$ $(2, 2) + (2, 2) = (2, 4)$ The location of $(2, m(2))$ is $(2, 4)$. The two points are at the intersection. Adding the output values of the two points equals $(2, 2 + 2)$.	$(2, 2) + 0 = (2, 2)$ The location of $(2, m(2))$ is $(2, 2)$. The lines intersect at one point. A point plus zero is itself.

Who is correct? Explain your reasoning.

When performing operations on two graphs, it isn't practical to consider all sets of ordered pairs. The process is much more efficient if you use key points. Some of the points considered in this problem, such as intercepts, zeros, and intersection points, are good examples of key points.

5. Sketch the graph of $m(x) = f(x) + g(x)$.

   a. Circle key points of the graphs of $f(x)$ and $g(x)$.

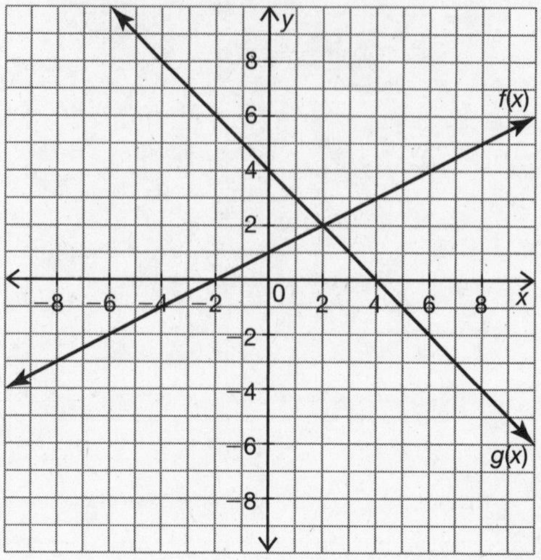

   b. Draw dashed vertical lines through your key points.

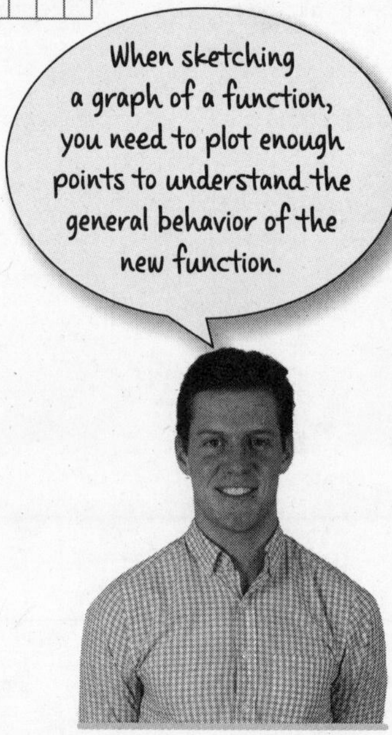

When sketching a graph of a function, you need to plot enough points to understand the general behavior of the new function.

   c. Add the corresponding y-values of $f(x)$ and $g(x)$ on each dashed vertical line to determine points on $m(x)$. Then sketch the graph of $m(x)$. Show or explain your work.

   d. Verify your graph of $m(x)$ using one or more pairs of points that are not key points.

   e. Compare the function you graphed in this question with the prediction you made in Question 1. Describe any errors you may have made in your prediction.

PROBLEM 2 Keep On Keeping On

Let's consider operations on different types of graphs. Let's look at a linear function and a constant function.

1. Analyze the graphs of $j(x)$ and $h(x)$.

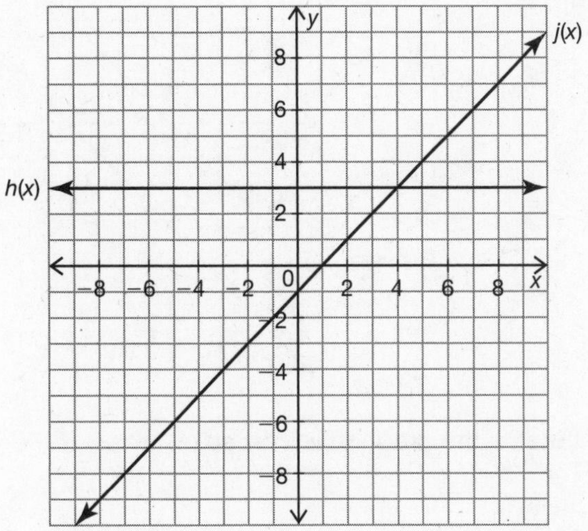

a. Predict the function family of $c(x)$ if $c(x) = j(x) + h(x)$. Then sketch the graph of $c(x)$.

b. Describe the relationship between original functions and $c(x)$. Explain the relationship between the functions in terms of their graphical and algebraic representations.

How will your process of sketching a graph change now that you are subtracting two functions?

c. Predict the function family of $n(x)$ if $n(x) = j(x) - h(x)$. Then sketch the graph of $n(x)$.

d. Describe the relationship between the original functions and $n(x)$. Explain the relationship between the functions in terms of their graphical and algebraic representations.

Now let's look at what happens when you add and subtract the outputs of two parallel lines.

2. Analyze the graphs of $s(x)$ and $v(x)$.

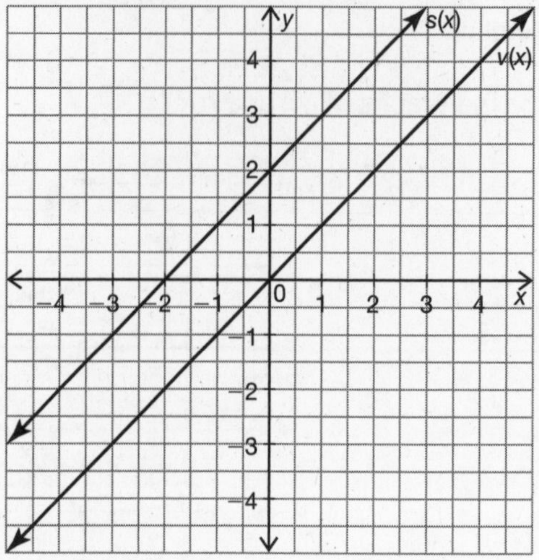

a. Sketch the graph of $w(x) = s(x) + v(x)$.

b. Describe the shape of $w(x)$ compared to $s(x)$ and $v(x)$. Explain why adding the output values changes the shape of the new graph in this way.

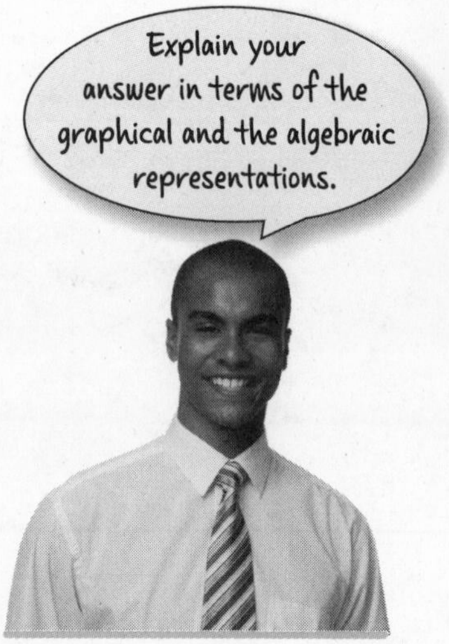

Explain your answer in terms of the graphical and the algebraic representations.

c. Sketch the graph of $m(x)$ if $m(x) = s(x) - v(x)$.

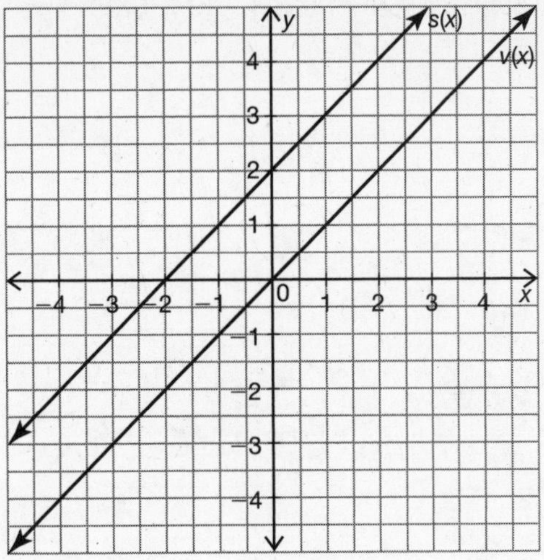

3

d. Sketch the graph of $n(x)$ if $n(x) = v(x) - s(x)$.

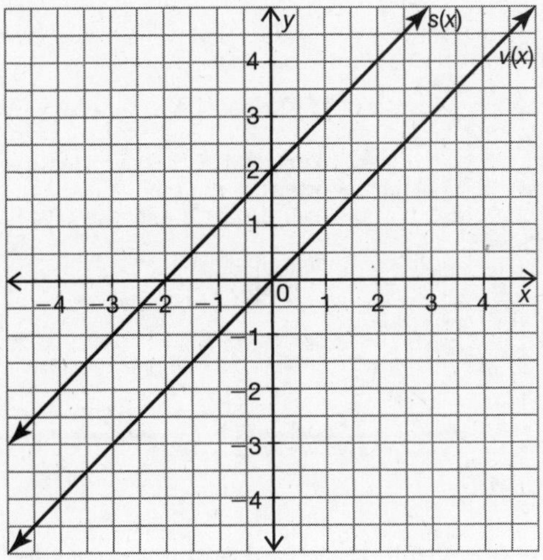

e. Describe the shape of the graph when you subtract $s(x)$ and $v(x)$. Will subtracting the output values of any two parallel lines have this same result? Explain your reasoning.

3. Mrs. Webb asked her students to determine $v(x) - s(x)$. Erik's and Lily's work is shown.

Erik

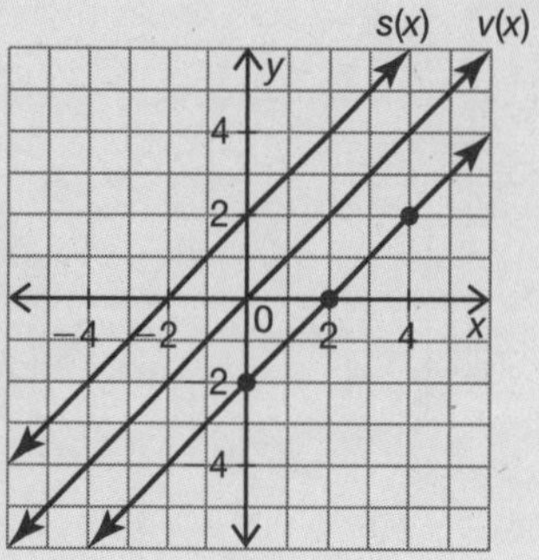

V(x)	t(x)	Differences
0	−2	−2
2	0	−2
4	2	−2

The new graph is located 2 units below V(x). I know this is correct because each point has a difference of −2

Lily

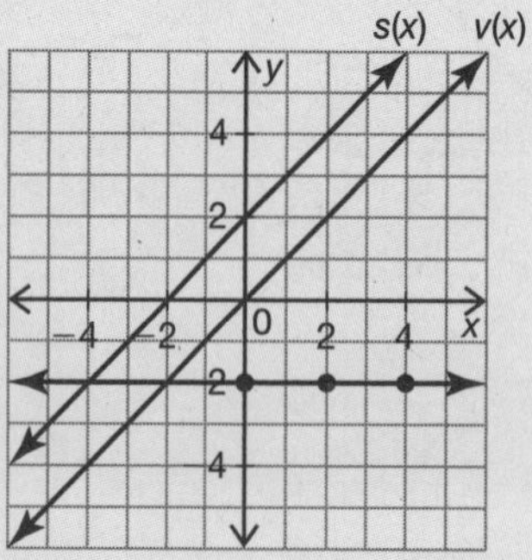

The new graph is located at $y = -2$.
I know this is correct because I subtracted several points and the y-value was always −2.

Who's correct? Explain why one graph is correct and the error made to create the other graph.

Now, let's work backwards.

4. Analyze the graphs of $h(x)$ and $k(x)$.

a. Draw the function $j(x)$ with outputs such that $h(x) + j(x) = k(x)$.

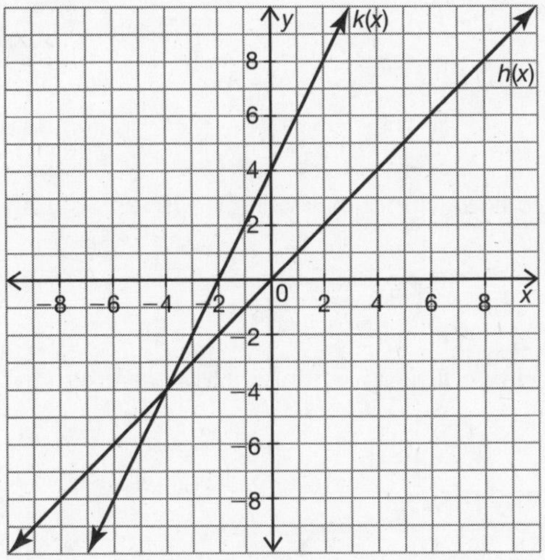

y
k(x)
h(x)
x
0
8
6
4
2
−2
−4
−6
−8

Hmmm . . . So this time you have to work backwards. Think about how to reverse what you did before. The additive identity and additive inverse may help you determine a couple output values for j(x).

b. Complete the table of values to verify that $h(x) + j(x) = k(x)$.

x	$h(x)$	$j(x)$	$k(x) = h(x) + j(x)$
−2			
−1			
0			
1			
2			

c. Describe examples of the additive inverse and additive identity properties for output values in this problem.

d. Use the graph or table of values to determine the algebraic expressions for $h(x)$, $j(x)$, and $k(x)$. Algebraically show that $h(x) + j(x)$ is equivalent to $k(x)$.

3

e. How can you determine from the graph, the table of values, and the algebraic expressions that the functions $h(x)$, $j(x)$, and $k(x)$ are all linear?

graph:

table:

equation:

f. Do you think adding two linear functions will always result in another linear function? Explain your reasoning.

So far, you have only considered two linear functions. Now let's explore a linear function and a quadratic function.

3

5. Analyze the graphs of $k(x)$ and $p(x)$.

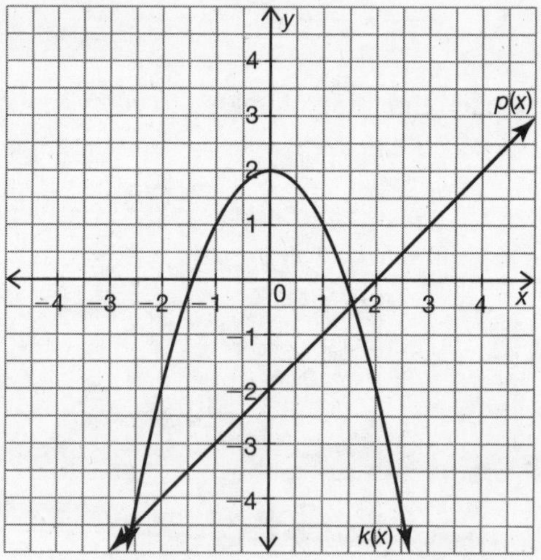

a. Predict the function family of $a(x)$ if $a(x) = k(x) + p(x)$. Explain your prediction.

b. Sketch the graph of function $a(x)$. Show or explain your work.

c. Do you think adding a linear function and a quadratic function will always result in a quadratic function? Explain your reasoning in terms of the algebraic and graphical representations of the functions.

6. Draw the graphs that meet the criteria provided.

a. Sketch the graph of two different functions whose sum is a parabola opening up. What conclusions can you make about the two functions?

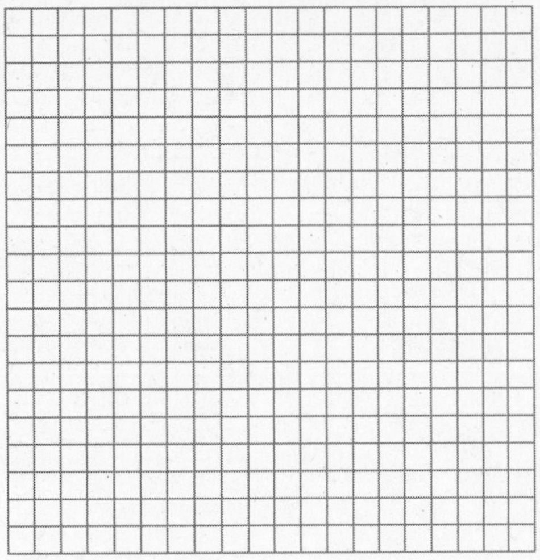

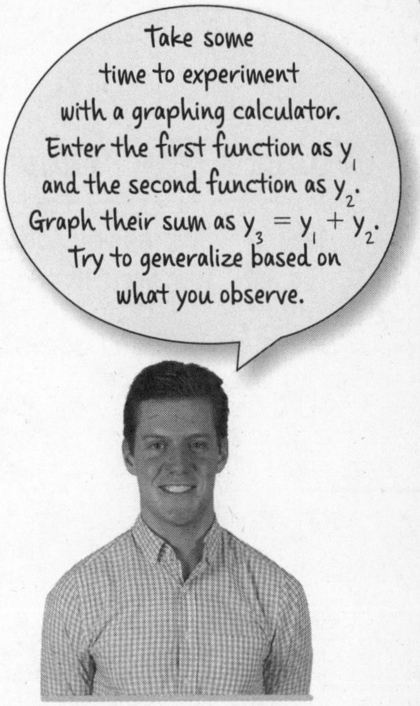
Take some time to experiment with a graphing calculator. Enter the first function as y_1 and the second function as y_2. Graph their sum as $y_3 = y_1 + y_2$. Try to generalize based on what you observe.

b. Sketch the graph of two functions whose sum is the horizontal line $y = 0$. What conclusions can you make about the two functions?

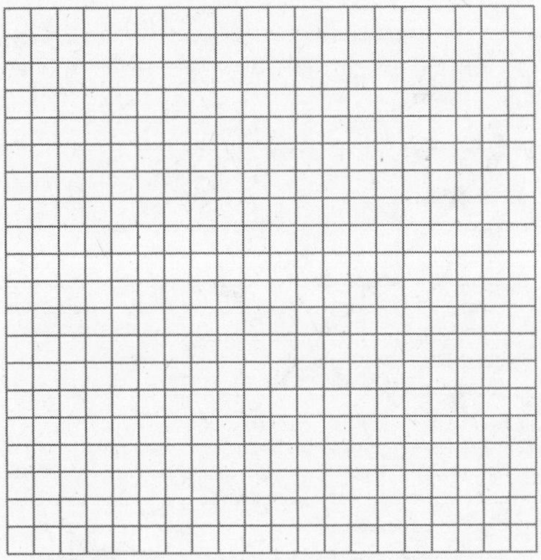

c. Sketch the graph of two functions whose sum is not a function. What conclusions can you make about the two functions?

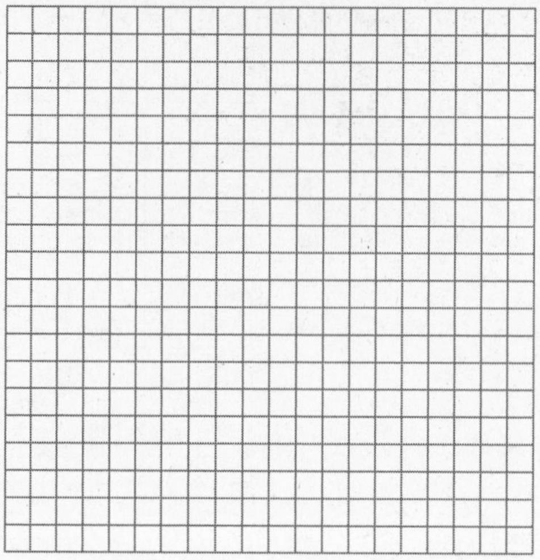

3

PROBLEM 3 They're Multiplying!!

Just as you added and subtracted functions in the previous problems, you can also build functions through multiplication.

1. Analyze the graphs of $f(x)$ and $g(x)$.

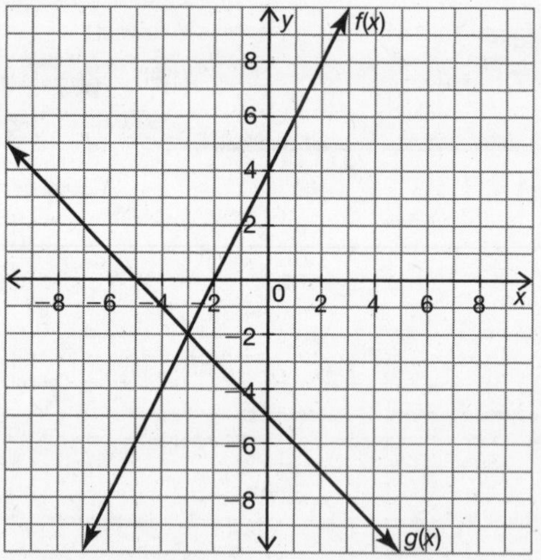

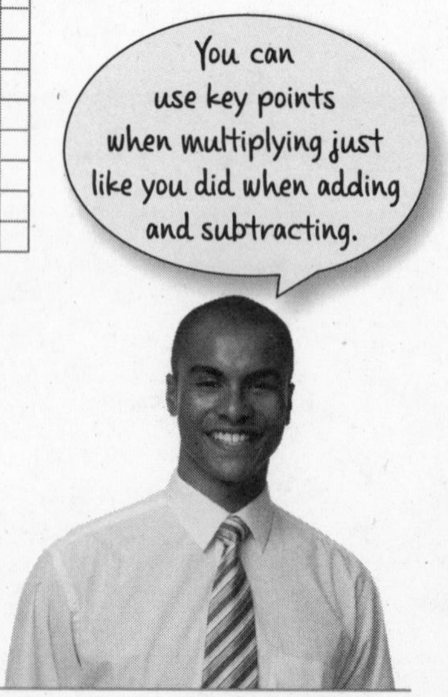

a. Predict the function family of $h(x)$ if $h(x) = f(x) \cdot g(x)$. Explain your reasoning.

b. Sketch the graph of $h(x)$. Show or explain your work.

c. Describe the differences between the graphs of $f(x)$ and $g(x)$ and the graph of $h(x)$.

d. Was your prediction in part (a) correct? What was the same/different after you multiplied the output values of key points?

3

2. You can analyze a table of values to determine the graphical behavior of functions.

a. Complete the table of values for $h(x) = f(x) \cdot g(x)$.

x	$f(x)$	$g(x)$	$h(x)$
−7	−10	2	
−6	−8	1	
−5	−6	0	
−4	−4	−1	
−3	−2	−2	
−2	0	−3	
−1	2	−4	
0	4	−5	

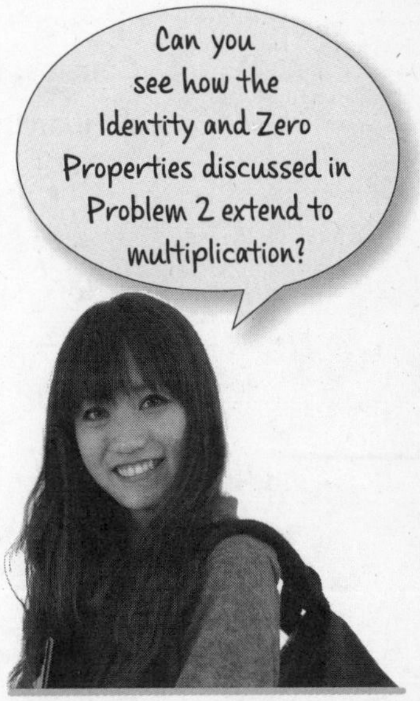

Can you see how the Identity and Zero Properties discussed in Problem 2 extend to multiplication?

b. What patterns do you notice in the table?

c. Analyze the first and second differences for each function. How do you know $f(x)$ and $g(x)$ are linear but $h(x)$ is not?

3. Consider the sign of the output values for each function in the table.

a. For which input values are the output values of $h(x)$ negative? For which input values are the output values of $h(x)$ positive?

This is just like multiplying real numbers.

b. How does the sign of the output values of $f(x)$ and $g(x)$ determine the sign of the output values of $h(x)$?

3

4. Consider the x-intercepts for $f(x)$, $g(x)$ and $h(x)$.

a. Identify the x-intercepts for each function.

$f(x)$:

$g(x)$:

$h(x)$:

b. What pattern do you notice in the x-intercepts?

Remember that the Zero Product Property is important for solving quadratic functions in factored form.

The **Zero Product Property** states that if the product of two or more factors is equal to zero, then at least one factor must be equal to zero.

c. How does the Zero Product Property relate to the x-intercepts of the three functions?

5. Analyze the graphs of $s(x)$ and $v(x)$.

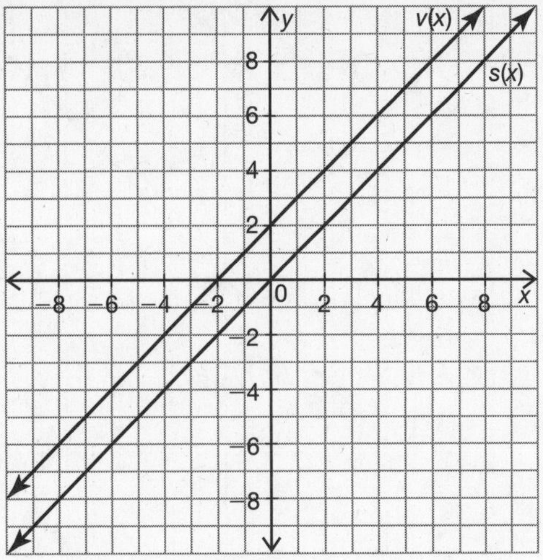

3

a. Sketch the graph of $p(x)$ if $p(x) = s(x) \cdot v(x)$.

b. Identify the x-intercepts of $p(x)$. Explain the relationship between the x-intercepts of $p(x)$ and the x-intercepts of $s(x)$ and $v(x)$.

c. Identify the vertex of $p(x)$. What is the relationship between the vertex of $p(x)$ and the functions $s(x)$ and $v(x)$?

d. In Problem 2 of this lesson, you added the functions $s(x)$ and $v(x)$ to create function $w(x)$. How is multiplication the same? How is it different?

6. Analyze the graphs of $a(x)$ and $b(x)$.

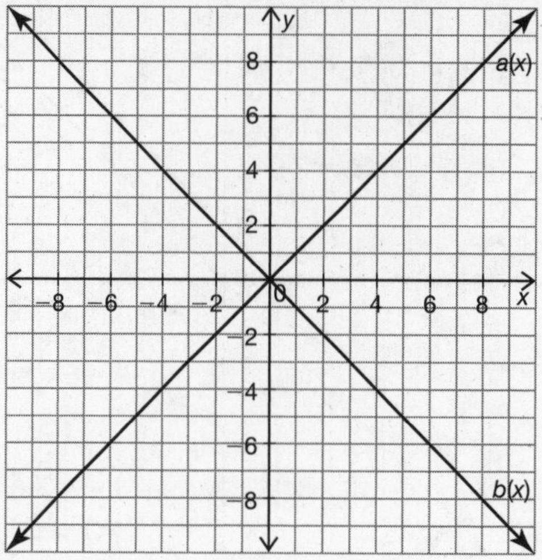

a. Sketch the graph of $c(x)$ if $c(x) = a(x) \cdot b(x)$.

b. Describe the shape of $c(x)$.

7. Analyze the graph of $r(x)$.

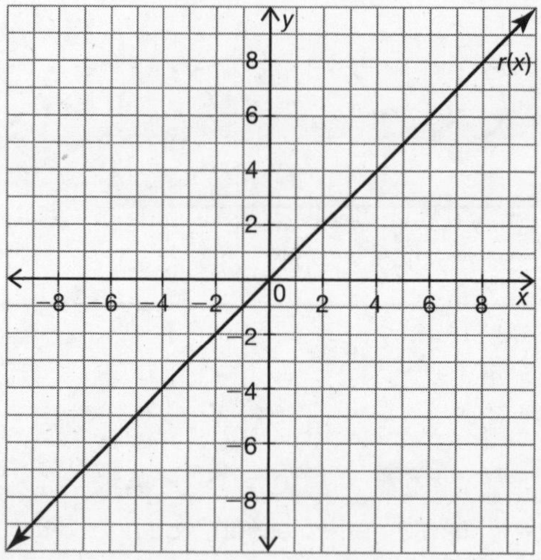

a. Sketch the graph of $d(x)$ if $d(x) = r(x) \cdot r(x)$.

b. Describe the shape of $d(x)$.

8. Analyze the graphs of $f(x)$ and $g(x)$.

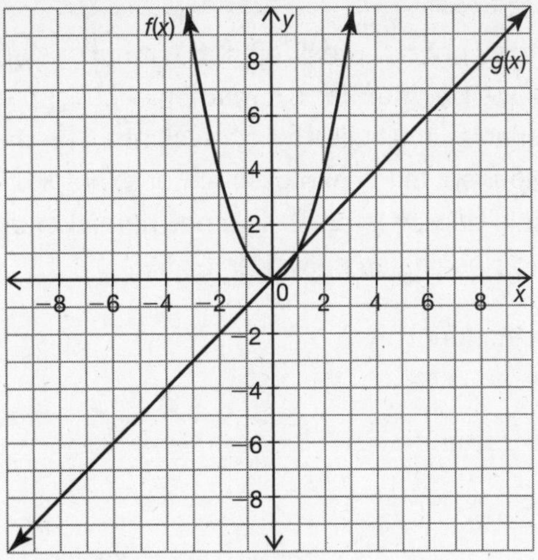

a. Sketch the graph of $m(x)$ if $m(x) = f(x) \cdot g(x)$.

b. Describe the shape of $m(x)$.

c. Do you think multiplying a quadratic function and a linear function will always result in a graph with this shape? Explain your reasoning.

3

Talk the Talk

While you may not have realized it, the functions you worked with throughout this lesson are *polynomials*. A **polynomial** is a mathematical expression involving the sum of powers in one or more variables multiplied by coefficients. The **degree** of a polynomial is the greatest variable exponent in the expression. For example, $4x^3 + 2x^2 + 5x + 1$ is a polynomial expression of degree three, $2x$ is a polynomial of degree 1, and a constant such as 5 has degree zero since it can be written as $5x^0$.

1. Given the functions,

- $y_1 = ax^2$,
- $y_2 = bx$, and
- $y_3 = c$

generalize the function family of the polynomial when:

a. $y_1 + y_2$

b. $y_1 + y_3$

c. $y_2 + y_3$

2. When two functions of different degree are added, what can you say about the degree of the resulting function?

Use a graphing calculator to explore functions of higher degree than 2. What are the shapes of functions with degree 3, 4, and higher? Do they keep this shape when other functions with lower degrees are added to them?

Be prepared to share your solutions and methods.

Chapter 3 Summary

KEY TERMS

- relation (3.3)
- function (3.3)
- function notation (3.3)
- Zero Product Property (3.5)
- polynomial (3.5)
- degree (3.5)

3.1 Identifying Patterns Within a Sequence

Patterns are found throughout nature and our everyday lives. Some patterns can be described numerically.

Example

Draw the next three terms for the pattern shown.

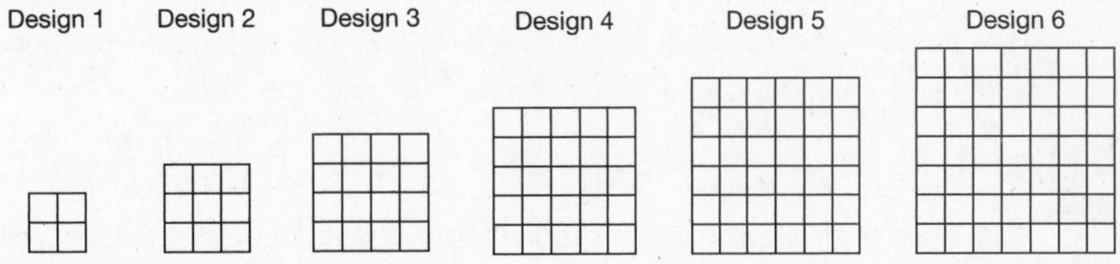

Design 1 is made of 4 small tiles, Design 2 is made of 9 small tiles, and so on. The total number of tiles in each pattern is a perfect square. So, the terms are $2^2 = 4$, $3^2 = 9$, $4^2 = 16$, $5^2 = 25$, $6^2 = 36$, and $7^2 = 49$.

3.1

Using Patterns to Solve Problems

Once you determine a pattern, you can predict the next term in the sequence.

Example

Ji is the coach for a soccer team. He wants to develop a phone tree for communicating with the team. He will call two people and each of those two people will call two more people. This pattern will continue until all team members and coaches have been contacted.

Rounds of Calls	Number of Calls Made	Cumulative Total Number of Calls Made
First round (Ji)	2	2
Second round (two teammates)	4	6
Third round (four teammates)	8	14
Fourth round (eight teammates)	16	30

The number of calls made each day is doubling. So, during the fifth round, $2 \cdot 16 = 32$ calls are made. During the sixth round, $2 \cdot 32 = 64$ calls are made.

3.2

Writing Algebraic Expressions to Describe Patterns

Algebraic expressions can be used when you want to predict patterns or represent real-life scenarios using mathematics.

Example

A website goes live and receives 83 visits in the first day. During the second day, the site receives 91 visits. The third day, the site receives 107 visits. Use an algebraic expression to represent the number of visits the site receives each day.

Day	Number of Visits to the Website
First day	83
Second day	91
Third day	107
Fourth day	139
Fifth day	203

The difference between each term in the pattern is $4(2^1)$ or 8, then $4(2^2)$ or 16, then $4(2^3)$ or 32, and so on. The first term is 8 more than 75. So, an expression to represent the number of visits the site receives each day is $4(2^x) + 75$.

3.2 Representing Patterns

Numeric patterns can be represented as expressions, tables, and graphs. After the pattern is graphed on a coordinate plane, the graph can be identified as linear, exponential, quadratic, or none of these.

Example

A salesperson works for four hours. During the first hour, she has 6 clients. During the second hour, she has 8 clients. During the third hour, she has 6 clients. During the fourth hour, she has 0 clients. The table shown represents the number of clients the salesperson has after each hour and also an expression to represent the number of clients the salesperson sees each hour. The graph represents a quadratic model of the data.

Time (hours)	Number of Clients
1	6
2	8
3	6
4	0
n	$-2n^2 + 8n$

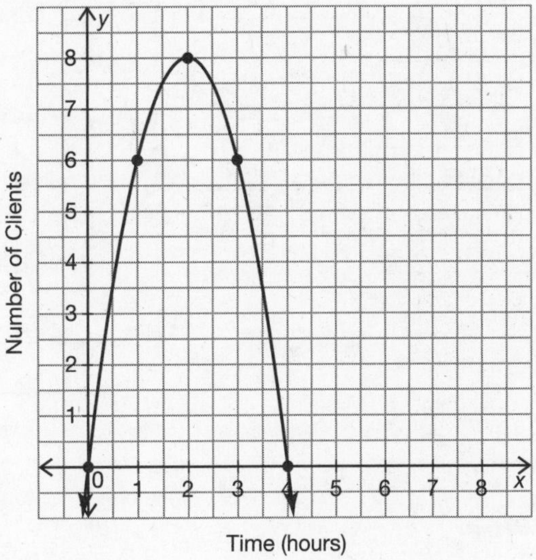

3

3.3 Identifying Functions

A relation describes how input values are mapped to output values in a pattern. A function is a relation that has only one output for each input. Function notation is a way to represent functions algebraically.

Example

The table and the graph represent relations. Because there is only one output for each input in the relations, they are functions. Because the same outputs are matched to each input, the functions are equivalent.

x	y
−3	25
−2	11
−1	3
0	1
1	5
2	15
3	31

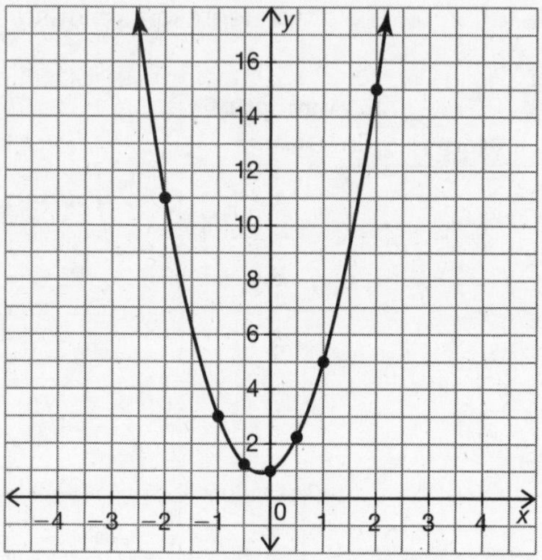

3.3 Modeling Real-World Scenarios

Tables, graphs, and equations can be used to represent real-world scenarios. A table shows the numeric values in columns. A graph shows the relation visually. The graph clearly shows whether the graph is a function or not. An equation uses numbers and variables to model the scenario.

Example

A store is having a sale on smartphones. The store opens at 8:00 AM and has 96 smartphones. After 1 hour, the store has 80 smartphones remaining. After 2 hours, the store has 64 smartphones remaining. If the pattern of sales continues at this rate, at what time will the store run out of smartphones? The number of smartphones in the store can be represented by a table and a graph. Based on the graph, the store will have zero smartphones after 6 hours.

Time	Time Since the Store Opened (hours)	Number of Smartphones Remaining
8:00 AM	0	96
9:00 AM	1	80
10:00 AM	2	64
11:00 AM	3	48
Noon	4	32
1:00 PM	5	16
2:00 PM	6	0

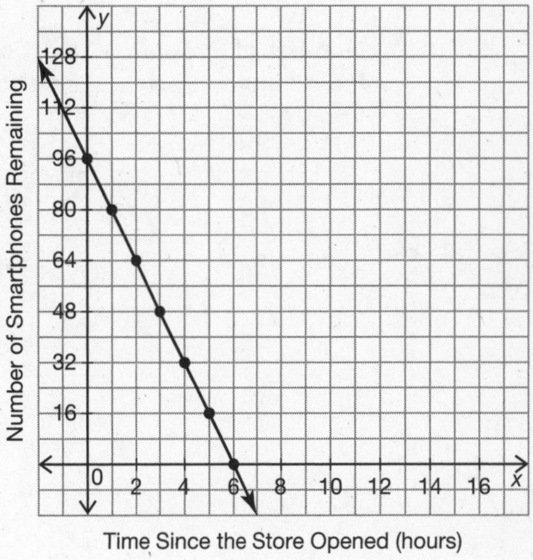

3

3.4 Graphing Functions

A table, graph, and equation can be used to represent real-world situations. Any of these forms can be used to analyze the situation.

Example

The cost of a party can be calculated by multiplying the number of people attending by 15 and then adding 24. An equation to model the situation is $y = 15x + 24$. The table lists the cost for specific numbers of people attending. The graph of the function is also shown. Based on the graph, the cost of the party will keep increasing as the number of people attending the party increases. Based on the table, for every 10 additional people attending the party, the cost of the party increases by $150.

Number of People Attending the Party	Cost of the Party (dollars)
10	174
20	324
30	474
40	624
50	774

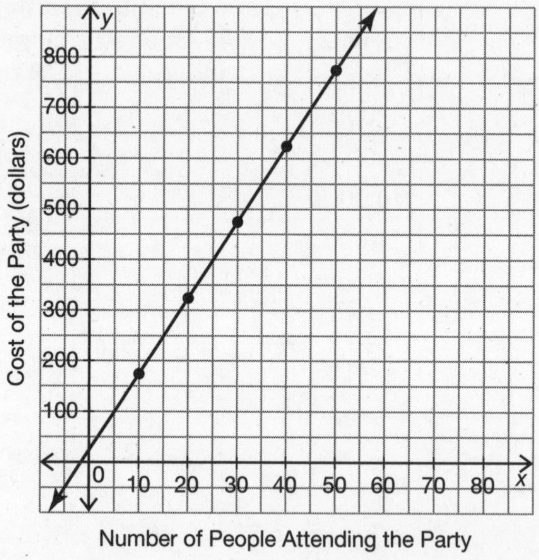

3.4 Using a Graph and Function to Analyze Problems

The table or graph for a situation can provide valuable information about the scenario. The minimum or maximum of a quadratic equation can provide context for the situation or aid in predicting or analyzing the scenario.

Example

Larissa is running a car wash as a fundraiser for her school. In the first hour, the group earns $12 in donations for car washes. The amount of money earned each hour is listed in the table and shown in the graph. The group earns a maximum of $28 in the third hour of the car wash.

Time Since the Car Wash Started (hours)	Amount of Money Earned Each Hour (dollars)
1	12
2	23
3	28
4	27
5	20
6	7

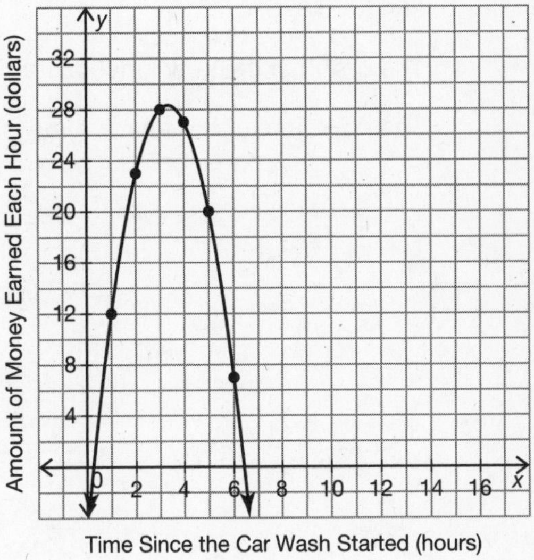

3

3.5 Adding or Subtracting Functions Graphically

To add or subtract two functions graphically, first identify several key points. Some key points include intersection points, x-intercepts, and y-intercepts. For each input value, add or subtract the output values for each function to calculate the output value of the new function. Then draw the graph of the new function.

Example

Add $g(x) = x + 2$ and $f(x) = 2x - 6$ graphically.

Use the key points $(-2, 0)$, $(-2, -10)$, $(0, 2)$, $(0, -6)$, $(3, 0)$, and $(3, 5)$.

The new function contains the points $(-2, 0 - 10)$ or $(-2, -10)$, $(0, 2 - 6)$ or $(0, -4)$, and $(3, 0 + 5)$ or $(3, 5)$.

The graph of the new function, $m(x)$ is shown.

The equation for the function $m(x)$ is $m(x) = 3x - 4$.

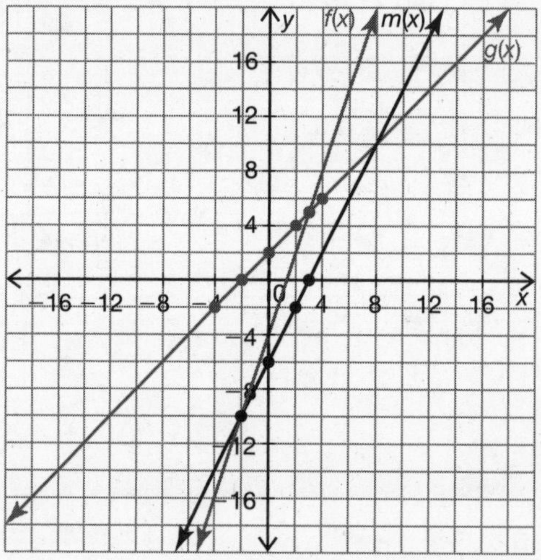

3.5 Multiplying Functions Graphically

To multiply two functions graphically, first identify several key points. Some key points include intersection points, x-intercepts, and y-intercepts. For each input value, multiply the output values for each function to calculate the output value of the new function. Then draw the graph of the new function.

Example

Multiply $j(x) = x + 3$ and $k(x) = 2x - 1$ to determine $f(x)$.

Use a table of values to graph the functions.

x	$j(x) = x + 3$	$k(x) = 2x - 1$	$f(x)$
−3	0	−7	0
−2	1	−5	−5
−1	2	−3	−6
0	3	−1	−3
1	4	1	4
2	5	3	15
3	6	5	30

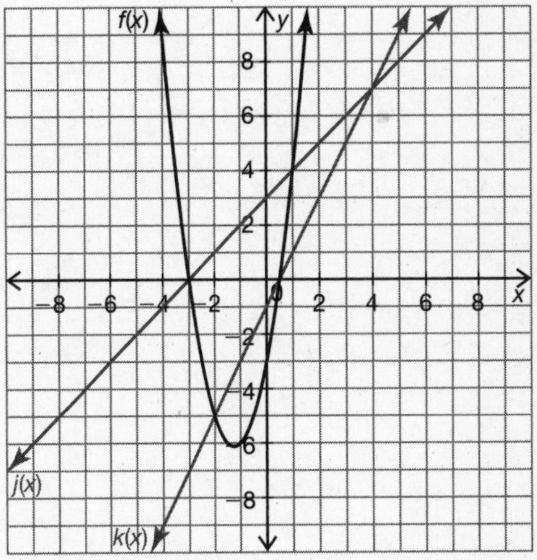

3

3

Quadratic Functions

4

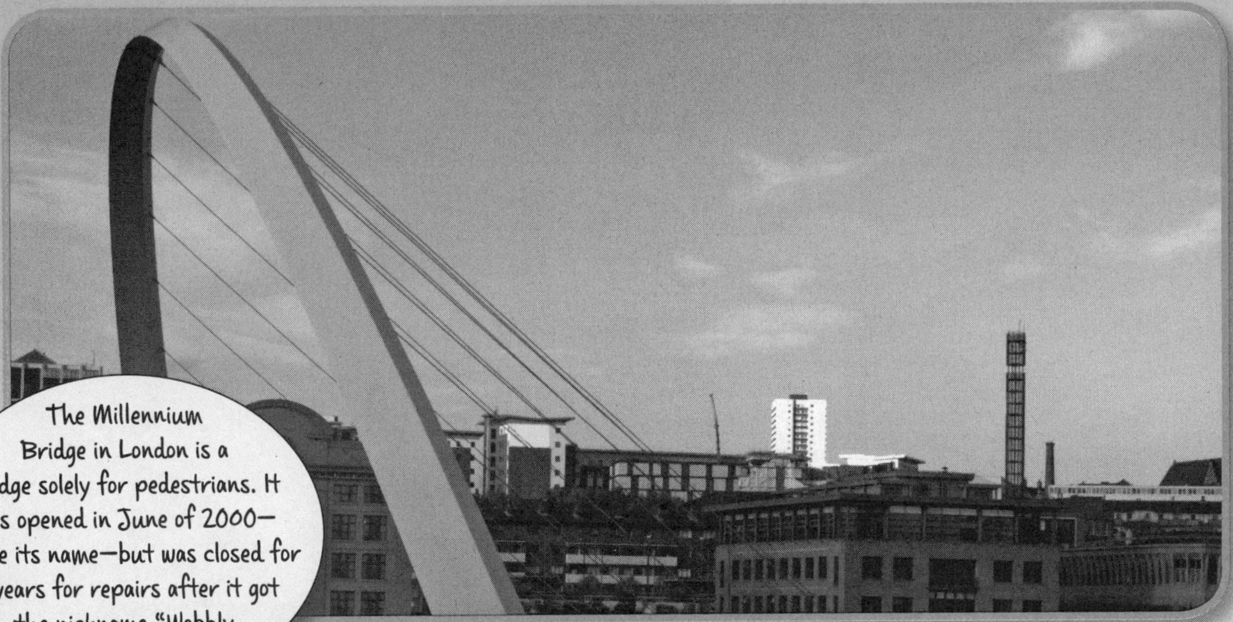

The Millennium Bridge in London is a bridge solely for pedestrians. It was opened in June of 2000—hence its name—but was closed for 2 years for repairs after it got the nickname "Wobbly Bridge."

4.1

Shape and Structure
Forms of Quadratic Functions

LEARNING GOALS

In this lesson, you will:

- Match a quadratic function with its corresponding graph.
- Identify key characteristics of quadratic functions based on the form of the function.
- Analyze the different forms of quadratic functions.
- Use key characteristics of specific forms of quadratic functions to write equations.
- Write quadratic functions to represent problem situations.

KEY TERMS

- standard form of a quadratic function
- factored form of a quadratic function
- vertex form of a quadratic function
- concavity of a parabola

Have you ever seen a tightrope walker? If you've ever seen this, you know that it is quite amazing to witness a person able to walk on a thin piece of rope. However, since safety is always a concern, there is usually a net just in case of a fall.

That brings us to a young French daredevil named Phillippe Petit. Back in 1974 with the help of some friends, he spent all night secretly placing a 450 pound cable between the World Trade Center Towers in New York City. At dawn, to the shock and amazement of onlookers, the fatigued 24-year old Petit stepped out onto the wire. Ignoring the frantic calls of the police, he walked, jumped, laughed, and even performed a dance routine on the wire for nearly an hour without a safety net! Mr. Petit was of course arrested upon climbing back to the safety of the ledge. When asked why he performed such an unwise, dangerous act, Phillippe said: "When I see three oranges, I juggle; when I see two towers, I walk."

You can see the events unfold in the 2002 Academy Award winning documentary Man on Wire by James Marsh.

Have you ever challenged yourself to do something difficult just to see if you could do it?

PROBLEM 1 It's All in the Form

1. Cut out each quadratic function and graph on the next page two pages.

   a. Tape each quadratic function to its corresponding graph.

Please do not use graphing calculators for this activity. What information can you tell from looking at the function and what can you tell by looking at each graph?

   b. Explain the method(s) you used to match the functions with their graphs.

a. $f(x) = 2(x + 1)(x + 5)$	**d.** $f(x) = (x - 1)^2$	**g.** $f(x) = -(x + 4)^2 - 2$
b. $f(x) = \frac{1}{3}x^2 + \pi x + 6.4$	**e.** $f(x) = 2(x - 1)(x - 5)$	**h.** $f(x) = -5x^2 - x + 21$
c. $f(x) = -2.5(x - 3)(x - 3)$	**f.** $f(x) = x^2 + 12x - 1$	**i.** $f(x) = -(x + 2)^2 - 4$

4

A.

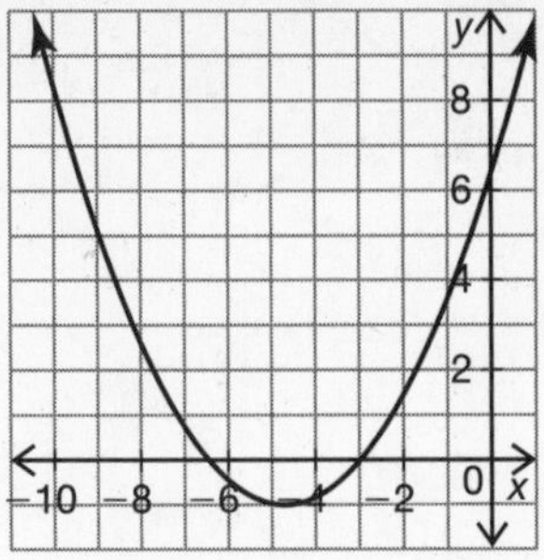

tape function here

B.

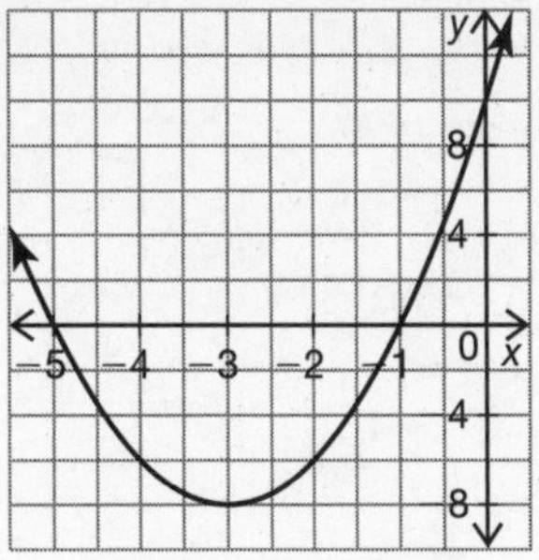

tape function here

C.

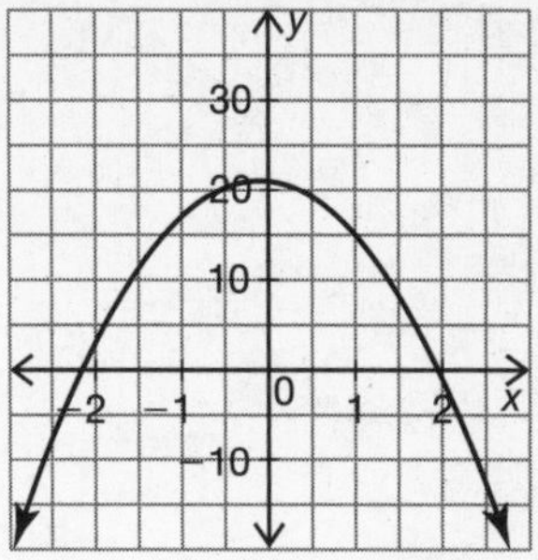

tape function here

D.

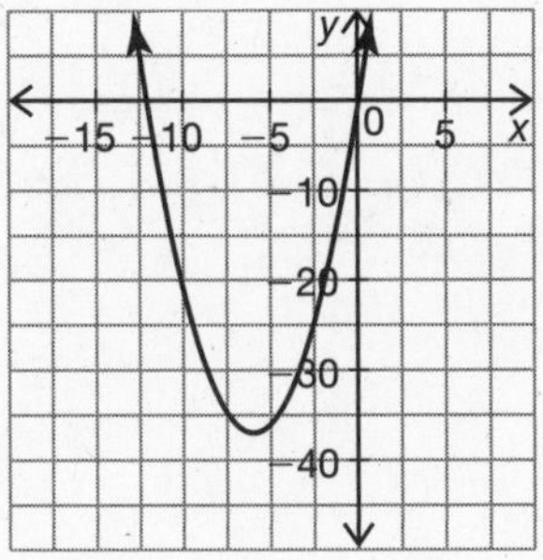

tape function here

E.

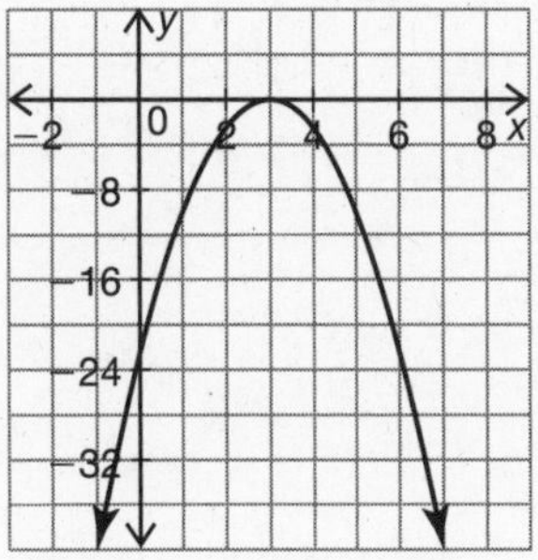

tape function here

F.

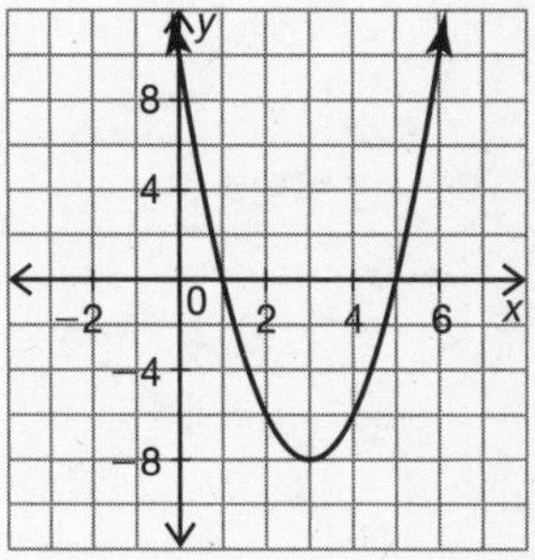

tape function here

G.

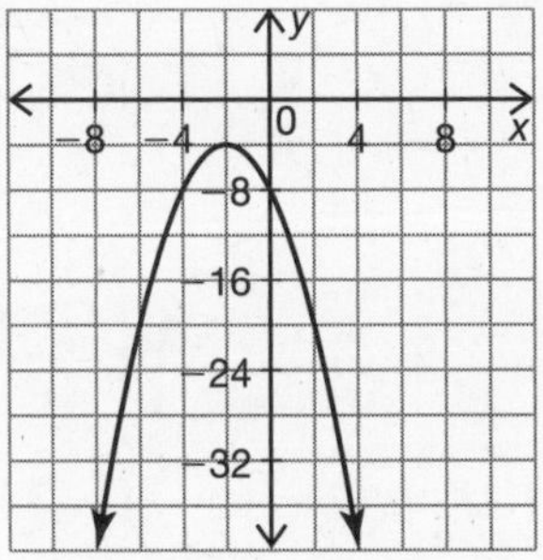

tape function here

H.

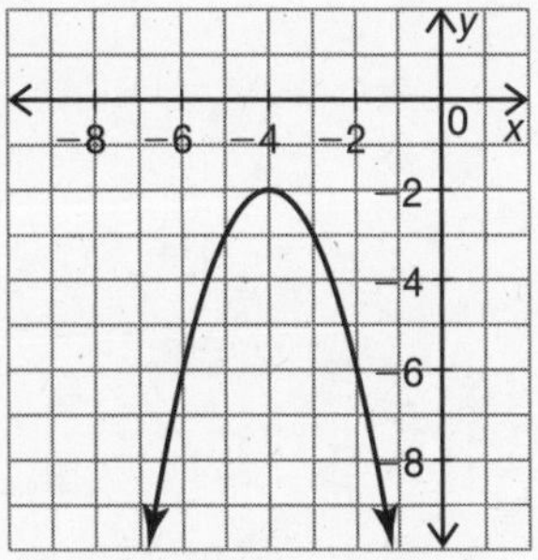

tape function here

I.

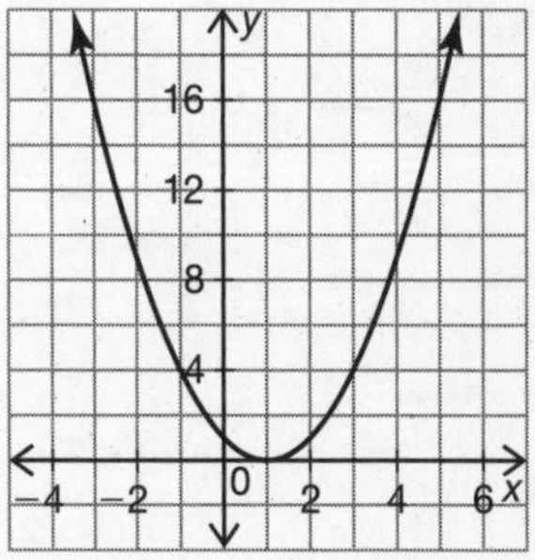

tape function here

4

Recall that quadratic functions can be written in different forms.

- **standard form:** $f(x) = ax^2 + bx + c$, where a does not equal 0.
- **factored form:** $f(x) = a(x - r_1)(x - r_2)$, where a does not equal 0.
- **vertex form:** $f(x) = a(x - h)^2 + k$, where a does not equal 0.

2. Sort your graphs with matching equations into 3 piles based on the function form.

Keep these piles; you will use them again at the end of this Problem.

The graphs of quadratic functions can be described using key characteristics:

- x-intercept(s),
- y-intercept,
- vertex,
- axis of symmetry, and
- concave up or down.

Concavity of a parabola describes whether a parabola opens up or opens down. A parabola is concave down if it opens downward; a parabola is concave up if it opens upward.

3. The form of a quadratic function highlights different key characteristics. State the characteristics you can determine from each.
   - standard form
   - factored form
   - vertex form

4. Christine and Kate were asked to determine the vertex of two different quadratic functions each written in different forms. Analyze their calculations.

Christine

$f(x) = 2x^2 + 12x + 10$

The quadratic function is in standard form. So I know the axis of symmetry is $x = \frac{-b}{2a}$.

$$x = \frac{-12}{2(2)}$$
$$= -3.$$

Now that I know the axis of symmetry, I can substitute that value into the function to determine the y-coordinate of the vertex.

$$f(-3) = 2(-3)^2 + 12(-3) + 10$$
$$= 2(9) - 36 + 10$$
$$= 18 - 36 + 10$$
$$= 8$$

Therefore, the vertex is $(-3, 8)$.

Kate

$g(x) = \frac{1}{2}(x + 3)(x - 7)$

The form of the function tells me the x-intercepts are -3 and 7. I also know the x-coordinate of the vertex will be directly in the middle of the x-intercepts. So, all I have to do is calculate the average.

$$x = \frac{-3 + 7}{2}$$
$$= \frac{4}{2} = 2$$

Now that I know the x-coordinate of the vertex, I can substitute that value into the function to determine the y-coordinate.

$$g(2) = \frac{1}{2}(2 + 3)(2 - 7)$$
$$= \frac{1}{2}(5)(-5)$$
$$= -12.5$$

Therefore, the vertex is $(2, -12.5)$.

a. How are these methods similar? How are they different?

b. What must Kate do to use Christine's method?

c. What must Christine do to use Kate's method?

4

5. Analyze each table on the following three pages. Paste each function and its corresponding graph from Question 2 in the "Graphs and Their Functions" section of the appropriate table. Then, explain how you can determine each key characteristic based on the form of the given function.

Standard Form
$f(x) = ax^2 + bx + c$, where $a \neq 0$

Graphs and Their Functions

		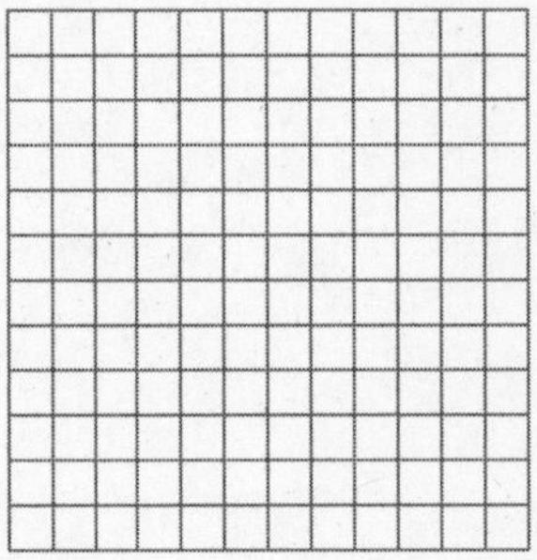

Methods to Identify and Determine Key Characteristics

Axis of Symmetry	*x*-intercept(s)	Concavity

Vertex	*y*-intercept

Factored Form

$f(x) = a(x - r_1)(x - r_2)$, where $a \neq 0$

Graphs and Their Functions		

Methods to Identify and Determine Key Characteristics		
Axis of Symmetry	***x*-intercept(s)**	**Concavity**

Vertex	***y*-intercept**

4

Vertex Form $f(x) = a(x - h)^2 + k$, where $a \neq 0$		
Graphs and Their Functions		
Methods to Identify and Determine Key Characteristics		
Axis of Symmetry	**x-intercept(s)**	**Concavity**
Vertex	**y-intercept**	

1. Analyze each graph. Then, circle the function(s) which could model the graph. Describe the reasoning you used to either eliminate or choose each function.

   a.

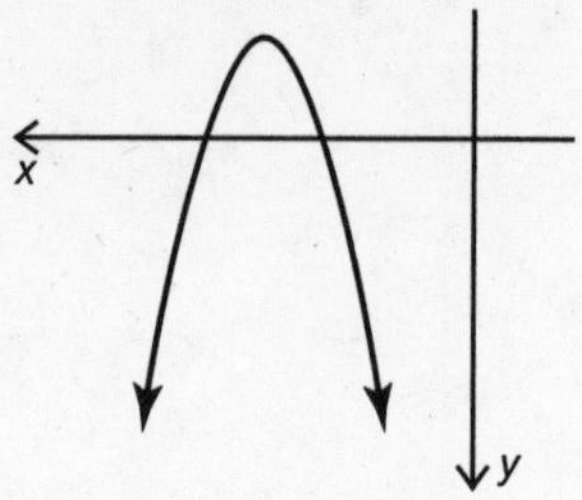

$$f_1(x) = -2(x + 1)(x + 4) \qquad f_2(x) = -\frac{1}{3}x^2 - 3x - 6 \qquad f_3(x) = 2(x + 1)(x + 4)$$

$$f_4(x) = 2x^2 - 8.9 \qquad\qquad f_5(x) = 2(x - 1)(x - 4) \qquad\qquad f_6(x) = -(x - 6)^2 + 3$$

Think about the information given by each function and the relative position of the graph.

$$f_7(x) = -3(x + 2)(x - 3) \qquad\qquad f_8(x) = -(x + 6)^2 + 3$$

b.

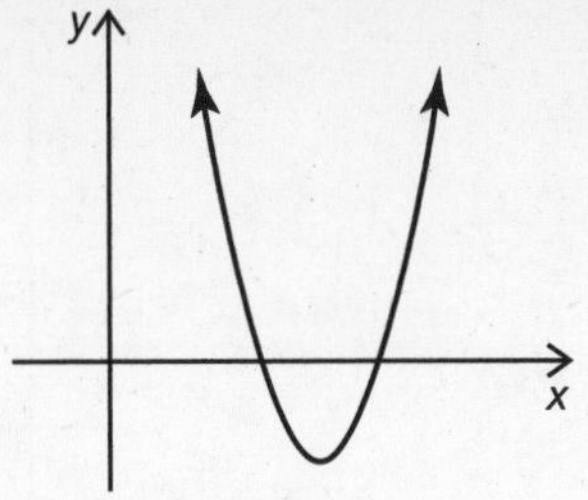

$f_1(x) = 2(x - 75)^2 - 92$ $f_2(x) = (x - 8)(x + 2)$ $f_3(x) = 8x^2 - 88x + 240$

$f_4(x) = -3(x - 1)(x - 5)$ $f_5(x) = -2(x - 75)^2 - 92$ $f_6(x) = x^2 + 6x - 2$

$f_7(x) = 2(x + 4)^2 - 2$ $f_8(x) = (x + 1)(x + 3)$

4

c.

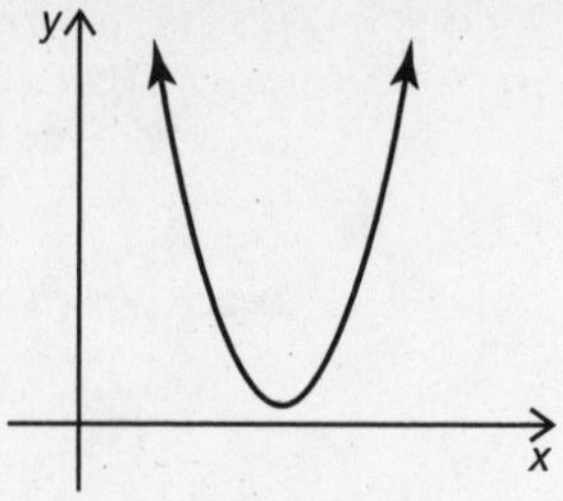

$f_1(x) = 3(x + 1)(x - 5)$ $f_2(x) = 2(x + 6)^2 - 5$ $f_3(x) = 4x^2 - 400x + 10{,}010$

$f_4(x) = 3(x + 1)(x + 5)$ $f_5(x) = 2(x - 6)^2 + 5$ $f_6(x) = x^2 + 2x - 5$

4

2. Consider the two functions shown from Question 1. Identify the form of the function given, and then write the function in the other two forms, if possible. If it is not possible, explain why.

   a. From part (a): $f_1(x) = -2(x + 1)(x + 4)$

   b. From part (c): $f_5(x) = 2(x - 6)^2 + 5$

4

PROBLEM 3 Unique . . . One and Only

1. George and Pat were each asked to write a quadratic equation with a vertex of (4, 8). Analyze each student's work. Describe the similarities and differences in their equations and determine who is correct.

George	Pat
$y = a(x - h)^2 + k$ $y = a(x - 4)^2 + 8$ $y = -\frac{1}{2}(x - 4)^2 + 8$	$y = a(x - h)^2 + k$ $y = a(x - 4)^2 + 8$ $y = (x - 4)^2 + 8$

4

2. Consider the 3 forms of quadratic functions and state the number of unknown values in each.

Form	Number of Unknown Values
$f(x) = a(x - h)^2 + k$	
$f(x) = a(x - r_1)(x - r_2)$	
$f(x) = ax^2 + bx + c$	

a. If a function is written in vertex form and you know the vertex, what is still unknown?

b. If a function is written in factored form and you know the roots, what is still unknown?

c. If a function is written in any form and you know one point, what is still unknown? State the unknown values for each form of a quadratic function.

d. If you only know the vertex, what more do you need to write a unique function? Explain your reasoning.

e. If you only know the roots, what more do you need to write a unique function? Explain your reasoning.

You can write a unique quadratic function given a vertex and a point on the parabola.

Write the quadratic function given the vertex (5, 2) and the point (4, 9).

Substitute the given values into the vertex form of the function.	$f(x) = a(x - h)^2 + k$ $9 = a(4 - 5)^2 + 2$
Then simplify.	$9 = a(-1)^2 + 2$ $9 = 1a + 2$ $7 = 1a$ $7 = a$
Finally, substitute the *a*-value into the function.	$f(x) = 7(x - 5)^2 + 2$

You can write a unique quadratic function given the roots and a point on the parabola.

Write a quadratic function given the roots (−2, 0) and (4, 0), and the point (1, 6).

Substitute the given values into the factored form of the function.	$f(x) = a(x - r_1)(x - r_2)$ $6 = a(1 - (-2))(1 - 4)$
Then simplify.	$6 = a(1 + 2)(1 - 4)$ $6 = a(3)(-3)$ $6 = -9a$ $-\frac{2}{3} = a$
Finally, substitute the *a*-value into the function.	$f(x) = -\frac{2}{3}(x + 2)(x - 4)$

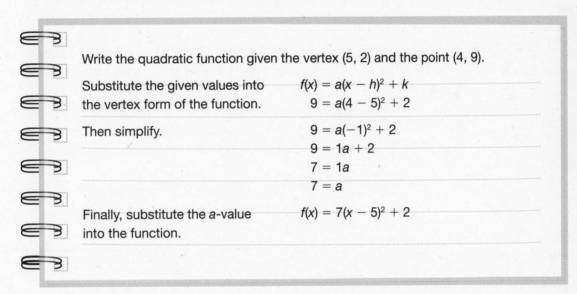

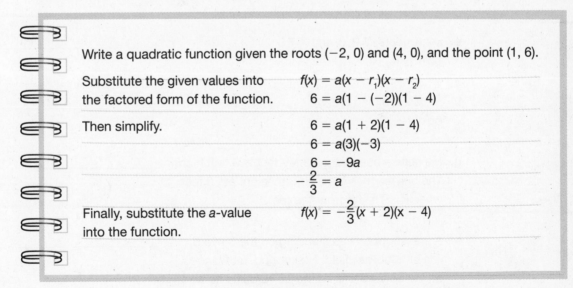

3. Explain why knowing the vertex and a point creates a unique quadratic function.

4. If you are given the roots, how many unique quadratic functions can you write? Explain your reasoning.

5. Use the given information to determine the most efficient form you could use to write the function. Write standard form, factored form, vertex form, or none in the space provided.

   a. minimum point (6, −75)
   y-intercept (0, 15) ____________________

   b. points (2, 0), (8, 0), and (4, 6) ____________________

   c. points (100, 75), (450, 75), and (150, 95) ____________________

   d. points (3, 3), (4, 3), and (5, 3) ____________________

   e. *x*-intercepts: (7.9, 0) and (−7.9, 0)
   point (−4, −4) ____________________

   f. roots: (3, 0) and (12, 0)
   point (10, 2) ____________________

   g. Max hits a baseball off a tee that is 3 feet high. The ball reaches a maximum height of 20 feet when it is 15 feet from the tee. ____________________

   h. A grasshopper was standing on the 35 yard line of a football field. He jumped, and landed on the 38 yard line. At the 36 yard line he was 8 inches in the air. ____________________

4

PROBLEM 4   Just Another Day at the Circus

Write a quadratic function to represent each situation using the given information. Be sure to define your variables.

1. The Amazing Larry is a human cannonball. He would like to reach a maximum height of 30 feet during his next launch. Based on Amazing Larry's previous launches, his assistant DaJuan has estimated that this will occur when he is 40 feet from the cannon. When Amazing Larry is shot from the cannon, he is 10 feet above the ground. Write a function to represent Amazing Larry's height in terms of his distance.

2. Crazy Cornelius is a fire jumper. He is attempting to run and jump through a ring of fire. He runs for 10 feet. Then, he begins his jump just 4 feet from the fire and lands on the other side 3 feet from the fire ring. When Cornelius was 1 foot from the fire ring at the beginning of his jump, he was 3.5 feet in the air. Write a function to represent Crazy Cornelius' height in terms of his distance. Round to the nearest hundredth.

3. Harsh Knarsh is attempting to jump across an alligator filled swamp. She takes off from a ramp 30 feet high with a speed of 95 feet per second. Write a function to represent Harsh Knarsh's height in terms of time.

> Remember, the general equation to represent height over time is $h(t) = -16t^2 + v_0 t + h_0$ where v_0 is the initial velocity in feet per second and h_0 is the initial height in feet.

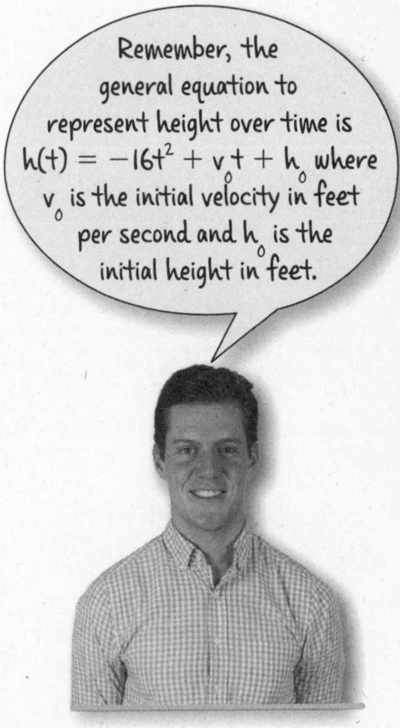

Be prepared to share your solutions and methods.

4

4.2

Function Sense

Translating Functions

LEARNING GOALS

In this lesson, you will:

- Analyze the basic form of a quadratic function.
- Identify the reference points of the basic form of a quadratic function.
- Understand the structure of the basic quadratic function.
- Graph quadratic functions through transformations.
- Identify the effect on a graph by replacing $f(x)$ by $f(x - C) + D$.
- Identify transformations given equations of quadratic functions.
- Write quadratic functions given a graph.

KEY TERMS

- reference points
- transformation
- rigid motion
- argument of a function
- translation

Have you ever taken a road trip? For most American children, some road trips were the bane of existence—especially with annoying siblings. Of course, on the drive back, kids might get excited by a point of reference such as a road sign indicating the number of miles remaining before getting home, or seeing a landscape that is comfortably familiar. Adults commonly use reference points on road trips as well. Most U.S. national map books give estimated hours of travel and distances between key cities across the country. These help motorists and truckers determine if they should continue on, or get off the highway for a bit of shut eye.

What types of reference points have you used? How did you use those reference points?

PROBLEM 1 It All Comes Down to the Basics

So far in this course, all the different forms of quadratic functions you have studied have been based on the function $f(x) = x^2$. This function is the basic form of a quadratic function. From the form of this function, you know the vertex is (0,0).

The pattern of this function is that for every input value, x, the output value, $f(x)$, is squared.

1. Let's consider the structure of $f(x) = x^2$ and its corresponding graph.

   a. Complete the table. Then plot and label the points on the coordinate plane.

x	$f(x) = x^2$
0	
1	
2	

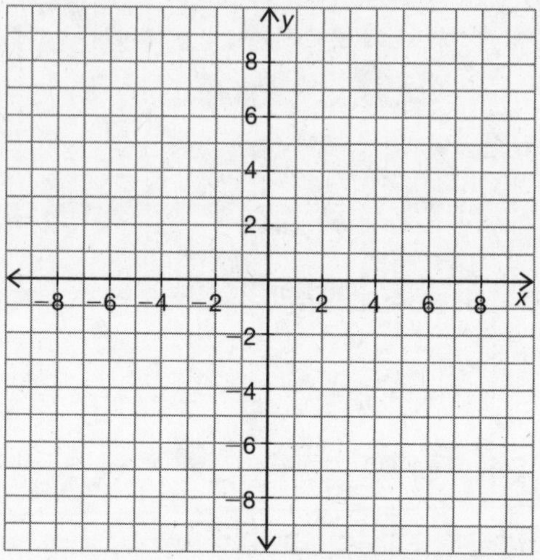

   b. Draw a dashed line to represent the axis of symmetry. Then plot and label all symmetric points. Finally, draw a smooth curve to represent $f(x) = x^2$.

PROBLEM 2 Up, Down, Left, Right

You just analyzed the basic form of a quadratic function, $f(x) = x^2$. For a quadratic function, if you know the vertex and any two points to the right of that vertex, you can use the axis of symmetry to identify the other half of the parabola. A set of key points that help identify the basic form of any function are called **reference points**. The reference points of the basic quadratic function are defined in the table shown.

Reference Points of the Basic Quadratic Function	
P	(0, 0)
Q	(1, 1)
R	(2, 4)

So, for quadratics I just need to remember the relationship between the vertex and two points. To plot Q, I go to the right 1 and up 1 from the vertex, and to plot point R, I go to the right 2 and up 4 from the vertex.

Now that you understand the structure of the basic quadratic function, let's explore how to apply *transformations* to graph new functions. Recall that a **transformation** is the mapping, or movement, of all the points of a figure in a plane according to a common operation. Translations, reflections, rotations, and dilations are examples of transformations. In previous courses, you studied the effects that transformations had on graphs of functions and various figures on the coordinate plane. A **rigid motion** is a transformation that preserves size and shape.

1. Identify which transformations are rigid motions that preserve size and shape.

Previously, you worked with the vertex form of quadratic functions, $f(x) = a(x - h)^2 + k$, which represent transformations of $f(x) = x^2$.

2. Given a quadratic function written in vertex form, $f(x) = a(x - h)^2 + k$, identify the effect the h- and k-values have on the graph of the basic quadratic function.

Which transformations are represented by the h- and k-values?

Vertex form is a specific form of a quadratic function. In this lesson, you will use the basic quadratic function to explore various function transformations. Eventually, you will learn how to generalize about transformations performed across many different function types, but first let's establish a form that will be representative of any function. Transformations performed on any function $f(x)$ to form a new function $g(x)$ can be described by the transformational function form:

$$g(x) = Af(B(x - C)) + D$$

where A, B, C, and D represent different constants.

Let's make some connections and compare the vertex form of a quadratic function, $f(x) = a(x - h)^2 + k$, to the transformational function form $g(x) = Af(B(x - C)) + D$, where $B = 1$.

3. How are the h- and k-values of the vertex form of the quadratic function represented in the transformational function form?

The goal is to understand the effects of transformations using a general function form, and then being able to apply that knowledge to any function family.

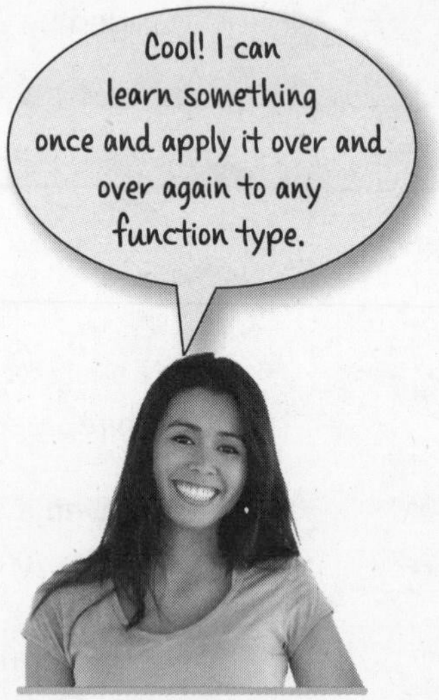
Cool! I can learn something once and apply it over and over again to any function type.

Let's consider the constants C and D, where A and B both equal 1 and the effects each value has on the graph of the basic quadratic function. Let A and B both equal 1.

$$\text{Given } f(x) = x^2$$

$$\text{Graph } g(x) = f(x - 4) + 2$$

In the function $g(x)$, $C = 4$ and $D = 2$. The C-value and the D-value will tell you how to translate the function. Notice, the value of 4 is on the *inside* of the function, or the *argument of the function*. The **argument of a function** is the variable, term, or expression on which the function operates. The value 2 is on the *outside* of the function. Recall values on the inside of a function affect the x-values of the function, and values on the outside affect y-values of the function. So, the C-value will tell you how many units to translate the function left or right, and the D-value will tell you how many units to translate the function up or down.

Remember, translations preserve the same size and shape of the function.

Given $f(x) = x^2$

Graph $g(x) = f(x - 4) + 2$

You can use reference points for $f(x)$ and your knowledge about transformations to graph the function $g(x)$.

From $g(x)$, you know that $C = 4$ and $D = 2$ which tells you the entire graph will translate 4 units to the right and 2 units up.

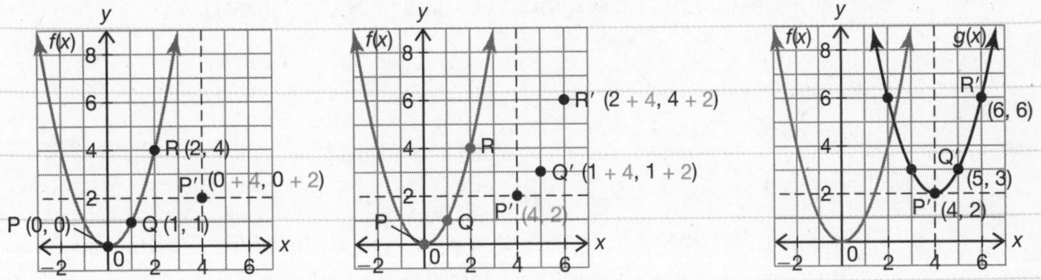

The function $f(x)$ is shown with its reference points. To begin to graph $g(x)$, plot the new vertex, (C, D). This point establishes the new set of axes.

Next, think about the pattern of the basic quadratic function. To plot point Q′, move right 1 unit, and up 1 unit from the vertex. To plot point R′, move right 2 units, and up 4 units from the vertex.

Finally, use symmetry to complete the graph.

You can think of the vertex of the transformed function as the "origin" of a new set of axes.

4

4. Analyze the worked example.

a. Complete the table of values to verify the graph.

Reference Points of Basic Quadratic Function		→	Apply the Transformations	Corresponding Points on $g(x)$	
P	(0, 0)	→	(0 + ____, 0 + ____)	P'	(4, 2)
Q	(1, 1)	→	(1 + ____, 1 + ____)	Q'	(5, 3)
R	(2, 4)	→	(2 + ____, 4 + ____)	R'	(6, 6)

b. Why is it important to establish a new set of axes?

c. Use C and D to write the equations that correspond to the new set of axes.

4

d. Name the two points symmetric to Q' and R'.

e. The function $g(x) = f(x - 4) + 2$ is written in terms of $f(x)$. Rewrite $g(x)$ in terms of x by substituting $(x - 4)$ for x into $f(x)$, and adding 2 onto $f(x)$.

5. Given $f(x) = x^2$, graph $h(x) = f(x - 2)$.

a. Identify the *C*- and *D*-values.

b. Complete the table.

Reference Points on *f*(*x*)	→	Corresponding Points on *h*(*x*)
(0, 0)	→	
(1, 1)	→	
(2, 4)	→	

c. Graph *h*(*x*) in the same 3 steps as the worked example. Provide the rationale you used below each graph.

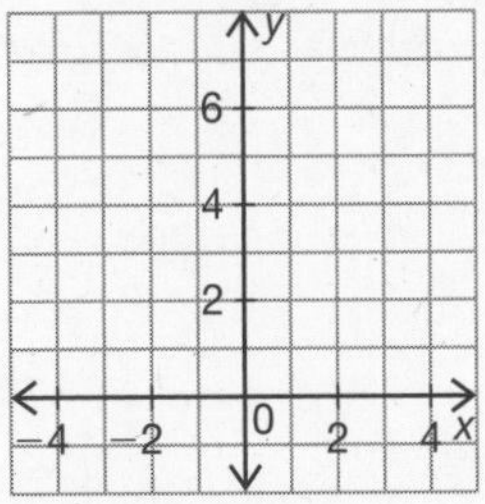

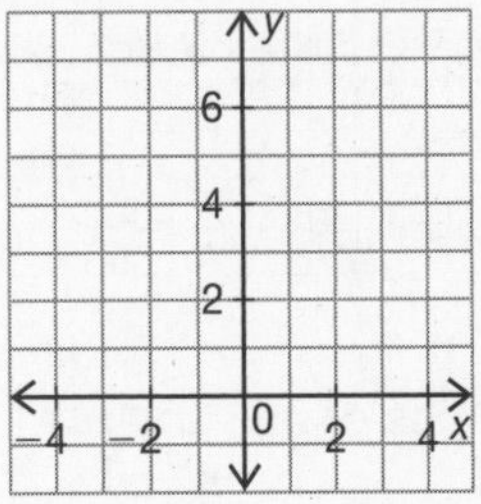

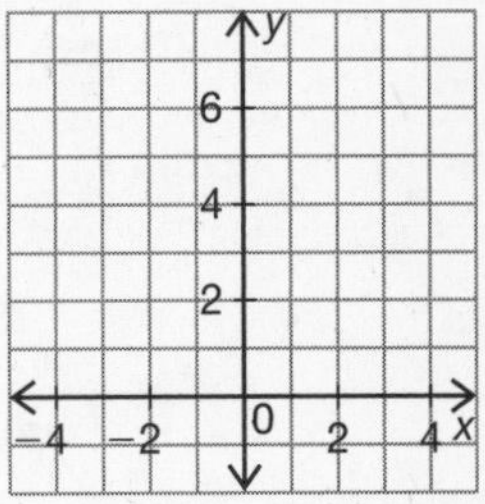

4

6. Given $f(x) = x^2$, graph the function $m(x) = f(x + 2) - 3$.

What does the form of m(x) tell you?

Reference Points on $f(x)$	→	Corresponding Points on $m(x)$
(0, 0)	→	
(1, 1)	→	
(2, 4)	→	

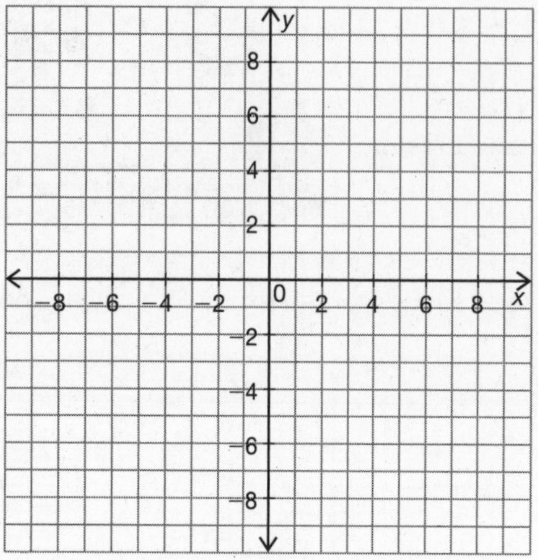

4

7. Analyze the graphs of $p(x)$ and $m(x)$.

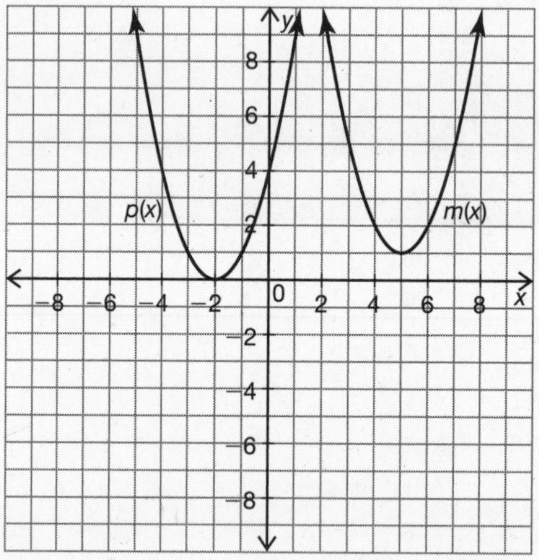
p(x)
m(x)

a. If $f(x) = x^2$, write $m(x)$ in terms of $f(x) = x^2$.

b. If $f(x) = x^2$, write $p(x)$ in terms of $f(x) = x^2$.

c. Write $p(x)$ in terms of $m(x)$.

d. Write $m(x)$ in terms of $p(x)$.

A **translation** is a type of transformation that shifts an entire figure or graph the same distance and direction.

Compared with the graph of $y = f(x)$, the graph of $y = f(x - C) + D$:

- shifts left C units if $C < 0$.
- shifts right C units if $C > 0$.
- shifts down D units if $D < 0$.
- shifts up D units if $D > 0$.

8. Given $y = f(x)$, write the coordinate notation represented in $y = f(x - C) + D$.

$(x, y) \rightarrow$ ____________________________

4

Be prepared to share your solutions and methods.

4

Up and Down

4.3

Vertical Dilations of Quadratic Functions

LEARNING GOALS

In this lesson, you will:

- Graph quadratic functions through vertical dilations.
- Identify the effect on a graph by replacing $f(x)$ by $Af(x)$.
- Write quadratic functions given a graph.

KEY TERMS

- vertical dilation
- vertical stretching
- vertical compression
- reflection
- line of reflection

Have you ever heard that people shrink as they get older? Shrinking can occur from a number of reasons like osteoporosis, or because of the spine compressing over time. What you might not know is that everybody shrinks, and everybody also stretches every single day! This stretching and shrinking occurs because of little discs in a person's spine. They are filled with water, acting as the body's shock absorbers. As the day passes, these little discs lose water, compressing the spine. Then during sleep, the water is replenished, and the spine stretches back to its original size.

Although elderly people do "shrink," and although people expand and contract on a daily basis, people have actually been getting taller. One proof of this observation is the height of doorways in 18th century homes—they were not very tall! This is because people were on average, shorter than today. Over the last 150 years, the average height of a person has increased by 4 inches.

Does this mean that 300 years from now people will be an average of 8 inches taller than what most people are now? Do you think that the average height will eventually reach 9 or 10 feet? Are we destined to become giants, or do you think that this trend will stop?

PROBLEM 1 Vertical Stretching and Compressing

Now, let's explore the effects of the *A*-value in the transformational function.

$$g(x) = Af(B(x - C)) + D$$

1. Analyze the transformational function. Where is the *A*-value positioned in terms of the function *f*: inside or outside the function? Based on the position of the *A*-value, do you think it will affect the *x*-values or the *y*-values? Explain your reasoning.

Let's consider various *A*-values to understand the effects on the basic function $f(x) = x^2$.

2. Use a graphing calculator to graph each quadratic function with $A > 0$. Sketch and label the graphs.

a.

$A \geq 1$
$2x^2$
$3x^2$
$4x^2$

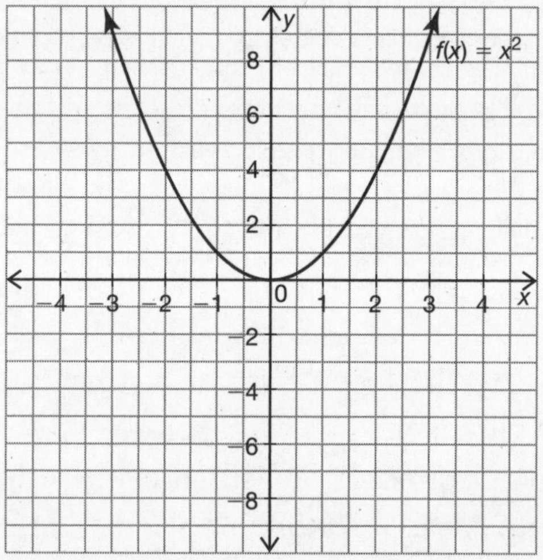

b.

$0 < A < 1$
$\frac{1}{4}x^2$
$\frac{1}{2}x^2$
$\frac{3}{4}x^2$

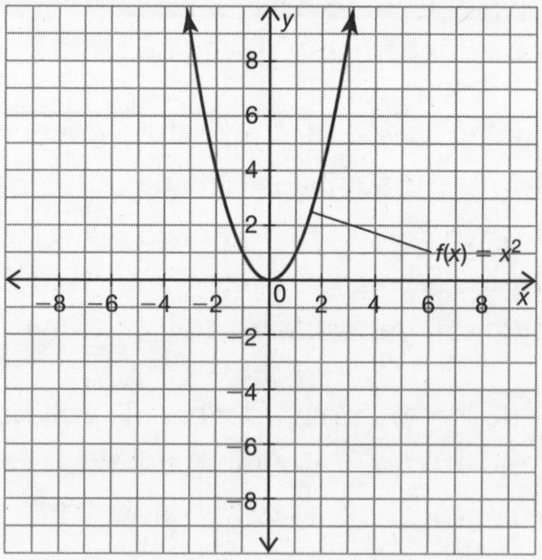

c. Consider the different A-values. How do the graphs in part (a) compare to those in part (b)?

d. Does the A-value affect the x-values or y-values? Explain your reasoning.

A **vertical dilation** is a type of transformation that stretches or compresses an entire figure or graph. In a vertical dilation, notice that the y-coordinate of every point on the graph of a function is multiplied by a common factor, A. You can also think about this as either a vertical stretch or vertical compression. **Vertical stretching** is the stretching of the graph away from the x-axis. **Vertical compression** is the squeezing of a graph towards the x-axis.

3. Is a dilation the type of transformation that preserves both the size and shape of a function? Explain your reasoning.

4. Consider the function $f(x) = \frac{3}{2}x^2$.
Dan says that the graph of this function will look more compressed than the graph of $f(x) = x^2$ because the A-value is a fraction. Jeannie says that the graph of this function will look more stretched because the A-value is greater than 1.
Who is correct? Explain your reasoning.

5. Choose a term that identifies the effect on the graph of replacing $f(x)$ with $Af(x)$:

vertical stretch	vertical compression

a. $A \geq 1$ ____________________

b. $0 < A < 1$ ____________________

6. Given the basic function $f(x) = x^2$, use a graphing calculator to graph each quadratic function with $A < 0$. Sketch and label the graphs. Also, use the TABLE feature and analyze each table of values.

a.

$A \leq -1$
$-2x^2$
$-3x^2$
$-4x^2$

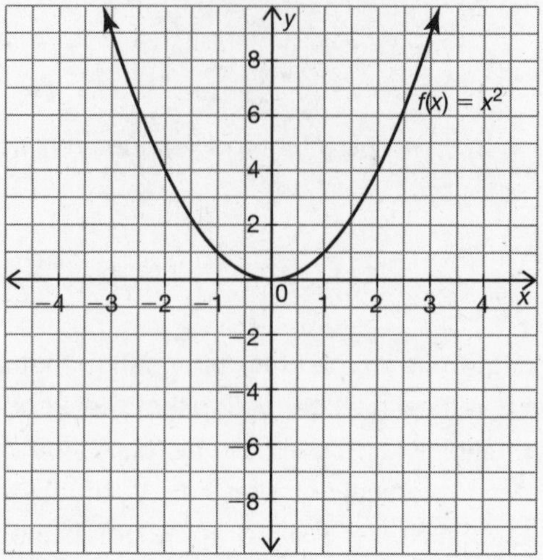

b.

$-1 < A < 0$
$-\frac{1}{4}x^2$
$-\frac{1}{2}x^2$
$-\frac{3}{4}x^2$

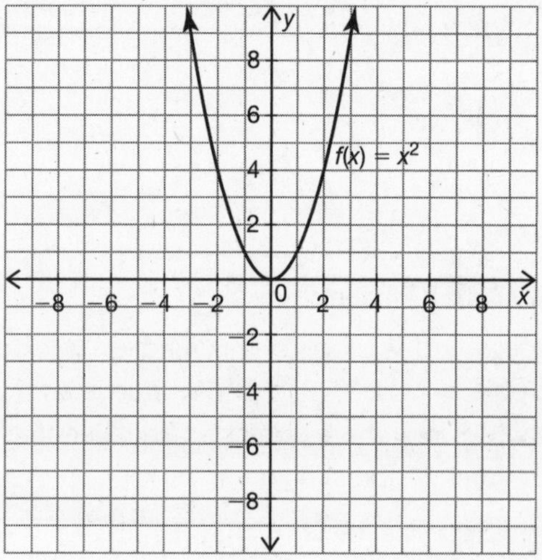

c. How did $A < 0$ affect the graph of the basic function.

d. How do the graphs in part (a) compare to the graphs in Question 2, part (a)?

e. How do the graphs in part (b) compare to the graphs in Question 2, part (b)?

A **reflection** of a graph is a mirror image of a graph across its *line of reflection*. A **line of reflection** is the line that a graph is reflected across.

7. Identify the line of reflection for each graph in Question 6.

Compared with the graph of $y = f(x)$, the graph of $y = Af(x)$ is:

- vertically stretched by a factor of $|A|$ if $|A| > 1$.
- vertically compressed by a factor of $|A|$ if $0 < |A| < 1$.

If $A < 0$, then the graph is also reflected across the x-axis.

4

8. Given $y = f(x)$, write the coordinate notation represented in $y = Af(x - C) + D$.

$(x, y) \rightarrow$ ______________________________

9. Use a graphing calculator to sketch each set of equations on the same coordinate plane.

a. $y_1 = x^2 + 2$
   $y_2 = -x^2 + 2$

How do the graphs of y_1 *and* y_2 compare?

b. $y_1 = x^2 + 2$
   $y_3 = -y_1$

How do the graphs of y_1 *and* y_3 compare?

10. Explain the differences between the lines of reflections used to produce y_2 and y_3 in Question 9.

Think about where the negative is positioned within the equation and how that affects your decision about applying the reflection.

11. Christian, Julia, and Emily each sketched a graph of the equation $y = -x^2 - 3$ using different strategies. Provide the step-by-step reasoning used by each student.

Christian

$A = -1$ and $D = -3$

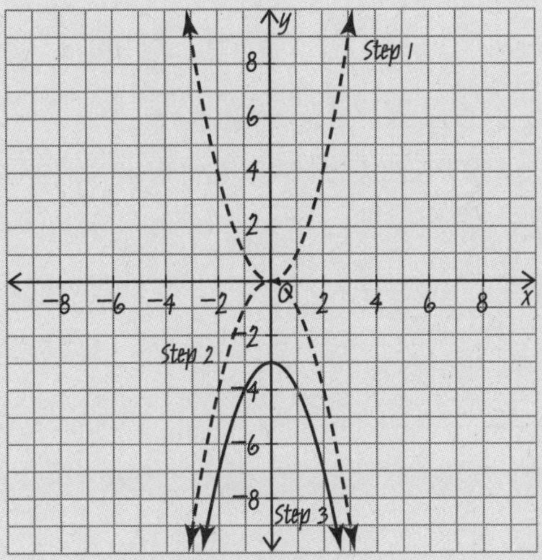

Step 1:

Step 2:

Step 3:

Julia

$D = -3$ and $A = -1$

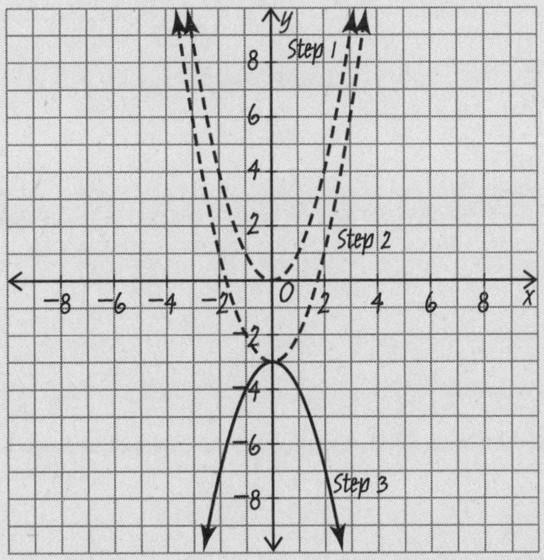

Step 1:

Step 2:

Step 3:

4

Emily

I rewrote the equation as $y = -(x^2 + 3)$.

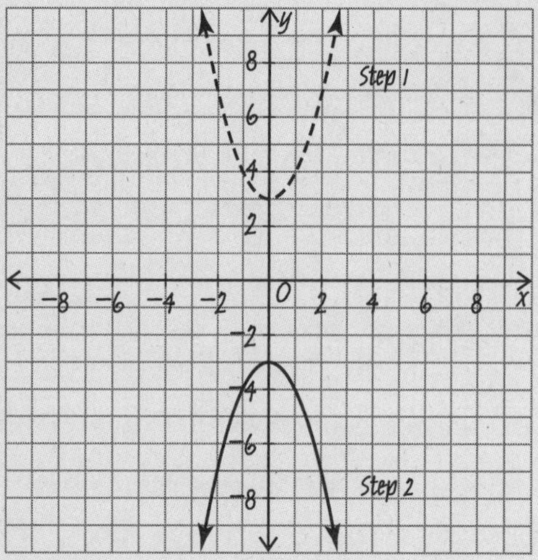

Step 1:

Step 2:

4

© Carnegie Learning

Given $y = f(x)$ is the basic quadratic function, you can use reference points to graph $y = Af(x - C) + D$ without the use of technology.

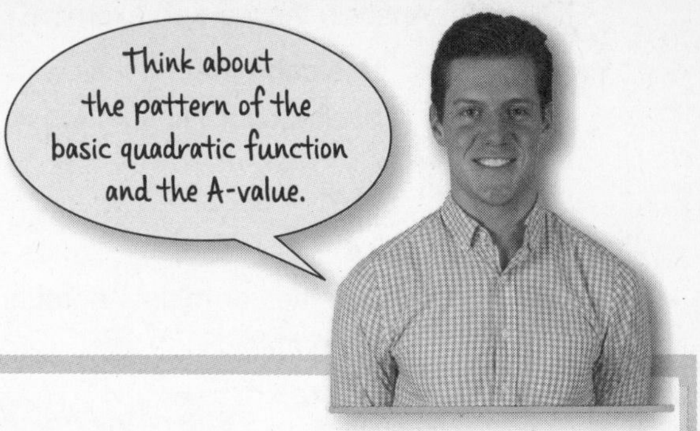

Given $f(x) = x^2$

Graph the function $g(x) = 2f(x - 3) + 4$

You can use reference points for $f(x)$ and your knowledge about transformations to graph the function $g(x)$.

From $g(x)$, you know that $A = 2$, $C = 3$, and $D = 4$.

The vertex for $g(x)$ will be at (3, 4). Notice $A > 0$, so the graph of the function will vertically stretch by a factor of 2.

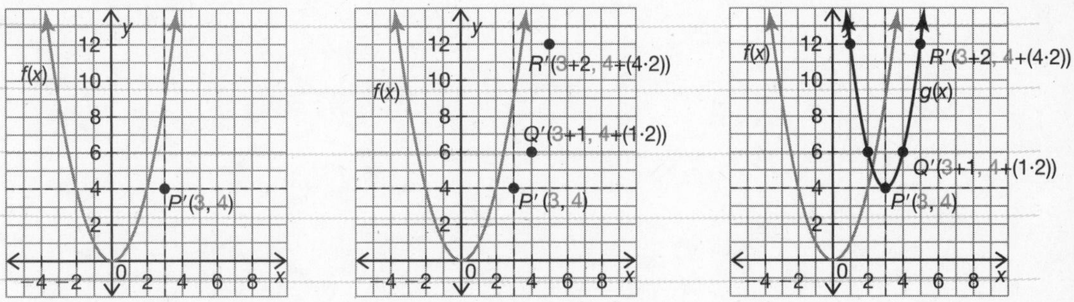

First, plot the new vertex, (C, D). This point establishes the new set of axes.

Next, think about the reference points for the basic quadratic function and that $A = 2$.

To plot point Q' move right 1 unit and up, not 1, but 1×2 units from the vertex P' because all y-coordinates are being multiplied by a factor of 2. To plot point R' move right 2 units from the P' and up, not 4, but 4×2 units.

Finally, use symmetry to complete the graph.

4

12. Analyze the worked example.

a. Use coordinate notation to represent how the *A*-, *C*-, and *D*-values transform the basic quadratic function to generate $g(x) = 2f(x - 3) + 4$.

$(x, y) \rightarrow$ ______________________________

b. Use the coordinate notation from part (a) to complete the table of values to verify the graph.

Reference Points of Basic Quadratic Function	→	Corresponding Points on $g(x)$
(0, 0)	→	
(1, 1)	→	
(2, 4)	→	

c. Rewrite $g(x)$ in terms of x.

4

13. Suppose function $d(x)$ has the same C- and D-values the function $g(x)$ in the worked example, but its A-value is $\frac{1}{2}$.

a. Write $d(x)$ in terms of $f(x)$.

b. How would the graph of $d(x)$ compare to the graph of $g(x)$? Explain your reasoning.

c. Complete the table of values.

Reference Points of Basic Quadratic Function	→	Corresponding Points on $d(x)$
(x, y)	→	
(0, 0)	→	
(1, 1)	→	
(2, 4)	→	

d. Sketch the graph of $d(x)$.

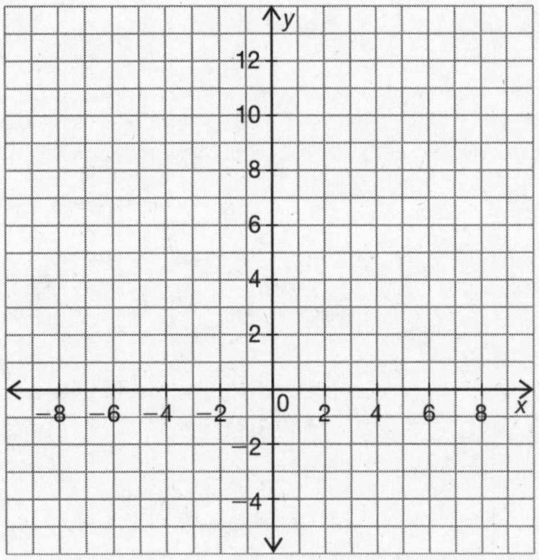

e. Rewrite $d(x)$ in terms of x.

14. Suppose a function, $r(x)$, has the same C- and D-values the function $g(x)$ in the worked example, but its A-value is -2.

a. Write $r(x)$ in terms of $f(x)$.

b. How would the graph of $r(x)$ compare to the graph of $g(x)$? Explain your reasoning.

c. Complete the table of values.

Reference Points of Basic Quadratic Function	→	Corresponding Points on $r(x)$
(x, y)	→	
(0, 0)	→	
(1, 1)	→	
(2, 4)	→	

d. Sketch the graph of $r(x)$.

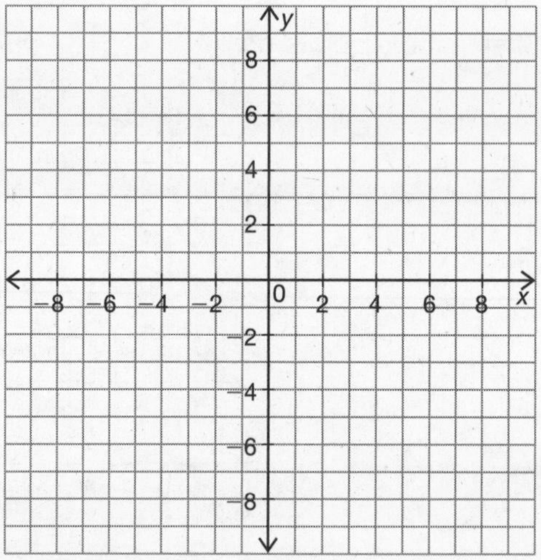

e. Rewrite $r(x)$ in terms of x.

15. Given the graph of $g(x) = 2(x - 3)^2 + 4$ from the worked example.

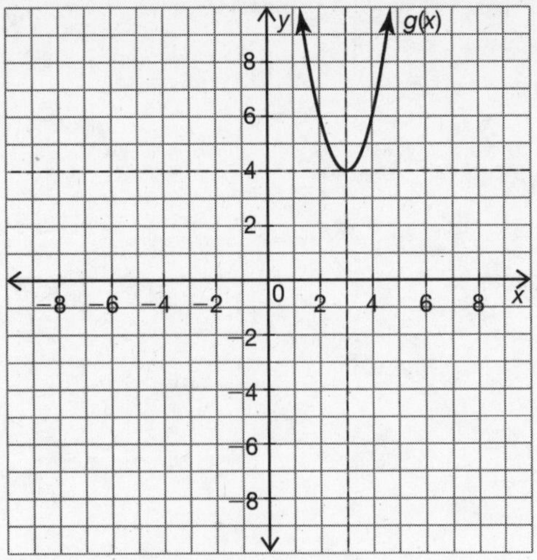

a. Graph $m(x) = -g(x)$.

b. How is the graph of $m(x)$ the same or different from the graph of $r(x)$ in Question 14?

c. Rewrite $m(x)$ in terms of x.

16. Graph $f(x) = \frac{1}{2}(x - 1)^2 + 3$.

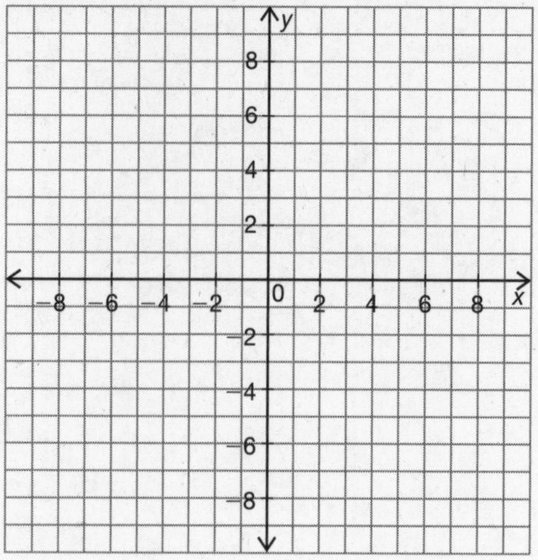

17. Write the functions that represent each graph.

a.

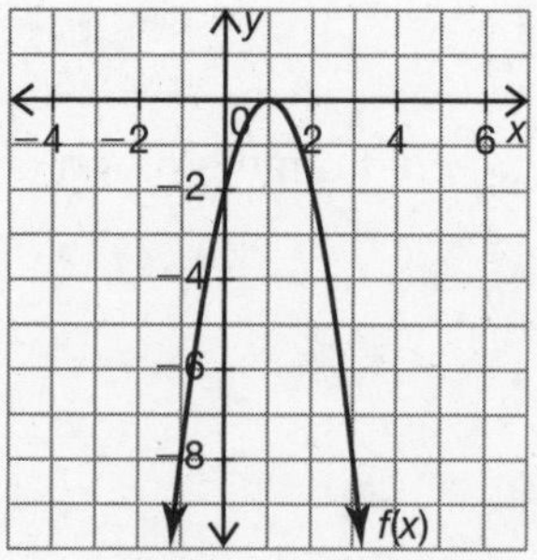

b.

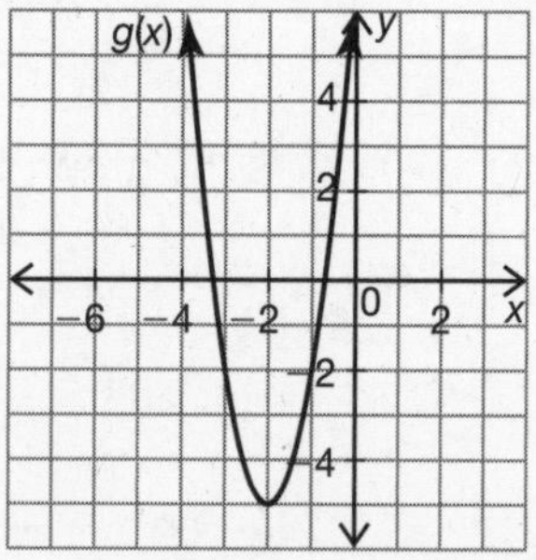

$f(x) =$ ______________

$g(x) =$ ______________

Be prepared to share your solutions and methods.

Side to Side

4.4

Horizontal Dilations of Quadratic Functions

LEARNING GOALS

In this lesson, you will:

- Graph quadratic functions through horizontal dilations.
- Identify the effect on a graph by replacing $f(x)$ by $f(Bx)$.
- Write quadratic functions given a graph.

KEY TERMS

- horizontal dilation
- horizontal stretching
- horizontal compression

Smile for the camera! FLASH! One of the most uncomfortable things about taking a picture indoors is using a flash. And if the picture-taker didn't quite get the shot, it is a double dose of bright lights! Flashes routinely do a number on your eyes—so does the sun. Even though your eyes routinely dilate depending on the light conditions, the sudden flash of light can be uncomfortable for most people. Of course, other things can make your eyes dilate. For example, if you are hungry and you see a commercial for a tantalizing meal, your eyes will involuntarily dilate. You may also know that your pupils dilate when you are sleeping.

What are other things that might cause your eyes to dilate? Have you ever wondered why a typical eye exam usually includes an eye dilation exam?

PROBLEM 1   Horizontal Stretching and Compressing

Now, let's explore the effect of the *B*- value in the transformational function $g(x) = Af(B(x - C)) + D$. The constant *B* is a multiplier.

Notice the *B*-value is on the inside of the function, so which values will be affected: *x* or *y*?

1. Compare the graph of $p(x) = x^2$ with $q(x) = (2x)^2$.

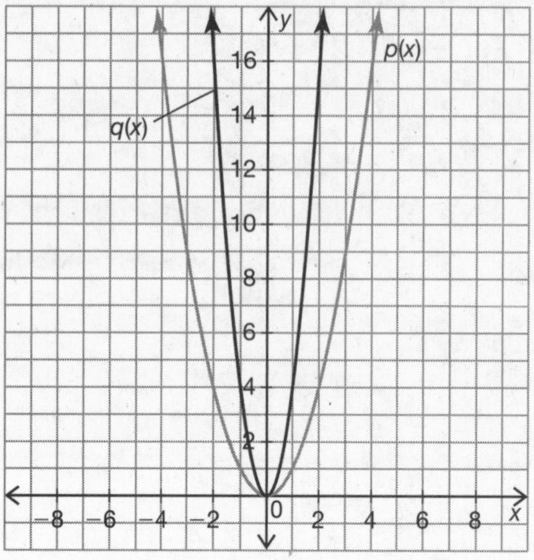

a. Analyze the table of values that correspond to the graph.

x	p(x)	q(x)
0	0	0
1	1	4
2	4	16
3	9	36
4	16	64
5	25	100
6	36	144

Notice when $p(x) = 4$ that $x = 2$, but when $q(x) = 4$ that $x = 1$.

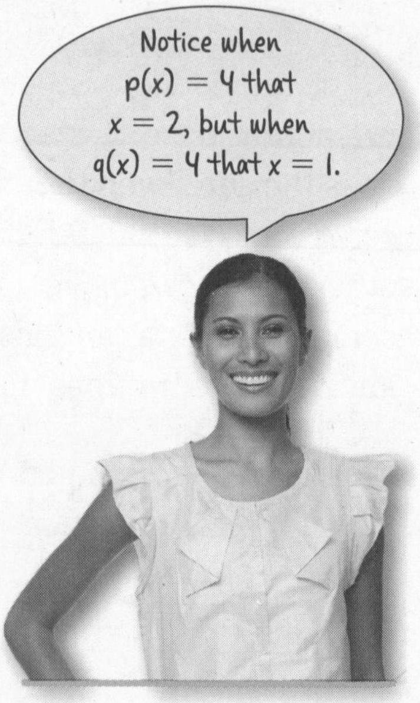

Circle other instances where the *y*-values for each function are the same. Then, list all the points where $p(x)$ and $q(x)$ have the same *y*-value.

b. How do the *x*-values compare when the *y*-values are the same?

4

A **horizontal dilation** is a type of transformation that stretches or compresses the entire graph. **Horizontal stretching** is the stretching of a graph away from the y-axis. **Horizontal compression** is the squeezing of a graph towards the y-axis.

c. Complete the statement.

The function $q(x)$ is a ______________________ of $p(x)$ by a

factor of __________.

d. How does the factor of stretching or compression compare to the B-value in $q(x)$?

2. Now, let's compare the graph of $p(x) = x^2$ with $r(x) = p\left(\frac{1}{2}x\right)$.

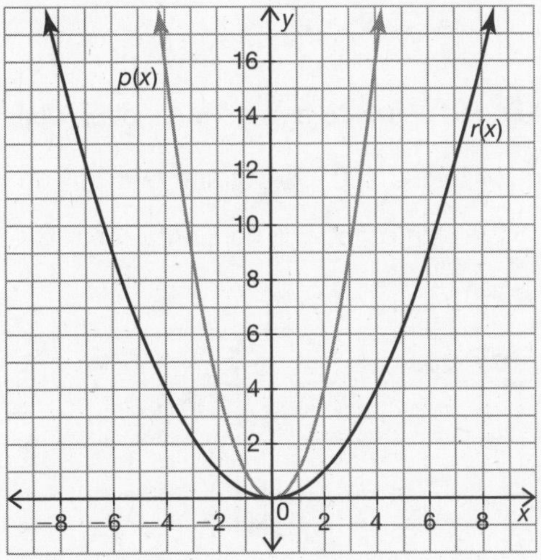

a. Analyze the table of values that correspond to the graph.

x	p(x)	r(x)
0	0	0
1	1	0.25
2	4	1
3	9	2.25
4	16	4
5	25	6.25
6	36	9

Circle instances where the y-values for each function are the same. Then, list all the points where $p(x)$ and $r(x)$ have the same y-value. The first instance has been circled for you.

b. How do the x-values compare when the y-values are the same?

c. Complete the statement.

The function $r(x)$ is a ______________________ of $p(x)$ by a factor of __________.

d. How does the factor of stretching or compression compare to the B-value in $q(x)$?

Compared with the graph of $y = f(x)$, the graph of $y = f(Bx)$ is:

- horizontally compressed by a factor of $\frac{1}{|B|}$ if $|B| > 1$.
- horizontally stretched by a factor of $\frac{1}{|B|}$ if $0 < |B| < 1$.

You can use reference points to graph the function $d(x) = f\left(\frac{1}{3}x\right)$ when $f(x) = x^2$.

From $d(x)$ you know that $C = 0$, $D = 0$, and $B = \frac{1}{3}$. The vertex for $d(x)$ is $(0, 0)$.

Notice $0 < |B| < 1$ so the graph will horizontally stretch by a factor of $\frac{1}{\frac{1}{3}}$ or 3.

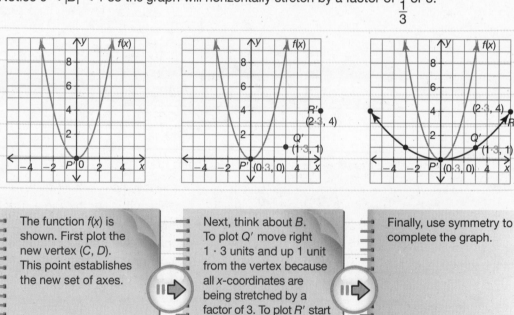

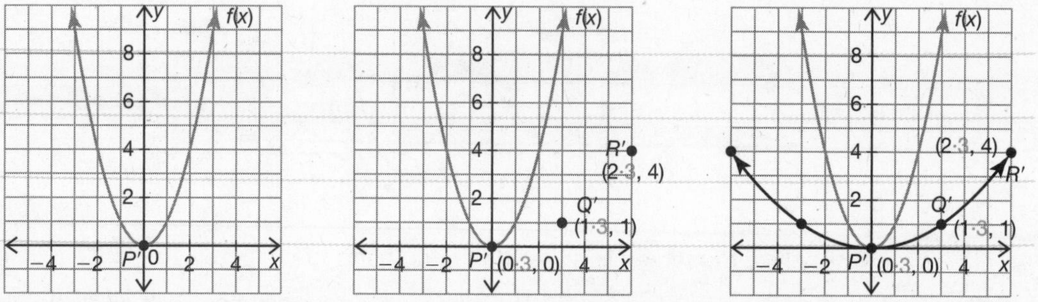

The function $f(x)$ is shown. First plot the new vertex (C, D). This point establishes the new set of axes.

Next, think about B. To plot Q' move right $1 \cdot 3$ units and up 1 unit from the vertex because all x-coordinates are being stretched by a factor of 3. To plot R' start at the vertex and move to the right $2 \cdot 3$ units and go up 4 units.

Finally, use symmetry to complete the graph.

3. List the corresponding points on $d(x)$ for the given points on $f(x)$ in the worked example.

$f(x)$	$d(x)$
(x, y)	
$(-3, 9)$	
$(-2, 4)$	
$(-1, 1)$	
$(0, 0)$	
$(1, 1)$	
$(2, 4)$	
$(3, 9)$	
$(4, 16)$	

4. In the worked example, you analyzed $d(x) = f\left(\frac{1}{3}x\right)$ when $f(x) = x^2$.

a. If you were asked to graph $h(x) = f(3x)$, describe how the graph would change.

b. List the corresponding points on $h(x)$ for the given points on $f(x)$.

$f(x)$	$h(x)$
(x, y)	
$(0, 0)$	
$(1, 1)$	
$(2, 4)$	
$(3, 9)$	

4

5. Analyze the graphs shown on the coordinate plane. Label each graph shown with its corresponding function.

a. $m(x) = \left(\frac{1}{4}x\right)^2$

b. $v(x) = (3x)^2$

c. $p(x) = \left(\frac{1}{3}x\right)^2$

d. $g(x) = \left(\frac{1}{2}x\right)^2$

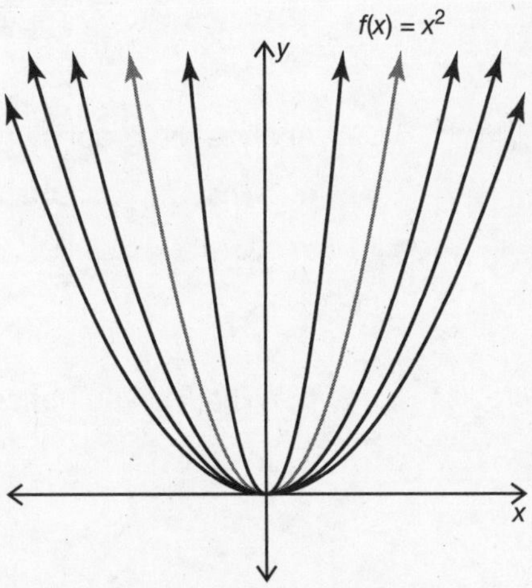

Now that you have studied how $B > 0$ affects the graph of a quadratic function, you will investigate what happens when $B < 0$.

6. Based on what you know about how $A < 0$ values affect the graph of x^2, make a conjecture about how you think $B < 0$ values will affect the graph of x^2.

7. List the corresponding points on $m(x)$ for the given points on $f(x)$.

$f(x) = x^2$		$m(x) = f(-x)$	
(x, y)		$(-x, y)$	
A	(−3, 9)	*A'*	
B	(−2, 4)	*B'*	
C	(−1, 1)	*C'*	
D	(0, 0)	*D'*	
E	(1, 1)	*E'*	
F	(2, 4)	*F'*	
G	(3, 9)	*G'*	

8. Plot and label the points of $f(x)$ and $m(x)$ on the two coordinate planes.

$f(x) = x^2$

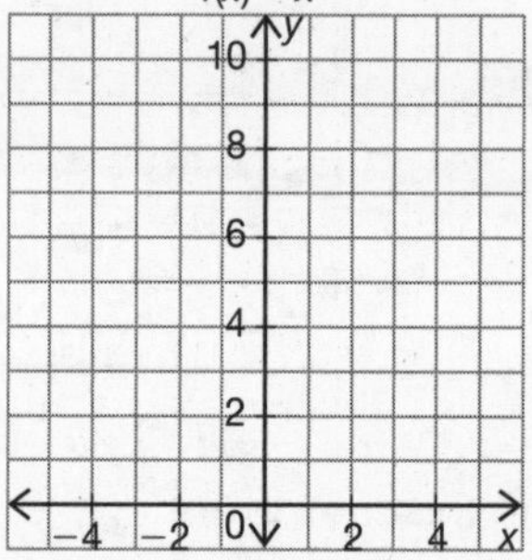

$m(x) = f(-x)$

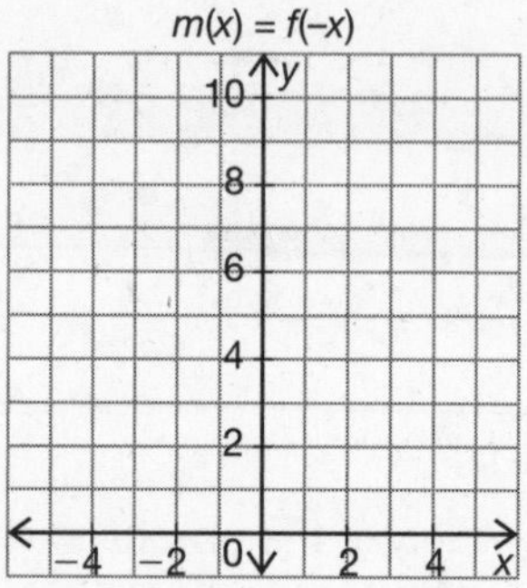

9. Analyze the graphs in Question 8.

   a. What do you notice about the graphs?

   b. What do you notice about the corresponding points in $f(x)$ and $m(x)$?

4

c. Did a transformation occur?

10. Given $f(x) = (x - 5)^2 + 3$.

a. Sketch $d(x) = f(-x)$. Then label A' and B' on your sketch.

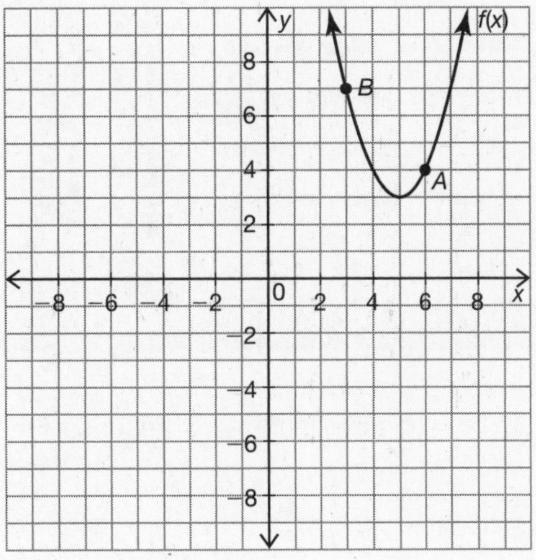

b. Write the function for $d(x)$ by substituting $(-x)$ into $f(x)$. Show all your work.

4

Compared with the graph of $y = f(x)$, the graph of $y = f(Bx)$ is:

- compressed horizontally by a factor of $\frac{1}{|B|}$ if $|B| > 1$.
- stretched horizontally by a factor of $\frac{1}{|B|}$ if $0 < |B| < 1$.
- reflected across the y-axis if $B < 0$.

11. Given $y = f(x)$, write the coordinate notation represented in $y = Af(B(x - C)) + D$.

$(x, y) \rightarrow$ ____________________

12. Connor and Jocelyn each describe the effects of the graph of $d(x) = f(3x + 12)$ when $f(x) = x^2$.

Connor

$d(x) = f(3x + 12)$

$d(x) = f(3(x + 4))$

The B-value is 3 so the graph will have a horizontal compression of $\frac{1}{3}$. The C value is -4, so the vertex will be shifted 4 units to the left at $(-4, 0)$.

Jocelyn

$d(x) = f(3x + 12)$

The B-value is 3 so the graph will have a horizontal compression of $\frac{1}{3}$. The C-value is -12, so the vertex will be shifted 12 units to the left at $(-12, 0)$.

a. Explain how Jocelyn incorrectly described the graph of $d(x)$.

b. Use transformations to sketch the graph of $d(x) = f(3(x + 4))$.

$f(x)$	$d(x)$
(0, 0)	
(1, 1)	
(2, 4)	

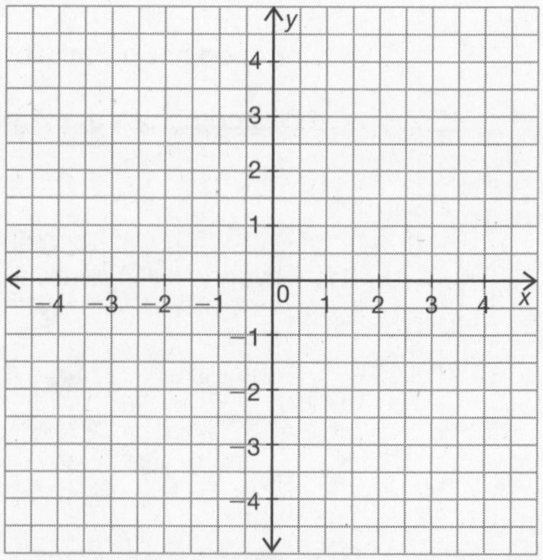

c. Rewrite $d(x)$ in terms of x.

Connor

I can rewrite the function $d(x)$ in terms of x in different ways.

$d(x) = (3x + 12)^2$ or

$d(x) = (3(x + 4))^2$ or

$d(x) = 9(x + 4)^2$

Explain Connor's reasoning.

d. Use transformations to sketch the graph of $d(x) = 9(x + 4)^2$.

f(x)	*d(x)*
(0, 0)	
(1, 1)	
(2, 4)	

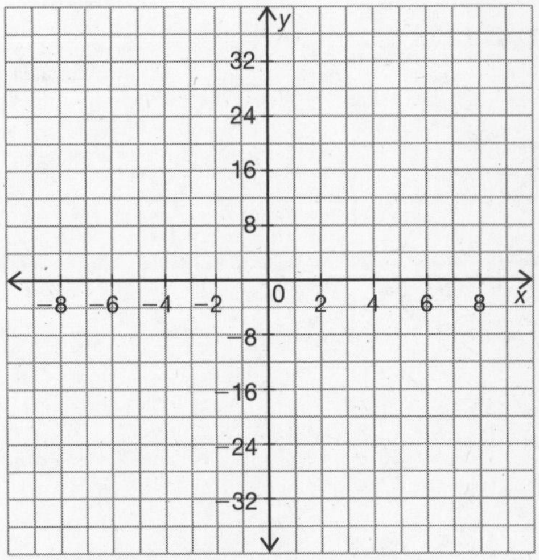

4

e. Use a graphing calculator to verify that your sketch for $d(x) = f(3(x + 4))$ given $f(x) = x^2$ and $d(x) = 9(x + 4)^2$ is the same.

Use the TABLE feature and analyze each table of values.

4

f. Why does it make sense that a quadratic function written in transformation notation with a B-value of 3 would produce the same graph as a quadratic function with an A-value of 9?

Talk the Talk

1. Complete the table to describe the graph of each function as a transformation on $y = f(x)$.

Function Form	Equation Information	Description of Transformation of Graph
$y = f(x) + D$	$D > 0$	
	$D < 0$	
$y = f(x - C)$	$C > 0$	
	$C < 0$	
$y = Af(x)$	$\lvert A \rvert > 1$	
	$0 < \lvert A \rvert < 1$	
	$A < 0$	
$y = f(Bx)$	$\lvert B \rvert > 1$	
	$0 < \lvert B \rvert < 1$	
	$B < 0$	

2. Given $y = f(x)$, sketch $m(x) = -f(x)$. Describe the transformations you performed.

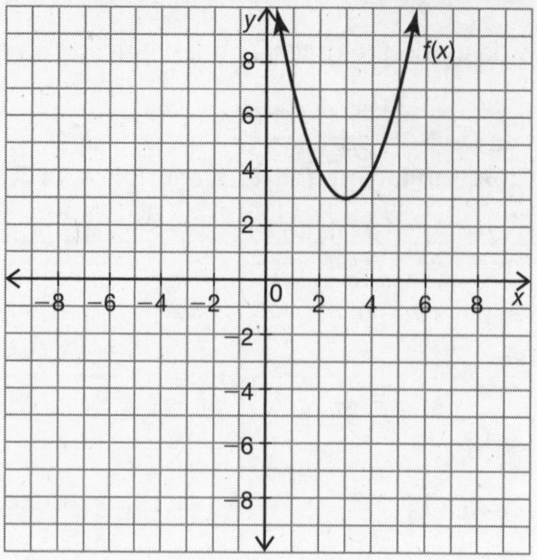

3. Given $y = p(x)$, sketch $m(x) = -p(x + 3)$. Describe the transformations you performed.

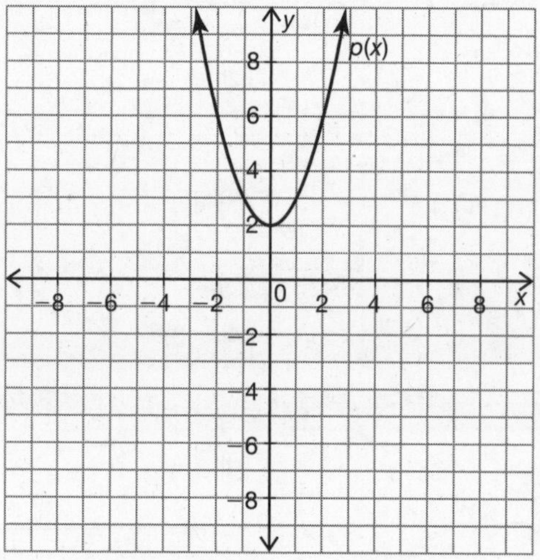

4

4. Write $m(x)$ in terms of $d(x)$.

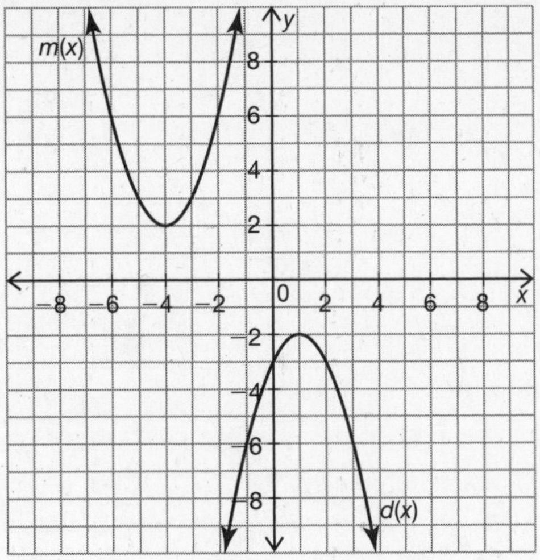

5. Write $m(x)$ in terms of $k(x)$.

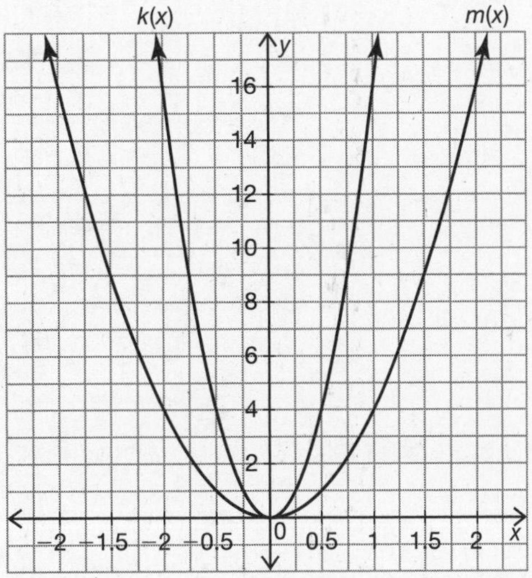

4

6. Given the graph of $f(x)$, sketch $g(x) = 3f(x + 1) - 6$ on the coordinate plane shown.

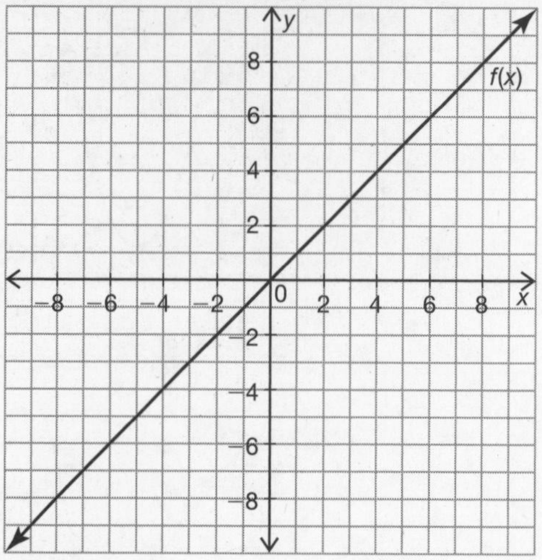

7. Given the graph of $f(x)$, sketch $g(x) = f(x - 2) + 3$ on the coordinate plane shown.

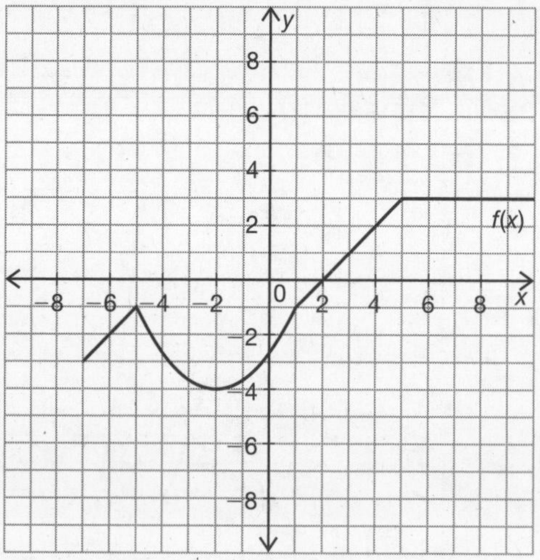

8. Given the graph of $f(x)$, sketch $m(x) = f(-x)$ on the coordinate plane shown. Label A'.

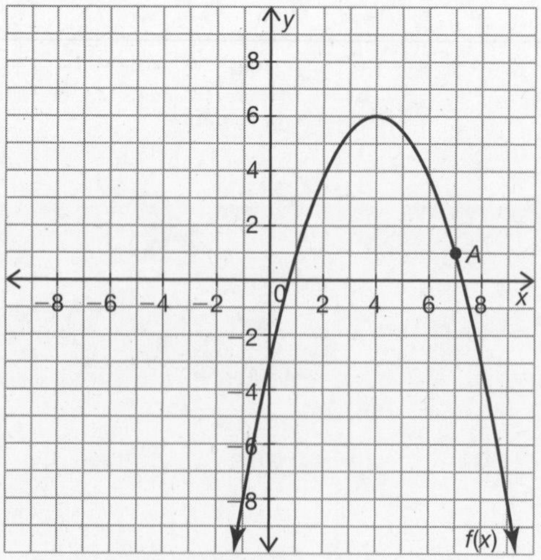

Be prepared to share your solutions and methods.

4.5

What's the Point?

Deriving Quadratic Functions

LEARNING GOALS

In this lesson, you will:

- Determine how many points are necessary to create a unique quadratic equation.
- Derive a quadratic equation given a variety of information using reference points.
- Derive a quadratic equation given three points using a system of equations.
- Derive a quadratic equation given three points using a graphing calculator to perform a quadratic regression.

No matter where you go to see professional baseball in the United States, the dimensions of the infield are all the same. The bases will always be ninety feet apart, and the pitcher's mound is 60.6 feet from home plate. The outfield, however, is a much different story! In fact, baseball is unique in that outfield dimensions, foul area, and outfield walls can be different depending on where the game is being played. For example, the distance from home plate to the right field wall in old Yankee Stadium was actually closer to home plate than its left field wall, making their left-handed power hitters very happy.

Have you ever seen an outfielder jump high above the left field wall to catch a potential homerun? They won't be able to do this in Boston, where the left field wall is 37 feet tall—earning the nickname "the Green Monster."

The dimensions of the field aren't the only differences you will find from stadium to stadium. Dodger Stadium in Los Angeles is built into a mountain side called Chavez Ravine. Turner Field in Atlanta has an arcade area called Scouts Alley. Coors Field in Denver is one mile above sea level that allows the fly balls to travel much further than they normally would because of the thin, dry air. The outfield of PNC Park in Pittsburgh opens up along the Monongahela River, making the city's beautiful skyline visible to all spectators.

Have you ever been to a Major League Baseball game? Did you notice anything unique about the stadium?

PROBLEM 1 A Dime A Dozen

1. Consider the family of linear functions. Use the given point(s) to sketch possible solutions.

   a. How many lines can you draw through point *A*?

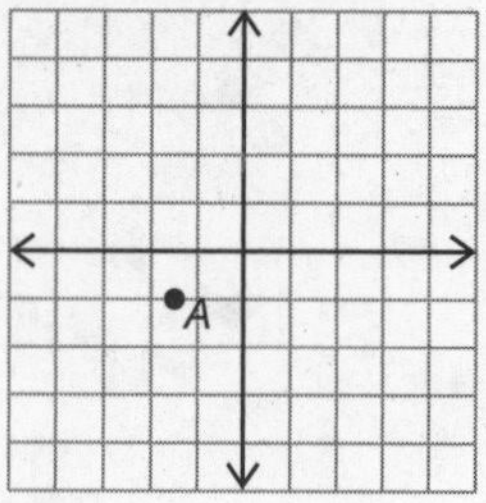

   b. How many lines can you draw through both points *A* and *B*?

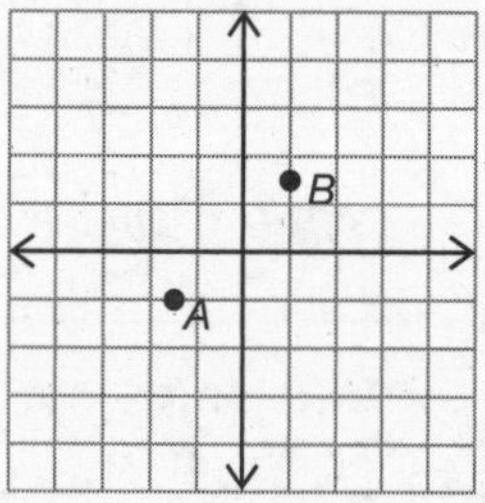

   c. How many lines can you draw through all points *A*, *B*, and *C*?

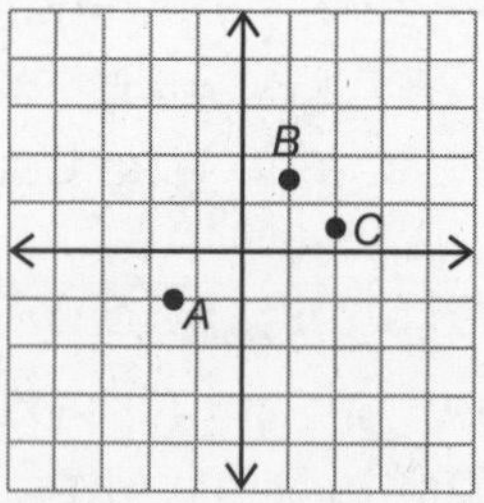

2. What is the minimum number of points you need to draw a unique line?

4

3. Consider the family of quadratic functions. Use the given point(s) to sketch possible solutions.

   a. How many parabolas can you draw through point A?

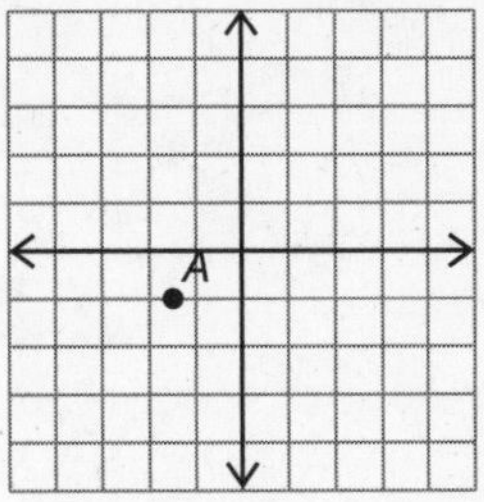

   b. How many parabolas can you draw through both points A and B?

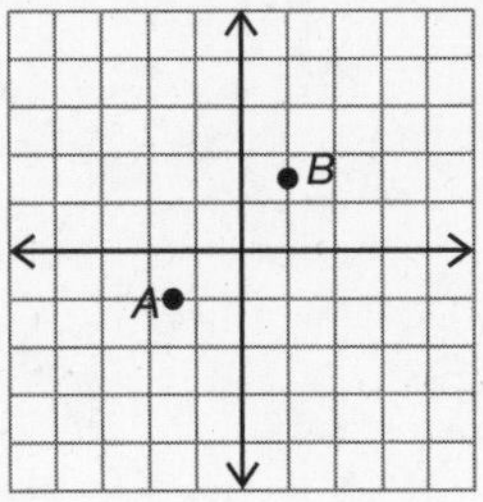

   c. How many parabolas can you draw through all points A, B, and C?

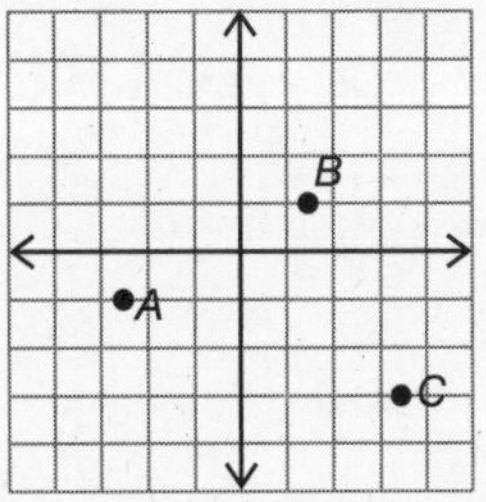

4

4

4. Use each coordinate plane and the given information to draw possible parabolas for Examples A through J.

If there is more than one parabola, draw it.

Example A

Given information: The vertex is (−3, 4).

Sketch:

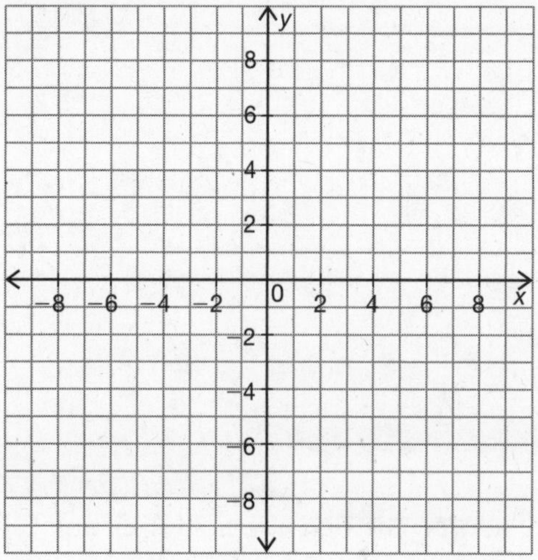

Example B

Given information: The vertex is (−3, 4) and (−4, 1) is a point on the parabola.

Sketch:

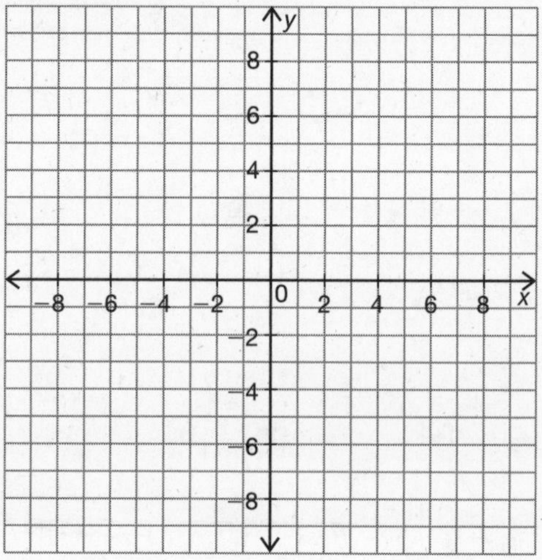

Example C

Given information: The vertex is (3, −2) and one of the two *x*-intercepts is (4, 0).

Sketch:

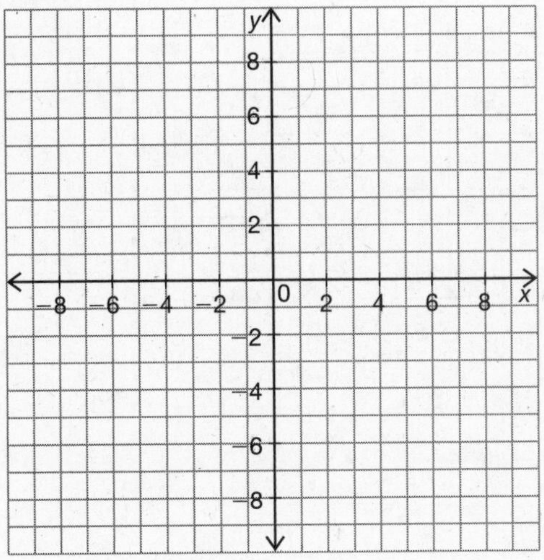

Example D

Given information: The parabola has exactly one *x*-intercept at (−4, 0) and a *y*-intercept at (0, 4).

Sketch:

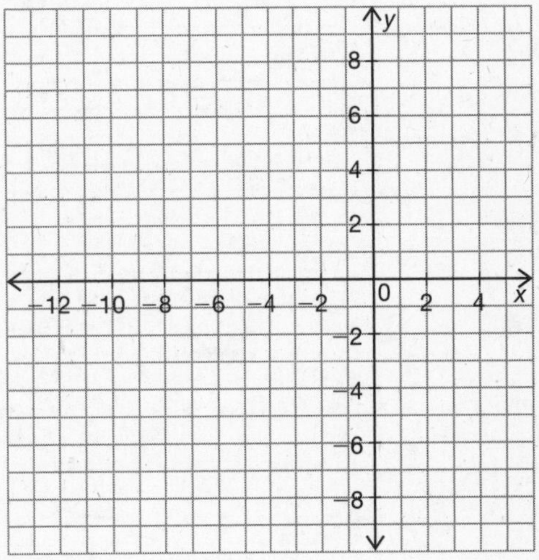

4

Example E

Given information: The *x*-intercepts are (−2, 0) and (2, 0).

Sketch:

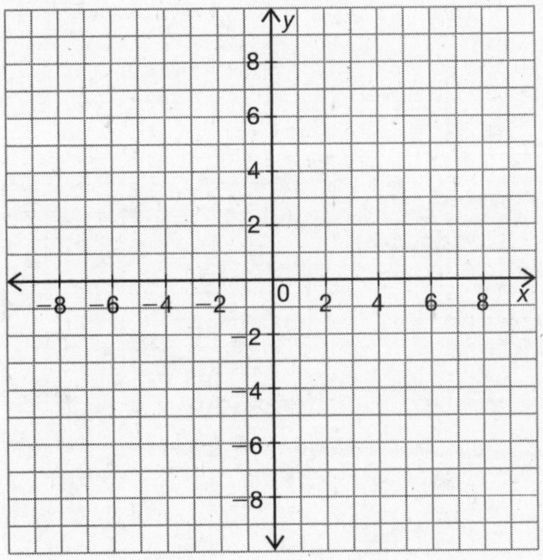

Example F

Given information: The *x*-intercepts are (−2, 0) and (2, 0), and (−1, −6) is a point on the parabola.

Sketch:

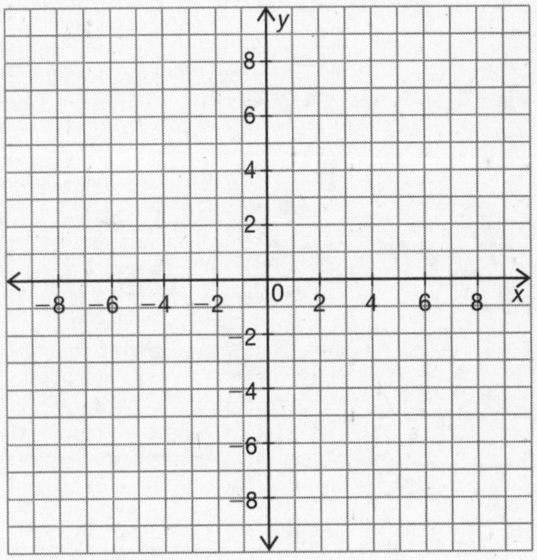

4

Example G

Given information: The axis of symmetry is $x = -5$ and $(-3, 6)$ is a point on the parabola.

Sketch:

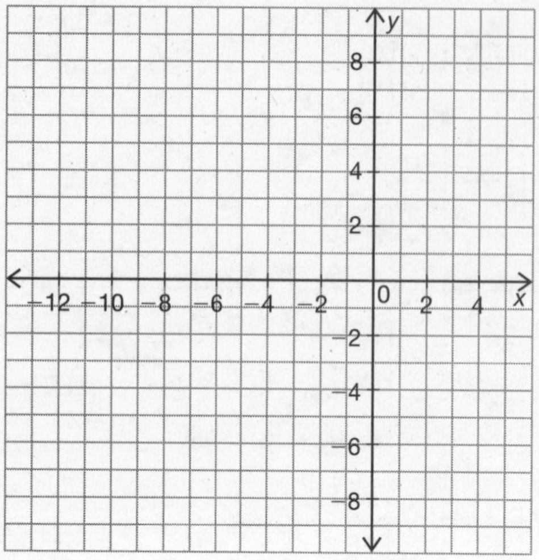

Example H

Given information: The axis of symmetry is $x = -5$, and $(-3, 6)$ and $(1, -10)$ are two points on the parabola.

Sketch:

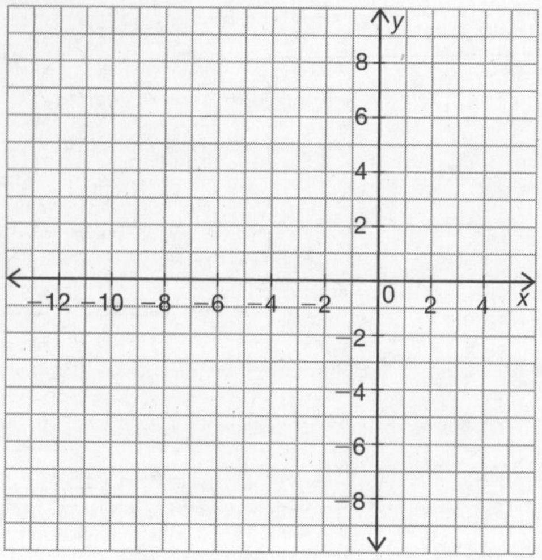

Example I

Given information: Three points on the parabola are $(2, 2)$, $(3, 4)$, and $(4, 6)$.

Sketch:

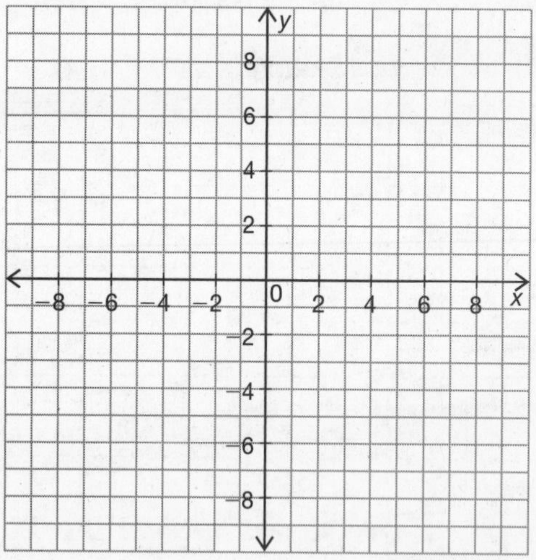

Example J

Given information: Three points on the parabola are $(-4, -8)$, $(0, 8)$, and $(7, -2.5)$.

Sketch:

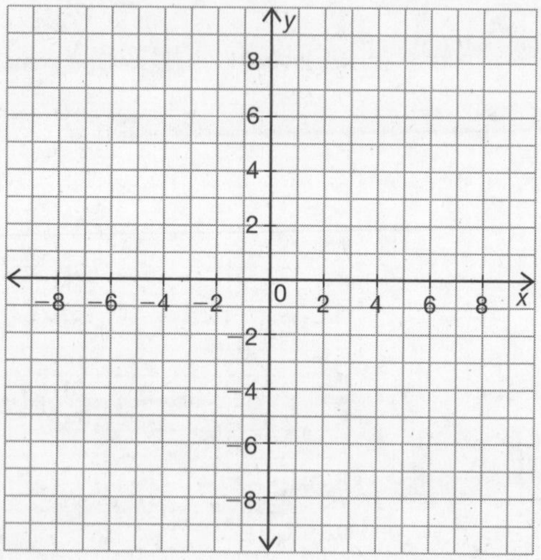

5. Review your work in Question 4.

a. List the example(s) in which you could draw more than one parabola. How many points were you given for the example(s) you listed?

b. List the example(s) in which you could draw only one parabola. How many points were you given for the example(s) you listed?

c. List the example(s) in which you could not draw a parabola. What did you notice that was different from the examples in which you were able to draw one or more parabolas?

6. Consider the examples in which you could draw only one parabola.

   a. Enter the example letter (A through J) and the given information in the appropriate columns of the table shown.

   b. For each example you listed, did you use the given information to determine any other points so that you could draw the parabola? If yes, enter the number of additional points you used in the appropriate column.

   c. Enter the total number of points you used to draw each parabola in the appropriate column.

Information that Determines A Unique Parabola				
Example	**Given Information**	**Number of Points Given**	**Number of Additional Points**	**Total Number of Points**

7. Summarize your results from Questions 1 through 6 to write a rule for the total number of points needed to determine a unique parabola.

PROBLEM 2 One of a Kind

Now that you learned how to determine a unique graph of a quadratic function, let's explore ways to write the function.

To write the quadratic function you will need to use the reference points and consider the vertical distance between each point. The basic quadratic function, the reference points, and the vertical distance between those points is shown.

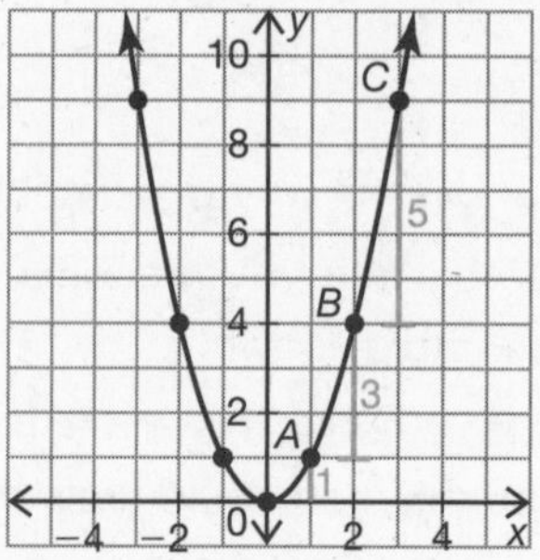

You can use reference points and the factored form of a quadratic function to write the function for the graph explained in Example F. The x-intercepts are $(-2, 0)$ and $(2, 0)$, and $(-1, -6)$ is a point on the parabola.

First, determine the axis of symmetry.
The axis of symmetry must be directly in the middle of the two x-intercepts.

$$x = \frac{r_1 + r_2}{2} = \frac{-2 + 2}{2}$$
$$= \frac{0}{2} = 0$$

The axis of symmetry is $x = 0$.

Plot the points and label the axis of symmetry on a coordinate plane.

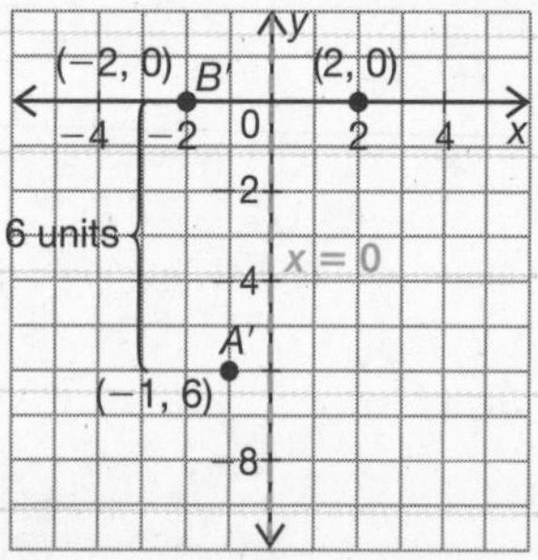

Point B' is two units away from the axis of symmetry, therefore corresponds to reference point B on the basic function.

Point A' is one unit away from the axis of symmetry, therefore corresponds to reference point A on the basic function.

Next, determine the a-value.

In the basic quadratic function, the vertical distance between reference point A and B is 3 units. The distance between A' and B' is 6 or 3×2 units, therefore $a = 2$.

You now know the values of r_1, r_2, and a, so you can create the unique quadratic function.

$$f(x) = a(x - r_1)(x - r_2)$$
$$f(x) = 2(x - 2)(x + 2)$$

1. Brayden, Max, and Ian are each writing quadratic functions that must satisfy the given information: x-intercepts at (3,0) and (9,0).

Brayden

I know the axis of symmetry is $x = 6$ because it is in the middle of the two x-intercepts. I substituted in the values of x and y for the point (9, 0) that is on the parabola to complete the vertex form.

$$f(x) = a(x - h)^2 + k$$
$$0 = a(3 - 6)^2 + 9$$
$$0 = a(-3)^2 + 9$$
$$0 = 9a + 9$$
$$-9 = 9a$$
$$a = -1$$
Therefore $f(x) = -1(x - 6)^2 + 9$

Max

I know the values for r_1 and r_2. So, all I need is the a-value. I randomly choose an a-value of 4. The function is:

$$f(x) = 4(x - 3)(x - 9)$$

Ian

I created a graph to model the situation, and choose to add the point (4, −10).

I know that the given point (3, 0) must be the C' because it is 3 units away from the axis of symmetry. By the same reasoning my new point must be B' because it is only 2 units away from the axis of symmetry. If the a-value was 1, the vertical distance between B' and C' would be 5. In this graph the vertical distance is 2 × 5, therefore the a-value must be 2.

The function is:

$$f(x) = 2(x - 3)(x - 9)$$

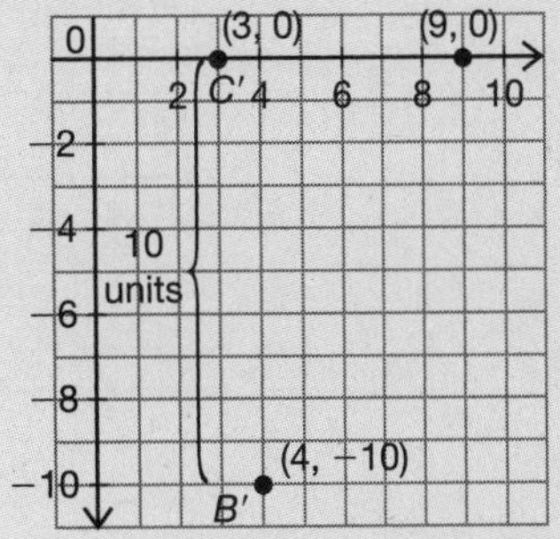

Who's method and quadratic function is correct? Explain your reasoning.

2. Use your knowledge of reference points to write a quadratic function for the examples previously identified as unique parabolas in Problem 1. If it is not possible to write a function, state why not.

a. Example B

Given: Vertex (−3, 4); point (−4, 1)

$f(x) =$ ____________________

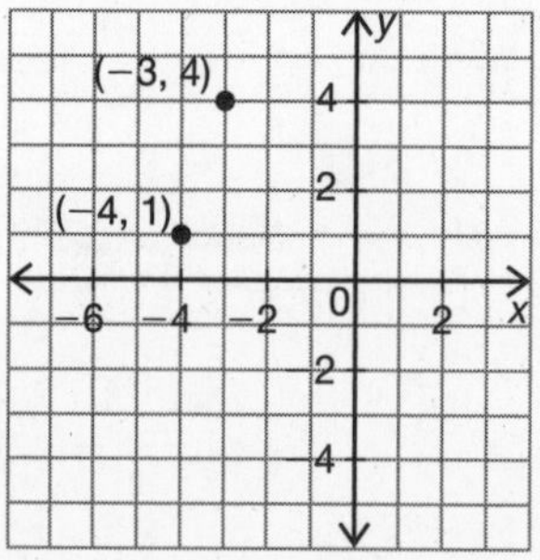

b. Example C

Given: Vertex (3, −2); one of two x-intercepts (4, 0)

$f(x) =$ ____________________

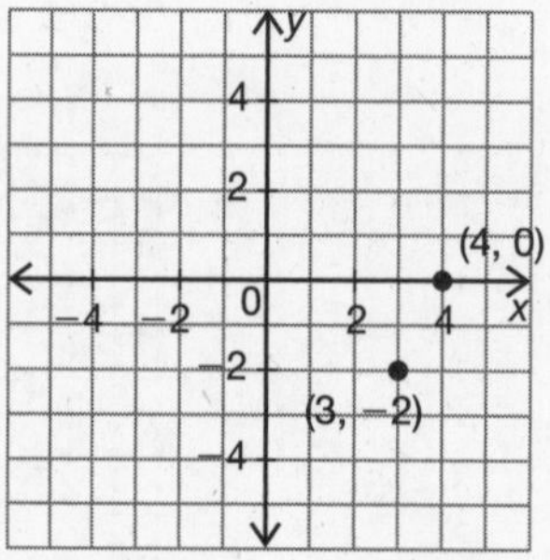

c. Example J

Given: Points $(-4, -8)$, $(0, 8)$, $(7, -2.5)$

$f(x) =$ ______________________

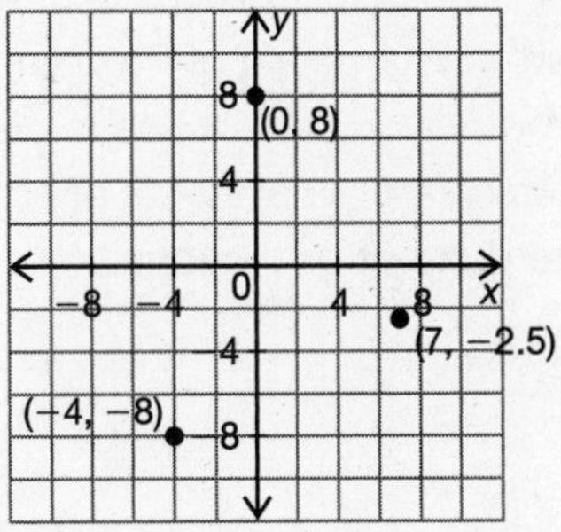

PROBLEM 3 Technology Whiz

Using reference points and the axis of symmetry to write the equation of a quadratic function is an efficient method to use when given certain points. However, this method will not always work. As you saw in Example J of Problem 2, if you do not know the axis of symmetry, you cannot use reference points. You can use a graphing calculator or systems of equations as two other methods to write quadratic functions.

Make sure you set the appropriate viewing window to view the graph.

You can use a graphing calculator to determine a quadratic regression equation given three points on the parabola.

Step 1: Diagnostics must be turned on so that all needed data is displayed. Press **2nd CATALOG** to display the catalog. Scroll to **DiagnosticOn** and press **ENTER**. Then press **ENTER** again. The calculator should display the word **Done**.

Step 2: Press **STAT** and then press **ENTER** to select **1:Edit**. In the **L1** column, enter the x-values by typing each value followed by **ENTER**. Use the right arrow key to move to the **L2** column. **ENTER** the y-values.

Step 3: Press **STAT** and use the right arrow key to show the **CALC** menu. Choose **5:QuadReg**. Press Enter. The values for a, b, and c will be displayed.

Step 4: To have the calculator graph the exact equation, press **Y=**, **VARS**, **5:Statistics**, scroll right to **EQ**, press **1:RegEQ**, **GRAPH**.

If there is already data in your L1 list, highlight the heading L1, Press CLEAR, then Press ENTER to delete it.

4

1. Use a graphing calculator to determine the quadratic equation for Example J.

2. Use a graphing calculator to determine the quadratic function for each set of three points that lie on a parabola.

a. points (−1, 36), (1, 12), and (2, 6)

b. points (0, 2), (−1, 9) and (3, 5)

c. points (2, 3), (3, 13) and (4, 29)

3. Van McSlugger needs one more homerun to advance to the next round of the home run derby. On the last pitch, he takes a swing and makes contact. Initially, he hits the ball at 5 feet above the ground. At 32 feet from home plate his ball was 23.7 feet in the air, and at 220 feet from home plate his ball was 70 feet in the air.

a. Draw a figure to represent this situation. Include any known data points.

b. Use a graphing calculator to write a function for the height of the ball in terms of its horizontal distance to home plate. Round to the nearest thousandth.

c. If Van's ball needs to travel a distance of 399 feet in order to get the homerun, did he succeed? Explain why or why not.

d. What was the maximum height of Van's baseball?

4

PROBLEM 4 All About the Algebra

You know that the method of using reference points to determine a quadratic equation does not always work. You know how to use a graphing calculator to create the equation, but what happened before the graphing calculator? What if you don't have graphing calculator, or needed to explain to somebody how to write the equation?

You can use algebra to solve! You can set up and solve systems of equations to determine a quadratic equation.

You now know that you need a minimum of 3 non-linear points to create a unique parabola. In order to create an equation to represent the parabola, you must use systems of equations.

Consider the three points $A(2, 1)$, $B(-1, -2)$, and $C(3, -10)$.

First, create a quadratic equation in the standard form $y = ax^2 + bx + c$ for each of the points:

Point A: $1 = a(2)^2 + b(2) + c$
$1 = 4a + 2b + c$ Equation A: $1 = 4a + 2b + c$

Point B: $-2 = a(-1)^2 + b(-1) + c$
$-2 = a - b + c$ Equation B: $-2 = a - b + c$

Point C: $-10 = a(3)^2 + b(3) + c$
$-10 = 9a + 3b + c$ Equation C: $-10 = 9a + 3b + c$

Now, use elimination and substitution to solve for a, b, and c.

STEP 1: Subtract Equation B from A:

$$\begin{aligned} 1 &= 4a + 2b + c \\ -(-2 &= a - b + c) \\ \hline 3 &= 3a + 3b \end{aligned}$$

STEP 2: Subtract Equation C from B:

$$\begin{aligned} -10 &= 9a + 3b + c \\ -(-2 &= a - b + c) \\ \hline -8 &= 8a + 4b \end{aligned}$$

STEP 3: Solve the equation from Step 1 in terms of a.

$$\begin{aligned} 3 &= 3a + 3b \\ 3 - 3b &= 3a \\ 1 - b &= a \end{aligned}$$

STEP 4: Substitute the value for a into the equation from Step 2.

$$\begin{aligned} -8 &= 8(1 - b) + 4b \\ -8 &= 8 - 4b \\ 16 &= 4b \\ 4 &= b \end{aligned}$$

STEP 5: Substitute the value for b into the equation from Step 3.

$$\begin{aligned} a &= 1 - (4) \\ a &= -3 \end{aligned}$$

STEP 6: Substitute the values for a and b into Equation A.

$1 = 4a + 2b + c$
$1 = 4(-3) + 2(4) + c$
$1 = -12 + 8 + c$
$1 = -4 + c$
$5 = c$

STEP 7: Substitute the values for a, b, and c into the standard form of a quadratic.

$y = -3x^2 + 4x + 5$

1. Create a system of equations and use algebra to create a quadratic equation with points $(-1, 5)$, $(0, 3)$, and $(3, 9)$.

4

2. Happy Homes Development Company has hired Splish Splash Pools to create the community pool for their new development of homes. The rectangular pool is to have one section with a 4-foot depth, and another section with a 9-foot depth. The pool will also have a diving board. By law, the regulation depth of water necessary to have a diving board is 9 feet. Happy Homes would like to have the majority of the pool to be a 4-feet depth in order to accommodate a large number of young children.

The diving board will be 3 feet above the edge of the pool's surface and extend 5 feet into the pool. After doing some research, Splish Splash Pools determined that the average diver would be 5 feet in the air when he is 8 feet from the edge of the pool, and 6 feet in the air when he is 10 feet from the edge of the pool. According to this dive model, what is the minimum length of 9 foot depth section of the pool?

a. Fill in the diagram with all known information.

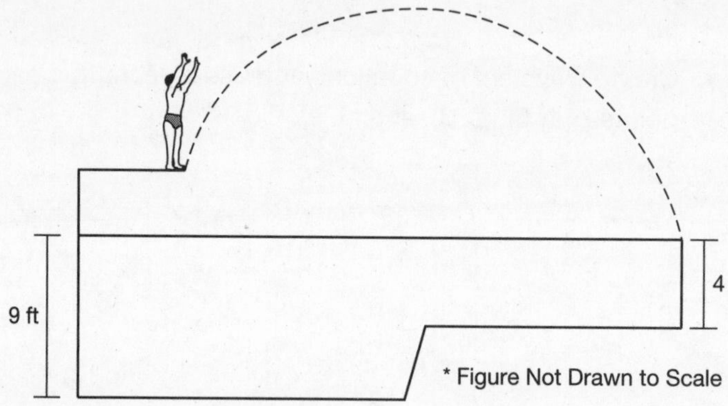

* Figure Not Drawn to Scale

b. Write a quadratic equation in standard form for each of the points you know.

c. Use substitution and elimination to solve the system of equations for variables a, b, and c.

d. Use your new equation to determine the minimum length of the 9 foot depth section of the pool.

Be prepared to share your solutions and methods.

4

© Carnegie Learning

Now It's Getting Complex . . . But It's Really Not Difficult!

4.6

Complex Number Operations

LEARNING GOALS

In this lesson, you will:

- Calculate powers of *i*.
- Interpret the real numbers as part of the complex number system.
- Add, subtract, and multiply complex numbers.
- Add, subtract, and multiply complex polynomial expressions.
- Understand that the product of complex conjugates is a real number.
- Rewrite quotients of complex numbers.

KEY TERMS

- the imaginary number *i*
- principal square root of a negative number
- set of imaginary numbers
- pure imaginary number
- set of complex numbers
- real part of a complex number
- imaginary part of a complex number
- complex conjugates
- monomial
- binomial
- trinomial

"Let me hear the downbeat!" might be something you hear the lead singer tell the band to start a song during a performance. In fact for centuries, bands, ensembles, barber shop quartets, and orchestras relied on tempo and beats to sync up with other band members. Well, this is true for band members today, but there is also music that doesn't have any band members—but a single musician mixing it up on turntables or on a laptop! Of course, these solo musicians are called DJs who have been mixing it since the late 1960s.

The cornerstone of almost any DJ's music is the art of sampling. Sampling is taking a portion or a "sample" of one sound recording and repurposing it into another song. One of the most common samples is taking the drum beats. Many DJs will take four measures of drum beats (with each measure having 4 beats per measure), and reuse it to become the spine of their new piece. Sometimes those four drum-beat measures are repeated for an entire piece—and sometimes these pieces can last 20 to 30 minutes in duration with the DJ infusing other samples of vinyl noise, ambient sound effects, record scratches, and lyrics.

Even more recently, artists have been using technology to create mashups. Mashups generally use two or more pre-recorded songs (not just samples, but entirely mixed songs) and arranging them together to create a new musical piece. Do you think that mashups use this same concept of 4 measures of music to create new musical pieces? Why do you think "4" is so special in creating music?

PROBLEM 1 The Powers of i

So far within this course, you have worked within the set of real numbers and determined real number solutions. Remember, the set of real numbers includes the sets of rational and irrational numbers.

So if it's not a real number, does that mean it's a fake number?

1. Consider the equation $x^2 = -1$.
   Is there a real number solution to this equation?
   Explain why or why not.

The imaginary number ***i*** is a number such that $i^2 = -1$. Because no real number exists such that its square is equal to a negative number, the number i is not a part of the real number system.

2. If $i^2 = -1$, what is the value of i?

4

3. Use the values of i and i^2 and the properties of exponents to calculate each power of i. Enter your results in the table and show your work.

Powers of i			
$i =$	$i^2 =$	$i^3 =$	$i^4 =$
$i^5 =$	$i^6 =$	$i^7 =$	$i^8 =$
$i^9 =$	$i^{10} =$	$i^{11} =$	$i^{12} =$

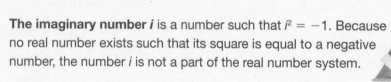

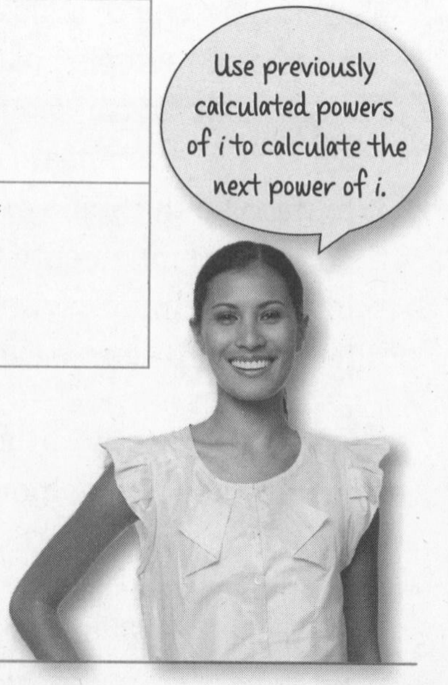

Use previously calculated powers of i to calculate the next power of i.

4. Describe any patterns you see in the table.

5. Tristan, Kira, and Libby calculated the power i^{15} using different methods as shown.

a. Explain why each student's method is correct.

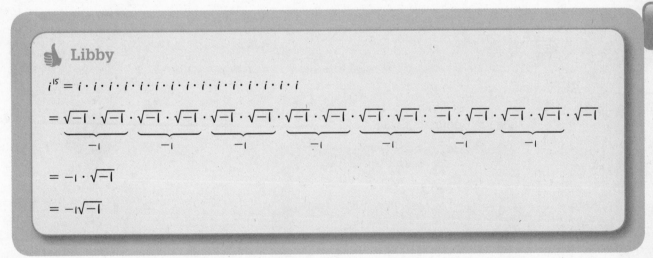

What's so special about multiplying by i^4?

Tristan

$$i^{15} = (i^4)^3 \cdot i^3$$
$$= (1)^3(-\sqrt{-1})$$
$$= 1(-\sqrt{-1})$$
$$= -\sqrt{-1}$$

Kira

The exponent of i^{15} is 15. When I divide 15 by 4, I have a remainder of 3. I know $i^3 = -\sqrt{-1}$. So, $i^{15} = i^3 = -\sqrt{-1}$.

4

Libby

$$i^{15} = i \cdot i \cdot i \cdot i \cdot i \cdot i \cdot i \cdot i \cdot i \cdot i \cdot i \cdot i \cdot i \cdot i \cdot i$$
$$= \underbrace{\sqrt{-1} \cdot \sqrt{-1}}_{-1} \cdot \underbrace{\sqrt{-1} \cdot \sqrt{-1}}_{-1} \cdot \underbrace{\sqrt{-1} \cdot \sqrt{-1}}_{-1} \cdot \underbrace{\sqrt{-1} \cdot \sqrt{-1}}_{-1} \cdot \underbrace{\sqrt{-1} \cdot \sqrt{-1}}_{-1} : \underbrace{\overline{-1} \cdot \sqrt{-1}}_{-1} \cdot \underbrace{\sqrt{-1} \cdot \sqrt{-1}}_{-1} \cdot \sqrt{-1}$$
$$= -1 \cdot \sqrt{-1}$$
$$= -1\sqrt{-1}$$

b. If you had to calculate i^{99}, whose method would you use and why?

6. Explain how to calculate any integer power of i.

7. Calculate each power of i.

a. $i^{93} =$

b. $i^{206} =$

c. $i^{400} =$

d. $i^{-2} =$

Here's a hint for part (e): Use the properties of exponents and your answer to part (d) to write an equivalent expression for i^{-1}.

Now that you know about i, you can rewrite expressions involving negative roots. For any positive real number n, the **principal square root of a negative number,** $-n$, is defined by $\sqrt{-n} = i\sqrt{n}$.

Determine the value of $\sqrt{-75}$.

$$\sqrt{-75} = \sqrt{(-1)(75)}$$
$$= \sqrt{-1} \cdot \sqrt{75}$$
$$= i\sqrt{25 \cdot 3}$$
$$= 5\sqrt{3}\,i$$

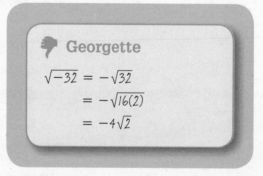

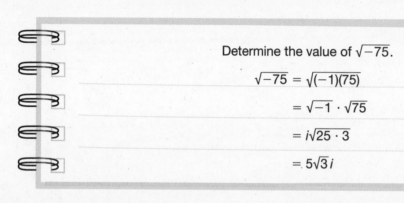

So, use the definition of the principal square root of a negative number before performing operations!

4

8. Analyze Georgette's work.

Georgette

$$\sqrt{-32} = -\sqrt{32}$$
$$= -\sqrt{16(2)}$$
$$= -4\sqrt{2}$$

Explain why she is incorrect.

9. Jen and Tami each rewrote the expression $\sqrt{-4} \cdot \sqrt{-4}$.

Jen	Tami
$\sqrt{-4} \cdot \sqrt{-4}$	$\sqrt{-4} \cdot \sqrt{-4}$
$= \sqrt{(-4)(-4)}$	$= 2i \cdot 2i$
$= \sqrt{16}$	$= 4i^2$
$= 4$	$= -4$

Who's correct? Explain the error in the other student's reasoning.

10. Rewrite each expression using *i*.

a. $\sqrt{64} - \sqrt{-63} =$

b. $\sqrt{-13} + 10 =$

c. $\dfrac{1 - \sqrt{-44}}{2} =$

4

PROBLEM 2 I Must Have Only Imagined this Was Complex

The **set of imaginary numbers** is the set of all numbers written in the form $a + bi$, where a and b are real numbers and b is not equal to 0. A **pure imaginary number** is a number of the form bi, where b is not equal to 0.

Why should I care about numbers that are imaginary?

1. Write the imaginary number i in the form $a + bi$. What are the values of a and b?

2. Give an example of a pure imaginary number.

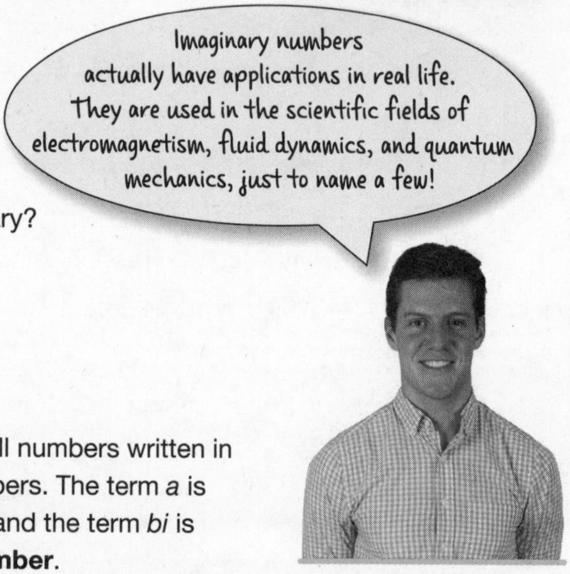
Imaginary numbers actually have applications in real life. They are used in the scientific fields of electromagnetism, fluid dynamics, and quantum mechanics, just to name a few!

3. Can a number be both real and imaginary? Explain why or why not.

The **set of complex numbers** is the set of all numbers written in the form $a + bi$, where a and b are real numbers. The term a is called the **real part of a complex number**, and the term bi is called the **imaginary part of a complex number**.

4. Identify whether each number is a complex number. Explain your reasoning.

a. i

b. 3

c. -5.5216

d. $\pi + 3.2i$

5. What is the difference between a complex number and an imaginary number?

6. Create a diagram to show the relationship between each set of numbers shown.

- complex numbers
- imaginary numbers
- integers
- irrational numbers
- natural numbers
- rational numbers
- real numbers
- whole numbers

7. Use the word box to complete each statement. Explain your reasoning.

always	sometimes	never

a. If a number is an imaginary number, then it is __________ a complex number.

b. If a number is a complex number, then it is __________ an imaginary number.

c. If a number is a real number, then it is __________ a complex number.

d. If a number is a real number, then it is __________ an imaginary number.

e. If a number is a complex number, then it is __________ a real number.

PROBLEM 3 Call the Doctor, Stat! It's Time to Operate!

You know how to perform the basic operations of addition, subtraction, multiplication, and division on the set of real numbers. You can also perform these operations on the set of complex numbers.

When operating with complex numbers involving i, combine like terms by treating i as a variable (even though it is a constant).

1. Simplify each expression. Show your work.

   a. $(3 + 2i) - (1 - 6i) =$

   b. $4i + 3 - 6 + i - 1 =$

   c. $5i(3 - 2i) =$

   d. $(5 + 3i)(2 - 3i) =$

2. Determine each product.

   a. $(2 + i)(2 - i) =$

   b. $\left(\frac{1}{2} + i\right)\left(\frac{1}{2} - i\right) =$

   c. $(3 + 2i)(3 - 2i) =$

   d. $(1 - 3i)(1 + 3i) =$

   e. What do you notice about each product?

4

You may have noticed that the products in Question 2 did not contain an imaginary number, even though the original expression contained imaginary numbers. Each pair of expressions in Question 2 are called *complex conjugates*.

Complex conjugates are pairs of numbers of the form $a + bi$ and $a - bi$. The product of a pair of complex conjugates is always a real number and equal to $a^2 + b^2$.

Remember that a polynomial is a mathematical expression involving the sum of powers in one or more variables multiplied by coefficients. The definition of a polynomial can now be extended to include imaginary numbers.

A polynomial in one variable is an expression of the form $a_0 + a_1x + a_2x^2 + \ldots + a_nx^n$, where the coefficients ($a_0, a_1, a_2, \ldots$) are complex numbers (real or imaginary) and the exponents are nonnegative integers.

A polynomial can have a special name, according to the number of terms it contains. A polynomial with one term is called **a monomial**. A polynomial with two terms is called a **binomial**. A polynomial with three terms is called a **trinomial**.

3. Maria says that the expression $3x + xi - 5$ is a trinomial because it has three terms. Dante says that the expression is a binomial because it can be rewritten as the equivalent expression $(3 + i)x - 5$, which has two terms. Jermaine says that it is not a polynomial. Who is correct? Explain your reasoning.

4. Identify each expression as a monomial, binomial, trinomial, or other. Explain your reasoning.

a. $3 + 5i$

b. $-4xi + 2x - 5i + 1$

c. $\frac{3}{2}x^2 - \frac{1}{4}x^2i$

d. $1.5x + 3i + 0.5x^3i$

4

You can simplify some polynomial expressions involving i using methods similar to those you used to operate with numerical expressions involving i.

5. Simplify each polynomial expression, if possible. Show your work.

a. $xi + xi =$

You just need to remember the rules for multiplying two binomials.

b. $xi + xy =$

c. $-2.5x + 3i - xi + 1.8i + 4x + 9 =$

4

d. $(x + 3i)^2 =$

e. $(2i - 4x)(i + x) =$

6. Analyze each method. Explain each student's reasoning. Then, identify which of the two methods seems more efficient and explain why.

a.

Shania

$$\begin{aligned}(2 - i)(1 + 2i)(2 + i) &= (2 - i)(2 + i)(1 + 2i) \\ &= (4 - i^2)(1 + 2i) \\ &= (4 - (-1))(1 + 2i) \\ &= 5(1 + 2i) \\ &= 5 + 10i\end{aligned}$$

Lindsay

$$\begin{aligned}(2 - i)(1 + 2i)(2 + i) &= (2 + 3i - 2i^2)(2 + i) \\ &= (2 + 3i - 2(-1))(2 + i) \\ &= (4 + 3i)(2 + i) \\ &= 8 + 10i + 3i^2 \\ &= 8 + 10i + 3(-1) \\ &= 5 + 10i\end{aligned}$$

4

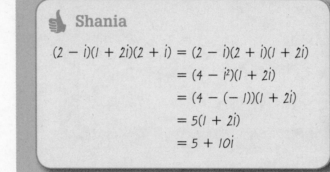

b.

Elijah

$(x + i)(x + 3) + (x + 3i)(x + 3)$

$= (x^2 + 3x + xi + 3i) + (x^2 + 3x + 3xi + 9i)$

$= (x^2 + x^2) + (3x + 3x) + (xi + 3xi) + (3i + 9i)$

$= 2x^2 + 6x + 4xi + 12i$

Aiden

$(x + i)(x + 3) + (x + 3i)(x + 3) = (x + 3)(x + i + x + 3i)$

$= (x + 3)(2x + 4i)$

$= 2x^2 + 4xi + 6x + 12i$

4

7. Simplify each expression.

a. $(2 - i)(1 + 2i)(2 + i)$

b. $(x + i)(x + 3) + (x + 3i)(x + 3)$

Division of complex numbers requires the use of complex conjugates, thus changing the divisor into a real number. Recall, the complex conjugate of $a + bi$ is $a - bi$.

1. For each complex number, write its conjugate. Then calculate each product.

a. $7 + i$

b. $-5 - 3i$

Remember that $(a + bi)(a - bi) = a^2 + b^2$.

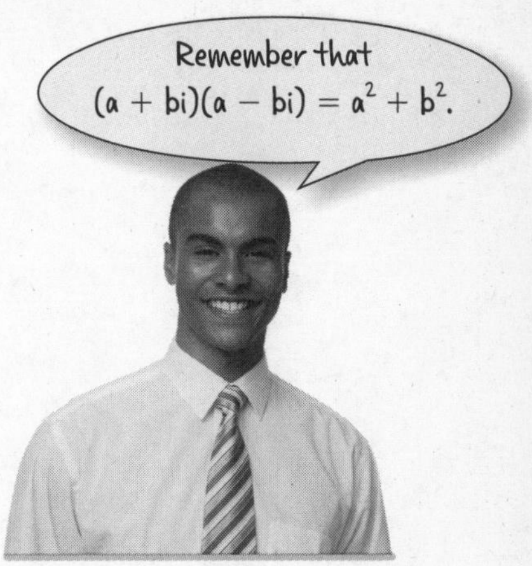

c. $12 + 11i$

d. $-4i$

You can rewrite the division of a complex number by multiplying both the divisor and the dividend by the conjugate of the divisor, thus changing the divisor into a real number.

You can rewrite $\dfrac{3 - 2i}{4 + 3i}$ without a complex number in the denominator.

You are just multiplying by a form of 1.

$$\frac{3 - 2i}{4 + 3i} = \frac{3 - 2i}{4 + 3i} \cdot \frac{4 - 3i}{4 - 3i}$$

$$= \frac{12 - 9i - 8i + 6i^2}{4^2 + 3^2}$$

$$= \frac{12 - 17i - 6}{16 + 9}$$

$$= \frac{6 - 17i}{25}$$

$$\frac{3 - 2i}{4 + 3i} = \frac{6}{25} - \frac{17}{25}i$$

2. Rewrite each quotient without a complex number in the denominator.

a. $\frac{2 - i}{3 + 2i}$

b. $\frac{3 - 4i}{2 - 3i}$

c. $\frac{5 + 2i}{1 + i}$

d. $\frac{20 - 5i}{2 - 4i}$

Be prepared to share your solutions and methods.

You Can't Spell "Fundamental Theorem of Algebra" without F-U-N!

4.7

Quadratics and Complex Numbers

LEARNING GOALS

In this lesson, you will:

- Determine the number and type of zeros of a quadratic function.
- Solve quadratic equations with complex solutions.
- Use the Fundamental Theorem of Algebra.
- Choose an appropriate method to determine zeros of quadratic functions.

KEY TERMS

- imaginary roots
- discriminant
- imaginary zeros
- Fundamental Theorem of Algebra
- double root

I'm sure you've heard these sayings: "That's it! I'm drawing a line in the sand!" or "You've crossed that line a long time ago!" So what is the human fascination with lines and boundaries and the implications if these boundaries are crossed?

You might remember that as a young child, you might have been told to stay within the lines of a drawing when coloring in your coloring book; though young toddlers seem to have a tough time with that motor skill. The implication of coloring *outside* of the lines was not a big deal—unless it just drove you crazy as a kid! However, crossing a line over international flying zones, at sea, or on the ground can have much greater impacts on global situations. For example, in 2009, three Americans were hiking in Iraqi Kurdistan when they inadvertently crossed the Iranian border. Upon doing so, Iranian border guards detained the hikers. A long ordeal of negotiating followed between the U.S. and Iranian governments led to the release of Sarah Shourd on September 2010, and the release of Shane Bauer and Joshua Fattal on September 21, 2011.

These of course are two extremes of crossing lines or boundaries. And of course, it is more than governments and conventions that establish lines and boundaries. People establish certain boundaries and etiquette in social settings. What are some social boundaries people have established? What are the implications when those boundaries are crossed?

PROBLEM 1 X-Axis Intersection Inspection

4

1. Analyze each graph. Identify the x-intercepts, if possible.

Group A

$g(x) = x^2 - 4$

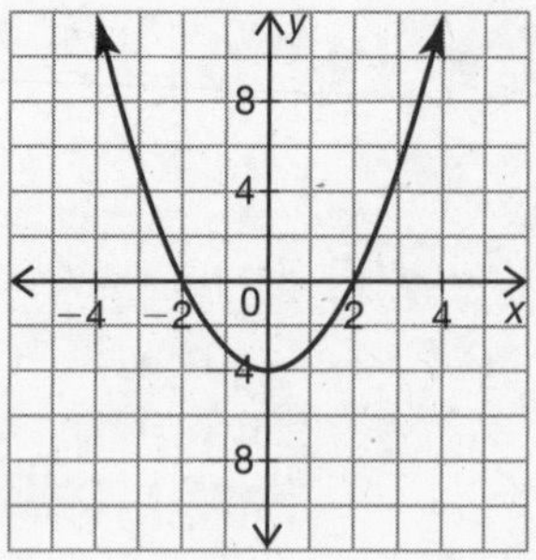

$h(x) = -x^2 - 6x$

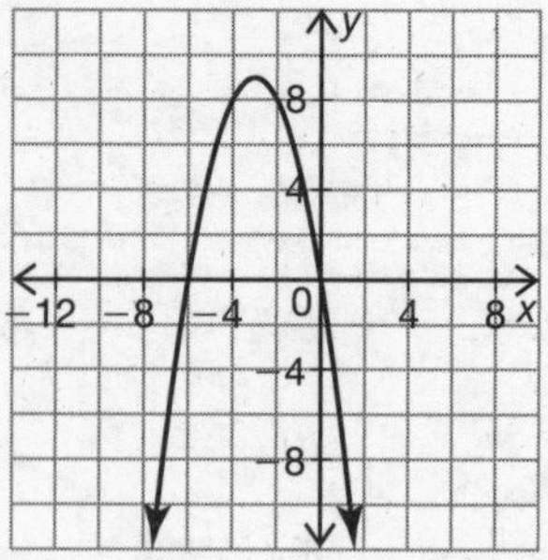

Group B

$m(x) = -x^2 - 6x - 9$

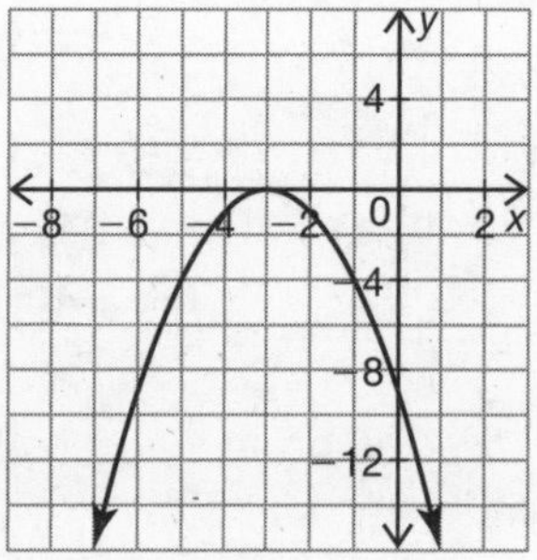

$n(x) = \frac{1}{2}x^2 - 4x + 8$

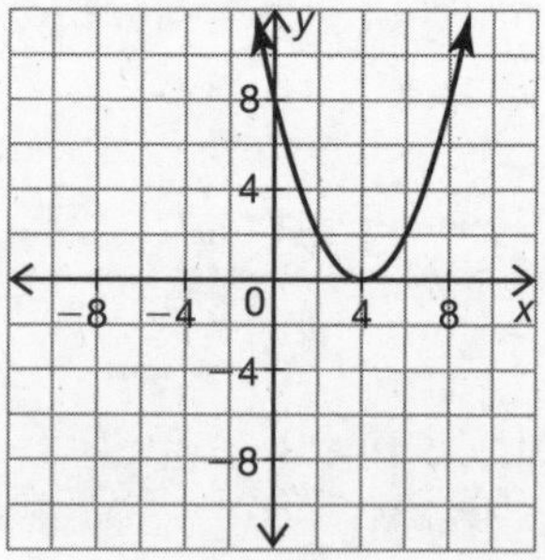

Group C

$p(x) = 2x^2 - 12x + 19$

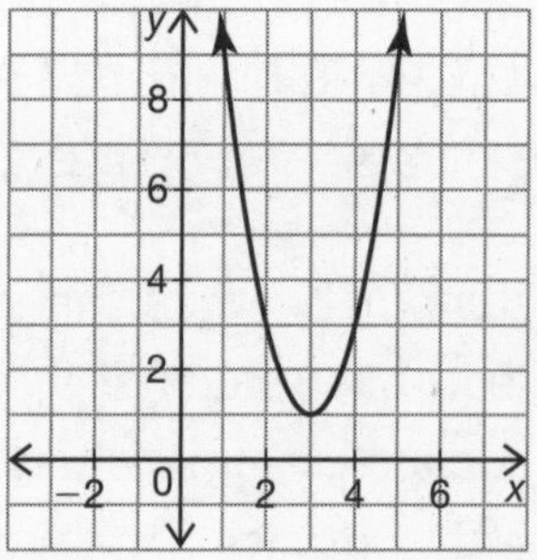

$q(x) = -\frac{1}{3}x^2 - \frac{4}{3}x - \frac{10}{3}$

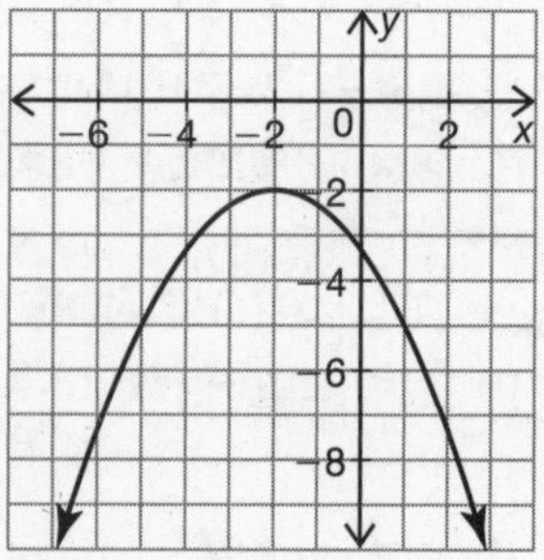

The x-intercepts of a quadratic function $f(x)$ are the solutions of the equation $f(x) = 0$.

2. If $f(x)$ is a quadratic function, explain how to determine the number of solutions of $f(x) = 0$ given the graph of $f(x)$.

3. Choose one of the two functions from each group in Question 1. Use the Quadratic Formula and what you know about imaginary numbers to solve an equation of the form $f(x) = 0$ for each function you choose.

Group A

$g(x) = x^2 - 4$ $\qquad$ $h(x) = -x^2 - 6x$

Group B

$m(x) = -x^2 - 6x - 9$ $\qquad$ $n(x) = \frac{1}{2}x^2 - 4x + 8$

4

Group C

$p(x) = 2x^2 - 12x + 19$ $\qquad$ $q(x) = -\frac{1}{3}x^2 - \frac{4}{3}x - \frac{10}{3}$

Equations that have imaginary solutions have **imaginary roots**.

4. Consider the three equations you chose to solve in Question 3.

   a. Which of the three equations have imaginary roots?

   b. When you used the Quadratic Formula to solve the equations, at what point did you know the solution was going to include an imaginary number?

The radicand expression in the Quadratic Formula, $b^2 - 4ac$, is called the **discriminant** because it "discriminates" the number and type of roots of a quadratic equation.

5. Describe how you can tell whether a quadratic equation has real or imaginary roots from the:

   a. discriminant.

   b. graph.

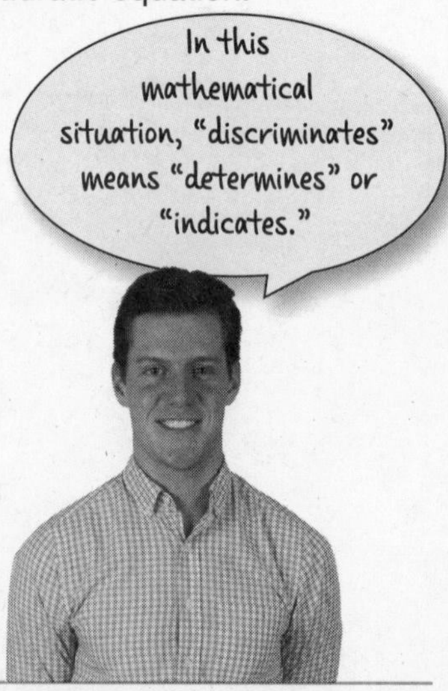

In this mathematical situation, "discriminates" means "determines" or "indicates."

6. Consider the three equations that you did not solve in Question 3. Use the discriminant to determine whether the roots are real or imaginary. Show your work. Then, look at each graph to verify.

Just as equations may have imaginary roots, functions may have *imaginary zeros*. **Imaginary zeros** are zeros of quadratic functions that do not cross the x-axis. Remember that zeros of a function $f(x)$ are the values of x for which $f(x) = 0$. Zeros, roots, and x-intercepts are all related.

Oh! So, graphs have x-intercepts, equations have roots, and functions have zeros!

7. Use any method to determine whether each function has real or imaginary zeros. You do not need to calculate the zeros.

a. $f(x) = -3x^2 + 2x - 1$

b. $f(x) = -\frac{1}{2}x^2 + x - \frac{1}{2}$

c. $f(x) = 2x^2 - 5x - 6$

Remember, a quadratic equation is a special type of polynomial equation. The degree of a polynomial equation is the greatest exponent in the polynomial equation.

8. What is the degree of a quadratic equation? a linear equation? a constant equation?

The *Fundamental Theorem of Algebra was* first proposed in the early 1600s, but would not be proven until almost two centuries later. The **Fundamental Theorem of Algebra** states that any polynomial equation of degree *n* must have exactly *n* complex roots or solutions; also, every polynomial function of degree *n* must have exactly *n* complex zeros. However, any root or zero may be a multiple root or zero.

Now that we have covered both real and imaginary roots and zeros, we can refer to them as complex roots and complex zeros.

9. Look at the graphs of the functions in Group B of Question 1. Even though the functions intersect the *x*-axis once, according to the Fundamental Theorem of Algebra, how many complex zeros do these functions have?

If the graph of a quadratic function *f*(*x*) has 1 *x*-intercept, the equation *f*(*x*) = 0 still has 2 real roots. In this case, the 2 real roots are considered a **double root.**

4

10. Analyze the discriminants of the quadratic functions in Question 1. What must be true about the discriminant of a quadratic equation that has a double root?

11. Explain why it is not possible for a quadratic equation to have 2 equal imaginary solutions, or a double imaginary root.

12. Circle the function(s) shown that could describe the given graph. Explain your reasoning.

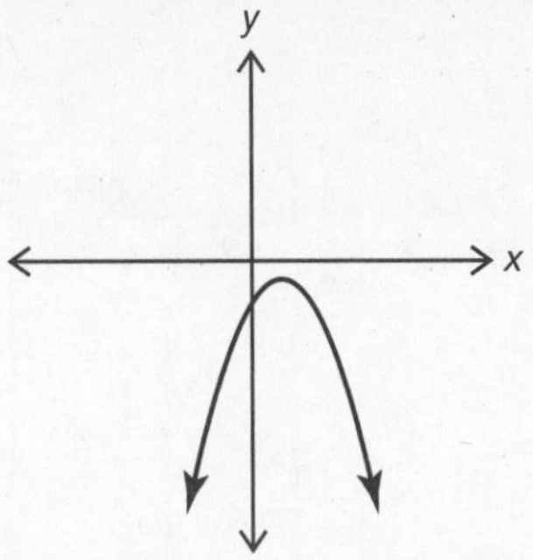

$h(x) = -2x^2 + 3x - 2$

$k(x) = -0.5x^2 + 1.5x + 1$

$t(x) = -\frac{1}{2}x^2 + 3x - \frac{9}{2}$

$w(x) = 2x^2 - 4x - 10$

4

PROBLEM 2 What Does the Form Tell Me?

1. Consider each quadratic function written in vertex form. Determine whether the zeros of each function are real or imaginary without calculating the zeros. Explain how you know.

   a. $f(x) = -2(x - 3)^2 - 4$

I'll give you a hint. Use the key characteristics of a function in vertex form to sketch a graph.

   b. $f(x) = 2(x - 3)^2 - 4$

   c. $f(x) = -2(x - 3)^2$

2. Complete the table to show how you can use the vertex form of a quadratic function to determine whether it has real or imaginary solutions. The first row has been completed for you.

Location of Vertex	Concavity	Sketch	Number of x-Intercepts	Number and Type of Roots	Number and Type of Zeros
Above the x-axis	Up	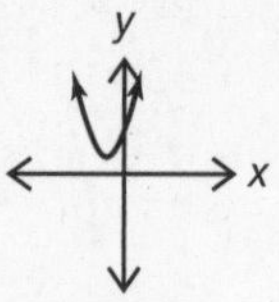	0	2 imaginary roots	2 imaginary zeros
	Down	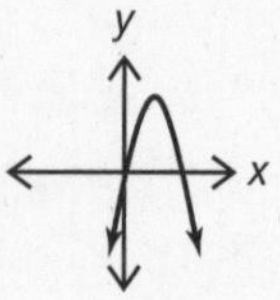			
Below the x-axis	Up	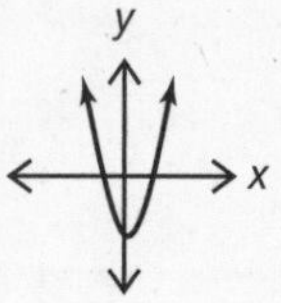			
	Down	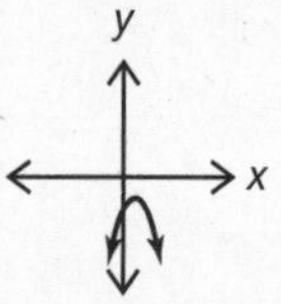			
On the x-axis	Up	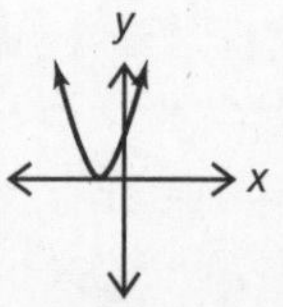			
	Down	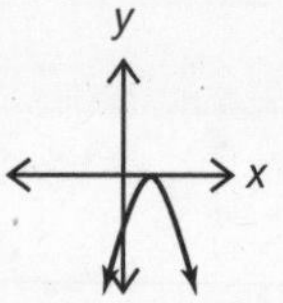			

3. Consider the quadratic function $f(x) = \frac{1}{2}(x - 3)(x + 2)$. Describe the type of zeros for this function. How do you know?

4. Tony and Ava each attempt to factor $f(x) = x^2 - 2x + 2$. Analyze their work.

Tony

I sketched the graph $f(x) = x^2 - 2x + 2$ and noticed there are no real zeros. So, $f(x) = x^2 - 2x + 2$ cannot be factored.

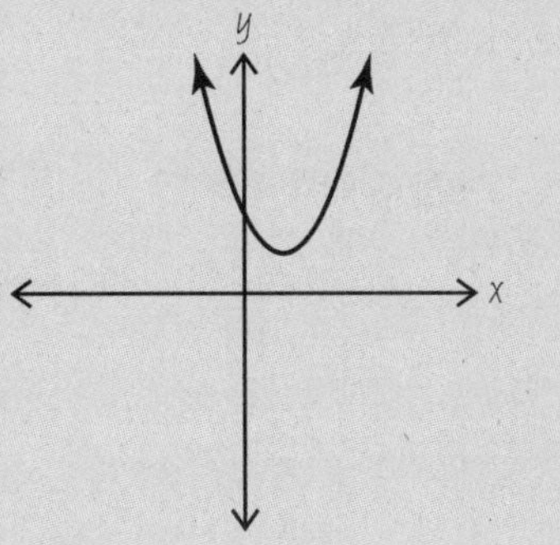

y
x

Eva

$x^2 - 2x + 2 = 0$

$$x = \frac{-(-2) \pm \sqrt{(-2)^2 - 4(1)(2)}}{2(1)}$$

$$x = \frac{2 \pm \sqrt{-4}}{2}$$

$$x = \frac{2 \pm 2i}{2}$$

$x = 1 \pm i$

The function in factored form is

$f(x) = [x - (1 + i)][x - (1 - i)]$.

a. If you consider the set of real numbers, who's correct? If you consider the set of imaginary numbers, who's correct? Explain your reasoning.

4

b. Use the distributive property to rewrite Eva's function to verify that the function in factored form is the same as the original function in standard form.

Remember, the set of complex numbers is the super set of numbers . . . it includes both real and imaginary numbers.

c. Identify the zeros of the quadratic function $f(x)$.

Some functions can be factored over the set of real numbers, while other functions can be factored over the set of imaginary numbers. However, all functions can be factored over the set of complex numbers.

5. Analyze each expression.

$x^2 + 4$	$x^2 - 4$	$x^2 + 2x + 5$	$x^2 + 4x - 5$
$-x^2 + x + 12$	$x^2 + 4x - 1$	$-x^2 + 6x - 25$	

a. Sort each expression based on whether it can be factored over the set of real numbers or the set of imaginary numbers.

Complex Factors	
Real Factors	**Imaginary Factors**

b. Factor each expression over the set of complex numbers.

6. Suppose that you know that one zero of a quadratic function $b(x)$ is $2 + 3i$.

   a. What is the other zero of the function $b(x)$? Explain how you know.

   b. Write the quadratic function $b(x)$ in standard form, using an a-value of 1.

   • Show all your work.

Talk the Talk

The table shown summarizes multiple methods to determine the complex zeros of a quadratic function based specific given information.

Given Information	Type of Zeros	Number of Complex Zeros of a Quadratic Function		
		Two Real Zeros		**Two Imaginary Zeros**
		Two Distinct Zeros	**Two Repeated Zeros**	**Two Distinct Zeros**
	Graph	two x-intercepts	one x-intercept	zero x-intercepts
	Equation in Standard Form: $f(x) = ax^2 + bx + c$	$b^2 - 4ac > 0$	$b^2 - 4ac = 0$	$b^2 - 4ac < 0$
	Equation in Vertex Form: $f(x) = a(x - h)^2 + k$	$k > 0$ and $a < 0$ or $k < 0$ and $a > 0$	$k = 0$	$k > 0$ and $a > 0$ or $k < 0$ and $a < 0$
	Equation in Factored Form: $f(x) = a(x - r_1)(x - r_2)$	$r_1 \neq r_2$, r_1 and r_2 are real numbers	$r_1 = r_2$, r_1 and r_2 are real numbers	$r_1 \neq r_2$, r_1 and r_2 are imaginary numbers

Determine the number of zeros and the type of zeros for each quadratic function. Justify your reasoning.

1. $k(x) = -2(x + 3)^2$

2. $v(x) = 0.5x^2 - 3x + 10$

3. $c(x) = -\frac{1}{3}x(x - 9)$

4. $p(x) = 5(x - 1)^2 + 6$

Be prepared to share your solutions and methods.

Chapter 4 Summary

KEY TERMS

- standard form of a quadratic function (4.1)
- factored form of a quadratic function (4.1)
- vertex form of a quadratic function (4.1)
- concavity of a parabola (4.1)
- reference points (4.2)
- transformation (4.2)
- rigid motion (4.2)
- argument of a function (4.2)
- translation (4.2)
- vertical dilation (4.3)
- vertical stretching (4.3)
- vertical compression (4.3)
- reflection (4.3)
- line of reflection (4.3)
- horizontal dilation (4.4)
- horizontal stretching (4.4)
- horizontal compression (4.4)
- the imaginary number *i* (4.6)
- principal square root of a negative number
- set of imaginary numbers (4.6)
- pure imaginary number (4.6)
- set of complex numbers (4.6)
- real part of a complex number (4.6)
- imaginary part of a complex number (4.6)
- complex conjugates (4.6)
- monomial (4.6)
- binomial (4.6)
- trinomial (4.6)
- imaginary roots (4.7)
- discriminant (4.7)
- imaginary zeros (4.7)
- Fundamental Theorem of Algebra (4.7)
- double root (4.7)

4

4.1 Using Characteristics of a Quadratic Function to Describe Its Graph

The graphs of quadratic functions can be described using key characteristics:

- *x*-intercept(s)
- *y*-intercept
- vertex
- axis of symmetry
- concave up or down

The *y*-intercept (c) and whether the parabola is concave up ($a > 0$) or down ($a < 0$) can be determined when the quadratic is in standard form, $f(x) = ax^2 + bx + c$.

The *x*-intercepts $(r_1, 0)$, $(r_2, 0)$, and whether the parabola is concave up ($a > 0$) or down ($a < 0$) can be determined when the quadratic is in factored form, $f(x) = a(x - r_1)(x - r_2)$.

The vertex (h, k), whether the parabola is concave up ($a > 0$) or down ($a < 0$), and the axis of symmetry ($x = h$) can be determined when the quadratic is in vertex form, $f(x) = a(x - h)^2 + k$.

The example shows that using the key characteristics of a graph can also determine the function represented by the graph.

Example

Analyze the graph. Then, circle the function(s) which could model the graph. Describe the reasoning you used to either eliminate or choose each function.

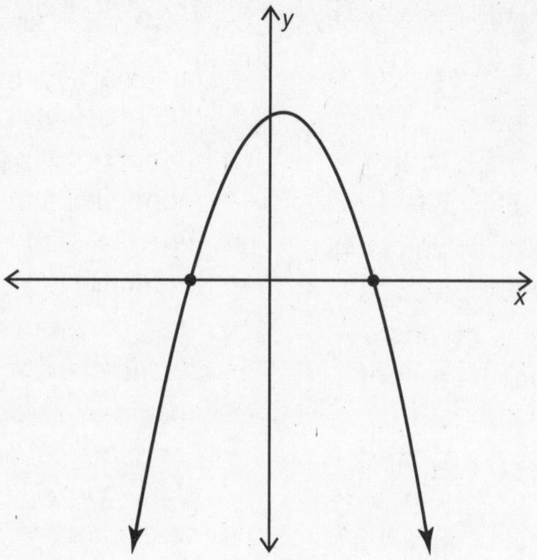

$f_1(x) = 2(x - 3)(x + 4)$

The function f_1 can be eliminated because the a-value is positive.

$f_2(x) = \frac{1}{2}(x + 3)(x - 4)$

The function f_2 can be eliminated because the a-value is positive.

$f_3(x) = -\frac{1}{2}(x + 3)(x - 4)$

The function f_3 is a possible function because it has a negative a-value and one positive and one negative x-intercept.

$f_4(x) = -\frac{1}{2}(x - 3)(x - 4)$

The function f_4 can be eliminated because it has two positive x-intercepts.

4

4.1 Determining the Best Form in Which to Write a Quadratic Function

Given the roots or x-intercepts and an additional point, a quadratic function can be written in factored form: $f(x) = a(x - r_1)(x - r_2)$.

Given a minimum or maximum point or vertex and an additional point, a quadratic function can be written in vertex form: $f(x) = a(x - h)^2 + k$.

Given a y-intercept and two additional points, a quadratic function can be written in standard form: $f(x) = ax^2 + bx + c$.

Example

vertex (2, −5) and point (3, 1): vertex form

points (2, 0), (6, 5), and (9, 0): factored form

y-intercept (0, −2) and points (−4, 3), (5, 2): standard form

4.1 Writing a Quadratic Function in Standard Form

When a quadratic function is in vertex or factored form, the function can be rewritten in standard form by multiplying the factors and combining like terms.

Example

$f(x) = (x - 2)(x + 8)$

$$\begin{aligned} f(x) &= (x - 2)(x + 8) \\ &= x^2 + 8x - 2x - 16 \\ &= x^2 + 6x - 16 \end{aligned}$$

$f(x) = -2(x - 3)^2 + 6$

$$\begin{aligned} f(x) &= -2(x - 3)^2 + 6 \\ &= -2(x^2 - 6x + 9) + 6 \\ &= -2x^2 + 12x - 18 + 6 \\ &= -2x^2 + 12x - 12 \end{aligned}$$

4.1 Writing a Quadratic Function to Represent a Situation

Determine the important information from the problem situation, including a possible vertex or *x*-intercepts. Substitute the information into either the vertex or factored form of a quadratic function and solve for *a*. Write the complete function.

Example

Hector launches a rocket from a platform 5 feet above the ground. The rocket reaches a maximum height of 50 feet at a distance of 75 feet. Write a function to represent the rocket's height in terms of its distance.

$$h(d) = a(d - 50)^2 + 75$$

$$5 = a(0 - 50)^2 + 75$$

$$5 = 2500a + 75$$

$$-70 = 2500a$$

$$\frac{-7}{250} = a$$

$$h(d) = -\frac{7}{250}(d - 50)^2 + 75$$

4.2 Identifying the Reference Points of a Quadratic Function

Reference points are a set of key points that help identify a basic function.

Reference Points of Basic Quadratic Function	
P	(0, 0)
Q	(1, 1)
R	(2, 4)

If the vertex of a quadratic function and two points to the right of that vertex are known, the axis of symmetry can be used to draw the other half of the parabola. These key points are reference points for the quadratic function family.

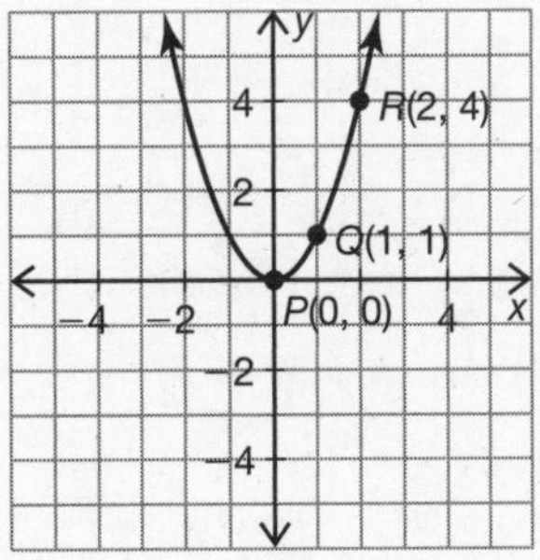

4

4.2 Understanding the Effect of the *C*-Value and the *D*-Value in the Transformational Function Form $g(x) = Af(B(x - C)) + D$

A translation shifts an entire graph the same distance and direction. When $f(x)$ is transformed to $g(x) = Af(B(x - C)) + D$, the *C*-value shifts the graph horizontally and the *D*-value shifts the graph vertically. When $C < 0$, the graph shifts left *C* units, and when $C > 0$, the graph shifts to the right *C* units. When $D < 0$, the graph shifts down *D* units, and when $D > 0$, the graph shifts up *D* units.

Example

$f(x) = x^2$

$m(x) = (x + 3) + 1$

$C = -3$ and $D = 1$

The original function $f(x)$ will translate to the left 3 units and translate up 1 unit.

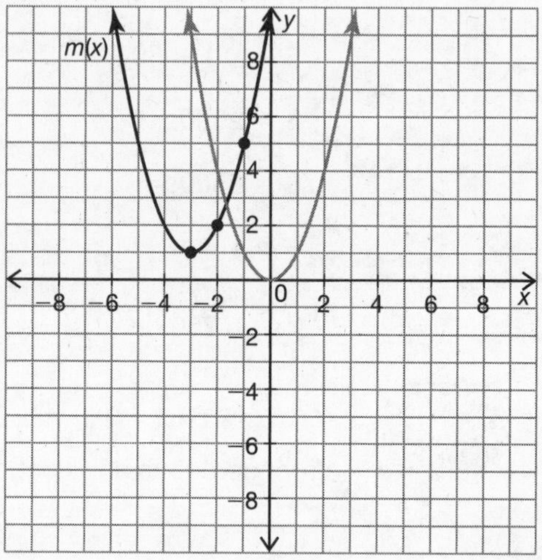

Reference Points on $f(x)$	→	Apply the Transformations	Corresponding Points on $m(x)$
(0, 0)	→	(0 − 3, 0 + 1)	(−3, 1)
(1, 1)	→	(1 − 3, 1 + 1)	(−2, 2)
(2, 4)	→	(2 − 3, 4 + 1)	(−1, 5)

4

4.2 Writing the Function of a Transformed Graph

Identify the location of the new vertex. Use the *x*- and *y*-coordinates of the new vertex as the *C*- and *D*-values. Write the transformed function in terms of the original function in the form $g(x) = f(x - C) + D$.

Example

Given $y = f(x)$

$g(x) = f(x - 2) - 4$

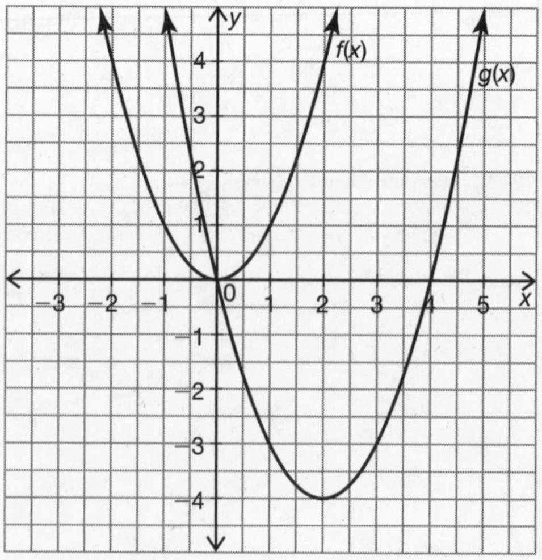

4.3 Understanding the Effect of the *A*-Value in the Transformational Function Form $g(x) = Af(B(x - C)) + D$

A translation shifts an entire graph the same distance and direction. When $f(x)$ is transformed to $g(x) = Af(B(x - C)) + D$, the *A*-value stretches or compresses the graph vertically. The *C*-value shifts the graph horizontally and the *D*-value shifts the graph vertically.
When $|A| \geq 1$, the graph stretches away from the *x*-axis, and when $0 < |A| < 1$, the graph compresses towards the *x*-axis. When $A < 0$, the graph is reflected across the *x*-axis or across the horizontal line $y = D$. Any point on the transformed graph can be represented in coordinate notation as

$$(x, y) \rightarrow \left(\frac{1}{B}x + C, Ay + D\right).$$

Example

$f(x) = x^2$

$b(x) = -4(f(x + 1) - 3$

The *C*-value is -1 and the *D*- value is -3 so the vertex will be translated 1 unit to the left and 3 units down to $(-1, -3)$.

The *A*-value is -4, so the graph will have a vertical stretch by a factor of 4 and will be reflected across the line $y = -3$.

$(x, y) = (x - 1, -4y - 3)$

4.3 Writing a Quadratic Function to Represent a Graph

Given $y = f(x)$, the coordinate notation represented in the transformational function $y = Af(x - C) + D$ is (x, y) becomes $(x + C, Ay + D)$. Using this coordinate notation and reference points, you can work backwards from the graph to write the function in vertex form.

Example

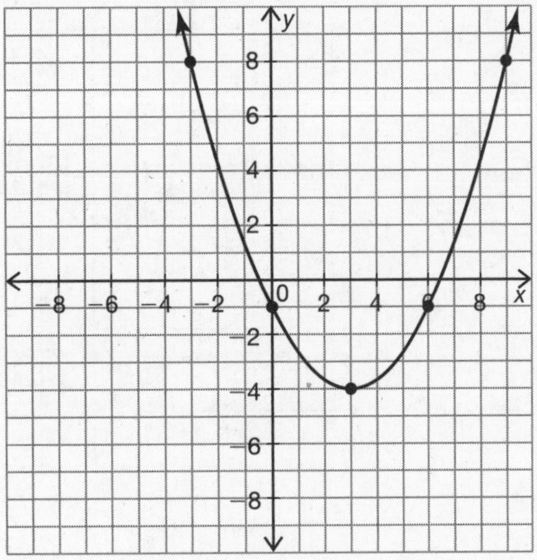

$f(x) = \frac{1}{3}(x - 3)^2 - 4$

4

4.4 Graphing Horizontal Dilations of Quadratic Functions

Considering the transformational function $g(x) = Af(B(x - C)) + D$, B determines the horizontal dilation.

- Horizontal stretching is the stretching of a graph away from the y-axis and happens when $0 < |B| < 1$.
- Horizontal compression is the squeezing of a graph towards the y-axis and happens when $|B| > 1$.

The factor of horizontal stretch or compression is the reciprocal of the B-value. When $B < 0$, the dilation will also include a reflection across the y-axis, but because a parabola is symmetric, it will look identical to the function when $B > 0$.

Example

$p(x) = f(2x)$

Reference Points on $f(x)$	→	Apply the Transformations	Corresponding Points on $p(x)$
(0, 0)	→	$\left(\frac{1}{2} \cdot 0, 0\right)$	(0, 0)
(1, 1)	→	$\left(\frac{1}{2} \cdot 1, 1\right)$	(0.5, 1)
(2, 4)	→	$\left(\frac{1}{2} \cdot 2, 4\right)$	(1, 4)
(3, 9)	→	$\left(\frac{1}{2} \cdot 3, 9\right)$	(1.5, 9)

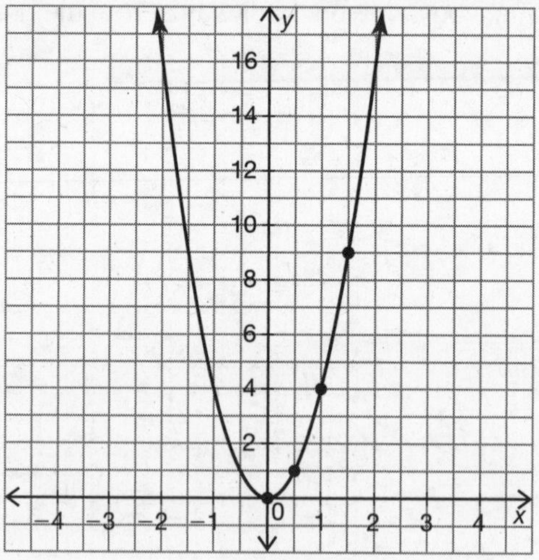

4

4.4 Identifying Multiple Transformations Given Quadratic Functions

Analyzing the transformations of $y = f(x)$, it is possible to graph a function from information given by the form of the equation.

Function Form	Equation Information	Description of Transformation of Graph
$y = Af(B(x - C)) + D$	$D > 0$	vertical shift up D units
	$D < 0$	vertical shift down D units
	$C > 0$	horizontal shift right C units
	$C < 0$	horizontal shift left C units
	$\|A\| > 1$	vertical stretch by a factor of A units
	$0 < \|A\| < 1$	vertical compression by a factor of A units
	$A < 0$	reflection across the line $y = k$
	$\|B\| > 1$	horizontal compression by a factor of $\frac{1}{\|B\|}$
	$0 < \|B\| < 1$	horizontal stretch by a factor of $\frac{1}{\|B\|}$
	$B < 0$	reflection across the y-axis

Example

$h(x) = -3(x + 7)^2 - 8$

The A value is -3 so the graph will have a vertical stretch by a factor of 3 and be reflected over the x-axis. The C-value is -7 and the D-value is -8, so the vertex will be shifted 7 units to the left and 8 units down to $(-7, -8)$. The A-value is -3 so the graph will have a vertical stretch by a factor of 3 and be reflected across the line $y = D$, or $y = -8$

Example

Given the graph of $y = f(x)$, the graph of $g(x) = -f\left(\frac{1}{2}(x - 4)\right) - 5$ is sketched.

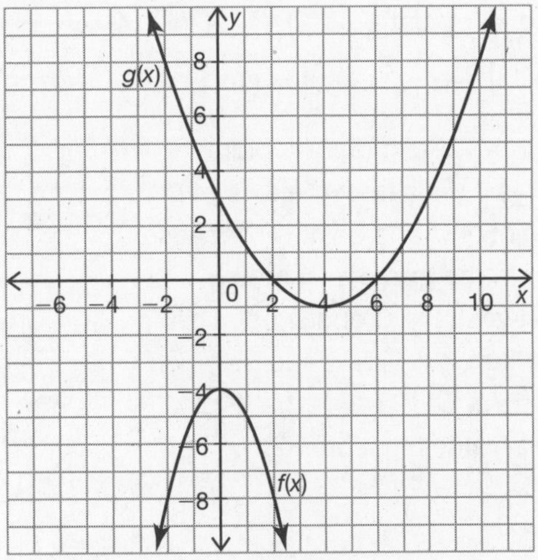

4.4 Writing Quadratic Functions in Terms of a Given a Graph

Determine by how much and in what direction the reference points of the graph have moved and if there has been a reflection, horizontal dilation, or vertical dilation. Use coordinate notation $\left(\frac{1}{B}x + C, Ay + D\right)$ to help identify A, B, C, and D values. Write the transformed function in terms of the original function in the form $g(x) = Af(B(x - C)) + D$.

Example

The function of $g(x)$ in terms of $f(x)$ is $g(x) = f(-x) - 5$, or $g(x) = f(x - 12) - 5$.

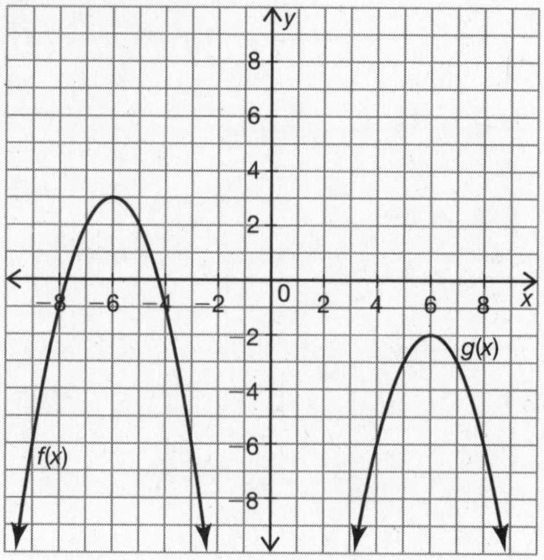

4.5 Deriving a Quadratic Equation Given Certain Information and Reference Points

To write a unique quadratic function, use the reference points of the basic quadratic function and consider the vertical distance between each point. If given the x-intercepts and another point on the parabola, a function can be written in factored form or if given the vertex and another point on the parabola, a function can be written in vertex form; but in both cases the a-value must also be determined. To do this, first determine the axis of symmetry as directly in the middle of the two x-intercepts or at the location of the vertex. Plot the axis of symmetry and points on a coordinate plane and assign each point a letter based on its horizontal distance from the line of symmetry. The vertical distance between A' and B' will be the vertical distance between A and B of the basic function times a.

Example

x-intercepts and 1 point: $(-3, 0)$, $(5, 0)$, $(4, 14)$

$\frac{r_1 + r_2}{2} = \frac{-3 + 5}{2} = \frac{2}{2} = 1$ so the axis of symmetry is $x = 1$. Point $(5, 0)$ is point D' because it is 4 units from the axis of symmetry. Point $(4, 14)$ is point C' because it is 3 units from the axis of symmetry. The range between the C and D point on the basic function is 7. The range between point D' and point C' is $7 \times (-2) = -14$, therefore the a-value must be -2.

$f(x) = -2(x + 3)(x - 5)$

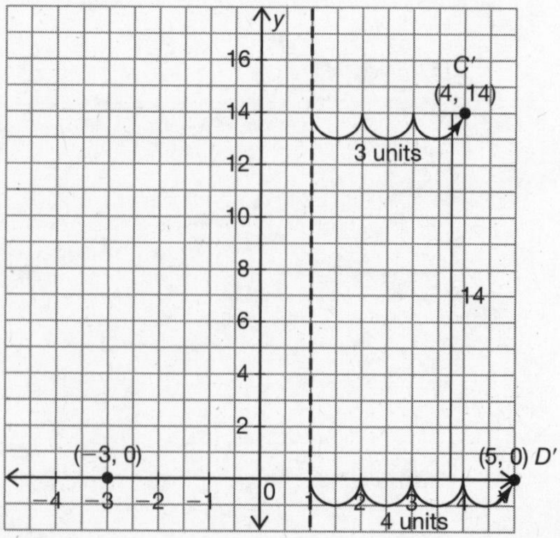

4.5 Deriving a Quadratic Equation Given Three Points Using a Graphing Calculator

You can use a graphing calculator to determine a quadratic regression equation given three points on the parabola.

Step 1: Diagnostics must be turned on so that all needed data is displayed. Press **2nd CATALOG** to display the catalog. Scroll to **DiagnosticOn** and press **ENTER**. Then press **ENTER** again. The calculator should display the word **Done**.

Step 2: Press **STAT** and then press **ENTER** to select **1:Edit**. In the **L1** column, enter the x-values by typing each value followed by **ENTER**. Use the right arrow key to move to the **L2** column. Enter the y-values.

Step 3: Press **STAT** and use the right arrow key to show the **CALC** menu. Choose **5:QuadReg**. Press Enter. The values for a, b, and c will be displayed.

Step 4: To have the calculator graph the exact equation for you, press **Y=**, **VARS**, **5:Statistics**, scroll right to **EQ**, press **1:RegEQ**, **GRAPH**.

Example

$(-8, 1), (-1, 13.25), (6, -48)$

$f(x) = -0.75x^2 - 5x + 9$

4.5 Deriving a Quadratic Equation Given Three Points Using a System of Equations

To use a system of equations, first create a quadratic equation in the form $y = ax^2 + bx + c$ for each of the points given. Then, use elimination and substitution to solve for a, b, and c.

Example

$(-1, -11), (2, -5), (4, -41)$

Equation 1: $-11 = a(-1)^2 + b(-1) + c$

$$-11 = a - b + c$$

Equation 2: $-5 = a(2)^2 + b(2) + c$

$$-5 = 4a + 2b + c$$

Equation 3: $-41 = a(4)^2 + b(4) + c$

$$-41 = 16a + 4b + c$$

Subtract Equation 1 from Equation 2 and solve in terms of a:

$$\begin{aligned} -5 &= 4a + 2b + c \\ -(-11 &= a - b + c) \\ \hline 6 &= 3a + 3b \\ 2 - b &= a \end{aligned}$$

Subtract Equation 2 from Equation 3:

$$\begin{aligned} -41 &= 16a + 4b + c \\ -(-5 &= 4a + 2b + c) \\ \hline -36 &= 12a + 2b \\ -18 &= 6a + b \end{aligned}$$

Substitute the value for a into this equation:

$$\begin{aligned} -18 &= 6(2 - b) + b \\ -18 &= 12 - 5b \\ -30 &= -5b \\ b &= 6 \end{aligned}$$

Substitute the value of b into the equation for the value of a:

$$\begin{aligned} a &= 2 - 6 \\ a &= -4 \end{aligned}$$

Substitute the values of a and b into Equation 1:

$$\begin{aligned} -11 &= -4 - 6 + c \\ -11 &= -10 + c \\ -1 &= c \end{aligned}$$

Substitute the values for a, b, and c into a quadratic equation in standard form:

$$f(x) = -4x^2 + 6x - 1$$

4.6 Calculating Powers of i

The imaginary number i is a number such that $i^2 = -1$. Because no real number exists such that its square is equal to a negative number, the number i is not a part of the real number system. The values of i^n repeat after every four powers of i, where $i = \sqrt{-1}$, $i^2 = -1$, $i^3 = -\sqrt{-1}$, and $i^4 = 1$.

Example

$$i^{25} = (i^4)^6(i^1)$$
$$= (1)^6(\sqrt{-1})$$
$$= \sqrt{-1}$$

4.6 Rewriting Expressions with Negative Roots Using i

Expressions with negative roots can be rewritten. For any positive real number n, the principal square root of a negative number, $-n$, is defined by $\sqrt{-n} = i\sqrt{n}$.

Example

$$\sqrt{-63} + \sqrt{-24} = i\sqrt{63} + i\sqrt{24}$$
$$= i\sqrt{(9)(7)} + i\sqrt{(6)(4)}$$
$$= 3\sqrt{7}i + 2\sqrt{6}i$$

4

4.6 Adding, Subtracting, and Multiplying on the Set of Complex Numbers

The set of complex numbers is the set of all numbers written in the form $a + bi$, where a and b are real numbers. The term a is called the real part of a complex number, and the term bi is called the imaginary part of a complex number. When operating with complex numbers involving i, combine like terms by treating i as a variable (even though it's a constant). Complex conjugates are pairs of numbers of the form $a + bi$ and $a - bi$. The product of a pair of complex conjugates is always a real number in the form $a^2 + b^2$.

Example

$$4x + (x + 3i)(x - 3i) - 5x + 7$$

$$4x + (x + 3i)(x - 3i) - 5x + 7 = 4x + x^2 - 9i^2 - 5x + 7$$
$$= x^2 + (4x - 5x) + (7 - 9(-1))$$
$$= x^2 - x + 16$$

4.6 Identifying Complex Polynomials

A polynomial is a mathematical expression involving the sum of powers in one or more variables multiplied by coefficients. The definition of a polynomial can be extended to include imaginary numbers. Some polynomials have special names, according to the number of terms they have. A polynomial with one term is called a monomial. A polynomial with two terms is called a binomial. A polynomial with three terms is called a trinomial. Combine like terms to name the polynomial.

Example

$5x - 3xi + x^2 - 3i + 9$

The expression is a trinomial because it can be rewritten as $x^2 + (5 - 3i)x + (9 - 3i)$, which shows one x^2 term, one x term, and one constant term.

4.6 Adding, Subtracting, and Multiplying Complex Polynomials

Some polynomial expressions involving i can be simplified using methods similar to those used to operate with numerical expressions involving i. Whenever possible, multiply the complex conjugates first to get a real number.

Example

$(3x + 7i)(2x + 5i)$

$$\begin{aligned}(3x + 7i)(2x + 5i) &= 6x^2 + 15xi + 14xi + 35i^2 \\ &= 6x^2 + 29xi + 35(-1) \\ &= 6x^2 + 29xi - 35\end{aligned}$$

4.6 Rewriting the Quotient of Complex Numbers

When rewriting the quotient of complex numbers, multiply both the divisor and the dividend by the complex conjugate of the divisor, thus changing the divisor into a real number. The product of a pair of complex conjugates is always a real number in the form $a^2 + b^2$.

Example

$$\begin{aligned}\frac{3 - i}{5 + 2i} &= \frac{3 - i}{5 + 2i} \cdot \frac{5 - 2i}{5 - 2i} \\ &= \frac{15 - 6i - 5i + 2i^2}{5^2 + 2^2} \\ &= \frac{15 - 11i - 2}{25 + 4} \\ &= \frac{13 - 11i}{29} \\ &= \frac{13}{29} - \frac{11}{29}i\end{aligned}$$

4

4.7 Using the Quadratic Formula to Determine the Zeros of a Function

If the graph of $f(x)$ intersects the x-axis 2 times, then the quadratic equation $f(x) = 0$ has 2 solutions, or roots. If the graph of $f(x)$ intersects the x-axis 1 time, then the quadratic equation $f(x) = 0$ has 1 solution and double roots. If the graph of $f(x)$ does not intersect the x-axis, then the quadratic equation $f(x) = 0$ has no solution, or imaginary roots. Use the Quadratic Formula and what you know about imaginary numbers to solve an equation of the form $f(x) = 0$ to calculate the roots, or zeros of the function.

Remember the Quadratic Formula is: $x = \frac{-b \pm \sqrt{b^2 - 4ac}}{2a}$.

Example

$g(x) = x^2 - 7x + 12$

$x^2 - 7x + 12 = 0$

$a = 1, b = -7, c = 12$

$$x = \frac{-b \pm \sqrt{b^2 - 4ac}}{2a}$$

$$x = \frac{-(-7) \pm \sqrt{(-7)^2 - 4(1)(12)}}{2(1)}$$

$$x = \frac{7 \pm \sqrt{1}}{2}$$

$x = 4, x = 3$

4

4.7 Determining Whether a Quadratic Function in Standard Form Has Real or Imaginary Zeros

The radicand in the Quadratic Formula, $b^2 - 4ac$, is called the discriminant because it "discriminates" the number and type of roots of a quadratic equation. If the discriminant is greater than or equal to zero, the quadratic equation has two real roots. If the discriminant is negative, the quadratic equation has two imaginary roots. If the discriminant is equal to zero, the quadratic equation appears to have only 1 root, but still has 2 real roots called a double root. The Fundamental Theorem of Algebra states that for any polynomial equation of degree n must have exactly n complex roots or solutions; also, every polynomial function of degree n must have exactly n complex zeros. Zeros of a function $f(x)$ are the values of x for which $f(x) = 0$ and are related to the roots of an equation.

Example

$f(x) = x^2 - 3x + 14$

$$\begin{aligned} b^2 - 4ac &= (-3)^2 - 4(1)(14) \\ &= 9 - 56 \\ &= -47 \end{aligned}$$

The discriminant is negative, so the function has two imaginary zeros.

4.7 Determining Whether a Quadratic Function in Vertex Form Has Real or Imaginary Zeros

If the graph of $f(x)$ intersects the x-axis 2 times, then the quadratic equation $f(x) = 0$ has 2 solutions, or roots. If the graph of $f(x)$ intersects the x-axis 1 time, then the quadratic equation $f(x) = 0$ has 1 solutions and double roots. If the graph of $f(x)$ does not intersect the x-axis, then the quadratic equation $f(x) = 0$ has no solution, or imaginary roots. So, by using C and D of vertex form to locate the vertex above or below the x-axis and using A to determine if the parabola is concave up or down, you can tell if the graph intersects the x-axis or not.

Example

$f(x) = -5(x - 2)^2 + 7$

Because the vertex (2, 7) is above the x-axis and the parabola is concave down ($a < 0$), it intersects the x-axis. So, the zeros are real.

4.7 Determining Whether a Quadratic Function in Factored Form Has Real or Imaginary Zeros

Some functions can be factored over the set of real numbers, while other functions can be factored over the set of imaginary numbers. However, all functions can be factored over the set of complex numbers. If necessary, use the Quadratic Formula to determine the roots and write the function in factored form.

Example

$p(x) = x^2 + 6x + 18$

$p(x) = [x - (-3 + 3i)][x - (-3 - 3i)]$

$x = -3 + 3i, x = -3 - 3i$

The function $p(x)$ has two imaginary zeros.

Polynomial Functions

5

5.1

Planting the Seeds

Exploring Cubic Functions

LEARNING GOALS

In this lesson, you will:

- Represent cubic functions using words, tables, equations, and graphs.
- Interpret the key characteristics of the graphs of cubic functions.
- Analyze cubic functions in terms of their mathematical context and problem context.
- Connect the characteristics and behaviors of cubic functions to its factors.
- Compare cubic functions with linear and quadratic functions.
- Build cubic functions from linear and quadratic functions.

KEY TERMS

- relative maximum
- relative minimum
- cubic function
- multiplicity

If you have ever been to a 3D movie, you know that it can be quite an interesting experience. Special film technology and wearing funny-looking glasses allow movie-goers to see a third dimension on the screen—*depth*. Three dimensional filmmaking dates as far back as the 1920s. As long as there have been movies, it seems that people have looked for ways to transform the visual experience into three dimensions.

However, your brain doesn't really need special technology or silly glasses to experience depth. Think about television, paintings, and photography—artists have been making two-dimensional works of art appear as three-dimensional for a long time. Several techniques help the brain perceive depth. An object that is closer is drawn larger than a similarly sized object off in the distance. Similarly, an object in the foreground may be clear and crisp while objects in the background may appear blurry. These techniques subconsciously allow your brain to process depth in two dimensions.

Can you think of other techniques artists use to give the illusion of depth?

PROBLEM 1 Business Is Growing

The Plant-A-Seed Planter Company produces planter boxes. To make the boxes, a square is cut from each corner of a rectangular copper sheet. The sides are bent to form a rectangular prism without a top. Cutting different sized squares from the corners results in different sized planter boxes. Plant-A-Seed takes sales orders from customers who request a sized planter box.

Each rectangular copper sheet is 12 inches by 18 inches. In the diagram, the solid lines indicate where the square corners are cut and the dotted lines represent where the sides are bent for each planter box.

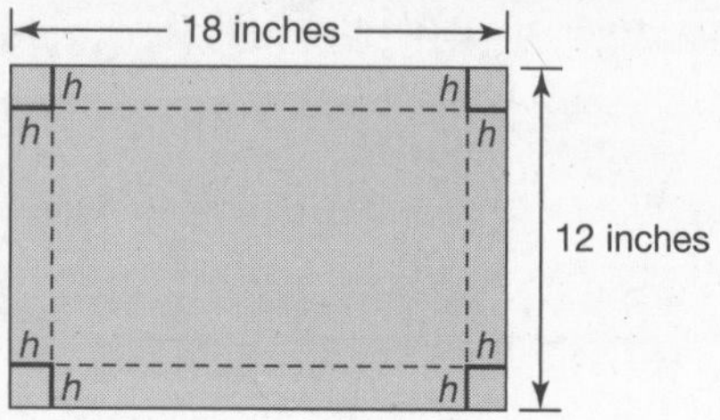
18 inches
12 inches
h
h
h
h
h
h
h
h

It may help to create a model of the planter by cutting squares out of the corners of a sheet of paper and folding.

1. Organize the information about each sized planter box made from a 12 inch by 18 inch copper sheet.

   a. Complete the table. Include an expression for each planter box's height, width, length, and volume for a square corner side of length h.

Square Corner Side Length (inches)	Height (inches)	Width (inches)	Length (inches)	Volume (cubic inches)
0				
1				
2				
3				
4				
5				
6				
7				
h				

Recall the volume formula V = lwh.

b. What patterns do you notice in the table?

2. Analyze the relationship between the height, length, and width of each planter box.

a. What is the largest sized square corner that can be cut to make a planter box? Explain your reasoning.

b. What is the relationship between the size of the corner square and the length and width of each planter box?

5

c. Write a function $V(h)$ to represent the volume of the planter box in terms of the corner side of length h.

3. Louis, Ahmed, and Heidi each used a graphing calculator to analyze the volume function, $V(h)$, and sketched their viewing window. They disagree about the shape of the graph.

Louis

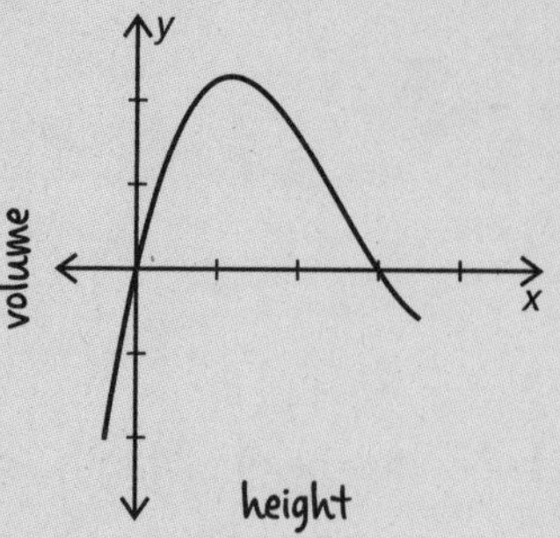

The graph increases and then decreases. It is a parabola.

Ahmed

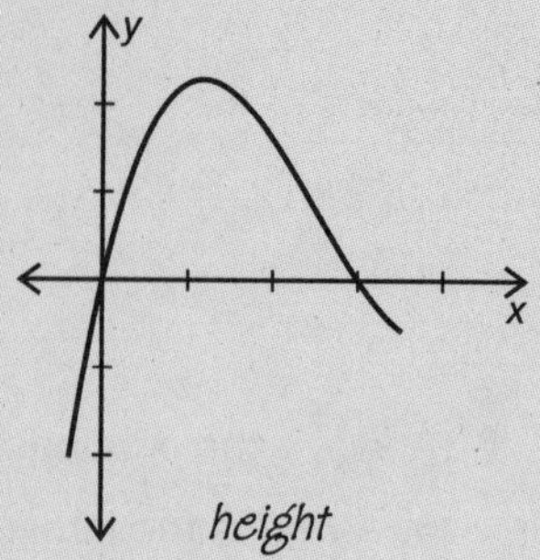

The graph lacks a line of symmetry, so it can't be a parabola.

Heidi

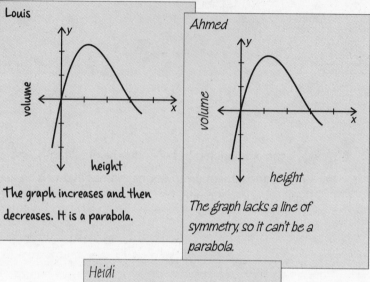

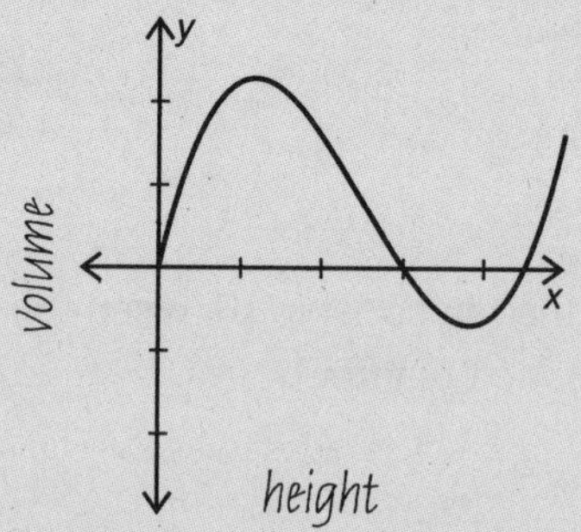

I noticed the graph curves back up so it can't be a parabola.

Evaluate each student's sketch and rationale to determine who is correct.
For the student(s) who is/are not correct, explain why the rationale is not correct.

5

4. Represent the function on a graphing calculator using the window $[-10, 15] \times [-400, 400]$.

   a. Describe the key characteristics of the graph?

In this problem you are determining the maximum value graphically, but consider other representations. How will your solution strategy change when using the table or equation?

   b. What is the maximum volume of a planter box? State the dimensions of this planter box. Explain your reasoning.

   c. Identify the domain of the function $V(h)$. Is the domain the same or different in terms of the context of this problem? Explain your reasoning.

   d. Identify the range of the function $V(h)$. Is the range the same or different in terms of the context of this problem? Explain your reasoning.

   e. What do the x-intercepts represent in this problem situation? Do these values make sense in terms of this problem situation? Explain your reasoning.

The key characteristics of a function may be different within a given domain. The function $V(h) = h(12 - 2h)(18 - 2h)$ has x-intercepts at $x = 0$, $x = 6$, and $x = 9$.

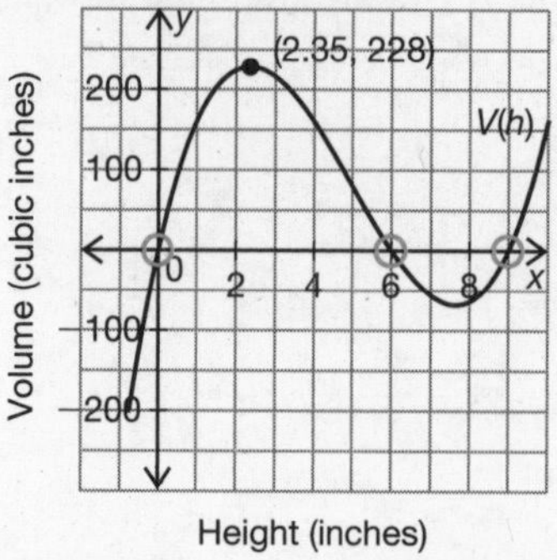

As the input values for height increase, the output values for volume approach infinity. Therefore, the function doesn't have a maximum; however, the point (2.35, 228) is a *relative maximum* within the domain interval of (0, 6). A **relative maximum** is the highest point in a particular section of a graph. Similarly, as the values for height decrease, the output values approach negative infinity. Therefore, a *relative minimum* occurs at (7.65, −68.16). A **relative minimum** is the lowest point in a particular section of a graph.

The function $v(h)$ represents all of the possible volumes for a given height h. A horizontal line is a powerful tool for working backwards to determine the possible values for height when the volume is known.

The given volume of a planter box is 100 cubic inches. You can determine the possible heights from the graph of $V(h)$.

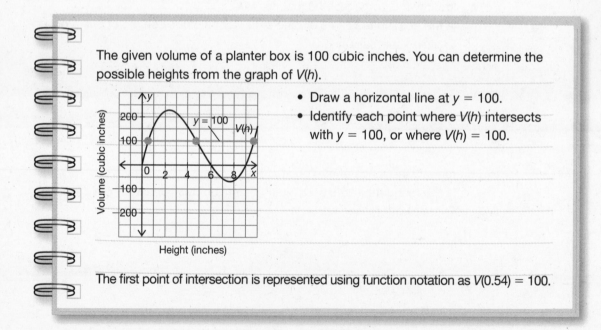

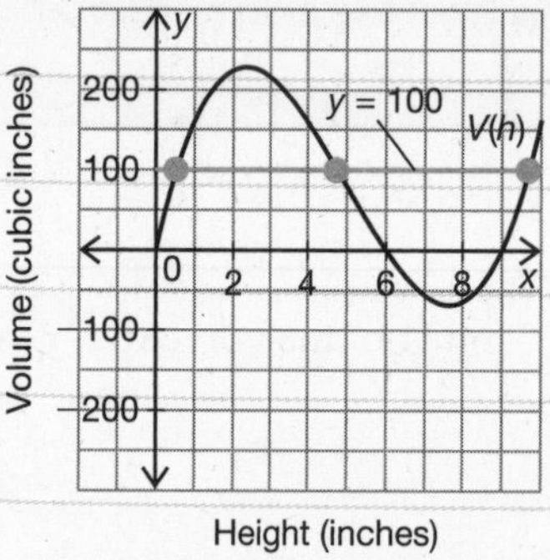

- Draw a horizontal line at $y = 100$.
- Identify each point where $V(h)$ intersects with $y = 100$, or where $V(h) = 100$.

The first point of intersection is represented using function notation as $V(0.54) = 100$.

5. A customer ordered a particular planter box with a volume of 100 cubic inches, but did not specify the height of the planter box.

   a. Use a graphing calculator to determine when $V(h) = 100$. Then write the intersection points in function notation. What do the intersection points mean in terms of this problem situation?

   b. How many different sized planter boxes can Plant-A-Seed make to fill this order? Explain your reasoning.

6. A neighborhood beautifying committee would like to purchase a variety of planter boxes with volumes of 175 cubic inches to add to business window sill store fronts. Determine the planter box dimensions that the Plant-A-Seed Company can create for the committee. Show all work and explain your reasoning.

5

7. Plant-A-Seed's intern claims that he can no longer complete the order because he spilled a cup of coffee on the sales ticket. Help Jack complete the order by determining the missing dimensions from the information that is still visible. Explain how you determined possible unknown dimensions of each planter box.

Plant-A-Seed
Sales Ticket

Base Area: 12 square inches
Height:
Length:
Width:
Volume:

8. A customer sent the following email:

> To Whom It May Concern,
> I would like to purchase several planter boxes, all with a height of 5 inches. Can you make one that holds 100 cubic inches of dirt? Please contact me at your earliest convenience.
>
> Thank you,
> Muriel Jenkins

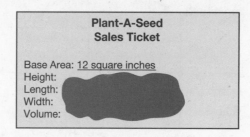

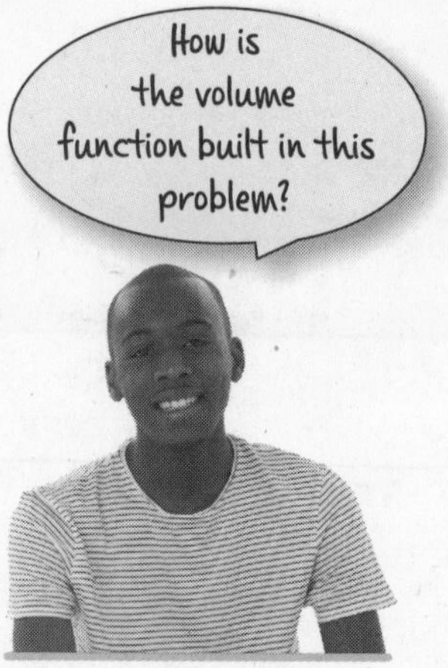

How is the volume function built in this problem?

Write a response to this customer, showing all calculations.

5

PROBLEM 2 A Dirty Business

The Plant-A-Seed Company also makes cylindrical shaped planters for city sidewalks and store fronts. The cylindrical shaped planters come in a variety of sizes, but all have a height to radius ratio of 2:1.

Recall from Geometry that this constant ratio makes the planters in this problem similar.

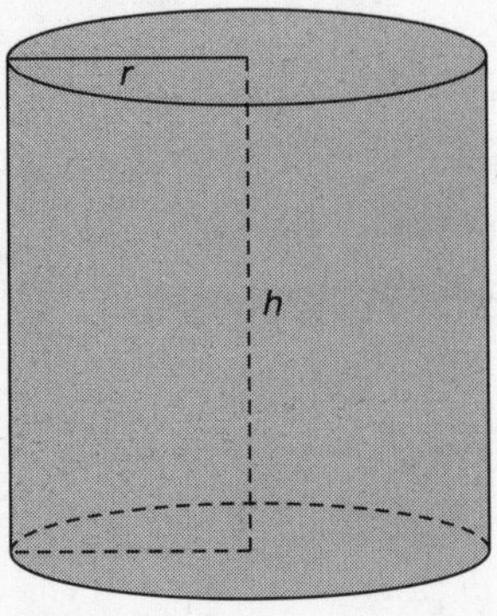

1. Why do you think Plant-A-Seed might want to manufacture different sizes of a product, but maintain a constant ratio, such as height to radius ratio of 2:1?

2. Consider different sized cylindrical planters.

   a. Complete the table.

   Recall the following formulas:
   Volume of a cylinder:
   $V = (base\ area)(height)$
   Area of a circle:
   $A = \pi r^2$

Radius	Height (inches)	Base Area (square inches)	Volume (cubic inches)
0			
1			
2			
3			
4			
			2000
x			

   b. Describe how you determined the volume when you are given the radius.

© Carnegie Learning

c. Describe your method to determine the base area and the height when you are given the volume.

d. Analyze your table of values. For every unit increase in the radius, describe the rate of change in the height, area, and volume of each planter.

3. The base area function $A(x) = 3.14x^2$ and the height function $h(x) = 2x$ are multiplied to build the volume function $V(x) = (3.14x^2)(2x)$. Let's analyze this problem situation graphically.

a. Sketch and label the functions $h(x)$, $A(x)$, and $V(x)$ on the same coordinate plane.

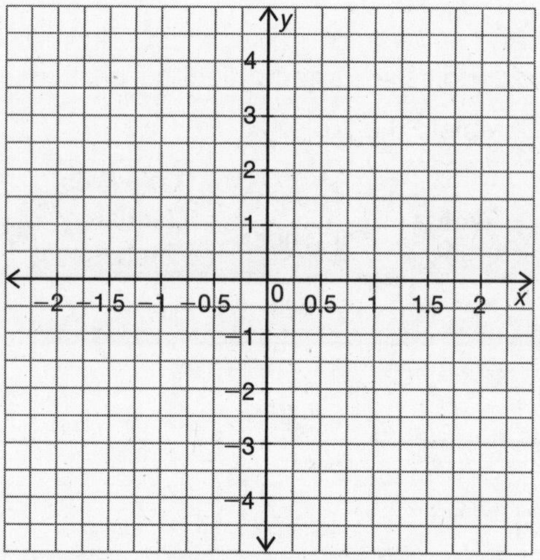

b. In what ways is the graph of $V(x)$ similar to the graph of $h(x)$? In what ways is it different?

5

c. In what ways is the graph of $V(x)$ similar to the graph of $A(x)$? In what ways is it different?

d. Does $V(x)$ have a relative maximum or relative minimum? Explain your reasoning in terms of the function and in terms of this problem situation.

e. Gene and Douglas disagree about the key characteristics of the graph of the cylindrical shaped planter compared to the graph of the rectangular planter box.

Gene

The volume function from the rectangular planter boxes had three x-intercepts, so the graph of the cylindrical shaped planter also must have three. If I extend my viewing window on my graphing calculator I can determine where this graph crosses the x-axis again.

Douglas

Both the linear and quadratic functions that built the volume function for the cylindrical shaped planter only cross the x-axis at (0, 0). A function can't have an x-intercept different from its factors, so (0, 0) is the only one.

Who is correct? Explain your reasoning.

The volume functions for the rectangular planter box and the cylindrical shaped planter are examples of *cubic functions*. A **cubic function** is a function that can be written in the standard form $f(x) = ax^3 + bx^2 + cx + d$ where $a \neq 0$. In other words, a cubic function is a polynomial function of degree 3.

The volume of the rectangular planter box was represented as $V(h) = h(12 - 2h)(18 - 2h)$. You can multiply the three factors to express the function in standard cubic form.

$$\begin{aligned} V(h) &= h(12 - 2h)(18 - 2h) \\ &= h(216 - 60h + 4h^2) \\ &= 216h - 60h^2 + 4h^3 \\ V(h) &= 4h^3 - 60h^2 + 216h \end{aligned}$$

The volume of the cylindrical shaped planter was represented as $V(x) = (3.14x^2)(2x)$. You can multiply the two factors to express the function in standard cubic form.

$$V(x) = 6.28x^3$$

The Fundamental Theorem of Algebra tells you that a cubic function must have 3 zeros. Roots may be any number in the set of complex numbers, and can even appear multiple times. **Multiplicity** is how many times a particular number is a zero for a given polynomial function. For example in the polynomial function that represents the volume of the cylindrical shaped planter, $V(x) = (3.14x^2)(2x)$, the zero, $x = 0$, has multiplicity 3.

4. The Fundamental Theorem states that a cubic function must have 3 zeros. Explain why the volume function in this problem crosses the x-axis only one time, yet still satisfies the Fundamental Theorem of Algebra.

5

5. When analyzing a table, the values in a linear function have a common first difference while quadratic functions have a common second difference. What pattern is present in cubic functions? Do you think this pattern always holds true? Explain your reasoning.

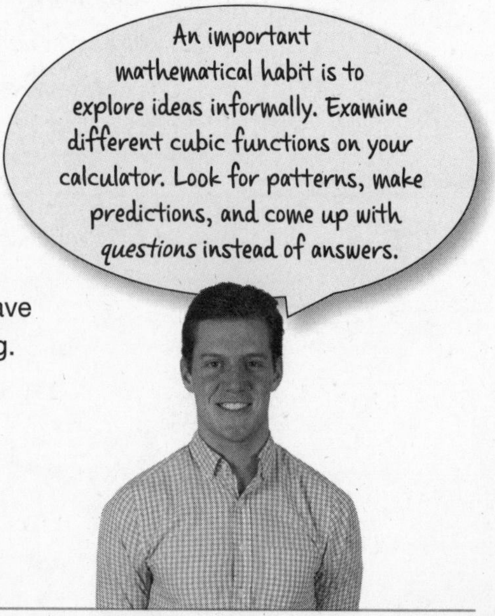
An important mathematical habit is to explore ideas informally. Examine different cubic functions on your calculator. Look for patterns, make predictions, and come up with questions instead of answers.

6. The graphs of linear functions are always lines while quadratic functions are always parabolas. How would you describe the shape of a cubic function? Do you think all cubic functions will have the same general shape? Explain your reasoning.

PROBLEM 3 Cubic Equivalence

Let's consider the volume formula from Problem 1, *Business is Growing*.

1. Three forms of the volume function $V(h)$ are shown.

$V(h) = h(18 - 2h)(12 - 2h)$	$V(h) = h(4h^2 - 60h + 216)$	$V(h) = 4h^3 - 60h^2 + 216h$
The product of three linear functions that represent height, length, and width.	The product of a linear function that represent the height and a quadratic function representing the area of the base.	A cubic function in standard form.

a. Algebraically verify the functions are equivalent. Show all work and explain your reasoning.

b. Graphically verify the functions are equivalent. Sketch all three functions and explain your reasoning.

c. Does the order in which you multiply factors matter? Explain your reasoning.

You can determine the product of the linear factors $(x + 2)(3x - 2)(4 + x)$ using multiplication tables.

Step 1:
Choose 2 of the binomials to multiply. Then combine like terms.

·	x	2
$3x$	$3x^2$	$6x$
-2	$-2x$	-4

Step 2:
Multiply the product from step 1 with the remaining binomial. Then combine like terms.

·	4	x
$3x^2$	$12x^2$	$3x^3$
$4x$	$16x$	$4x^2$
-4	-16	$-4x$

$$(x + 2)(3x - 2)(4 + x) = 3x^3 + 16x^2 + 12x - 16.$$

2. Analyze the worked example for the multiplication of three binomials.

   a. Use a graphing calculator to verify graphically that the expression in factored form is equivalent to the product written in standard form.

   b. Will multiplying three linear factors always result in a cubic expression? Explain your reasoning.

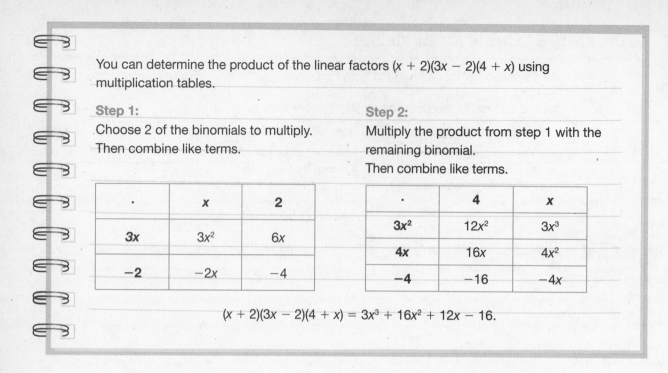

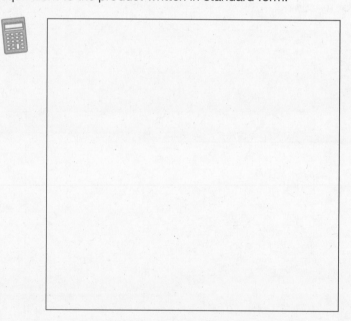

3. Determine each product. Show all your work and then use a graphing calculator to verify your product is correct.

a. $(x + 2)(-3x + 2)(1 + 2x)$

b. $(10 + 2x)(5x + 7)(3x)$

5

4. Determine the product of the linear and quadratic factors. Then verify graphically that the expressions are equivalent.

a. $(x - 6)(2x^2 - 3x + 1)$

b. $(x)(x + 2)^2$

5. Max determined the product of three linear factors.

Max

The function $f(x) = (x + 2)^3$ is equivalent to $f(x) = x^3 + 8$

a. Explain why Max is incorrect.

b. How many x-intercepts does the function $f(x) = (x + 2)^3$ have? How many zeros? Explain your reasoning.

5

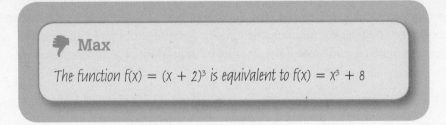

Talk the Talk

In this lesson, you represented the cubic function for volume of a rectangular prism as the product of three linear functions, volume = (length)(width)(height). You also represented the cubic function for volume of a cylinder as the product of a quadratic function and a linear function, volume = (base area)(height).

1. How are cubic functions similar to linear functions? How are they different?

Consider all representations: graph, table, equation, and context.

2. How are cubic functions similar to quadratic functions? How are they different?

Be prepared to share your solutions and methods.

5.2

Polynomial Power

Power Functions

LEARNING GOALS

In this lesson, you will:

- Determine the general behavior of the graph of even and odd degree power functions.
- Derive a general statement and explanation to describe the graph of a power function as the value of the power increases.
- Use graphs and algebraic functions to determine symmetry of even and odd functions.
- Determine whether a function is even or odd based on an algebraic function or graph.
- Understand the structure of the basic cubic function.
- Graph the basic cubic function using reference points and symmetry.

KEY TERMS

- power function
- end behavior
- symmetric about a line
- symmetric about a point
- even function
- odd function

How strong are you? Did you ever try to pick something up just to see if you could lift it? Often times, the weight a person can lift depends on that person's weight. People who weigh more tend to be able to lift more.

Powerlifting, a sport originating in the 1950's, developed separate weight classes for competitors in order to maintain a sense of fairness. Powerlifting consists of athletes competing in specific lifts: squat, bench press, and deadlift. The USA Powerlifting competition starts in high school, where young men in the 114 pound weight class are able to bench press over 250 pounds; while men in the 181 pound weight class have benched over 400 pounds. This competition is not only for men—high school women compete as well. Women in the 132 pound weight class have benched over 215 pounds.

PROBLEM 1 What Odd Behavior . . . or Is It Even?

You have studied linear functions, quadratic functions, and now you will explore more polynomial functions. A common type of polynomial function is a *power function*. A **power function** is a function of the form $P(x) = ax^n$, where n is a non-negative integer.

For the purpose of this lesson, you will only focus on power functions where $a = 1$ and -1. In the next lesson you will investigate power functions with various a-values.

1. Consider each power function and its graph in the sequence shown.

$y = x$

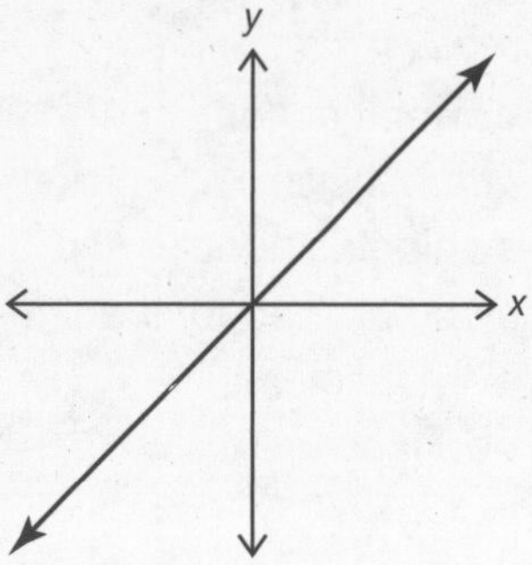

$y = x^2$

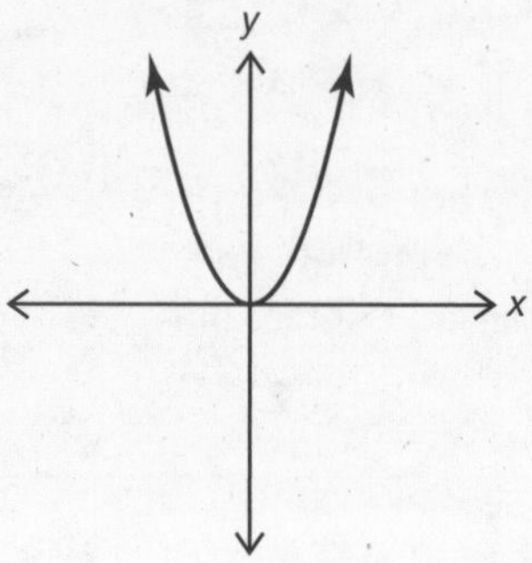

$y = x^3$

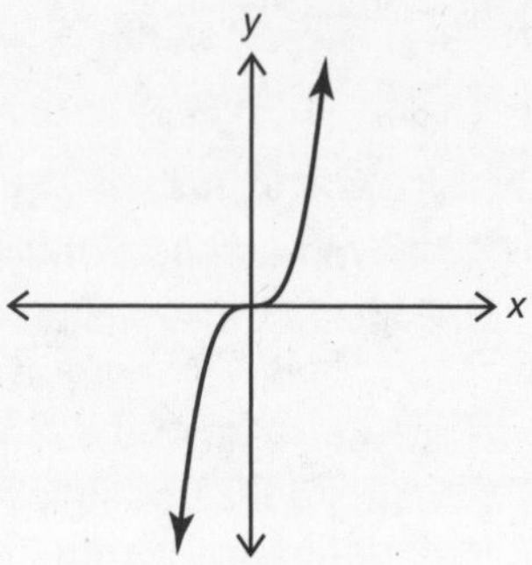

$y = x^4$

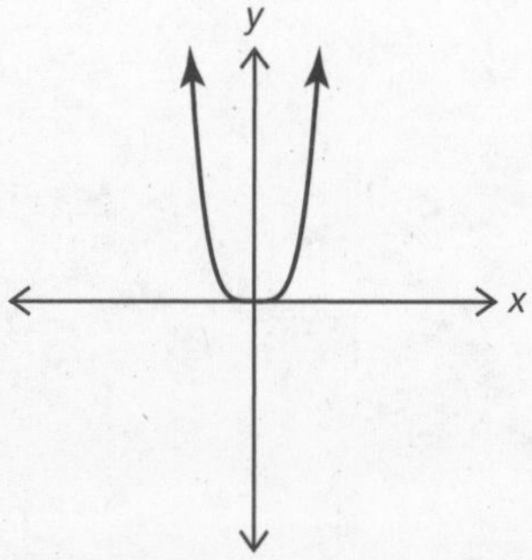

$y = x^5$

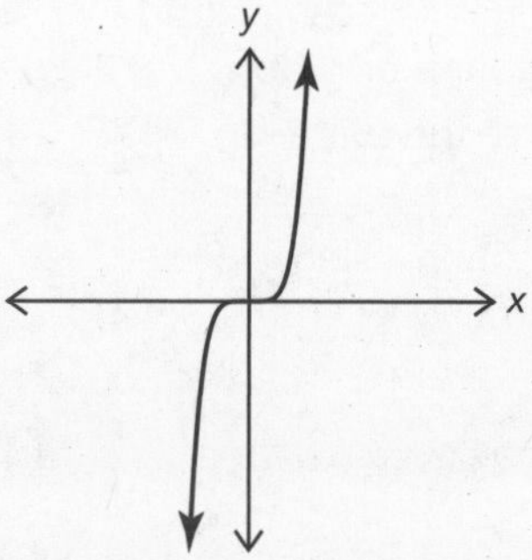

$y = x^6$

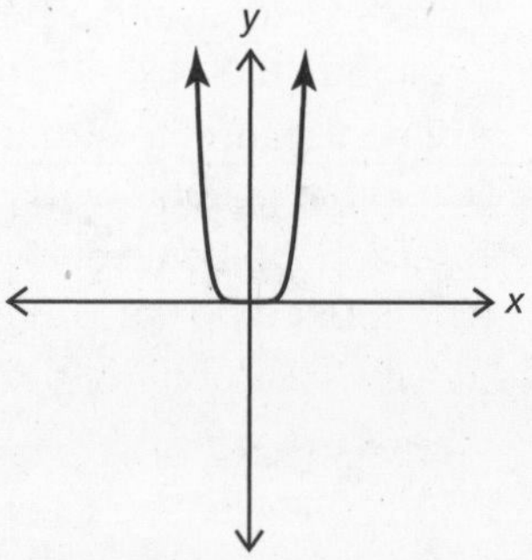

a. Sketch and label the next two graphs in the sequence.

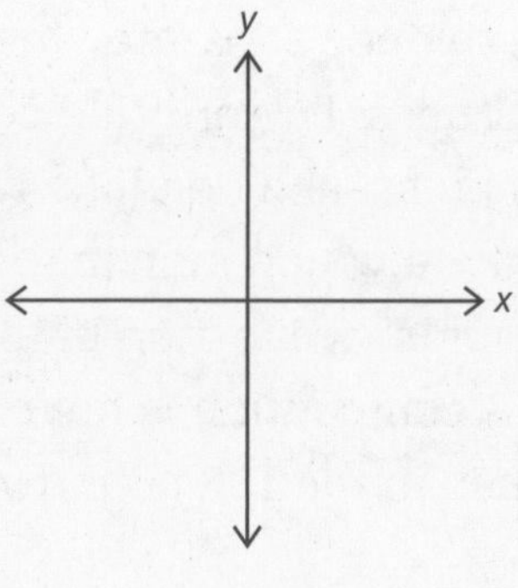

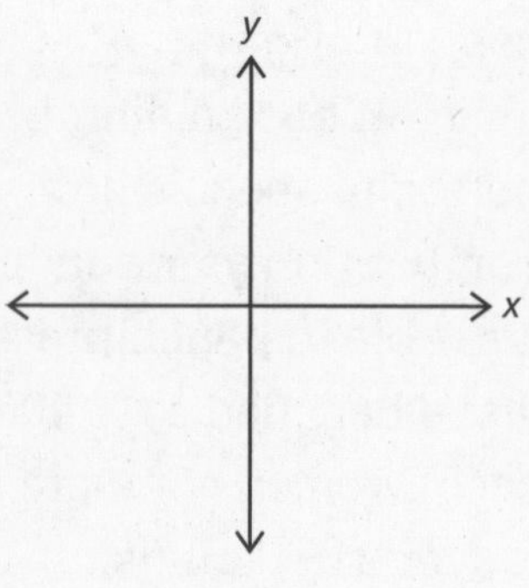

b. State any observations or patterns that you notice about the graphs in the sequence.

c. Make a general statement about the graph of a power function raised to an odd degree.

d. Make a general statement about the graph of a power function raised to an even degree.

2. Based on you work in Question 1, sketch the graph of x^n when:

a. $n = 12$

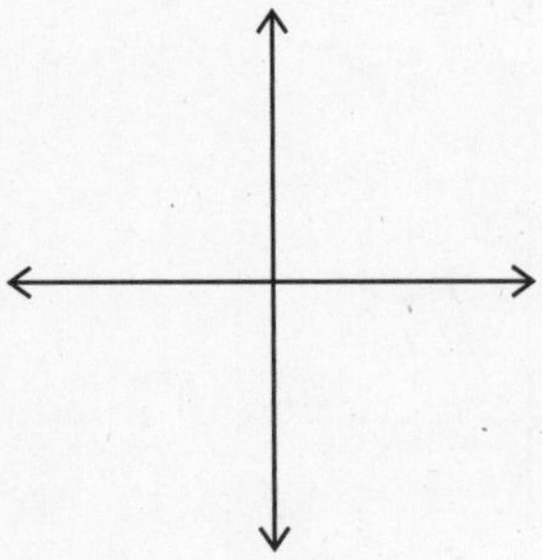

b. $n = 27$

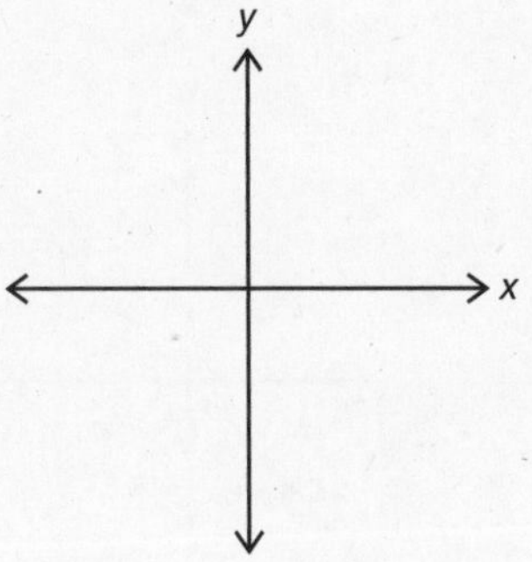

c. $n = 2m$, where m is an integer greater than 0

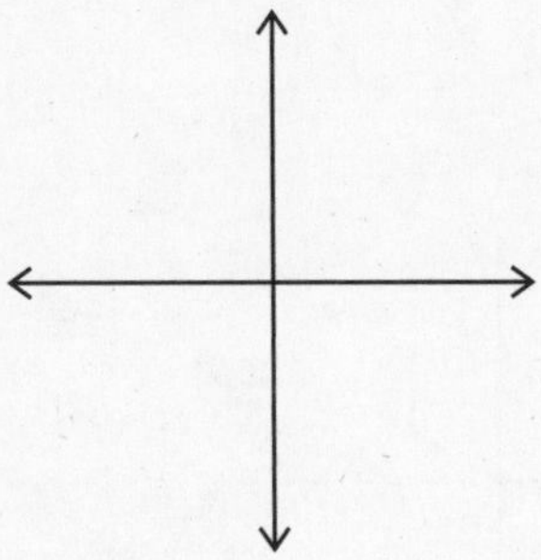

d. $n = 2m + 1$, where m is an integer greater than 0

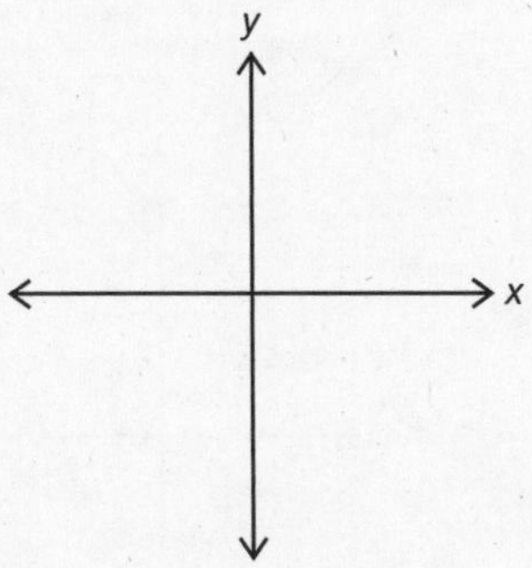

5

The **end behavior** of a graph of a function is the behavior of the graph as x approaches infinity and as x approaches negative infinity.

You can write the end behavior of this polynomial function using the notation:

As $x \to \infty$, $f(x) \to \infty$.

As $x \to -\infty$, $f(x) \to -\infty$.

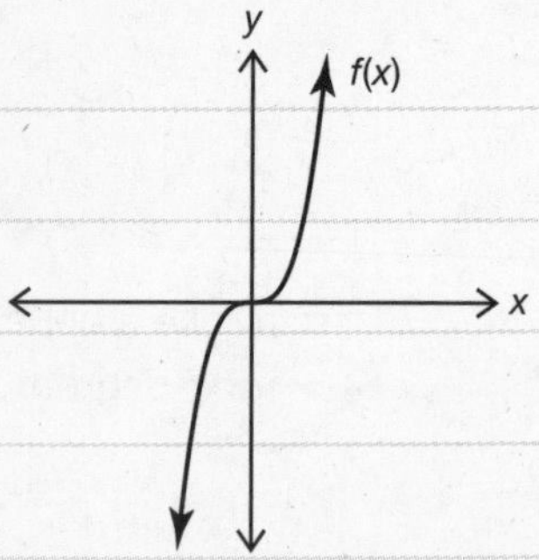

3. Explain in words what the end behavior in the worked example means.

4. Consider the sequence of graphs shown.

$f_1(x) = x$

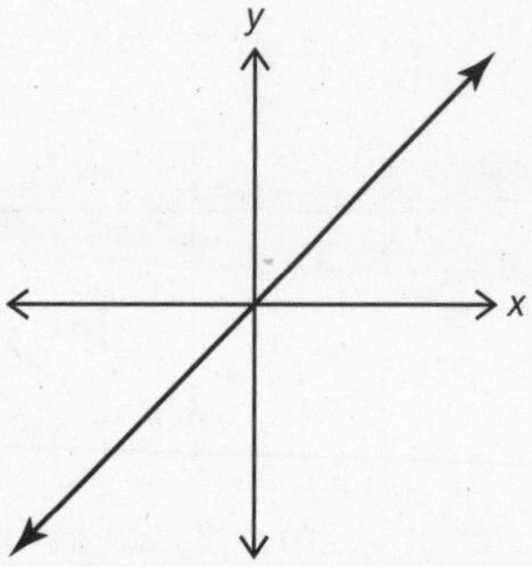

$f_2(x) = x^2$

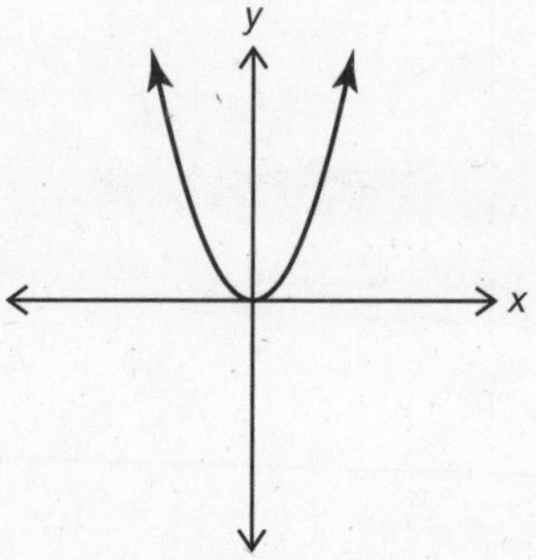

$f_3(x) = x^3$

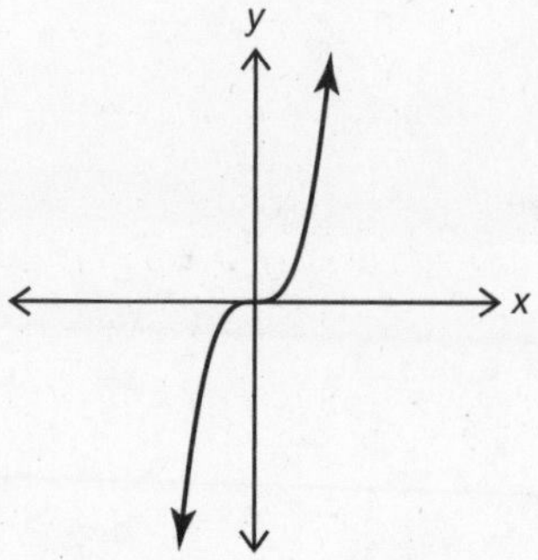

a. Write each function in terms of x, and then sketch it.

$-f_1(x) =$ ________

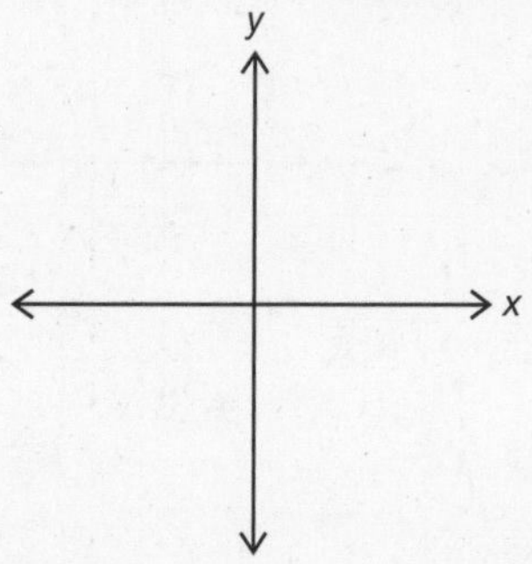

$-f_2(x) =$ ________

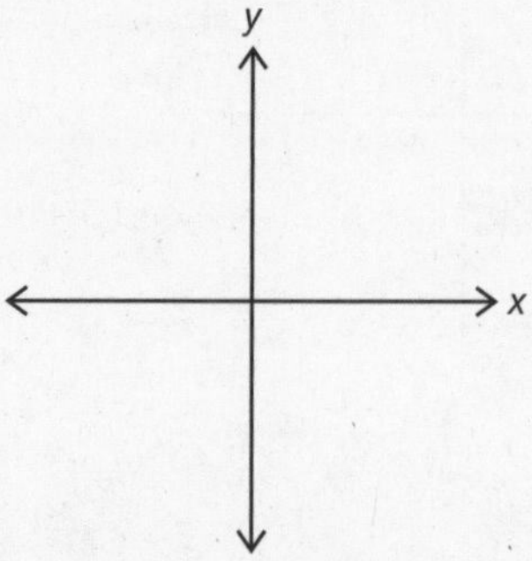

$-f_3(x) =$ ________

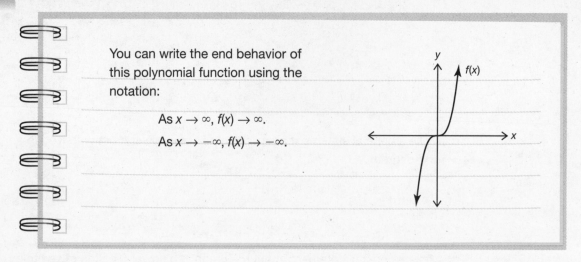

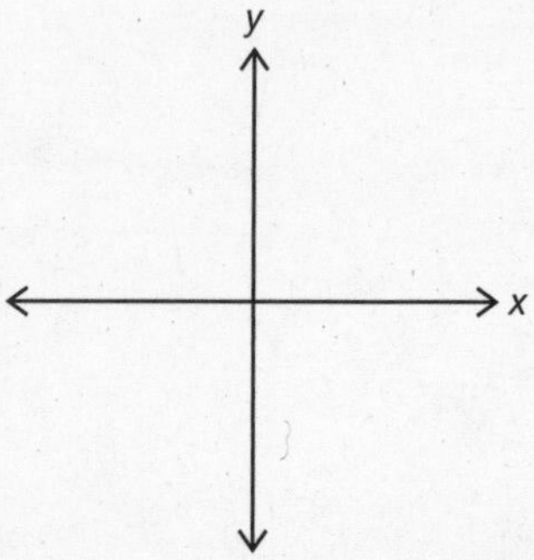

b. Complete the table to describe the end behavior for any polynomial function.

	Odd Degree Power Function	Even Degree Power Function
$a > 0$		
$a < 0$		

PROBLEM 2 If It's Flat, Then How Is It Rising?

1. The function, $f(x) = x^2$, has been graphed for you. Complete the tables for $g(x) = x^4$ and $h(x) = x^6$. Then use your knowledge of the axis of symmetry to graph and label each function on the same coordinate plane shown.

x	$g(x) = x^4$
0	
0.5	
1	

x	$h(x) = x^6$
0	
0.5	
1	

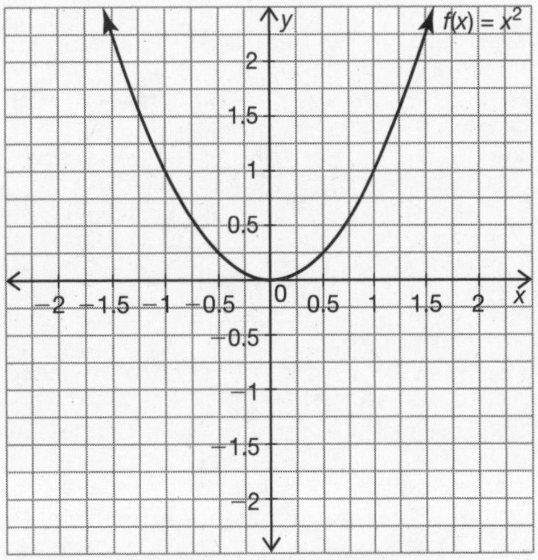

a. Notice how all 3 graphs intersect at (0, 0), therefore $f(0) = g(0) = h(0) = 0$. Describe any other intersection points using function notation.

b. As the even degree power increases, what do you notice about the graph?

c. Sketch the graph of $k(x) = x^{12}$ on the same coordinate plane as $g(x)$ and $h(x)$.

5

d. Explain why the graphs of the even degree functions flatten as the degree increases for values of x between -1 and 1.

e. Explain why the graphs of the greater even degree functions steepen when the distance from x exceeds 1.

2. The function, $f(x) = x^3$, has been graphed for you. Complete the tables for $g(x) = x^5$ and $h(x) = x^7$. Then use your knowledge of the axis of symmetry to graph and label each function on the same coordinate plane.

x	$g(x) = x^5$
0	
0.5	
1	

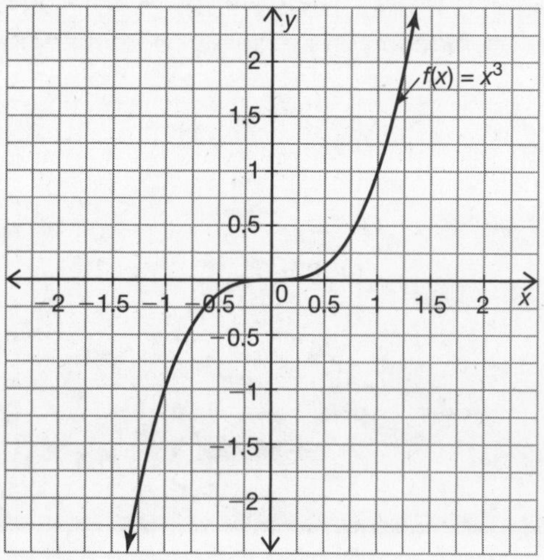

x	$h(x) = x^7$
0	
0.5	
1	

a. Notice how all 3 graphs intersect at (0, 0), therefore $f(0) = g(0) = h(0) = 0$. Describe any other intersection points using this function notation.

b. As the odd degree power increases, what do you notice about the graph?

c. Sketch and label the graph of $k(x) = x^{13}$ on the same coordinate plane as $g(x)$ and $h(x)$.

d. Explain why the graphs of the odd degree functions flatten as the degree increases for values of x between -1 and 1.

e. Explain why the graphs of the greater odd degree functions steepen when the distance from x exceeds 1.

PROBLEM 3 Where's the Other Half?

Recall that the axis of symmetry divides the graph into two parts that are mirror images of each other. If you do a reflection across an axis and the graph looks exactly the same as the original, it means that the graph is symmetric with respect to that axis.

1. Sketch 2 graphs that are symmetric to:

a. the x-axis

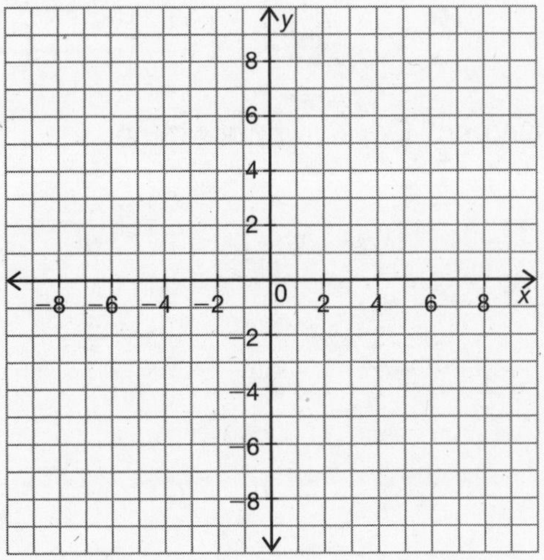

b. the line $y = 0$

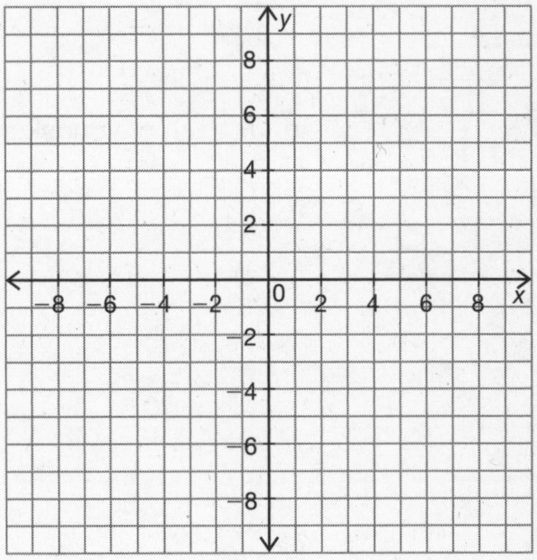

c. the line $x = 3$

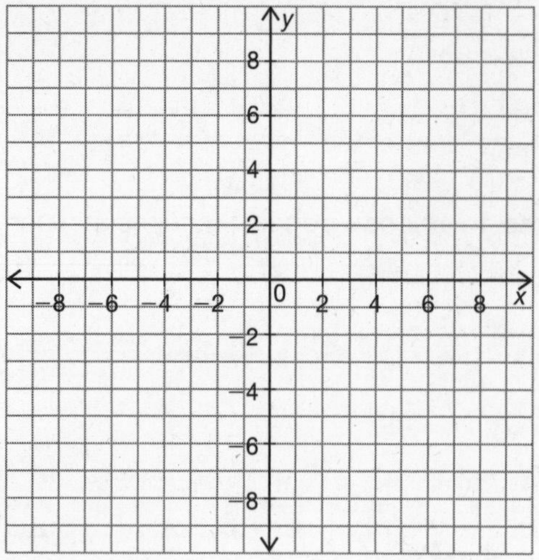

d. the line $y = 0$

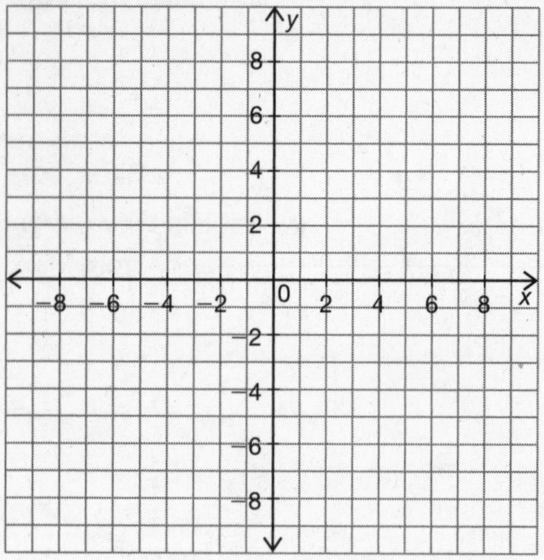

e. the line $x = -4$

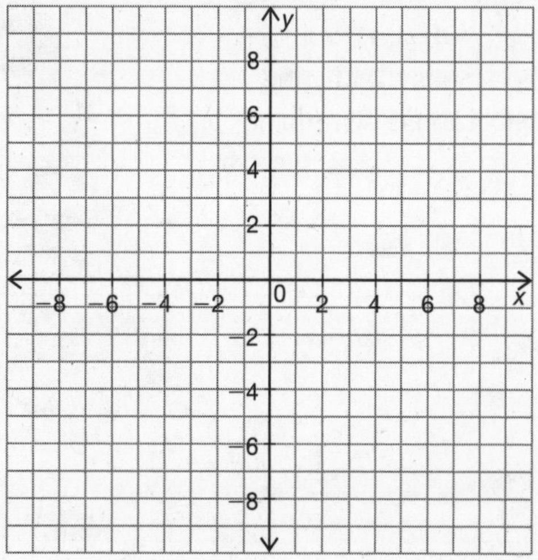

f. the line $y = 2$

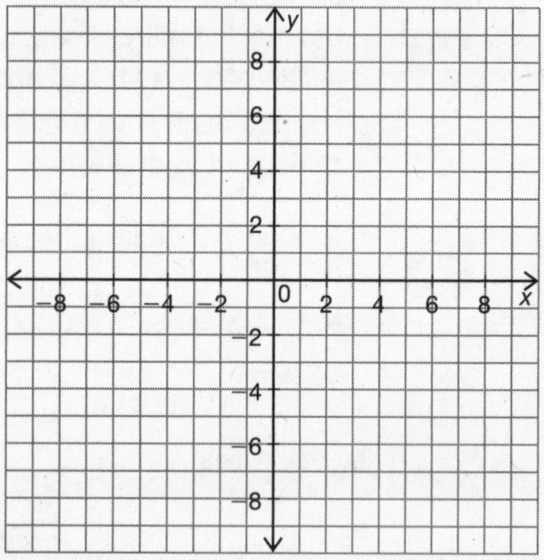

g. Is each of your sketches a function? Explain why or why not.

2. Analyze the graph shown.

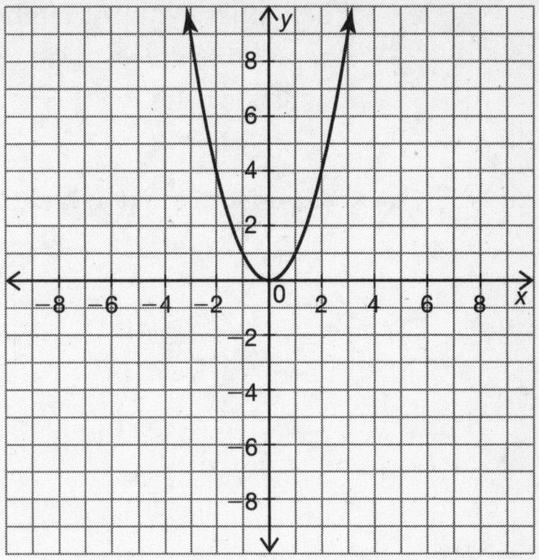

a. Identify 2 symmetric points.

b. If one point is (x, y) what are the coordinates of the other symmetric point?

c. What do you notice about the y-values when you replace x with $-x$?

d. Write a general statement to explain the relationship between any two points symmetrical to the line $x = 0$.

3. Analyze the graph shown.

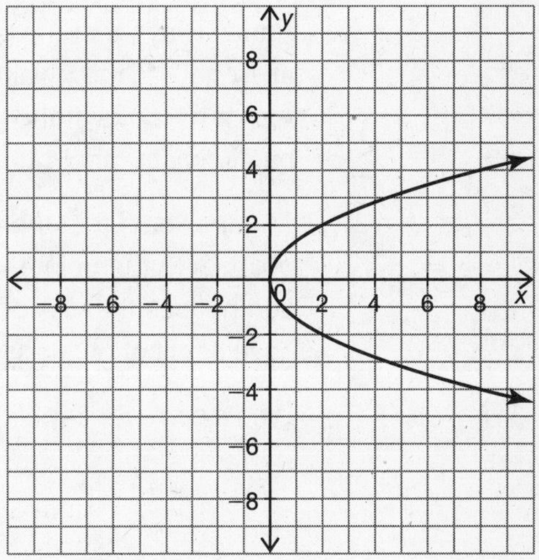

a. Identify 2 symmetric points.

b. If one point is (x, y) what are the coordinates of the other symmetric point?

c. What do you notice about the x-values when you replace y with $-y$?

d. Write a general statement to explain the relationship between any two points symmetrical to the line $y = 0$.

5

If a graph is **symmetric about a line**, the line divides the graph into two identical parts. Special attention is given to the line of symmetry when it is the y-axis as it tells you that the function is even.

4. Analyze the graph shown.

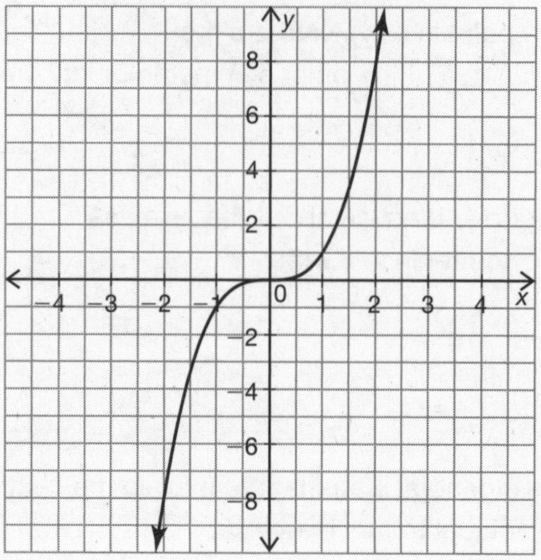

Olivia says that the graph has no line of symmetry because if she reflected the graph across the x- or y-axis, it would just change the graph to look like an odd degree power function with a negative a-value, thus not looking like a mirror image.

Randall says that the graph has no line of symmetry because if he looks at the x-value at 1 and -1, the y-value is not the same, so there can't be symmetry about the y-axis. Also if he looks at the y-value at 8 and -8, the x-value is not the same, so there can't be symmetry about the x-axis.

Shedrick said that there is some type of symmetry. He notices that if he looks at the point (2, 8) the point (-2, -8) is also on the graph. Likewise he looks at the point (1, 1) and notices that the point (-1, -1) is also on the graph. He concluded that it must have a reflection across the x- and y-axis at the same time.

Who's correct? Explain your reasoning.

5

The graph of an odd degree basic power function is *symmetric about a point*, in particular the origin. A function is **symmetric about a point** if each point on the graph has a point the same distance from the central point, but in the opposite direction. Special attention is given when the central point is the origin as it determines that the function is odd. When the point of symmetry is the origin, the graph is reflected across the x-axis and the y-axis. If you replace both (x, y) with $(-x, -y)$, the function remains the same.

You can think of the point of symmetry about the origin, as a double reflection.

$f_1(x) = x^3$

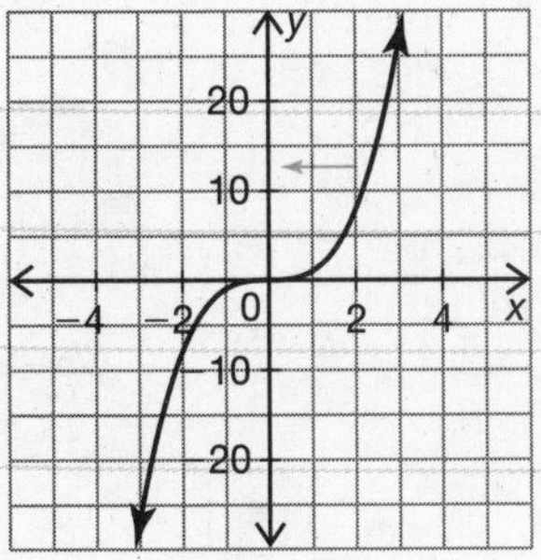

The function $f_1(x)$ is shown.

$f_2(x) = f_1(-x)^3$

$= (-x)^3$

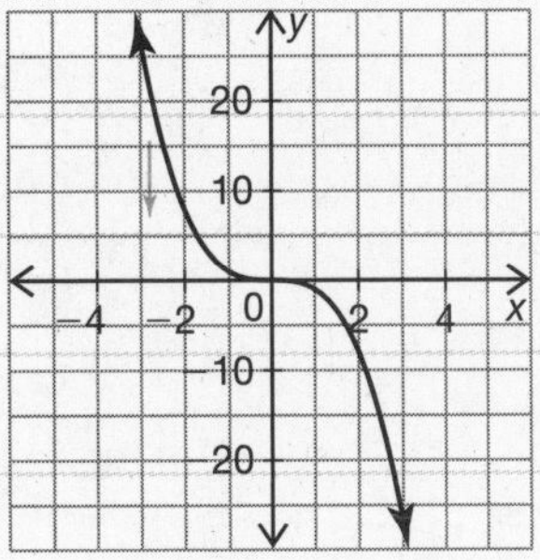

The function $f_1(x)$ is reflected across the y-axis to produce f_2.

$f_3(x) = -f_2(x)$

$= x^3$

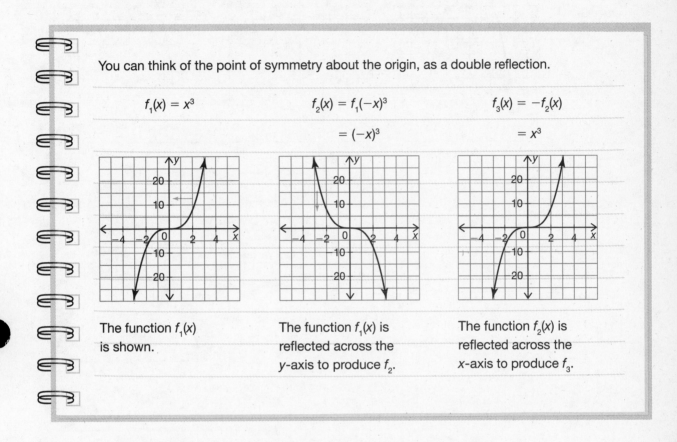

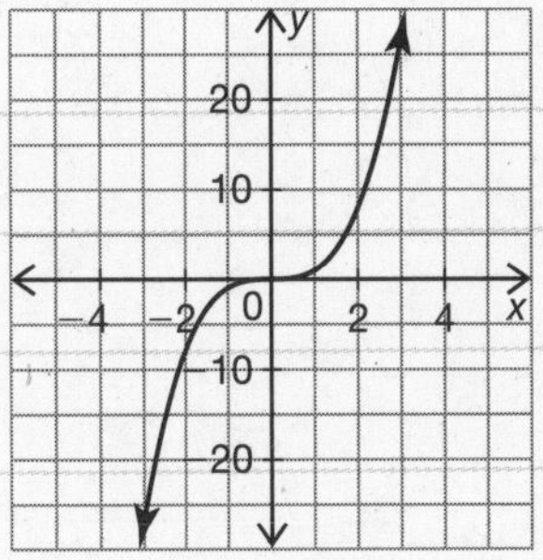

The function $f_2(x)$ is reflected across the x-axis to produce f_3.

An **even function** has a graph symmetric about the y-axis, thus $f(x) = f(-x)$.

An **odd function** has a graph symmetric about the origin, thus $f(x) = -f(-x)$.

5. Which graph in Questions 2 through 4 represents an even function? Explain your reasoning.

6. Which graph in Questions 2 through 4 represents an odd function? Explain your reasoning.

7. State whether the graph of each function shown is even, odd, or neither.

a.

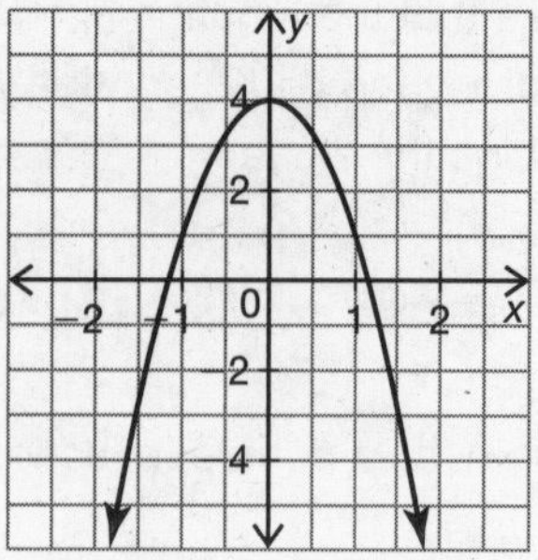

____

b.

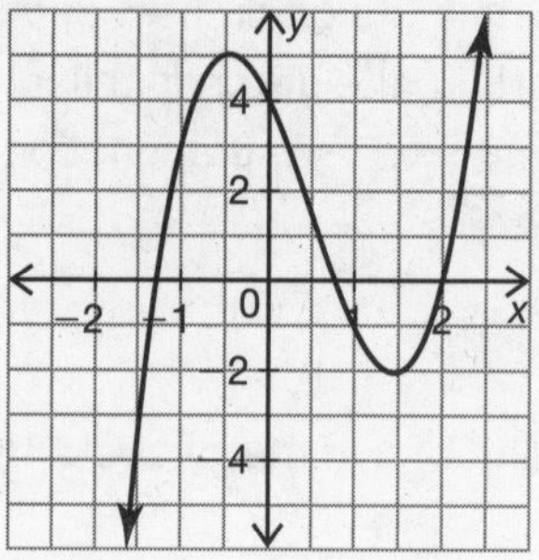

____

c.

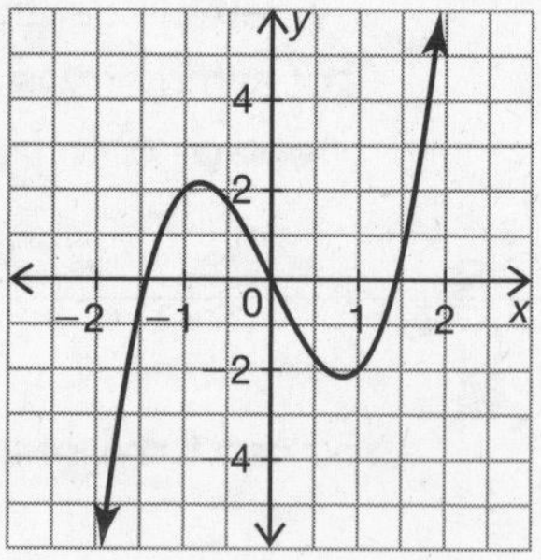

____

Odd and even functions are NOT the same as odd and even degree functions.

5

8. Lillian and Destiny are working on the problem shown.

Determine algebraically whether the polynomial function $f(x) = 3x^4 - 2x^3 + 4x - 6$ is even, odd, or neither.

Lillian

$f(x) = 3x^4 - 2x^3 + 4x - 6$

$f(x) = 3x^4 - 2x^3 + 4x - 6$
$f(-x) = 3(-x)^4 - 2(-x)^3 + 4(-x) - 6$
$f(-x) = 3x^4 + 2x^3 - 4x - 6$

$-f(x) = -(3x^4 - 2x^3 + 4x - 6)$
$-f(x) = -3x^4 + 2x^3 - 4x + 6$

$f(x) \neq f(-x)$ or $-f(x)$ thus
$f(x)$ is neither even or odd.

Destiny

$f(x) = 3x^4 - 2x^3 + 4x - 6$

$f(x) = 3x^4 - 2x^3 + 4x - 6$
$f(-x) = 3(-x^4) - 2(-x^3) + 4(-x) - 6$
$f(-x) = -3x^4 + 2x^3 - 4x - 6$

$-f(x) = -(3x^4 - 2x^3 + 4x - 6)$
$-f(x) = -3x^4 + 2x^3 - 4x + 6$

$f(x) \neq f(-x)$ or $-f(x)$ thus
$f(x)$ is neither even or odd.

a. Explain why Destiny's work is incorrect.

5

b. How can you use algebra to determine whether a function is even or odd?

9. Determine algebraically whether the functions are even, odd, or neither.

a. $f(x) = 2x^3 - 3x$

Take your time
and check your
substitutions.

b. $g(x) = 6x^2 + 10$

c. $h(x) = x^3 - 3x^2 - 2x + 7$

5

Be prepared to share your solutions and methods.

5.3

Function Makeover

Transformations and Symmetry of Polynomial Functions

LEARNING GOALS

In this lesson, you will:

- Dilate, reflect, and translate cubic and quartic functions.
- Understand that not all polynomial functions can be formed through transformations.
- Explore differences between even and odd functions, and even and odd degree functions.
- Use power functions to build cubic, quartic, and quintic functions.
- Explore the possible graphs of cubic, quartic, and quintic functions, and extend graphical properties to higher-degree functions.

KEY TERMS

- polynomial function
- quartic function
- quintic function

M. C. Escher is a well-known artist with a unique visual perspective. Many of his works display elusive connections, peculiar symmetry, and tessellations. Tessellations are symmetric designs with a repeated pattern.

You can find many images of Escher's work on the World Wide Web. Take a look and enjoy! Make sure to take a close look, because things may not be as straightforward as they seem.

PROBLEM 1 Refer to the Reference Points

Recall that reference points are a set of points that are used to graph a basic function. Previously, you used reference points and the key characteristics of a parabola to graph the basic quadratic function. You learned that the reference points for the basic quadratic function are (0, 0), (1, 1), and (2, 4). The basic quadratic function is symmetric about the y-axis; that is, $f(x) = f(-x)$. Therefore, you can use symmetry to graph two other points of the basic function, $(-1, 1)$, $(-2, 4)$.

Let's consider a set of reference points and the property of symmetry to graph the basic cubic function.

To complete Questions 1 and 2, consider the basic cubic function, $f(x) = x^3$.

1. Complete the table for the given reference points. Then graph the points on the coordinate plane shown.

x	$f(x) = x^3$
0	
1	
2	

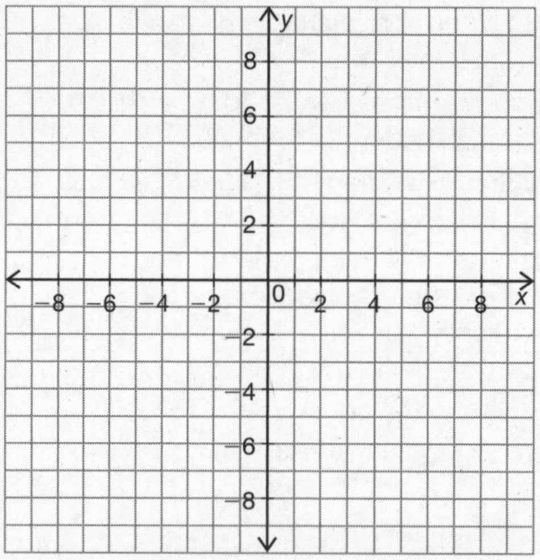

The pattern for a basic cubic function is to cube the input value to get the output value. So, from the origin, move over 1 unit and up 1 unit. For the next point, start at the origin, move over 2 units and up 8 units.

5

2. The graph of the basic cubic function is symmetric about the origin. So, $f(x) = -f(-x)$. Use the property of symmetry to determine 2 other points from the reference points. Then, use these points to graph the basic cubic function on the coordinate plane shown.

PROBLEM 2 Will Symmetry Prevail?

Transformations performed on a function $f(x)$ to form a new function $g(x)$ can be described by the transformational function:

$$g(x) = Af(B(x - C)) + D.$$

Previously, you graphed quadratic functions using this notation. You can use this notation to identify the transformations to perform on any function.

Recall that the constants A and D affect the *outside* of the function (the output values). For instance, if $A = 2$, then you can multiply each y-coordinate of $f(x)$ by 2 to determine the y-coordinates of $g(x)$.

The constants B and C affect the inside of the function (the input values). For instance, if $B = 2$, then you can multiply each x-coordinate of $f(x)$ by $\frac{1}{2}$ to determine the x-coordinates of $g(x)$.

Function Form	Equation Information	Description of Transformation of Graph
$y = Af(x)$	$\lvert A\rvert > 1$	vertical stretch of the graph by a factor of A units
	$0 < \lvert A\rvert < 1$	vertical compression of the graph by a factor of A units
	$A < 0$	reflection across the x-axis
$y = f(Bx)$	$\lvert B\rvert > 1$	compressed horizontally by a factor of $\frac{1}{\lvert B\rvert}$
	$0 < \lvert B\rvert < 1$	stretched horizontally by a factor of $\frac{1}{\lvert B\rvert}$
	$B < 0$	reflection across the y-axis
$y = f(x - C)$	$C > 0$	horizontal shift right C units
	$C < 0$	horizontal shift left C units
$y = f(x) + D$	$D > 0$	vertical shift up D units
	$D < 0$	vertical shift down D units

1. Complete the table to show the coordinates of $g(x) = Af(B(x - C)) + D$ after each type of transformation performed on $f(x)$.

Type of Transformation Performed on $f(x)$	Coordinates of $f(x) \rightarrow$ Coordinates of $g(x)$
Vertical Dilation by a Factor of A	$(x, y) \rightarrow$ (__________, __________)
Horizontal Dilation by a Factor of B	$(x, y) \rightarrow$ (__________, __________)
Horizontal Translation of C units	$(x, y) \rightarrow$ (__________, __________)
Vertical Translation of D units	$(x, y) \rightarrow$ (__________, __________)
All four transformations: A, B, C, and D	$(x, y) \rightarrow$ (__________, __________)

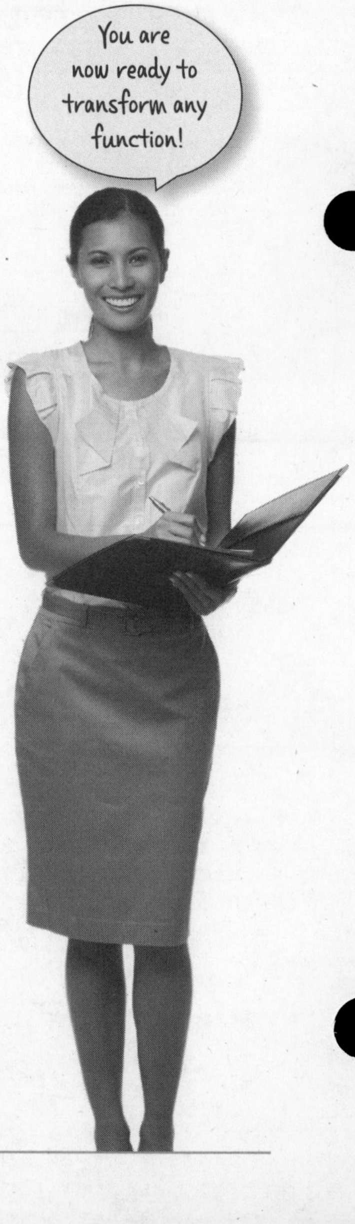

You are now ready to transform any function!

5

2. The graph of the basic cubic function $c(x) = x^3$ is shown.

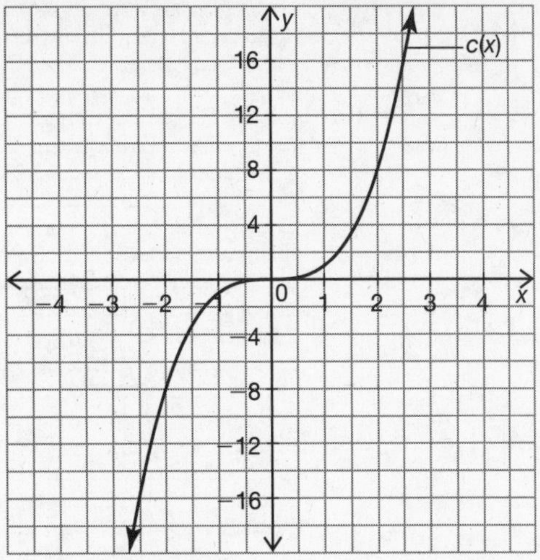

a. Suppose that $g(x) = 2c(x)$. Use reference points and properties of symmetry to complete the table of values for $g(x)$. Then, graph and label $g(x)$ on the same coordinate plane as $c(x)$.

Reference Points on c(x)	→	Corresponding Points on g(x)
(0, 0)	→	
(1, 1)	→	
(2, 8)	→	

b. Suppose that $h(x) = \frac{1}{2}c(x)$. Use reference points and properties of symmetry to complete the table of values for $h(x)$. Then, graph and label $h(x)$ on the same coordinate plane as $c(x)$ and $g(x)$.

Reference Points on c(x)	→	Corresponding Points on h(x)
(0, 0)	→	
(1, 1)	→	
(2, 8)	→	

5

c. Describe the symmetry of $g(x)$ and $h(x)$. How does the symmetry of $g(x)$ and $h(x)$ compare to the symmetry of $c(x)$?

d. Determine whether $g(x)$ and $h(x)$ are even functions, odd functions, or neither. Verify your answer algebraically.

3. The graph of the basic cubic function $c(x) = x^3$ is shown.

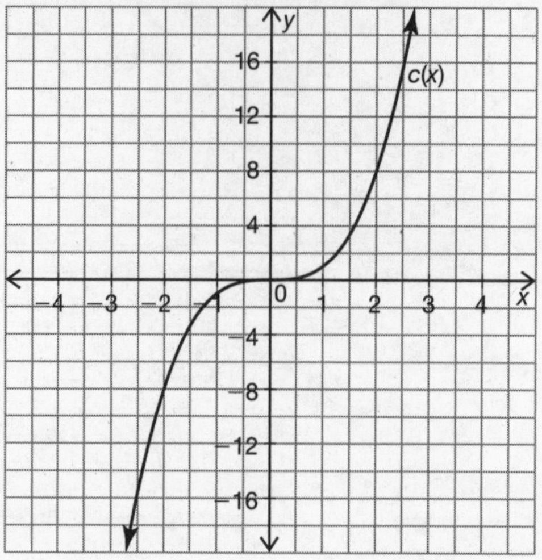

a. Suppose that $u(x) = c(2x)$. Use reference points and properties of symmetry to complete the table of values for $u(x)$. Then, graph and label $u(x)$ on the same coordinate plane as $c(x)$.

Reference Points on $c(x)$	→	Corresponding Points on $u(x)$
(0, 0)	→	
(1, 1)	→	
(2, 8)	→	

b. Suppose that $v(x) = c\left(\frac{1}{2}x\right)$. Use reference points and properties symmetry to complete the table of values for $v(x)$. Then, graph and label $v(x)$ on the same coordinate plane as $c(x)$ and $u(x)$.

Reference Points on $c(x)$	→	Corresponding Points on $v(x)$
(0, 0)	→	
(1, 1)	→	
(2, 8)	→	

5

c. Describe the symmetry of $u(x)$ and $v(x)$. How does the symmetry of $u(x)$ and $v(x)$ compare to the symmetry of $c(x)$?

d. Determine whether $u(x)$ and $v(x)$ are even functions, odd functions, or neither. Verify your answer algebraically.

4. The graph of the basic cubic function $c(x) = x^3$ is shown.

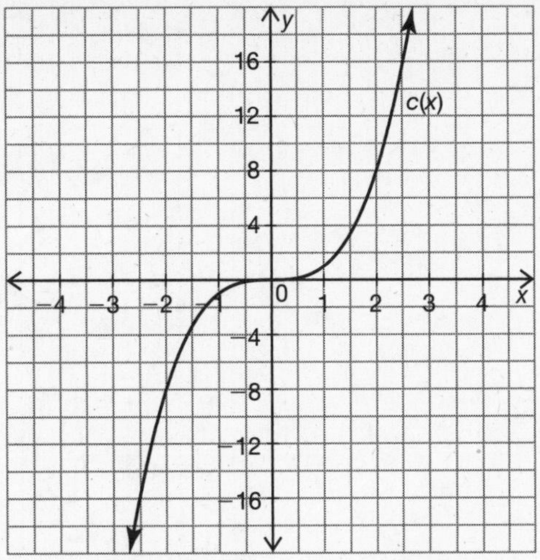

a. Suppose that $a(x) = -c(x)$. Use reference points and properties of symmetry to complete the table of values for $a(x)$. Then, graph and label $a(x)$ on the same coordinate plane as $c(x)$.

Reference Points on $c(x)$	→	Corresponding Points on $a(x)$
(0, 0)	→	
(1, 1)	→	
(2, 8)	→	

b. Suppose that $b(x) = c(-x)$. Use reference points and properties symmetry to complete the table of values for $b(x)$. Then, graph and label $b(x)$ on the same coordinate plane as $c(x)$ and $a(x)$.

Reference Points on $c(x)$	→	Corresponding Points on $b(x)$
(0, 0)	→	
(1, 1)	→	
(2, 8)	→	

5

c. Describe the symmetry of $a(x)$ and $b(x)$. How does the symmetry of $a(x)$ and $b(x)$ compare to the symmetry of $c(x)$?

d. Determine whether $a(x)$ and $b(x)$ are even functions, odd functions, or neither. Verify your answer algebraically.

5. The graph of the basic cubic function $c(x) = x^3$ is shown.

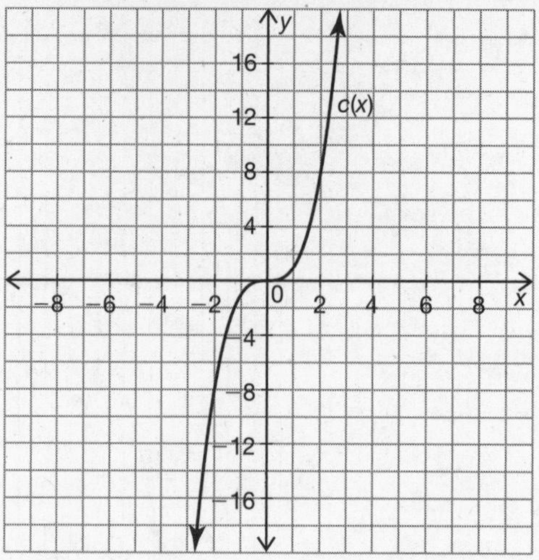

a. Suppose that $m(x) = c(x - 5)$. Use reference points and properties of symmetry to complete the table of values for $m(x)$. Then, graph and label $m(x)$ on the same coordinate plane as $c(x)$.

Reference Points on $c(x)$	$\rightarrow$	Corresponding Points on $m(x)$
(0, 0)	$\rightarrow$	
(1, 1)	$\rightarrow$	
(2, 8)	$\rightarrow$	

b. Suppose that $n(x) = c(x + 5)$. Use reference points and properties of symmetry to complete the table of values for $n(x)$. Then, graph and label $n(x)$ on the same coordinate plane as $c(x)$ and $m(x)$.

Reference Points on $c(x)$	$\rightarrow$	Corresponding Points on $n(x)$
(0, 0)	$\rightarrow$	
(1, 1)	$\rightarrow$	
(2, 8)	$\rightarrow$	

5

c. Describe the symmetry of $m(x)$ and $n(x)$. How does the symmetry of $a(x)$ and $b(x)$ compare to the symmetry of $c(x)$?

d. Determine whether $m(x)$ and $n(x)$ are even functions, odd functions, or neither. Verify your answer algebraically.

6. The graph of the basic cubic function $c(x) = x^3$ is shown.

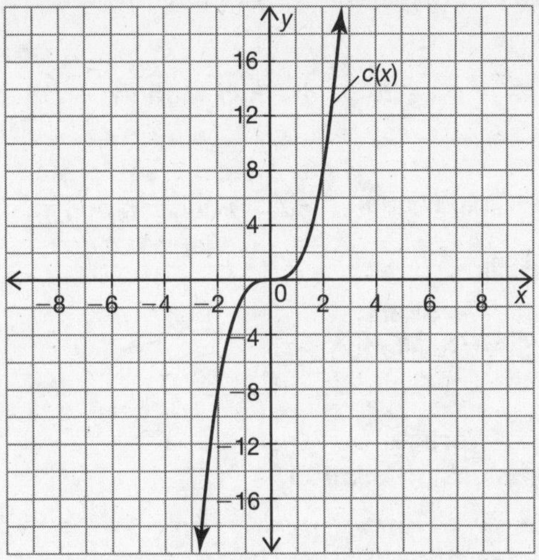

a. Suppose that $j(x) = c(x) + 5$. Use reference points and properties of symmetry to complete the table of values for $j(x)$. Then, graph and label $j(x)$ on the same coordinate plane as $c(x)$.

Reference Points on $c(x)$	→	Corresponding Points on $j(x)$
(0, 0)	→	
(1, 1)	→	
(2, 8)	→	

b. Suppose that $k(x) = c(x) - 5$. Use reference points and properties of symmetry to complete the table of values for $k(x)$. Then, graph and label $k(x)$ on the same coordinate plane as $c(x)$ and $j(x)$.

Reference Points on $c(x)$	→	Corresponding Points on $k(x)$
(0, 0)	→	
(1, 1)	→	
(2, 8)	→	

5

c. Describe the symmetry of $j(x)$ and $k(x)$. How does the symmetry of $j(x)$ and $k(x)$ compare to the symmetry of $c(x)$?

d. Determine whether $j(x)$ and $k(x)$ are even functions, odd functions, or neither. Verify your answer algebraically.

7. Complete the table to summarize the effects that transformations have on the basic cubic function $c(x) = x^3$. The first row has been completed for you.

Effects of Rigid Motions on the Basic Cubic Function $c(x) = x^3$			
Rigid Motion	**New Transformed Function $p(x)$ in Terms of $c(x)$**	**Description of Symmetry of $p(x)$**	**Is $p(x)$ Even, Odd, or Neither?**
Vertical Stretch Dilation	$p(x) = Ac(x)$, $A > 1$	Symmetric about the point (0, 0)	Odd
Vertical Compression Dilation			
Horizontal Stretch Dilation			
Horizontal Compression Dilation			
Reflection across x-axis			
Reflection across y-axis			
Vertical Translation			
Horizontal Translation			

5

8. Do you think that your results in Question 7 would be the same for *any* odd power function? Explain your reasoning.

9. The graph of the basic quartic function $q(x) = x^4$ and its reference points are shown. Use the graph to sketch the function after dilations, reflections, and translations. Pay special attention to the symmetry after the transformations. Record your conclusions by completing the table that follows. The first row has been completed for you.

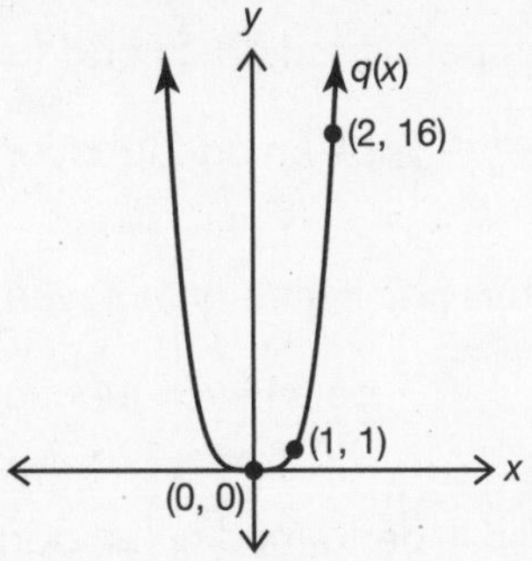

Effects of Rigid Motions on the Basic Cubic Function $q(x) = x^4$			
Rigid Motion	**New Transformed Function $p(x)$ in Terms of $q(x)$**	**Description of Symmetry of $p(x)$**	**Is $p(x)$ Even, Odd, or Neither?**
Vertical Stretch Dilation	$p(x) = Ac(x)$, $A > 1$	Symmetric about the y-axis	Even
Vertical Compression Dilation			
Horizontal Stretch Dilation			
Horizontal Compression Dilation			
Reflection across x-axis			
Reflection across y-axis			
Vertical Translation			
Horizontal Translation			

10. Do you think that your results in Question 9 would be the same for *any* even power function? Explain your reasoning.

11. Use the appropriate word from the box to complete each statement.

always	sometimes	never

a. If a dilation is performed on an odd function $f(x)$ to produce $g(x)$, then $g(x)$ will ________________ be an odd function.

b. If a reflection is performed on an even function $f(x)$ to produce $g(x)$, then $g(x)$ will ________________ be an even function.

c. If a translation is performed on an odd function $f(x)$ to produce $g(x)$, then $g(x)$ will ________________ be an odd function.

d. If a translation is performed on an even function $f(x)$ to produce $g(x)$, then $g(x)$ will ________________ be an even function.

PROBLEM 3 Multiple Transformations

1. Analyze the graphs of $f(x)$ and $g(x)$. Describe the transformations performed on $f(x)$ to create $g(x)$. Then, write an equation for $g(x)$ in terms of $f(x)$. For each set of points shown on $f(x)$, the corresponding points after the rigid motions are shown on $g(x)$.

a. $g(x) =$ ________________

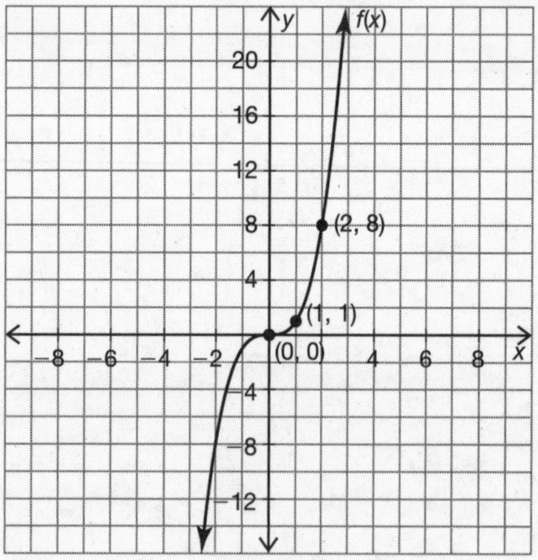

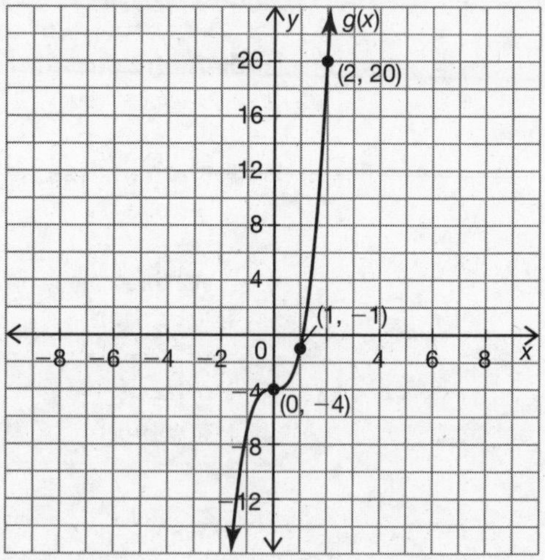

5

b. $g(x) =$ ________________

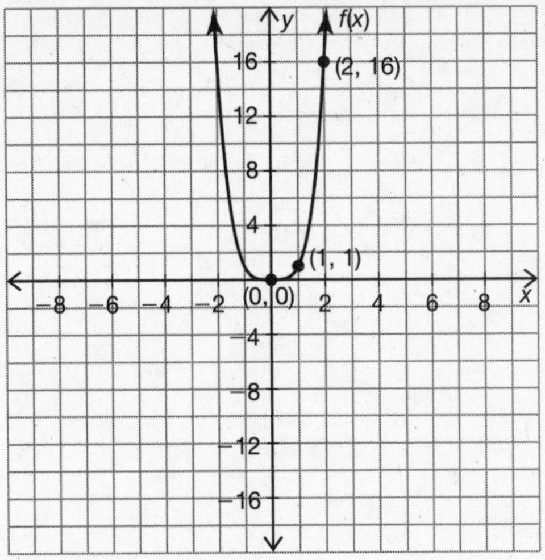

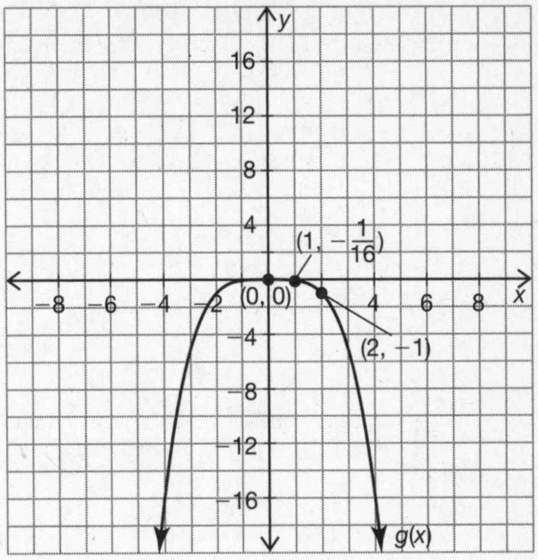

c. $g(x) =$ ____________________

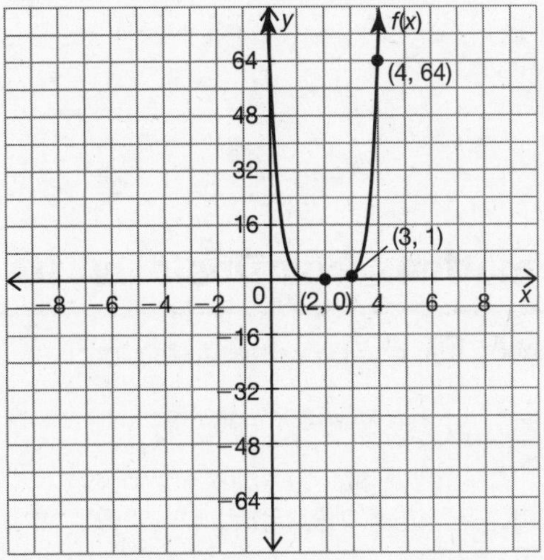

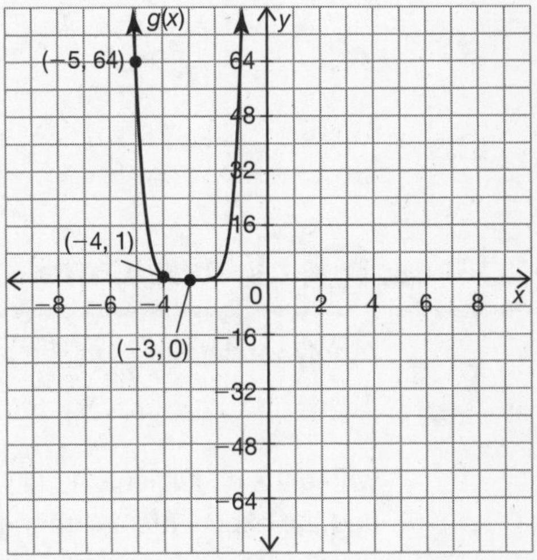

5

2. The equation for a polynomial function $p(x)$ is given. The equation for the transformed function $t(x)$ in terms of $p(x)$ is also given. Describe the transformation(s) performed on $p(x)$ that produced $t(x)$. Then, write an equation for $t(x)$ in terms of x.

a. $p(x) = x^5$

$t(x) = 0.5p(-x)$

b. $p(x) = x^4$

$t(x) = 2p(x + 3)$

c. $p(x) = x^3$

$t(x) = -p(x - 2) + 4$

PROBLEM 4 When Transformations Just Don't Cut It

A **polynomial function** is a function that can be written in the form

$$p(x) = a_n x^n + a_{n-1} x^{n-1} + \cdots + a_2 x^2 + a_1 x + a_0,$$

where the coefficients $a_n, a_{n-1}, \ldots a_2, a_1, a_0$ are complex numbers and the exponents are nonnegative integers. The form shown here is called the standard form of a polynomial.

All of the polynomial functions in this course will have real number coefficients.

You already know that a third-degree polynomial function has a special name—a cubic function. A **quartic function** is a fourth degree polynomial function, while a **quintic function** is a fifth degree polynomial function.

You can describe any linear or quadratic functions in terms of the transformations performed on the basic functions. Is this true for *any* polynomial function? That is, can you derive any polynomial function by transforming a basic function?

1. Consider the polynomial function $p(x) = x^3 + 2x^2 - 3x$.

a. Predict what the graph of $p(x)$ looks like. Describe the number of x-intercepts and end behavior.

b. Use a graphing calculator to graph $p(x)$. Were your predictions accurate?

c. Can you describe which transformations were performed on $f(x) = x^3$ that results in the graph of $p(x)$?

Transformations on basic functions cannot be used to derive any polynomial. Therefore, you will need to consider another method.

Use each basic power function shown to complete Questions 2 through 6.

$f(x) = x$	$g(x) = x^2$	$h(x) = x^3$	$j(x) = x^4$	$k(x) = x^5$

2. Consider the function $a(x)$, where $a(x) = h(x) + 2g(x)$.

a. The functions $g(x)$ and $h(x)$ are shown. Complete the table of values and sketch $a(x)$ on the coordinate plane shown. The first row has been completed for you.

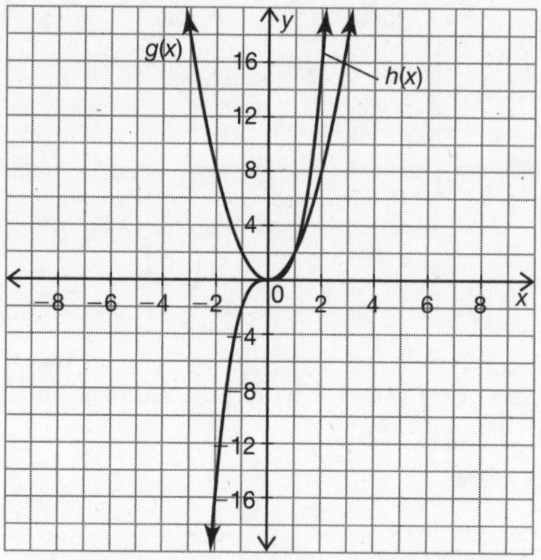

x	$h(x)$	$g(x)$	$a(x)$
−2	−8	4	−8 + 2(4) = 0
−1			
0			
1			
2			

b. Write the equation for $a(x)$.

c. Explain any differences between the graph of $a(x)$ and the graph of the basic power function of the same degree as $a(x)$.

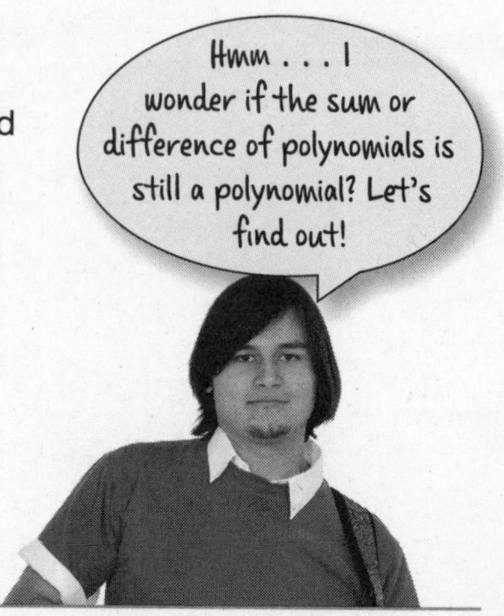

$f(x) = x$ $g(x) = x^2$ $h(x) = x^3$ $j(x) = x^4$ $k(x) = x^5$

3. Consider the function $b(x)$, where $b(x) = 2f(x) - h(x)$.

   a. The functions $f(x)$ and $h(x)$ are shown. Complete the table of values and sketch $b(x)$ on the coordinate plane.

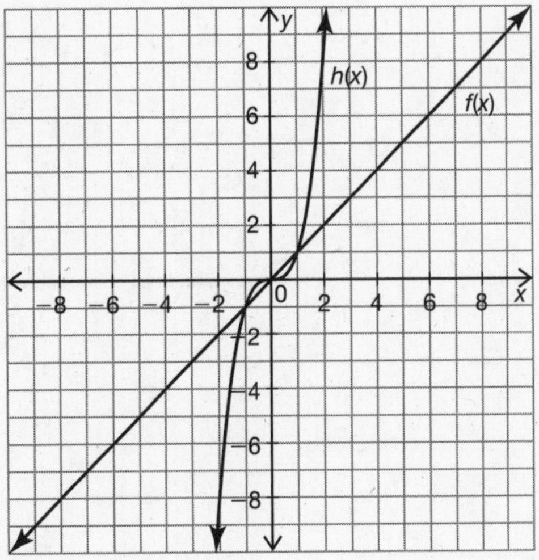

x	$f(x)$	$h(x)$	$b(x)$
−2			
−1			
0			
1			
2			

   b. Write the equation for $b(x)$.

   c. Explain any differences between the graph of $b(x)$ and the graph of the basic power function of the same degree as $b(x)$.

5

$f(x) = x$	$g(x) = x^2$	$h(x) = x^3$	$j(x) = x^4$	$k(x) = x^5$

4. Consider the function $c(x)$, where $c(x) = j(x) + 0.5h(x) - 2g(x)$.

   a. The functions $g(x)$, $h(x)$, and $j(x)$ are shown. Complete the table of values and sketch $c(x)$ on the coordinate plane.

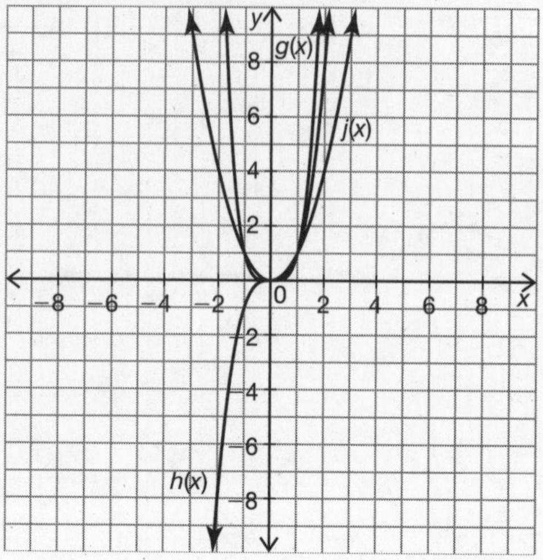

x	j(x)	h(x)	g(x)	c(x)
−2				
−1				
0				
1				
2				

5

   b. Write the equation for $c(x)$.

   c. Explain any differences between the graph of $c(x)$ and the graph of the basic power function of the same degree as $c(x)$.

$f(x) = x$	$g(x) = x^2$	$h(x) = x^3$	$j(x) = x^4$	$k(x) = x^5$

5. Consider the function $d(x)$, where $d(x) = -j(x) + 3g(x) - 1$.

a. The functions $g(x)$ and $j(x)$ are shown. Complete the table of values and sketch $d(x)$ on the coordinate plane.

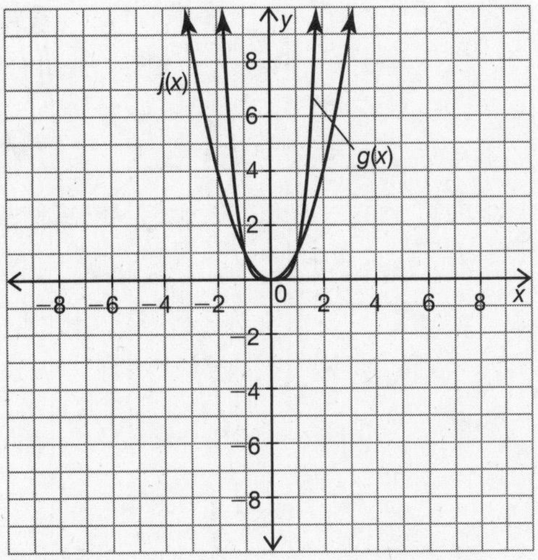

x	j(x)	g(x)	d(x)
−2			
−1			
0			
1			
2			

b. Write the equation for $d(x)$. Is $d(x)$ a polynomial?

c. Explain any differences between the graph of $d(x)$ and the graph of the basic power function of the same degree as $d(x)$.

$f(x) = x$	$g(x) = x^2$	$h(x) = x^3$	$j(x) = x^4$	$k(x) = x^5$

6. Consider the function $z(x)$, where $z(x) = k(x) + 2j(x) - 4h(x) - 6g(x)$.

a. The functions $g(x)$, $h(x)$, $j(x)$, and $k(x)$ are shown. Complete the table of values and sketch $z(x)$ on the coordinate plane.

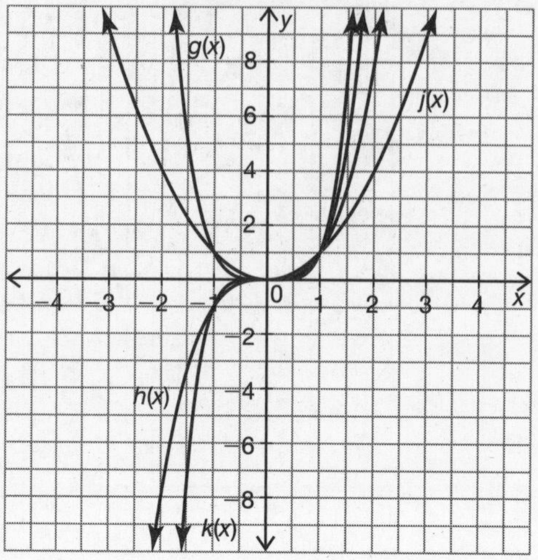

x	k(x)	j(x)	h(x)	g(x)	z(x)
−3					
−2					
−1					
0					
1					
2					
3					

b. Write the equation for $z(x)$.

c. Explain any differences between the graph of $z(x)$ and the graph of the basic power function of the same degree as $z(x)$.

Talk the Talk

The possible shapes of linear, quadratic, cubic, quartic, and quintic functions are shown.

Linear Functions

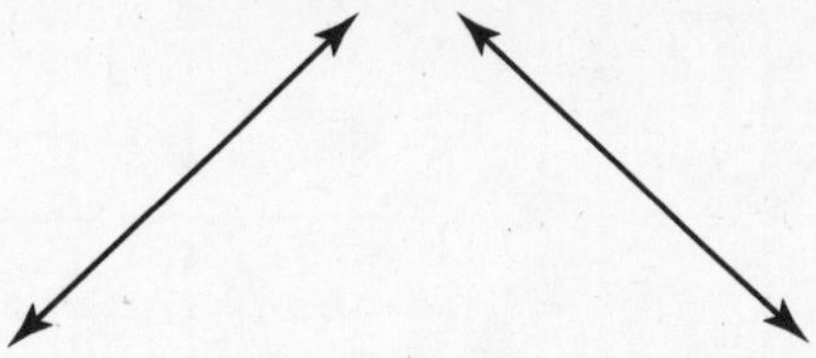

Quadratic Functions

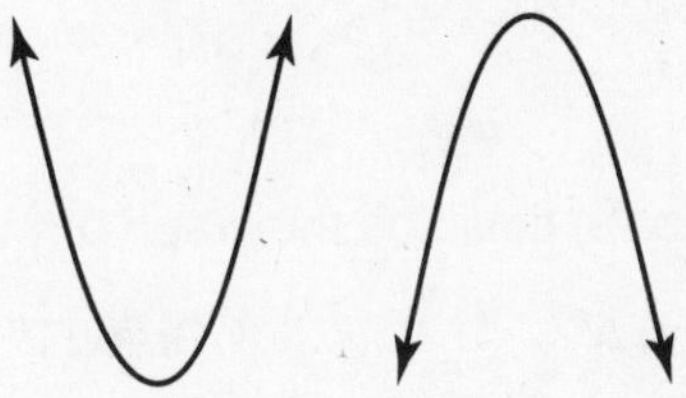

Cubic Functions

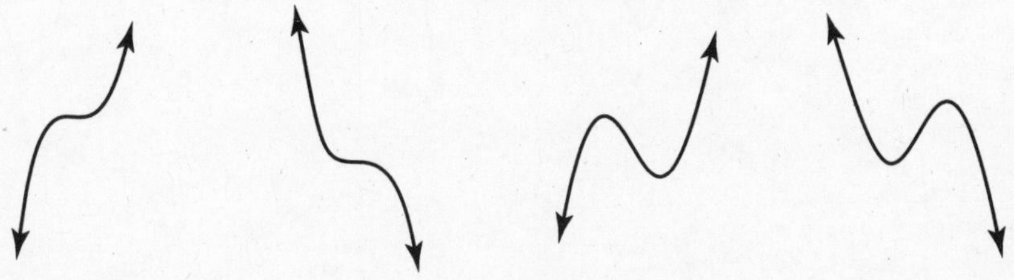

Quartic Functions

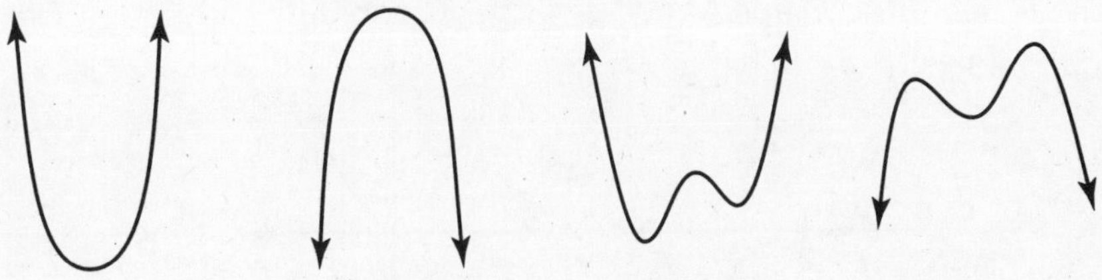

Quintic Functions

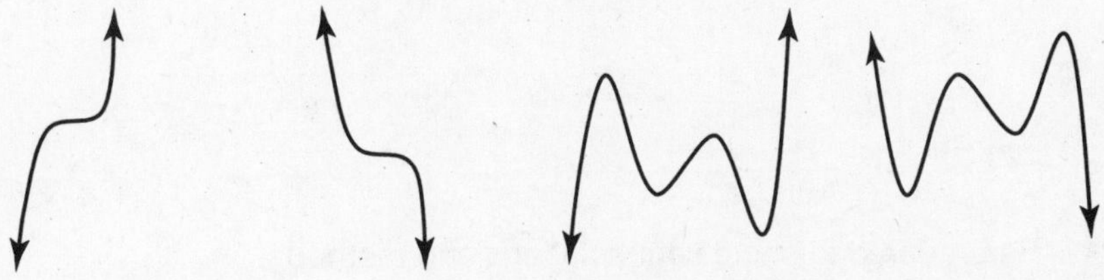

1. Choose the possible graph(s) for each given polynomial function $f(x)$.

   a. Which graph(s) could be the graph of $f(x) = 2x^2$?

Graph A

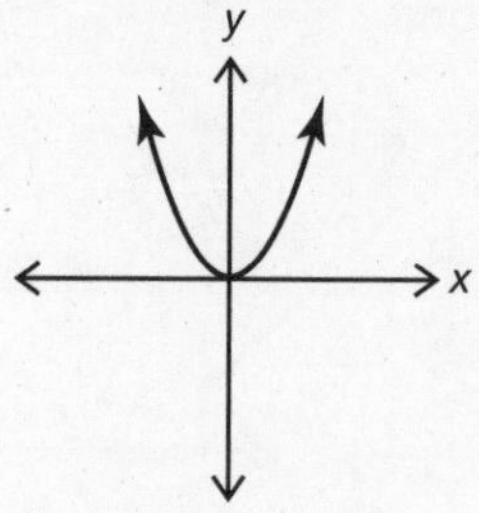

Graph B

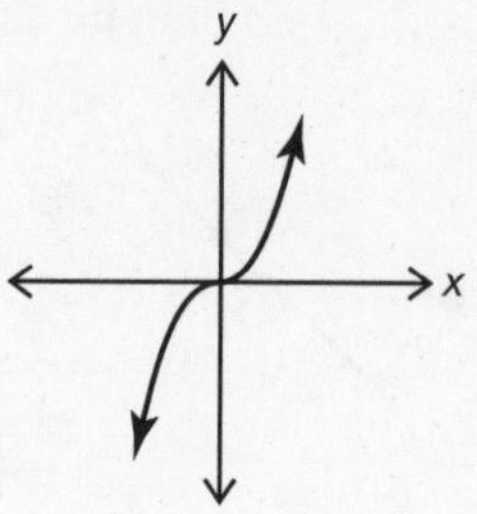

Graph C

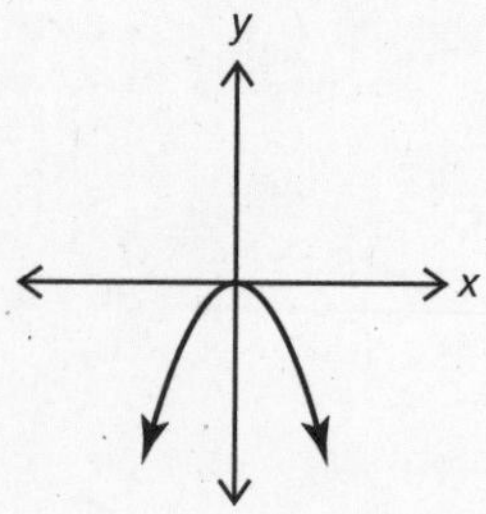

   b. Which graph(s) could be the graph of $f(x) = -x^3 - x^2 + 6x$?

Graph A

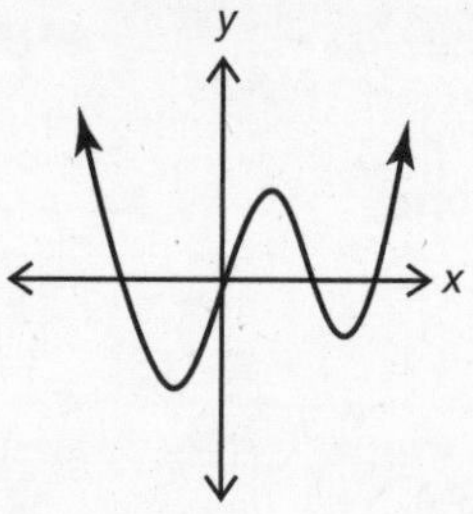

Graph B

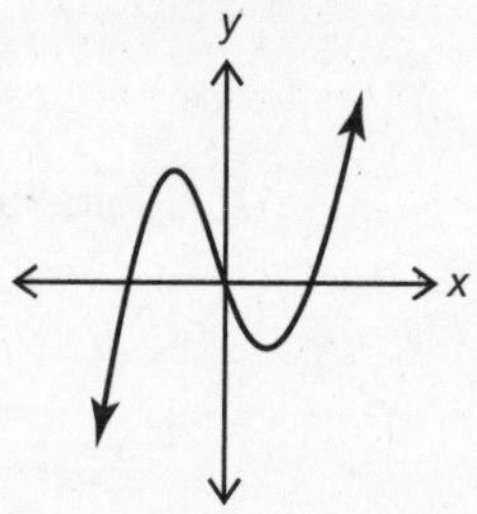

Graph C

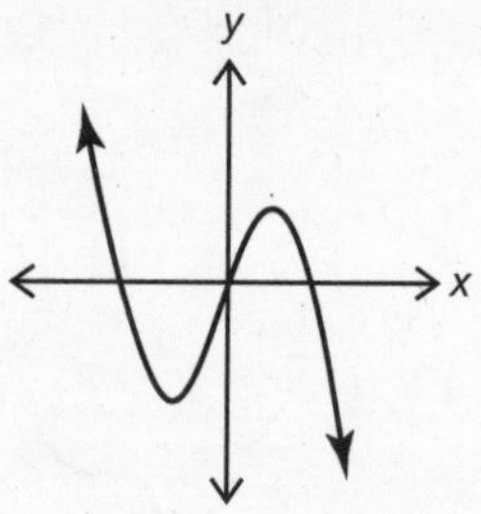

   c. Which graph(s) could be the graph of $f(x) = x^4 + 1$?

Graph A

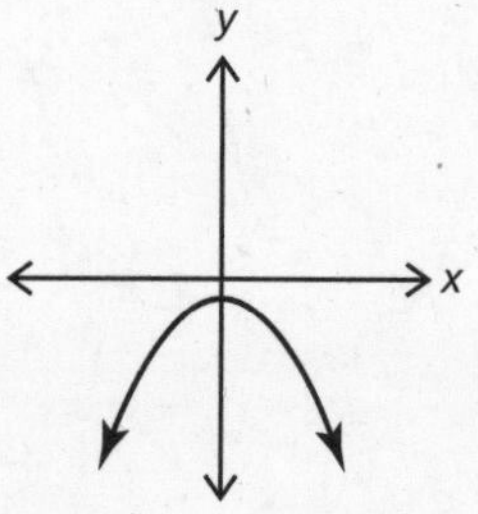

Graph B

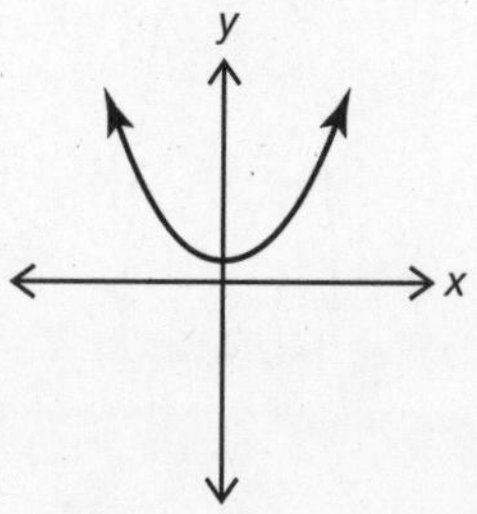

Graph C

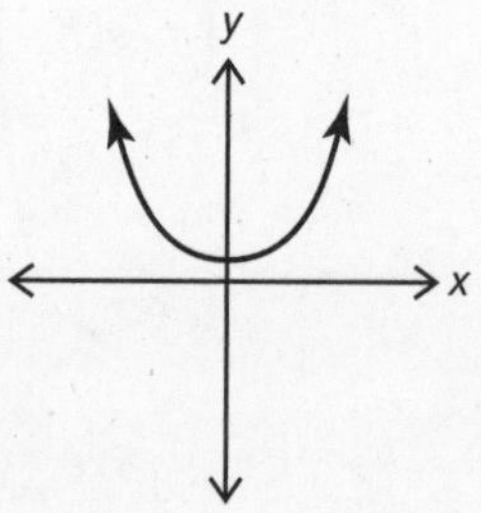

Be prepared to share your solutions and methods.

5.4

Polynomial DNA

Key Characteristics of Polynomial Functions

LEARNING GOALS

In this lesson, you will:

- Interpret polynomial key characteristics in the context of a problem situation.
- Generalize the key characteristics of polynomials.
- Sketch the graph of any polynomial given certain key characteristics.

KEY TERMS

- absolute maximum
- absolute minimum
- extrema

Children typically resemble their parents because of the inheritance of genes from parent to offspring. Scientists know of over 200 hereditary traits that are transmitted across generations of families. The genes that carry these traits are in specific strands of DNA. You can witness these traits by crossing your hands. Is your left thumb over your right thumb? If it is, you have the dominant trait. People with the recessive trait will cross their right thumb over their left thumb. Try it the opposite way, it feels awkward doesn't it?

Did you ever work with Punnett squares in biology to determine the probability of an offspring having a particular characteristic like blue eyes versus brown eyes or eyelash length? Being able to roll your tongue is actually a dominant genetic feature. Some other dominant genetic human traits are non-cleft chins, widow's peaks, broad eyebrows, freckles, dimples, and unattached ear lobes to name a few. When you look at the specific genotype of a species you can determine or predict what the offspring may look like.

The same thing is true for polynomials! If you know certain characteristics about the polynomial, you can predict what the graph will look like, as well as other key characteristics.

The data shown represents the population of a rare, endangered species of frog called the glass frog. In order to better understand the glass frog's fertilization habits, scientists performed a study and recorded the average number of frog eggs over the span of 44 months.

Month of Study	Average Number of Glass Frog Eggs	Month of Study	Average Number of Glass Frog Eggs
0	10,534	19	14,330.5
1	5500	20	13,845.1
2	5033	21	13,893.1
3	2600	22	14,546.3
4	239.4	23	11,815.8
6	137.3	23	13,086.2
7	108.4	24	15,966.9
8	667.1	29	9904.4
9	387.4	29	8257.3
12	4813.1	31	5297.5
14	9539.5	32	2494.1
15	11,318.6	33	1805.4
16	8953.3	34	665
18	15,402.5	43	4813

The data has been plotted for you and a quartic regression was used to generate the polynomial function to best represent the data. The quartic regression option calculates the best-fit equation of the form $y = ax^4 + bx^3 + cx^2 + dx + e$.

Glass Frog Eggs Recorded

$y = 0.2251x^4 - 19.747x^3 + 528.95x^2 - 4292x + 10445$
$R^2 = 0.9515$

◆ Series1
— Poly. (Series1)

Average Number of Eggs Observed

Number of Months

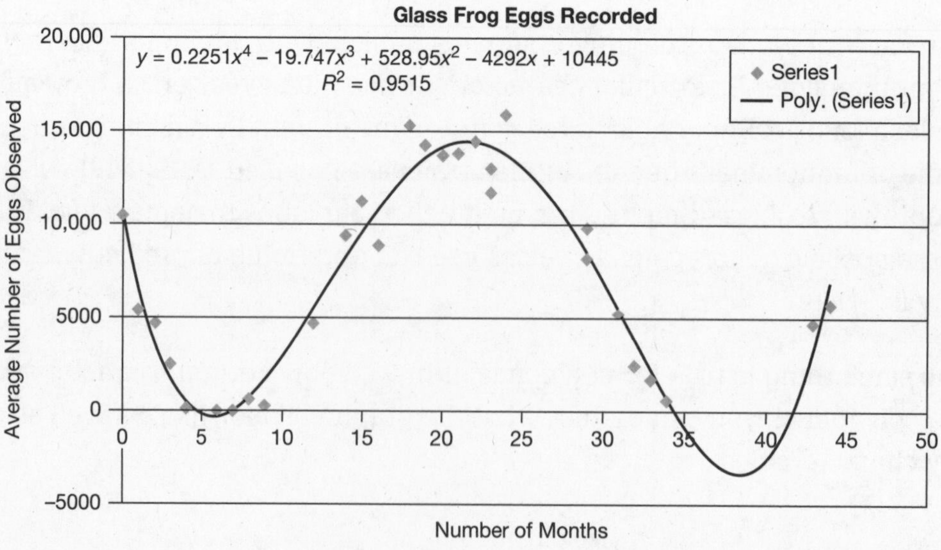

1. Consider the graph and equation to answer each question.

   a. What is the domain and range of the study?

   b. Explain what the domain and range represent in the context of this problem.

   c. What is the domain and range of the function?

   d. At what month in the study were the most frog eggs observed? How many eggs were recorded?

   e. At what month in the study were the least frog eggs observed? How many eggs were recorded?

   f. If the study lasted for 50 months, how many frog eggs would there be according to the function?

   g. If the study lasted forever, how many eggs would there be according to the function?

   h. How many frog eggs appeared between months 35 and 40?

   i. At what month(s) of the study were there approximately 4800 glass frog eggs observed?

2. Use a graphing calculator to determine the x-intercepts of the function. What do the x-intercepts mean in the context of this problem situation?

5

3. State the end behavior of the function. Does this make sense in the context of this problem scenario? Explain your reasoning.

4. How many frog eggs were observed at the beginning of the study? Explain the mathematical meaning of your answer.

5. Describe the interval when the frog's egg population is:

   a. increasing.

   b. decreasing.

PROBLEM 2 A Polynomial is Born

So far in this chapter, you have learned a great deal about polynomial functions. You have learned about minimums, maximums, zeros, end behavior, and the general shapes of their graphs. Now, you will combine all that information to generalize the key characteristics for any degree polynomial.

5

Recall the definition of a relative maximum is the highest point in a particular section of a function's graph, and a relative minimum is the lowest point in a particular section of the graph. Similarly, the **absolute maximum** is the highest point in the entire graph, and the **absolute minimum** is the lowest point in the entire graph. The set of absolute maximums, absolute minimums, relative maximums, and relative minimums may also be referred to as **extrema**. The extrema are also called extreme points and extremum.

1. Consider the graph that represents the average number of glass frog eggs in Problem 1.

   a. State all relative maximums and minimums.

   b. State all absolute maximums and minimums.

c. Do the absolute minimums and/or maximums make sense in the context of this problem situation? Explain your reasoning.

2. Determine the number of extrema in each polynomial.

Don't forget to look for relationships!

4th Degree Polynomials

$g_1(x) = x^4$

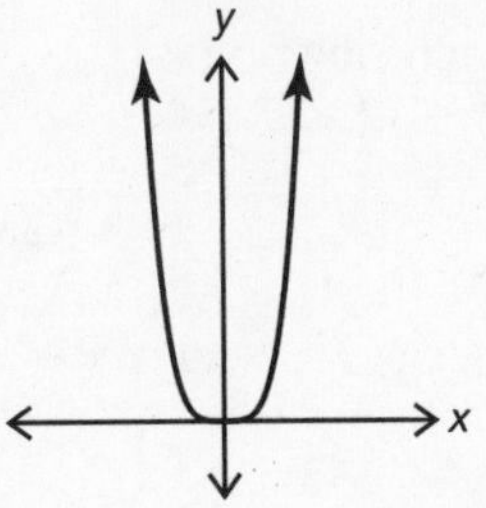

$g_2(x) = x^4 - 3x^2$

Number of Extrema _____ _____

5th Degree Polynomials

$f_1(x) = x^5$

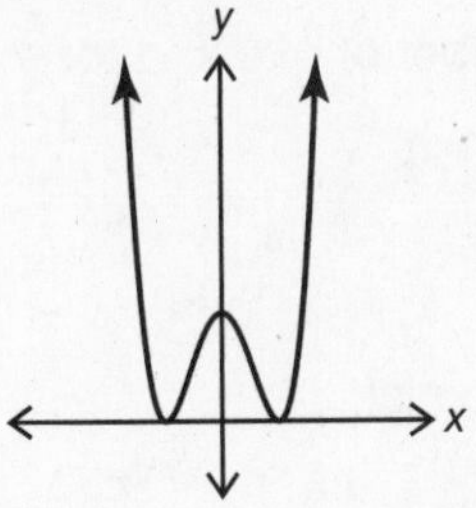

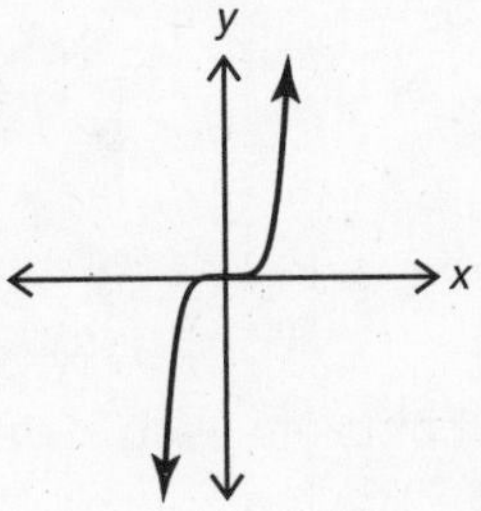

$f_2(x) = x^5 + 4x^2$

$f_3(x) = x^5 - 5x^3 + 5x + 1.18$

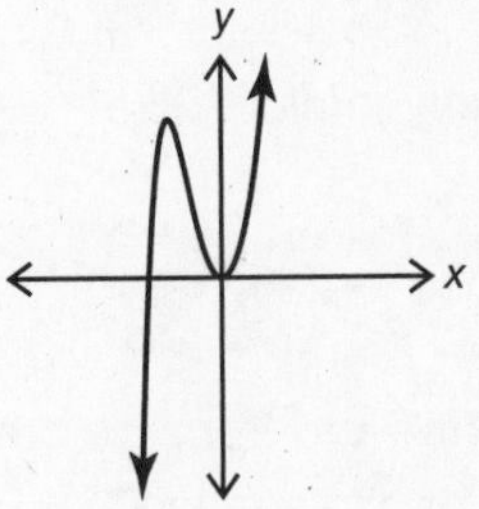

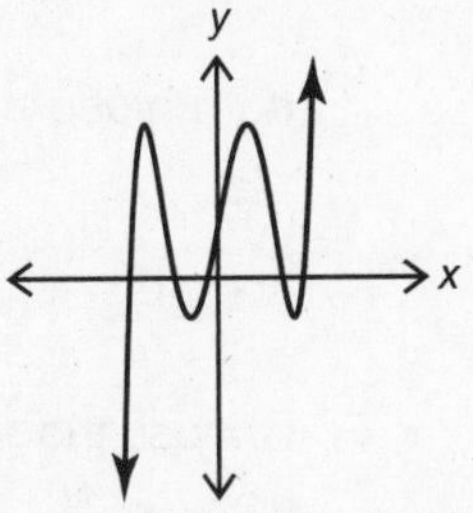

Number of Extrema _____ _____ _____

6th Degree Polynomials

$h_1(x) = x^6$

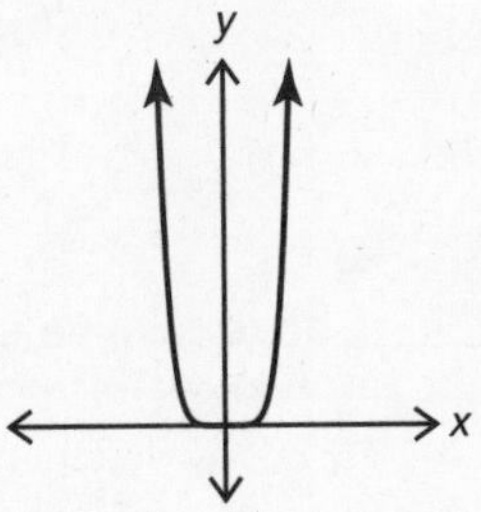

$h_2(x) = x^6 - 3x^2$

$h_3(x) = 2x^6 - 13x^5 + 26x^4 - 7x^3 - 2$

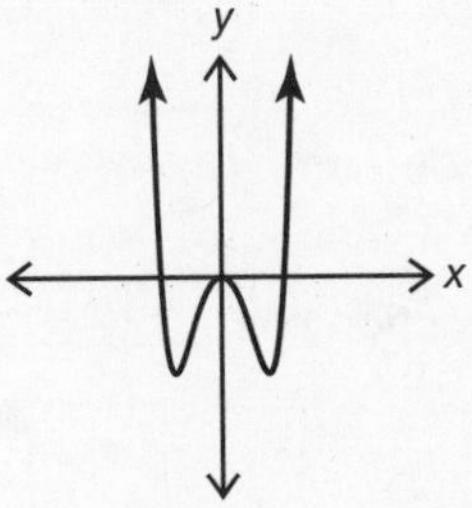

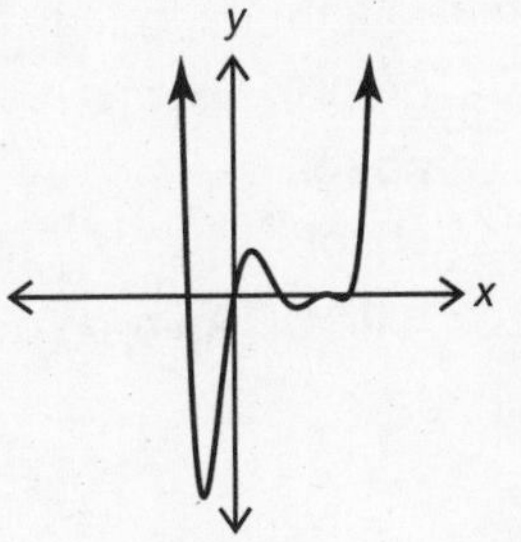

Number of Extrema _____ _____ _____

5

3. List any observations you notice about the possible number of extrema and the degree of the polynomial.

4. List the possible number of extrema for the each polynomial.

a. 9th degree polynomial

b. 18th degree polynomial

c. nth degree odd polynomial

d. nth degree even polynomial

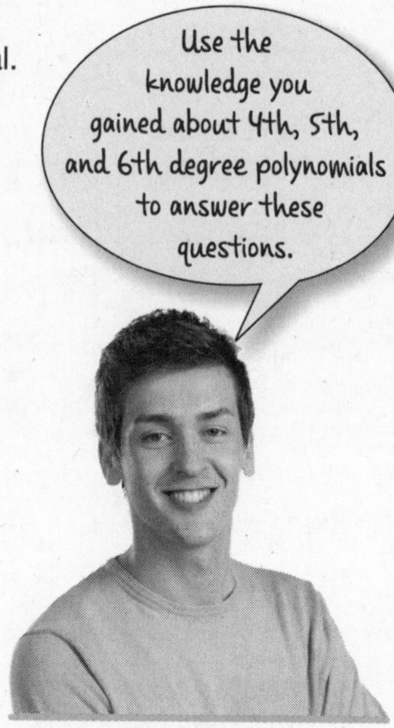

5. Choose the appropriate word from the box to complete each statement. Justify your answer with a sketch or explanation.

always	sometimes	never

a. An odd degree function will ______________ have absolute extrema.

b. An even degree function will ______________ have relative extrema.

c. An even degree function will ______________ have 3 or more relative extrema.

d. An even degree function will ______________ have absolute extrema.

e. An odd degree function will ______________ have relative extrema.

f. An odd degree function will ______________ one have relative extrema.

6. Analyze the graphs shown.

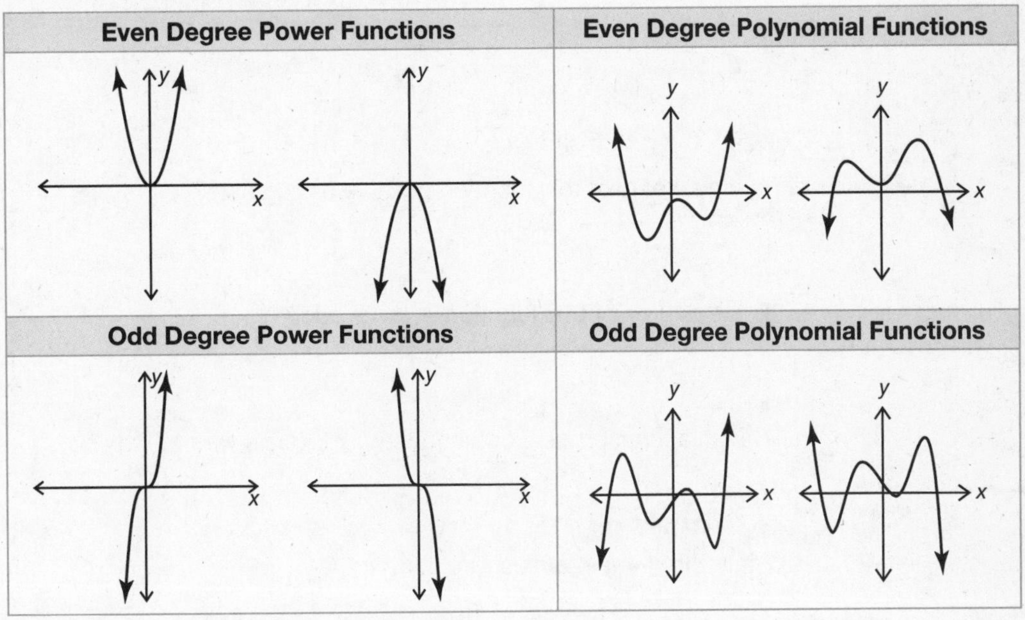

a. State the similarities and differences you notice between the power functions and the polynomial functions.

b. What conclusions can you make about the end behavior of all even degree polynomial functions?

c. What conclusions can you make about the end behavior of all odd degree polynomial functions?

d. What conclusions can you make about the domain and range of all even degree polynomial functions?

e. What conclusions can you make about the domain and range of all odd degree polynomial functions?

7. Consider the graph shown.

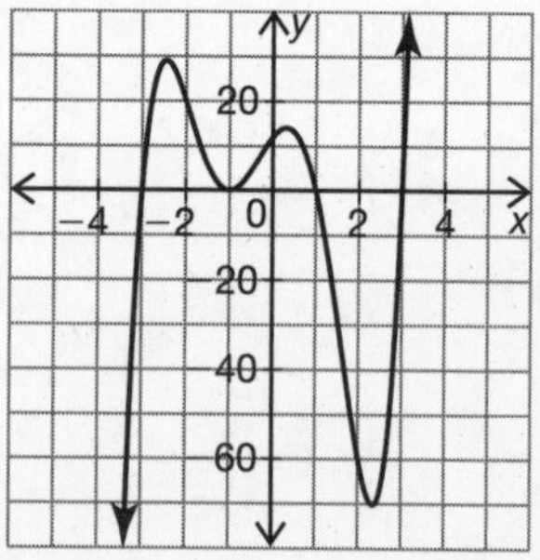

a. Is the *a*-value of this function positive or negative?

b. Is the degree of this function even or odd?

c. Can this function be a cubic function? Explain why or why not.

d. State the domain of this function.

e. State the range of this function.

f. Determine the number of relative extrema in this graph.

g. Determine the number of absolute extrema in this graph.

h. State the intervals where the graph is increasing.

8. Consider the graph shown.

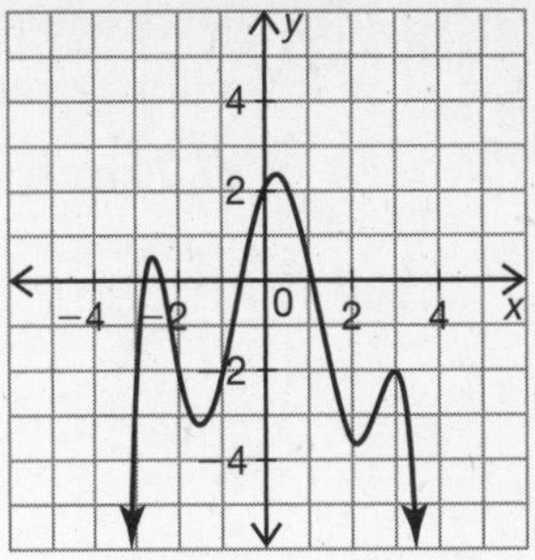

a. Is the a-value of this function positive or negative?

b. Is the degree of this function even or odd?

c. Can this function be a 6th degree polynomial function? Explain why or why not.

d. State the domain of this function.

e. State the range of this function.

f. Determine the number of relative extrema in this graph.

g. Determine the number of absolute extrema in this graph.

h. State the intervals where the graph is decreasing.

9. Complete the table on the next page to represent the graphs of various polynomials.

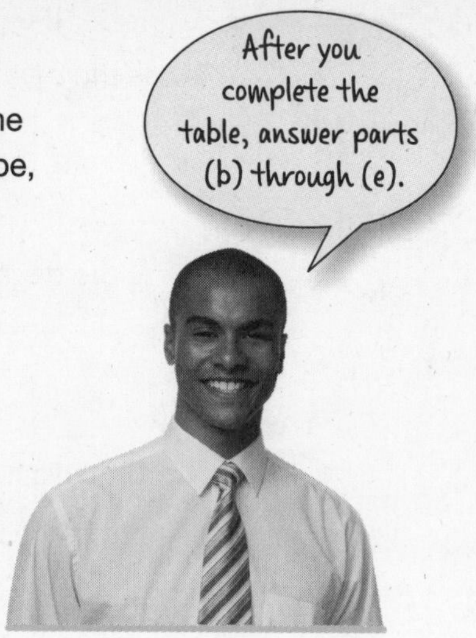
After you complete the table, answer parts (b) through (e).

a. Sketch the basic shape on each set of axes, given the number of zeros. If you cannot sketch the basic shape, explain why.

b. Compare your graphs with a partner. State the similarities and differences.

c. What do you notice about the maximum number of x-intercepts and the degree of the function?

5

d. Use your graphs to determine the greatest number of extrema (absolute and relative) in each degree polynomial.

Type of Polynomial Function	Number of Extrema
Linear	
Quadratic	
Cubic	
Quartic	
Quintic	

e. What do you notice about the number of extrema and the degree of a polynomial? Write a statement to generalize the possible number of extrema in any degree polynomial function.

	No Zeros	1 Zero	Exactly 2 Zeros	Exactly 3 Zeros	Exactly 4 Zeros	Exactly 5 Zeros
Linear						
Quadratic						
Cubic						
Quartic						
Quintic						

PROBLEM 3 Who Am I?

1. Use the coordinate plane to sketch a graph with the characteristics given. If the graph is not possible to sketch, explain why.

   a. Characteristics:

   - degree 4
   - starts in quadrant III
   - ends in quadrant IV
   - relative maximum at $x = -4$
   - absolute maximum at $x = 3$

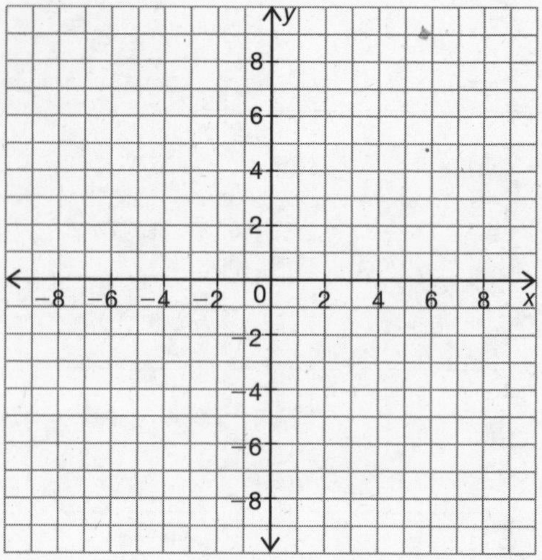

   b. Characteristics:

   - always increasing
   - y-intercept at 5
   - x-intercept at -1.7

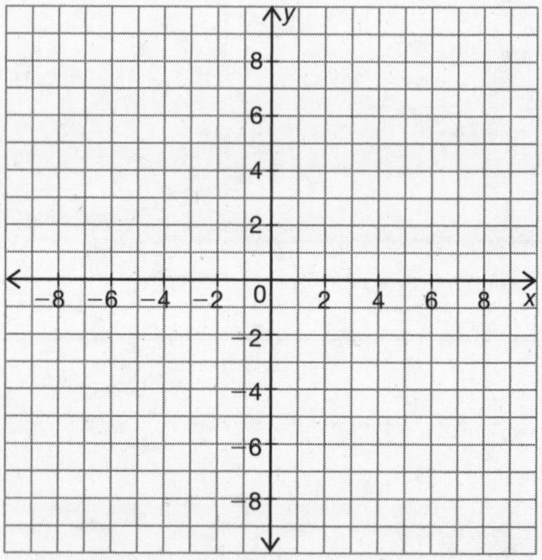

5

c. Characteristics:

- odd degree
- increases to $x = -3$, then decreases to $x = 3$, then increases
- absolute maximum at $y = 4$

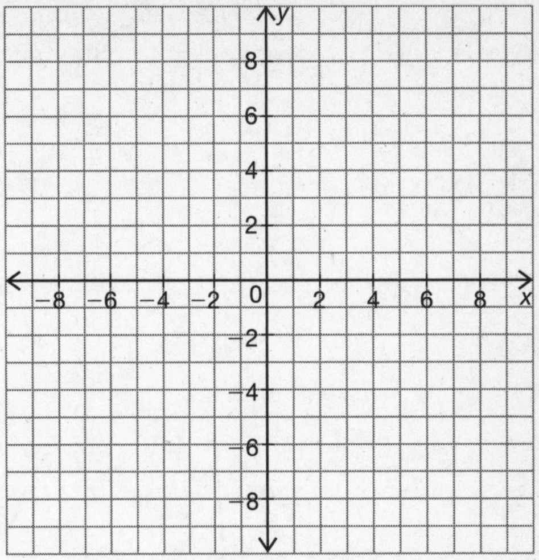

d. Characteristics:

- as $x \to \infty$, $f(x) \to \infty$
  as $x \to -\infty$, $f(x) \to \infty$
- 4 x-intercepts
- relative maximum at $y = 3$

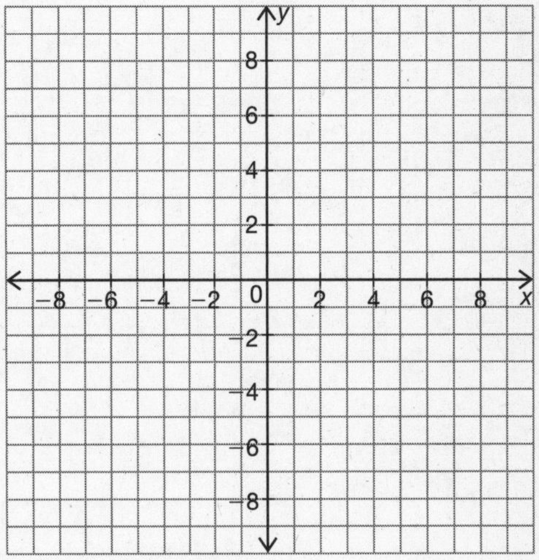

5

e. Characteristics:

- x-intercepts at -2, 2 and 5
- negative a value
- degree 2

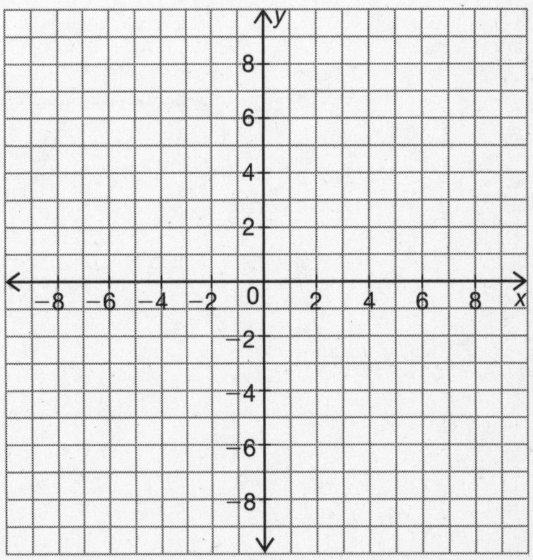

2. Analyze each graph. Circle the function(s) which could model the graph. Describe your reasoning to either eliminate or choose each function.

a.

$f_1(x) = -3x^5 - 2x^2 + 4x + 7$

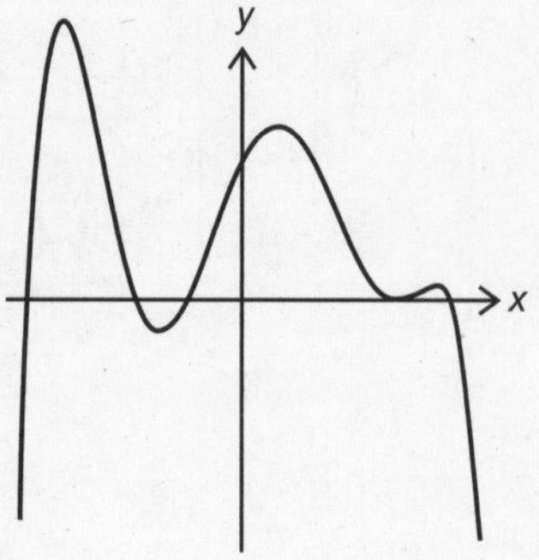

$f_2(x) = -(x + 2)(x + 1.5)(x + 0.5)(x - 2.5)^2 (x - 3)$

$f_3(x) = -3x^4 - 2x^2 + 4x + 7$

b.

$f_1(x) = 0.5(x + 7)(x + 1)(x - 5) - 3$

5

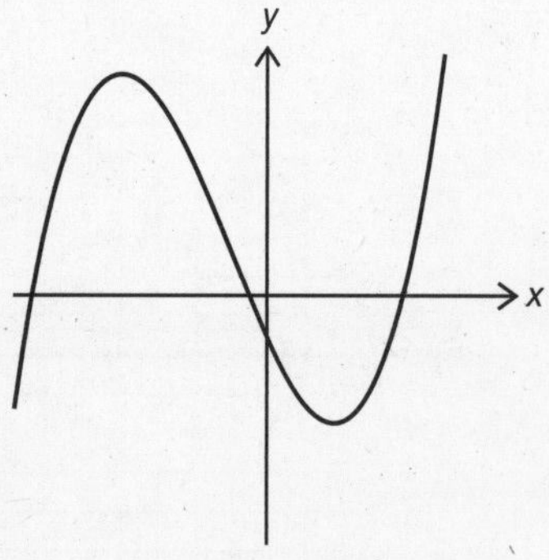

$f_2(x) = -2(x + 7)(x + 1)(x - 5) - 3$

$f_3(x) = 2(x + 7)(x + 1)(x - 5)(x - 3)$

Talk the Talk

Complete each table to summarize the key characteristics for quartics and quintics. The cubics table has been done for you.

Cubics	
All possible end behavior	As $x \to \infty$, $f(x) \to \infty$. As $x \to -\infty$, $f(x) \to -\infty$. As $x \to \infty$, $f(x) \to -\infty$. As $x \to -\infty$, $f(x) \to \infty$.
Possible number of x-intercept(s)	3, 2, or 1
Possible number of y-intercept(s)	1
Possible intervals of increase and decrease	• Always increasing • Always decreasing • Increasing, decreasing, increasing • Decreasing, increasing, decreasing
Number of possible relative extrema	2 or none
Number of possible absolute extrema	None

5

Quartics	
All possible end behavior	
Possible number of *x*-intercept(s)	
Possible number of *y*-intercept(s)	
Possible intervals of increase and decrease	
Number of possible relative extrema	
Number of possible absolute extrema	

Quintics	
All possible end behavior	
Possible number of *x*-intercept(s)	
Possible number of *y*-intercept(s)	
Possible intervals of increase and decrease	
Number of possible relative extrema	
Number of possible absolute extrema	

Be prepared to share your solutions and methods.

5.5

That Graph Looks a Little Sketchy

Building Cubic and Quartic Functions

LEARNING GOALS

In this lesson, you will:

- Construct cubic functions graphically from three linear functions.
- Construct cubic functions graphically from one quadratic and one linear function.
- Connect graphical behavior of a cubic function to key characteristics of its factors.
- Construct quartic polynomial functions.
- Determine the number of real and imaginary roots for a polynomial function based on its factors.

People in the world today use a lot of energy, much more than previous generations. Consider modern conveniences people in the U.S. have in public spaces such as heating, air conditioning, lights, and electronic devices. Also, consider food products, clothes, and other goods that often travel halfway around the world on planes, ships, or trucks before ending up in U.S. shopping malls. Quite a bit of energy goes into getting these resources to you. People also travel much more these days than ever before. You may ride a bus to school and shop at a mall; adults may commute 30+ miles to work; business people may fly across the country to attend a conference. Compare this lifestyle to how people lived throughout the vast majority of history. People generally grew their own food, traveled on foot, and made their own clothes and wares. Is our lifestyle sustainable? In other words, can we continue using this much energy forever?

We use approximately 1.2 trillion gallons of gasoline each year. We also use tremendous amounts of coal and natural gas. The world's current energy consumption is so large that the numbers are difficult to even comprehend. The unit of measure Cubic Mile of Oil was developed to help make sense of it. A CMO is literally the amount of energy released by burning a cubic mile of oil. To visualize a cubic mile, imagine a huge cube-shaped container with length, width, and height of approximately 18 football fields. The energy from burning three of these containers of oil is the amount of energy we currently use in just one year. At this rate of consumption our natural gas reserves will be gone by 2080. Coal reserves will run out by 2150.

It is hard to imagine people voluntarily returning to a world without the conveniences we have today. However, natural resources are limited. What options do we have if we want our children to live a life filled with the conveniences that we currently enjoy?

PROBLEM 1 They Don't Build Cubics Like They Used To!

So far in this chapter you've built a cubic function by multiplying three linear functions and by multiplying a linear function and a quadratic function. Let's explore how the properties of linear and quadratic functions determine the key characteristics of cubic functions.

1. Sketch a set of functions whose product builds a cubic function with the given characteristics. Explain your reasoning. Then list similarities and differences between your graphs and your classmates' graphs.

   a. zeros: $x = 0$, $x = 2$, and $x = -5$

   Explanation:

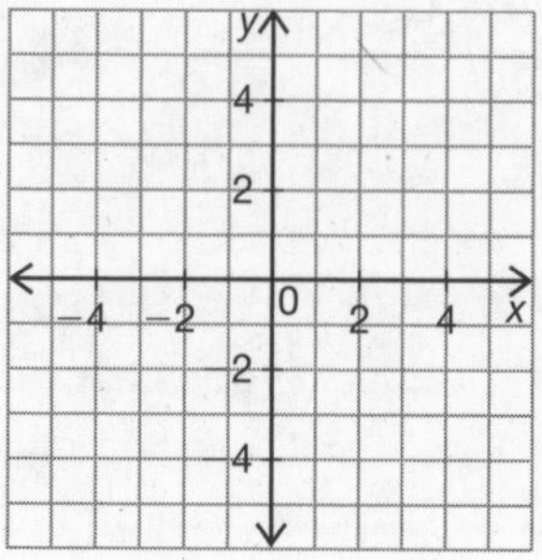

   Similarities/Differences:

Remember, you are not graphing the cubic—just the linear or quadratic functions that build it. Precise drawings aren't necessary here, just sketches with key characteristics.

You will learn more as you work through the lesson. At this point if you are unsure, experiment on your calculator, discuss with partners, and try a few things . . . that's how mathematicians work!

5

b. zeros: $x = -3$, $x = 4$ (multiplicity 2)

Explanation:

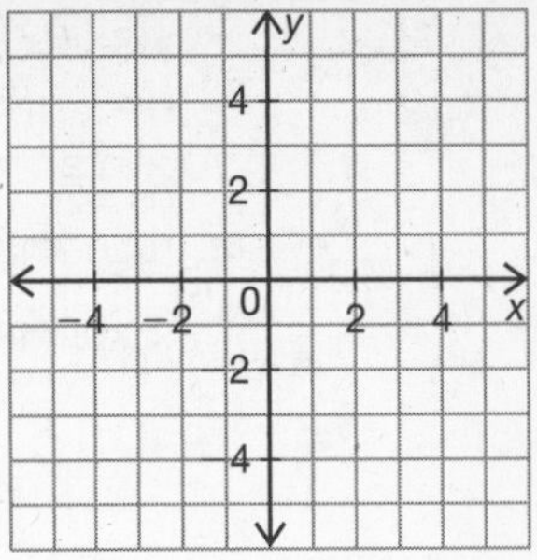

Which mathematical property guarantees that the zeros of a function must be the same as the zeros of its factors?

Similarities/Differences:

2. Alex and Derek disagree over which functions when multiplied together build a cubic function with zeros $x = 5$, $x = -1$ (multiplicity 2).

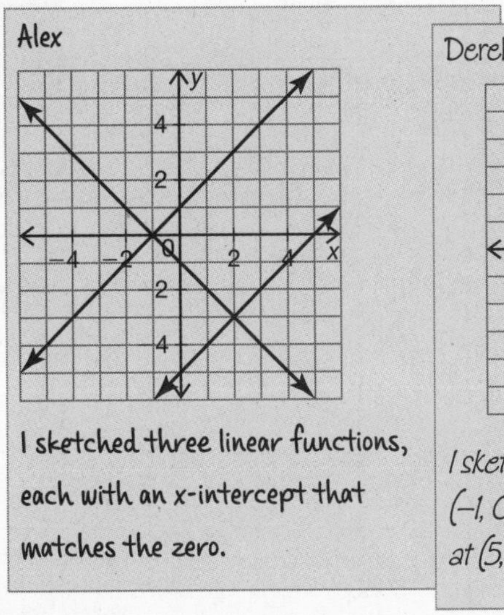
Alex
I sketched three linear functions, each with an x-intercept that matches the zero.

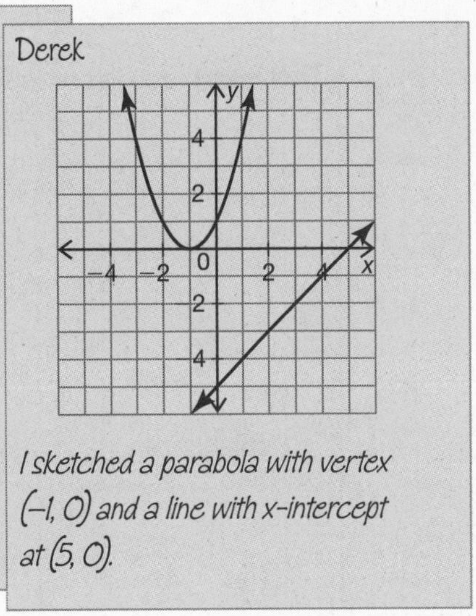
Derek
I sketched a parabola with vertex (–1, 0) and a line with x-intercept at (5, 0).

Who is correct? Explain your reasoning.

3. Sketch a set of functions whose product builds a cubic function with the given characteristics. Explain your reasoning. Then list similarities and differences between your graphs and your classmates' graphs.

a. two imaginary zeros and a real zero

Explanation:

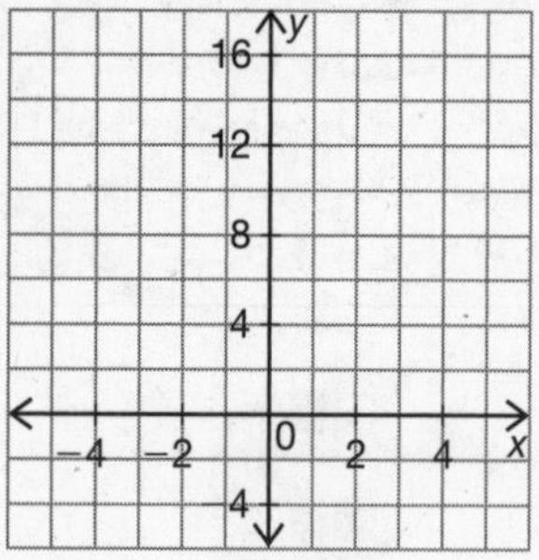

Similarities/Differences:

b. y-intercept of (0, 12)

Explanation:

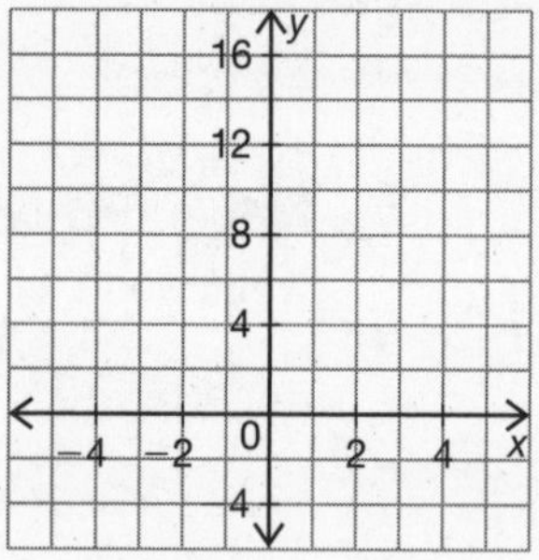

Similarities/Differences:

5

c. zero: $x = -4$ (multiplicity 3)

Explanation:

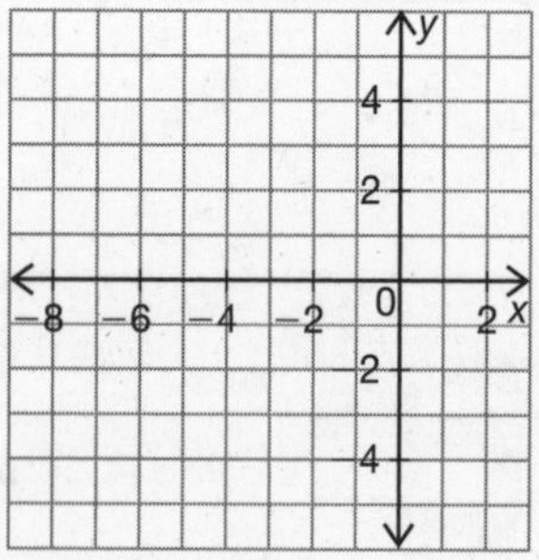

Similarities/Differences:

d. The cubic function is in Quadrants II and IV only.

Explanation:

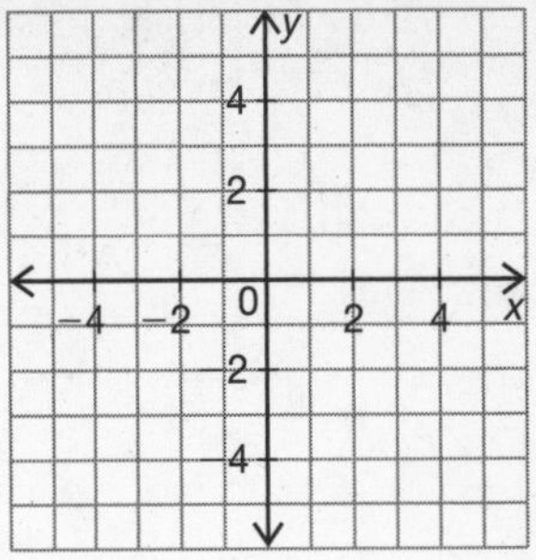

The product has to be in Quadrants II and IV, not necessarily the functions that build it. What determines direction? What determines the intercepts?

Similarities/Differences:

e. 3 imaginary roots

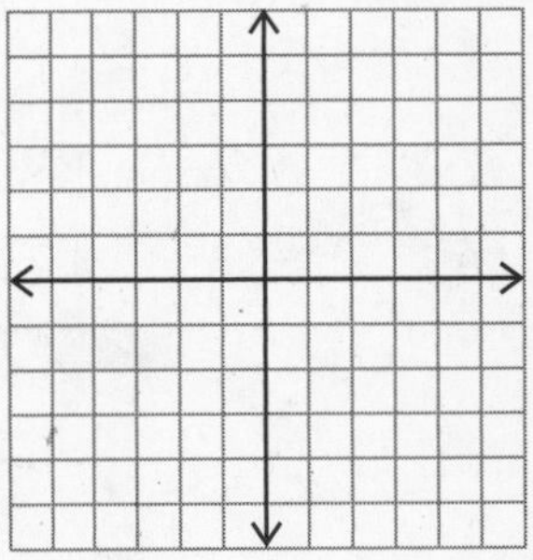

Explanation:

Similarities/Differences:

5

4. What are the possible combinations of real and imaginary roots that a cubic function can have? Explain your reasoning in terms of the functions that can build a cubic function.

Remember to include multiple roots.

5. Emily makes an observation about the number of imaginary zeros a cubic function may have.

Emily

A cubic function must have three zeros. I know this from the Fundamental Theorem. However, the number of real and imaginary zeros can vary. The function may have 0, 1, 2, or 3 imaginary zeros.

Explain the error in Emily's reasoning.

6. Augie, Kathryn, and Chili each wrote a cubic function with zeros at $x = 3$, $x = 1$, and $x = -4$.

Augie

The cubic function $f(x) = (x - 3)(x - 1)(x + 4)$ has the three zeros given. I can verify this by solving the equations $x - 3 = 0$, $x - 1 = 0$, and $x + 4 = 0$.

Kathryn

The cubic function $g(x) = 5(x - 3)(x - 1)(x + 4)$ has the three zeros given.

Chili

The cubic function $j(x) = (2x - 6)(3x - 3)(x + 4)$ has the three zeros given.

5

a. How does multiplying by a constant affect the graph of the function?

b. Why do the zeros remain the same after multiplying by a constant?

c. How many different cubic functions can you write from a given set of zeros?

7. Write two different cubic functions with the given characteristics.

a. zeros: $x = 2$, $x = 0$ and $x = -4$

b. zeros: $x = 0$, $x = 2i$, $x = -2i$

c. zeros: $x = 6$ (multiplicity 2) and $x = -5$

d. zeros: $x = 2$, $x = 3$, $x = 1$ and a y-intercept $(0, -24)$

e. the point $(1, 12)$ lies on the graph of the function

5

The factors and roots determine the general shape of a cubic function. The table summarizes all possible combinations of roots and factors for a cubic function.

Roots	Factors	Graph
1 real 2 imaginary	(linear factor) × (quadratic factor with 0 real roots)	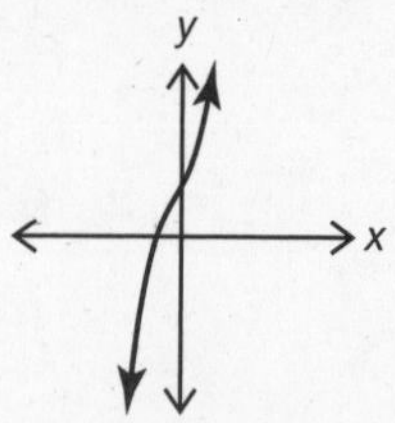
1 real (multiplicity 1) 1 real (multiplicity 2)	(linear factor) × $(\text{linear factor})^2$	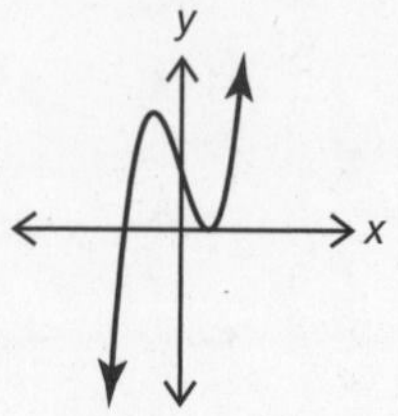
1 real (multiplicity 3)	$(\text{linear factor})^3$	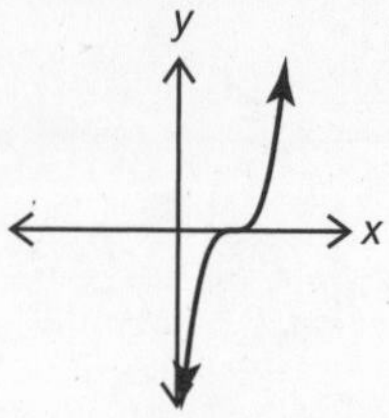
3 real distinct	(linear factor) × (linear factor) × (linear factor)	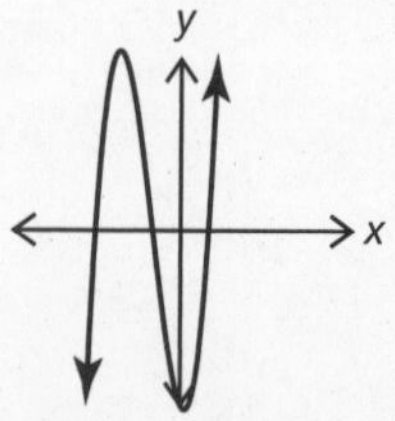

PROBLEM 2 I Like My Cubics Built the Old-Fashioned Way

Recall that the volume function $V(x) = x(18 - 2x)(12 - 2x)$ from Plant-A-Seed was built by multiplying three linear functions representing length, width, and height. It was also built from a quadratic function representing the area of the base and a linear function representing the height. You can sketch the graph of a cubic function by determining the x-intercepts and the intervals for which the output values of the factors are positive or negative.
The Plant-A-Seed example is shown.

The linear functions that represent the length, width, and height of the planter boxes from Plant-A-Seed are shown on the graph.

<table>
<tr><th>Description</th><th>Graphical Display</th></tr>
<tr><td>Graph each factor as an individual function.
• The x-intercepts for each function are circled.</td><td>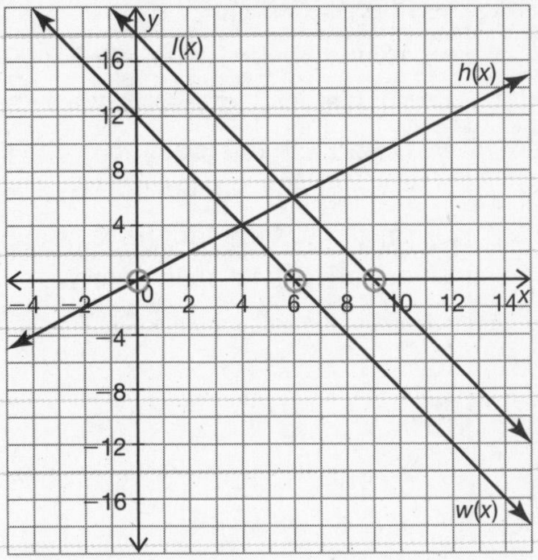
</td></tr>
<tr><td>Draw dashed vertical lines through the x-intercepts.
• The coordinate plane is now divided into 4 sections: $(-\infty, 0)$, $(0, 6)$, $(6, 9)$ and $(9, \infty)$.</td><td>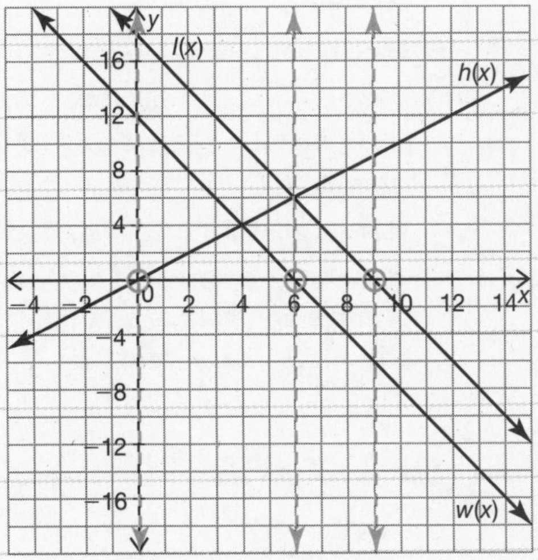
</td></tr>
</table>

5

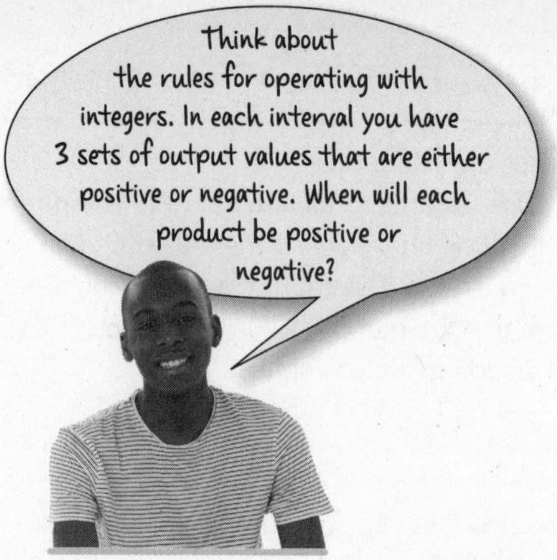

Determine whether the output values for each function in the interval are positive or negative.

- Values above the x-axis are positive.
- Values below the x-axis are negative.
- Determine the location of the cubic function by calculating whether the product of the factors is positive or negative over each interval.

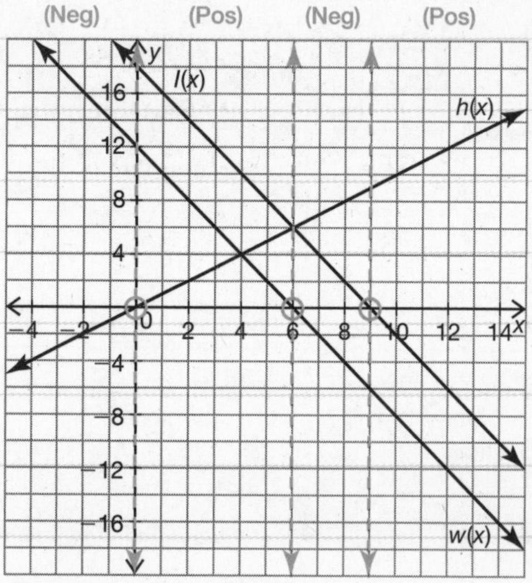

- Use the x-intercepts and the sign of the output value over each interval to sketch the graph.
- The new function will cross the x-axis at each of the x-intercepts as the factors.
- The graph will increase or decrease depending on whether the output is positive or negative as it moves from one interval to the next.

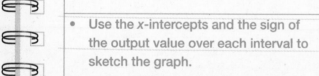

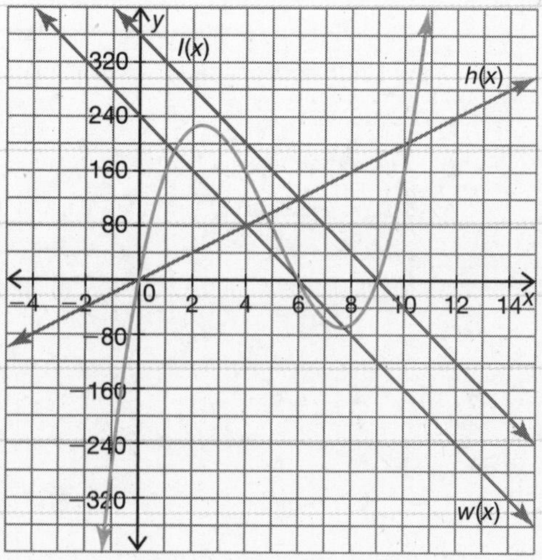

1. Analyze the worked example.

   a. Given the three functions $l(x)$, $w(x)$, and $h(x)$, summarize how to determine when $V(x)$ lies above or below the x-axis.

   b. Why must the volume function intersect the x-axis at (0, 0), (6, 0), (9, 0)?

   c. Is it possible for a function to have a zero that is different from its factors? Explain your reasoning.

2. Sketch the graph of the cubic function that is the product of the 3 linear functions shown. Show all work and explain your reasoning.

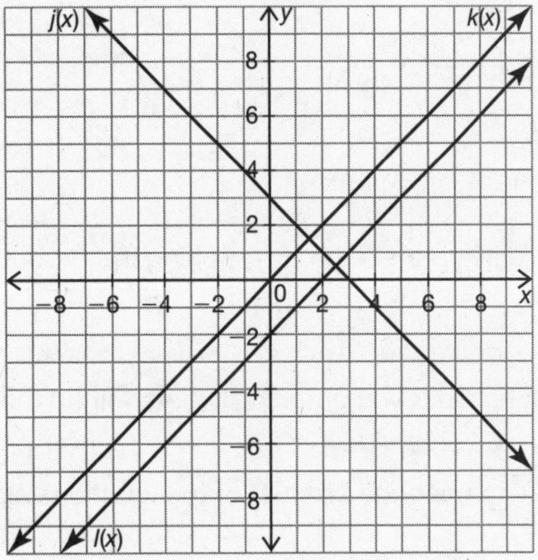

3. Sketch the graph of the cubic function that is the product of the quadratic and linear functions shown. Show all work and explain your reasoning.

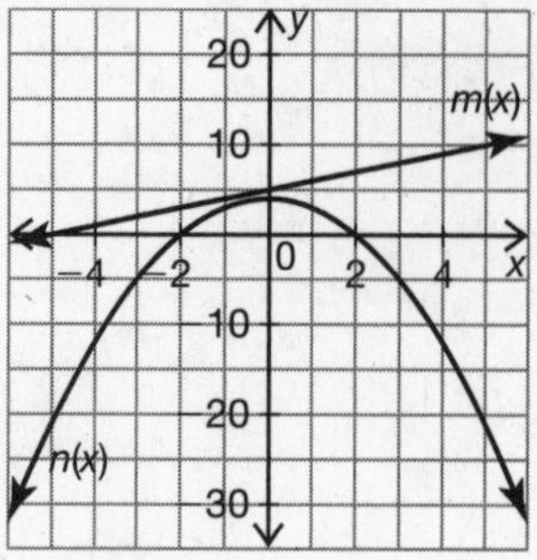

The process is the same as before. Focus on the zeros and the intervals over which the output is positive or negative.

4. In Question 2 you graphically determined the product of the functions $f(x) = 3 - x$, $g(x) = x$ and $h(x) = x - 2$.

a. Determine the product of the functions algebraically.

5

b. Verify your sketch by graphing the product on a graphing calculator.

5. In Question 3 you graphically determined the product of the functions $j(x) = 4 - x^2$ and $k(x) = x + 5$

a. Determine the product of the functions algebraically.

b. Verify your sketch by graphing the product on a graphing calculator.

PROBLEM 3 Anyone Have Change for a Quartic?

In Problems 1 and 2, you determined that a cubic function has 3 zeros. The zeros may be real, imaginary, or have multiplicity depending on the key characteristics of the functions that built it. Similarly, the Fundamental Theorem of Algebra guarantees that a quartic function has 4 zeros. The key characteristics of the quartic function also vary depending on the functions that built it.

1. Analyze the linear, quadratic, and cubic functions that are shown.

$f(x) = x$	$g(x) = -x + 2$	$m(x) = x^2 - 2x - 5$
$p(x) = x^2 + 4$	$r(x) = (x + 2)^2$	$w(x) = x^3$

a. List the number and type of zeros for each function provided.

b. List 5 possible sets of functions from the list that multiply to build a quartic function.

You may use a function more than once.

5

2. Complete each statement with *always, sometimes,* or *never*. Explain your reasoning.

   a. A quartic function _______________ has 4 real roots.

   b. A function of the nth degree _______________ has n roots.

   c. The number of x-intercepts _______________ matches the number of roots of a function.

   d. A function _______________ has imaginary roots.

   e. A function _______________ has an odd number of imaginary roots.

3. Analyze the table shown. The function $h(x)$ is the product of $f(x)$ and $g(x)$.

x	$f(x)$	$g(x)$	$h(x) = f(x) \cdot g(x)$
−2	8	4	32
−1	5	1	5
0	4	0	0
1	5	1	5
2	8	4	32
3	13	9	117

   a. Determine whether $h(x)$ is a quartic function. Explain your reasoning.

   b. Determine the number of real and imaginary zeros of $h(x)$. Explain your reasoning.

   c. Describe the end behavior of $h(x)$. How does this help you determine whether the function is quartic or not?

4. Analyze the table shown. The function $m(x)$ is the product of $j(x)$ and $k(x)$.

x	$j(x)$	$k(x)$	$m(x) = j(x) \cdot k(x)$
−2	4	−1	−4
−1	0	0	0
0	−2	1	−2
1	−2	2	−4
2	0	3	0
3	4	4	16

a. Determine whether $m(x)$ is a quartic function. Explain your reasoning.

b. Determine the number of real and imaginary zeros for the function $m(x)$. Explain your reasoning.

c. Describe the end behavior of $m(x)$. How does this help you determine whether the function is quartic or not?

5

5. Gavin explains the relationship between the imaginary zeros of a polynomial function and the table of values for that function. Henry disagrees.

Gavin

A polynomial function with imaginary zeros has imaginary numbers in the table of values. For example, the function $x^2 + 4$ has 2 imaginary zeros. These values appear in the table.

Henry

It is impossible for a polynomial function to have imaginary numbers in the table of values. A real input value must have a real output value.

Who is correct? Explain your reasoning.

5

6. Sketch a set of functions whose product builds a quartic function with the given characteristics. Explain your reasoning. Determine similarities and differences between your graphs and your classmates' graphs.

a. two imaginary roots and a double root

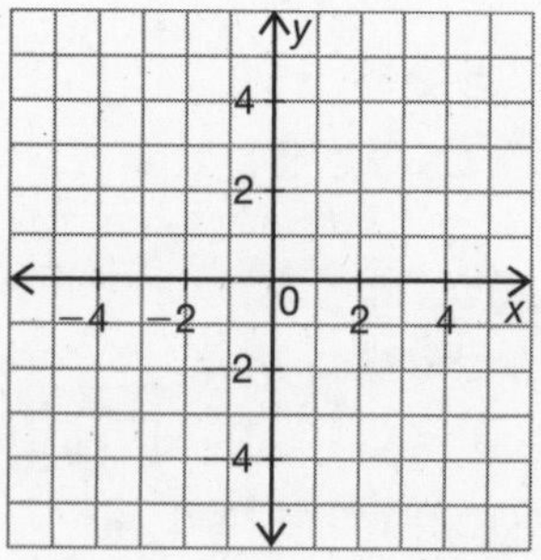

Explanation:

Similarities/Differences:

b. four distinct roots and a y-intercept of $(0, -24)$

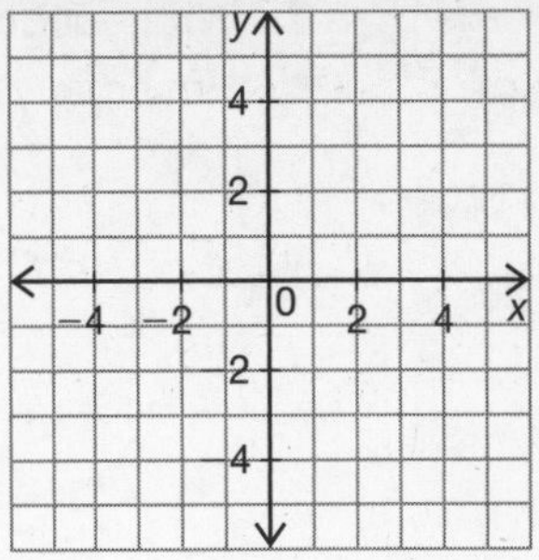

Explanation:

Similarities/Differences:

c. located in Quadrants III and IV only

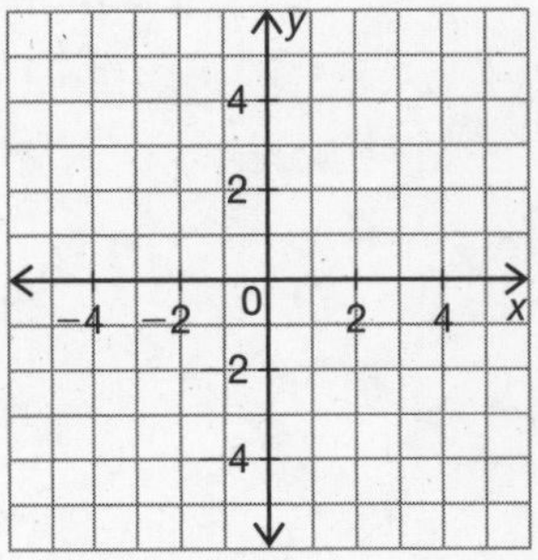

Explanation:

Similarities/Differences:

d. located in quadrants II and IV only

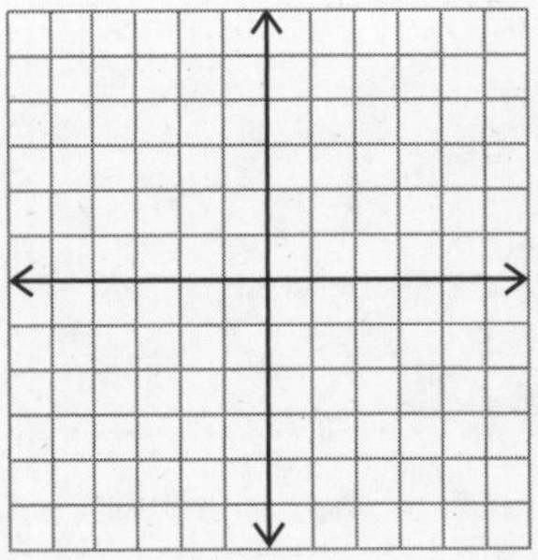

Explanation:

Similarities/Differences:

5

7. What function types can be multiplied together to build a new function of degree 5? How many total zeros will the function have? How many can be imaginary?

8. Explain the possible ways to build a function of degree n?

5

Be prepared to share your solutions and methods.

5.6

Closing Time

The Closure Property

LEARNING GOALS

In this lesson, you will:

- Compare functions that are closed under addition, subtraction, and multiplication to functions that are not closed under these operations.
- Analyze the meaning for polynomials to be closed under an operation.
- Compare integer and polynomial operations.

KEY TERM

- closed under an operation

The word "closure" can mean many things depending on the context.

- In business, closure is a process in which an organization can no longer operate. For instance, closure for a business may be caused by an organization going bankrupt.
- In psychology, closure is a person's emotional need for the conclusion of a difficult event in their life.
- In government, closure, which is also referred to as "cloture," is a procedure by which the Senate can vote to place a time limit on consideration of a bill.

Closure is also an important term in mathematics. Can you think of any other meanings for the word closure?

PROBLEM 1 Closed for Business

In this chapter you have learned the properties of polynomials in different representations.

Graphically, polynomials are:	Algebraically, polynomials are:	In a table of values, polynomials are:
• smooth • continuous • increase or decrease to infinity as x approaches positive or negative infinity	• written in the form $ax^n + bx^{n-1} + \cdots$	• made up of real numbers • increase or decrease to infinity as x approaches positive or negative infinity

You have studied many different types of functions. A function has a unique output for every input value. However, a function does not necessarily have to be a polynomial function.

1. Sketch the graphs of two functions that are not polynomial functions. Explain your reasoning.

a.

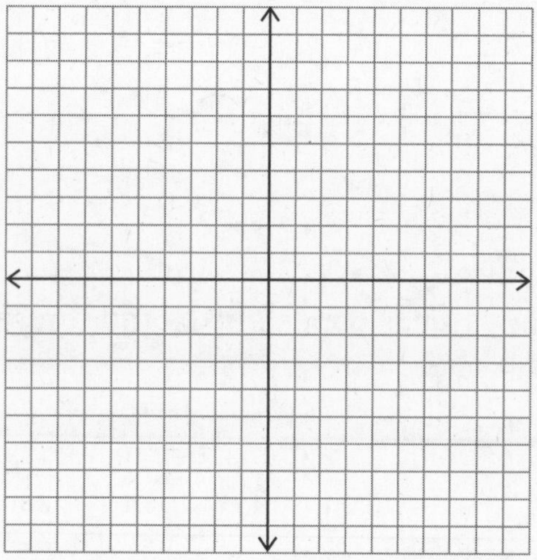

b.

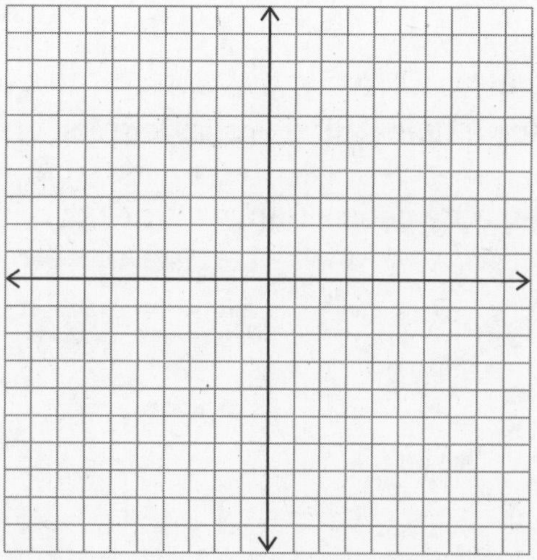

5

2. Analyze the graphs of the functions shown. Describe why each function is not a polynomial function.

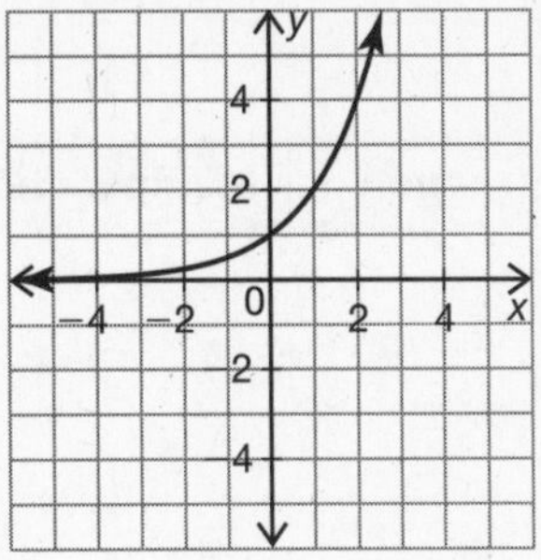

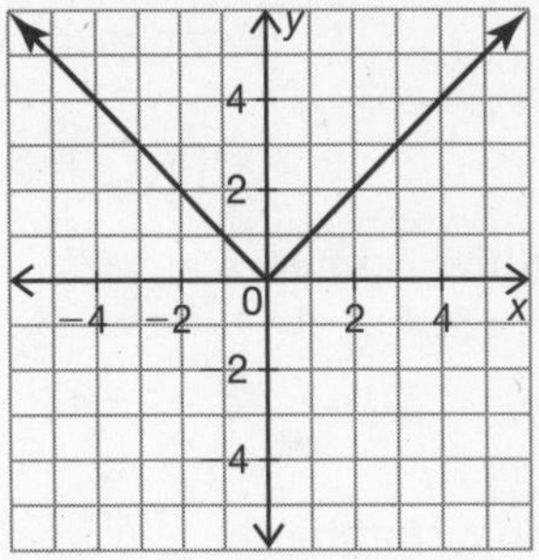

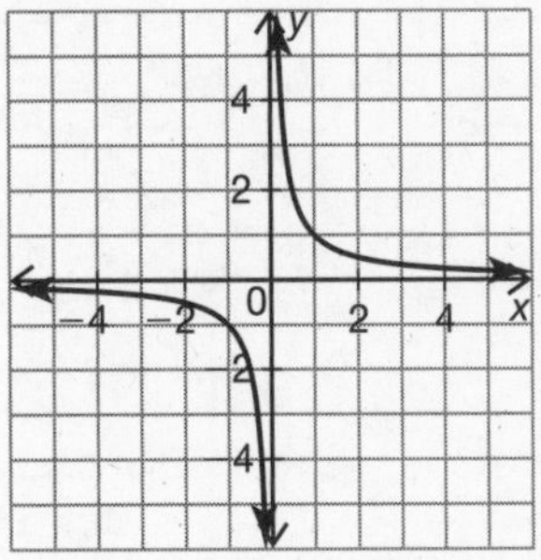

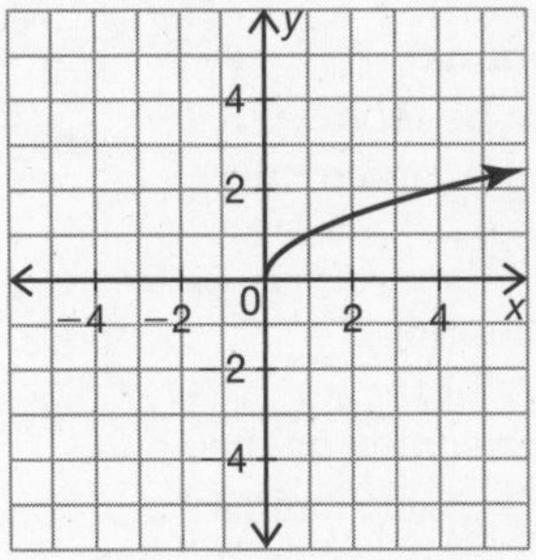

Throughout this chapter you added, subtracted, or multiplied two or more polynomial functions to build a new polynomial function. You did this using a graph, algebra, and a table of values. When an operation is performed on any number or expression in a set and the result is in the same set, it is said to be **closed under that operation**. Are polynomials closed under addition, subtraction, and multiplication? In other words, when you add, subtract, or multiply polynomial functions, will you *always* create another polynomial function?

Before answering this question, let's analyze closure within the real number system.

Recall how it is a useful mathematical practice to compare abstract topics to what we already know about real numbers.

3. Determine whether each set within the Real Number System is closed under addition, subtraction, multiplication, and division.

a. Complete the table. If a set is not closed under a given operation, provide a counterexample.

	Addition	Subtraction	Multiplication	Division
Natural Numbers {1, 2, 3, 4, . . .}				
Whole Numbers {0, 1, 2, 3, . . .}	Yes	No $2 - 3 = -1$		
Integers {. . . −2, −1, 0, 1, 2 . . .}				
Rational Can be represented as the ratio of two integers				
Irrational Cannot be represented as the ratio of two integers				

b. What patterns do you notice?

The sum of 2 whole numbers is always another whole number. Therefore, whole numbers are closed under addition. Whole numbers are not closed under subtraction. The counterexample is 2 − 3 = −1, since −1 is not a whole number. Experiment with other sets of numbers to determine whether they are closed.

4. Determine whether polynomial functions are closed under addition, subtraction, multiplication, and division?

a. Write 5 polynomials with various degrees that you will use to explore closure.

$y_1 =$ ________	$y_2 =$ ________
$y_3 =$ ________	
$y_4 =$ ________	$y_5 =$ ________

b. Determine whether the polynomials are closed under addition, subtraction, multiplication, and division. Show all work and explain your reasoning.

Take some time to explore closure by performing operations with various polynomials. Experiment algebraically and graphically and see what happens, then make a conjecture – that's what mathematicians do!

c. How do you know when a polynomial is not closed under a given operation? Explain your reasoning in terms of the graph, table, and algebraic representation.

d. Have you proven that polynomials are closed under a given operation? Have you proven that polynomials are not closed under a given operation? Explain your reasoning.

In the previous problem, *Closed For Business*, you conjectured that integers and polynomials are both closed under addition, subtraction, and multiplication. You also determined through counterexamples that integers and polynomials are not closed under division.

1. Similarities between integer and polynomial operations are shown in the table.

	Integer Example	Polynomial Example
Addition	$\begin{array}{r} 400 + 30 + 7 \\ +20 + 5 \\ \hline 400 + 50 + 12 \end{array}$	$\begin{array}{r} 4x^2 + 3x + 7 \\ +2x + 5 \\ \hline 4x^2 + 5x + 12 \end{array}$
Subtraction	$\begin{array}{r} 400 + 30 + 7 \\ -(20 + 5) \\ \hline 400 + 10 + 2 \end{array}$	$\begin{array}{r} 4x^2 + 3x + 7 \\ -(2x + 5) \\ \hline 4x^2 + x + 2 \end{array}$
Multiplication	$\begin{array}{r} 400 + 30 + 7 \\ \times20 + 5 \\ \hline 2000 + 150 + 35 \\ 8000 + 600 + 140 \\ \hline 8000 + 2600 + 290 + 35 \end{array}$	$\begin{array}{r} 4x^2 + 3x + 7 \\ \times2x + 5 \\ \hline 20x^2 + 15x + 35 \\ 8x^3 + 6x^2 + 14x \\ \hline 8x^3 + 26x^2 + 29x + 35 \end{array}$
Division	$\dfrac{437}{25} = 17\,R12$	$\dfrac{4x^2 + 3x + 7}{2x + 5} = (2x - 3)\,R(-x + 22)$

a. Describe the similarities between polynomial and integer operations.

b. In what ways is the distributive property essential to performing operations with integers and polynomials?

For part d, consider the integer example. How would you verify that $\dfrac{437}{25} = 17\,R12$?

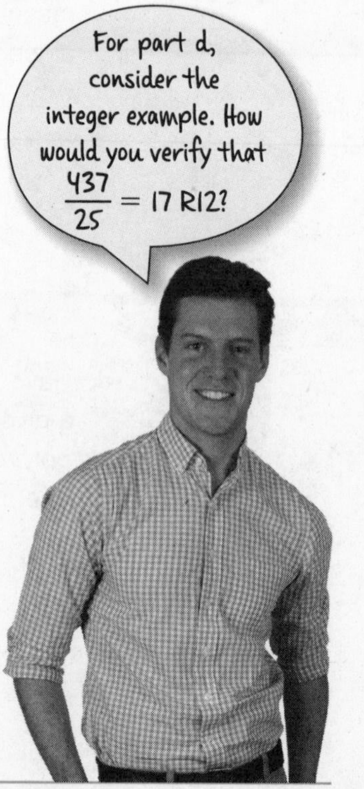

c. How does this example demonstrate that polynomials are not closed under division?

d. Verify that the polynomial division was performed correctly.

You have explored operations under various polynomials. It appears as though polynomials are closed under addition, subtraction, and multiplication, but these examples do not constitute a proof. The real number system is closed, but discovering that polynomials are analogous to the real number system does not allow you to assume that polynomials are also closed. The worked example shows you how to formally prove that polynomials are closed under addition.

Consider the two polynomial functions $f(x)$ and $g(x)$.

$f(x) = a_n x^n + a_{n-1}x^{n-1} + \cdots + a_1 x + a_0$

$g(x) = b_n x^n + b_{n-1}x^{n-1} + \cdots + b_1 x + b_0$

You can show that the polynomials are closed under addition.

Step 1: Write the sum $f(x) + g(x)$. Because the polynomials have multiple terms, it is best to arrange the sum vertically.

$$\begin{array}{r} a_n x^n + a_{n-1}x^{n-1} + \cdots + a_1 x + a_0 \\ +\ b_n x^n + b_{n-1}x^{n-1} + \cdots + b_1 x + b_0 \\ \hline \end{array}$$

Step 2: Add the polynomials by combining like terms.

$$\begin{array}{r} a_n x^n + a_{n-1}x^{n-1} + \cdots + a_1 x + a_0 \\ +\ b_n x^n + b_{n-1}x^{n-1} + \cdots + b_1 x + b_0 \\ \hline (a_n + b_n)x^n + (a_{n-1} + b_{n-1})x^{n-1} + \cdots + (a_1 + b_1)x + (a_0 + b_0) \end{array}$$

Step 3: In the sum, each coefficient is of the form $a_n + b_n$. A coefficient $a_n + b_n$ is a real number because a_n and b_n are real numbers, and the real numbers are closed under addition.

Step 4: The sum of the polynomials $f(x)$ and $g(x)$ is in the form of a polynomial function with a real coefficient. Therefore, polynomials are closed under addition.

5

Remember, like terms are terms that have identical variables and exponents.

2. Consider the two polynomial functions $f(x)$ and $g(x)$.

$$f(x) = a_n x^n + a_{n-1} x^{n-1} + \cdots + a_1 x + a_0$$
$$g(x) = b_n x^n + b_{n-1} x^{n-1} + \cdots + b_1 x + b_0$$

a. Prove that polynomials are closed under subtraction.

b. Use the multiplication table to prove that polynomials are closed under multiplication.

$\bullet$	$a_n x^n$	$a_{n-1} x^{n-1}$	$\cdots$	$a_1 x$	a_0
$b_n x^n$					
$b_{n-1} x^{n-1}$					
$\vdots$					
$b_1 x$					
b_0					

Be prepared to share your solutions and methods.

Chapter 5 Summary

KEY TERMS

- relative maximum (5.1)
- relative minimum (5.1)
- cubic function (5.1)
- multiplicity (5.1)
- power function (5.2)
- end behavior (5.2)
- symmetric about a line (5.2)
- symmetric about a point (5.2)
- even function (5.2)
- odd function (5.2)
- polynomial function (5.3)
- quartic function (5.3)
- quintic function (5.3)
- absolute maximum (5.4)
- absolute minimum (5.4)
- extrema (5.4)
- closed under an operation (5.6)

5.1 Representing Cubic Functions Using Words, Tables, and Equations and Identifying Key Characteristics

The formula for volume: $V = l \cdot w \cdot h$ can represent a cubic function when length and width are given in terms of height. Each value can be shown in a table and the final formula as a function of one variable. The key characteristics of a function may be different within a given domain. As the input values for height increase, the output values for volume approach infinity. Therefore, the function doesn't have a maximum. But, it can have a relative maximum, or a highest point in a particular section of a graph. Similarly, as the values for height decrease, the output values approach negative infinity. Therefore, a relative minimum can occur at the lowest point in that particular section of a graph.

Example

The relative maximum is circled.

Height of Box (in.)	Width of Box (in.)	Length of Box (in.)	Volume of Box (cu. in.)
0	6	12	0
1	5	11	55
2	4	10	80
3	3	9	81
4	2	8	64
5	1	7	35
6	0	6	0
h	$6 - h$	$12 - h$	$h(6 - h)(12 - h)$

5.1 Building Cubic Functions From Linear and Quadratic Functions

A cubic function is a polynomial function of degree three. When multiplying three linear factors, the result is always a cubic function. First choose two of the factors to multiply and combine like terms. Then, multiply that product with the remaining factor and combine like terms. The original expression and the new expression can be graphed to verify that they are equivalent.

Example

$$\begin{aligned}(2x - 1)(3x + 2)(x - 5) &= (6x^2 + 4x - 3x - 2)(x - 5)\\ &= (6x^2 + x - 2)(x - 5)\\ &= 6x^3 - 30x^2 + x^2 - 5x - 2x + 10\\ &= 6x^3 - 29x^2 - 7x + 10\end{aligned}$$

The graph of the original expression and the final expression are the same, so the product is correct.

$$\begin{aligned}(12 - 5x - x^2)(3x + 1) &= 36x + 12 - 15x^2 - 5x - 3x^3 - x^2\\ &= -3x^3 - 16x^2 + 31x + 12\end{aligned}$$

The graph of the original expression and the final expression are the same, so the product is correct.

5.2 Determining the General Behavior of the Graph of Even and Odd Degree Power Functions

A power function is a function of the form $P(x) = ax^n$, where n is a non-negative integer. The graph of a power function raised to an odd degree increases from left to right (or right to left if $a < 0$), flattening near the origin, as the absolute value of the power increases. The graph of a power function raised to an even degree is a concave up (or down if $a < 0$) parabola, flattening near the origin as the absolute value of the power increases. The end behavior for even and odd degree power functions can be described as:

	Odd Degree Power Function	Even Degree Power Function
$a > 0$	As $x \to \infty$, $f(x) \to \infty$. As $x \to -\infty$, $f(x) \to -\infty$.	As $x \to \infty$, $f(x) \to \infty$. As $x \to -\infty$, $f(x) \to \infty$.
$a < 0$	As $x \to \infty$, $f(x) \to -\infty$. As $x \to -\infty$, $f(x) \to \infty$.	As $x \to \infty$, $f(x) \to -\infty$. As $x \to -\infty$, $f(x) \to -\infty$.

5

Example

x^{12}

As $x \to \infty$, $f(x) \to \infty$.

As $x \to -\infty$, $f(x) \to \infty$.

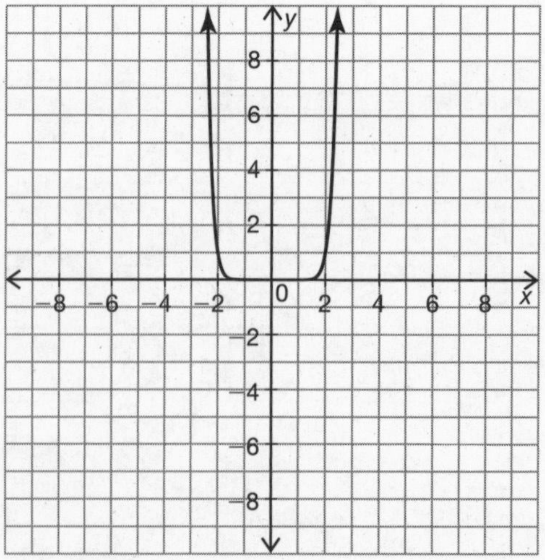

5.2 Using a Graph to Determine the Symmetry of Even and Odd Functions

If a graph is symmetric about a line, the line divides the graph into two identical parts. Special attention is given to the line of symmetry when it is the *y*-axis, as it tells you that the function is even. The graph of an odd degree basic power function is symmetric about a point, in particular the origin. A function is symmetric about a point if each point on the graph has a point the same distance from the central point but in the opposite direction. Special attention is given when the central point is the origin as it determines that the function is odd. When the point of symmetry is the origin, the graph is reflected across the *x*-axis and the *y*-axis. If you replace both (x, y) with $(-x, -y)$, the function remains the same. You can think of the point of symmetry about the origin, as a double reflection. An even function has a graph symmetric about the y-axis, thus $f(x) = f(-x)$. An odd function has a graph symmetric about the origin, thus $f(x) = -f(-x)$.

Example

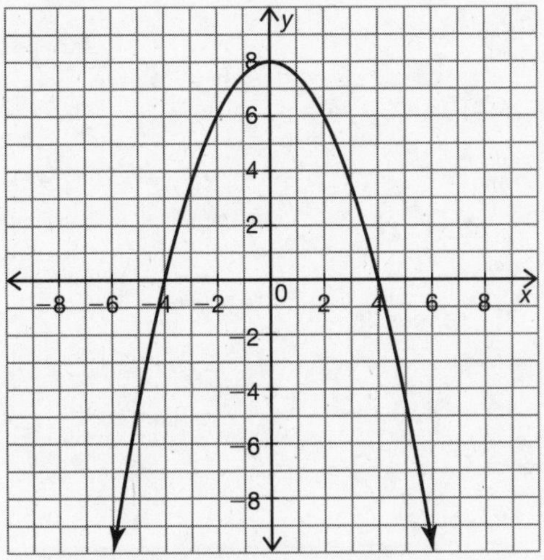

The function is even because it is symmetrical about the *y*-axis.

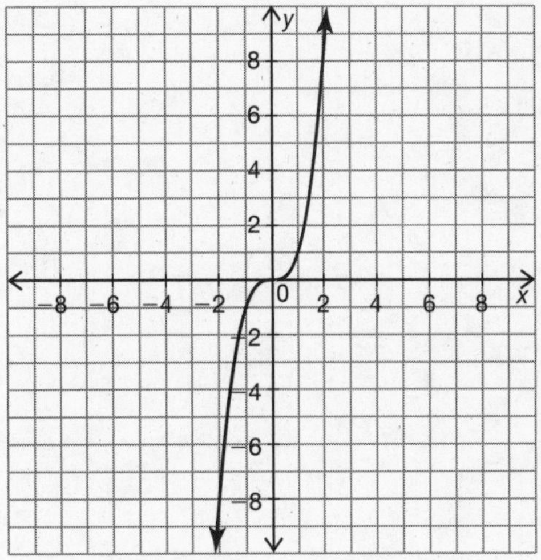

The function is odd because it is symmetrical about the origin.

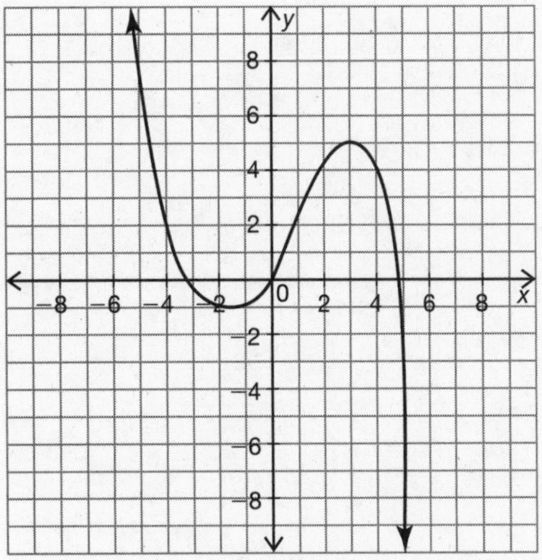

The function is neither even nor odd because it is not symmetrical.

An even function has a graph symmetric about the y-axis, thus $f(x) = f(-x)$. An odd function has a graph symmetric about the origin, thus $f(x) = -f(-x)$. So, solve $f(x)$ for $-x$ and solve for $-f(x)$ and compare.

Example

$$m(x) = 4x^5 - 2x^2$$

$$m(-x) = 4(-x)^5 - 2(-x)^2$$

$$m(-x) = -4x^5 + 2x^2$$

$$-m(x) = -(4x^5 - 2x^2)$$

$$-m(x) = -4x^5 + 2x^2$$

$m(-x) = -m(x)$ thus $m(x)$ is odd.

5.3 Using Reference Points to Dilate, Reflect, and Translate Cubic and Quartic Functions

Reference points are a set of points of a basic function that are used to graph the function. The graph of the basic cubic function is symmetric about the origin. So, $f(x) = -f(-x)$. Use symmetry to determine two other points from the reference points. Rigid motions performed on a function $f(x)$ to form a new function $g(x)$ can be described by $g(x) = Af(B(x - C)) + D$. The table shows the coordinates of $g(x)$ after each type of rigid motion performed on $f(x)$.

Type of Rigid Motion Performed on $f(x)$	Coordinates of $f(x)$ → Coordinates of $g(x)$
Vertical Dilation by a Factor of A	$(x, y) \rightarrow (x, Ay)$
Horizontal Dilation by a Factor of B	$(x, y) \rightarrow \left(\frac{1}{B}x, y\right)$
Horizontal Translation of C units	$(x, y) \rightarrow (x + C, y)$
Vertical Translation of D units	$(x, y) \rightarrow (x, y + D)$
All four rigid motions (A, B, C, and D)	$(x, y) \rightarrow \left(\frac{1}{B}x + C, Ay + D\right)$

Example

$m(x) = x^4$

$p(x) = -m(x) + 2$

Reference Points on $m(x)$	→	Corresponding Points on $p(x)$
(0, 0)	→	(0, 2)
(1, 1)	→	(1, 1)
(2, 16)	→	(2, −14)

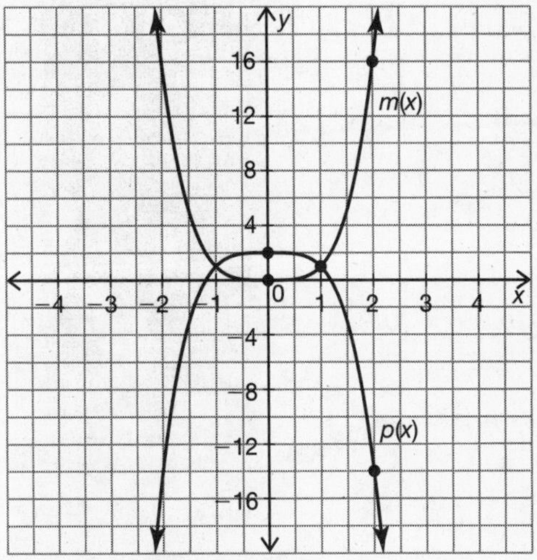

The line of reflection is $y = 2$.
The function $p(x)$ is an even function.

5.3 Describing the Rigid Motions and Writing Cubic and Quartic Functions That Have Been Dilated, Reflected, or Translated

The table shows the effects of rigid motions on basic cubic and quartic functions. Rigid motions performed on a function $f(x)$ to form a new function $g(x)$ can be described by $g(x) = Af(B(x - C)) + D$. Observe how corresponding points have changed on a graph and use the data to write the new function. Or, describe the rigid motions based on the equation of the transformed function in terms of the original function.

Rigid Motion	New Transformed Function $p(x)$ in Terms of $q(x)$
Vertical Stretch Dilation	$p(x) = Aq(x)$, $A > 1$
Vertical Compression Dilation	$p(x) = Aq(x)$, $0 < A < 1$
Horizontal Stretch Dilation	$p(x) = q(Bx)$, $0 < B < 1$
Horizontal Compression Dilation	$p(x) = q(Bx)$, $B > 0$
Reflection across x-axis	$p(x) = -q(x)$
Reflection across y-axis	$p(x) = q(-x)$
Vertical Translation	$p(x) = q(x) + D$
Horizontal Translation	$p(x) = q(x - C)$

5

Example

$g(x) = x^3$

$f(x) = 0.5g(x - 1) + 2$

$A = 0.5$
$C = 1$
$D = 2$

$(x, y) \rightarrow (x + 1, 0.5y + 2)$

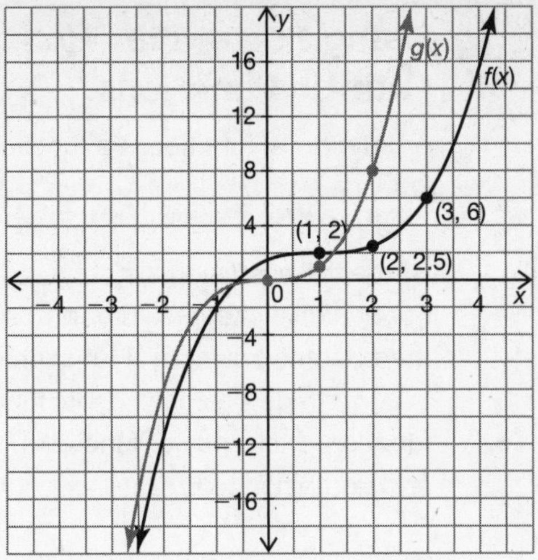

The graph of the function $g(x)$ has been vertically compressed by a factor of 0.5, translated 1 unit to the right, and 2 units up.

$$f(x) = 0.5g(x - 1) + 2$$
$$= 0.5(x - 1)^3 + 2$$
$$= 0.5(x^3 - 3x^2 + 3x - 1) + 2$$
$$= 0.5x^3 - 1.5x^2 + 1.5x + 1.5$$

5.3 Using Power Functions to Build Cubic, Quartic, and Quintic Functions

A polynomial function is a function that can be written in the form

$$p(x) = a_n x^n + a_{n-1} x^{n-1} + \cdots + a_2 x^2 + a_1 x + a_0$$

where the coefficients $a_n, a_{n-1}, \ldots a_2, a_1, a_0$ are complex numbers and the exponents are nonnegative integers. The form shown here is called the standard form of a polynomial. A third degree polynomial function has a special name—a cubic function. A quartic function is a fourth degree polynomial function. A quintic function is a fifth degree polynomial function. Basic power functions, such as $f(x) = x^2$, $f(x) = x^3$, $f(x) = x^4$, etc, can be transformed and combined to create more complex polynomial functions.

Example

$f(x) = x$; $g(x) = x^2$

$a(x) = 2g(x) - 3f(x)$

x	g(x)	f(x)	a(x)
−2	4	−2	14
−1	1	−1	5
0	0	0	0
1	1	1	−1
2	4	2	2

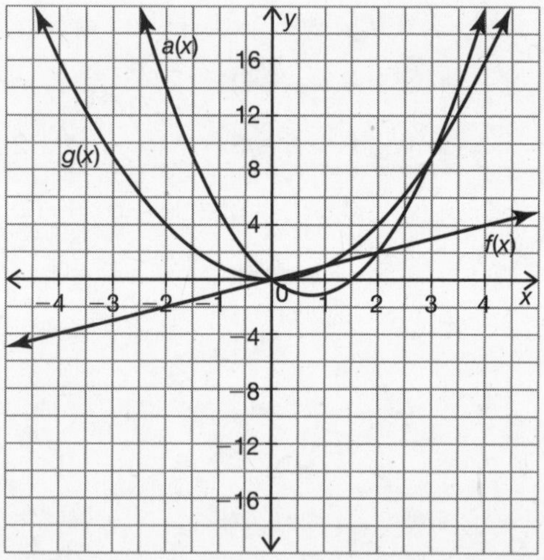

$a(x) = 2x^2 - 3x$

5.4 Determining the Number of Possible Extrema for a Polynomial

The relative maximum and minimum are the highest and lowest point in a particular section of a graph. Similarly, absolute maximum is the highest point in the entire graph, and absolute minimum is the lowest point in the entire graph. The set of absolute maximums, absolute minimums, relative maximums, and relative minimums may also be referred to as extrema. The extrema are also called extreme points and extremum. The maximum number of extrema is one less than the degree of the polynomial. The possible number of extrema is always a difference of 2. The possible number of extrema for an odd degree polynomial is even. The possible number of extrema for an even degree polynomial is odd.

Example

A 9th degree polynomial can have 0, 2, 4, 6, or 8 extrema.

© Carnegie Learning

5.4 Determining the Correct Graph and Function of a Polynomial Given Key Characteristics

Key characteristics of polynomial function such as the number and kind of extrema, the end behavior, the *a*-value, degree of the function, intercepts, etc., can be used to sketch the graph of the polynomial. These characteristics can also be gleaned from the function and the correct polynomial function matched to the graph.

Example

Characteristics:

- even degree polynomial
- negative *a*-value
- *y*-intercept of -2
- *x*-intercepts of 1 and 2

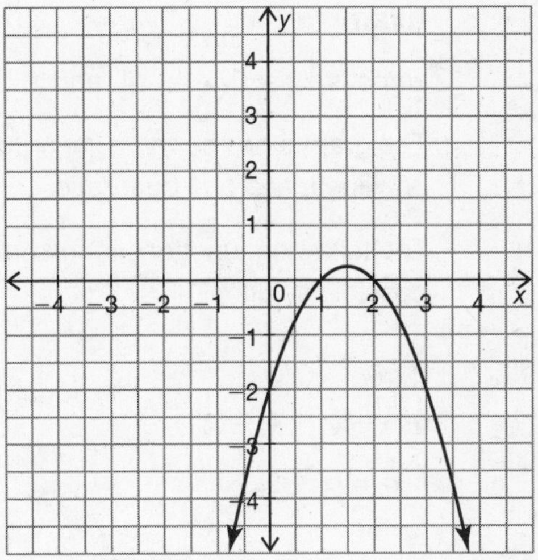

Circle the possible function(s) to represent the graph:

$f_1(x) = (x - 1)(x - 2)$

This function can be eliminated because it does not have a negative *a*-value.

$f_2(x) = -x^2 + 3x - 2$

This function matches the graph because it has a negative *a*-value, an even degree, a *y*-intercept of -2, and can be factored into $(-x + 1)(x - 2)$ which gives *x*-intercepts of 1 and 2.

$f_3(x) = -x^3 + 2x^2 - x + 1$

This function can be eliminated because it has an odd degree.

5

5.5 Determining Linear and Quadratic Functions That Would Construct a Cubic Function With Key Characteristics

Cubic functions can be built by multiplying three linear functions or by multiplying a linear function and a quadratic function. Key characteristics of cubic functions, such as zeros and *y*-intercepts can be used to determine the linear and quadratic functions whose product builds that cubic function.

Example

zeros are $x = 0$, $x = -4$, and $x = 2$

The graphs can be three linear functions or one linear and one quadratic.

The following functions represent one possible solution.

$f(x) = x$

$g(x) = (x + 4)$

$h(x) = (x - 2)$

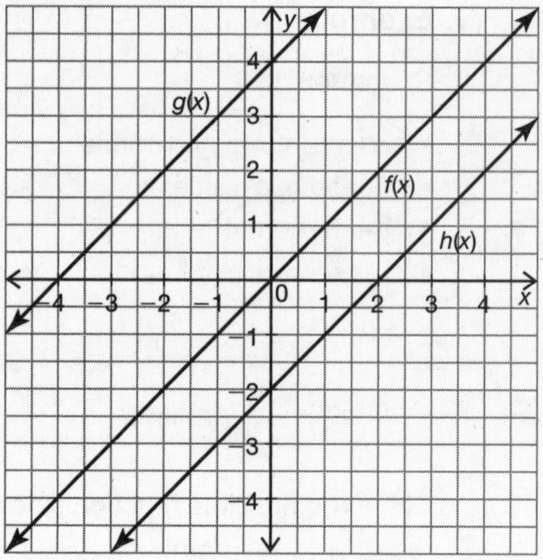

5.5 Constructing Cubic Functions Graphically From Linear and Quadratic Functions

The graph of a cubic function can be sketched by graphing the linear and quadratic factors of the function. Divide the graph into vertical sections at the *x*-intercepts. Determine whether the output values for each function in the interval are positive or negative. Values above the *x*-axis are positive. Values below the *x*-axis are negative. Determine the location of the cubic function by calculating whether the product of the factors is positive or negative over each interval. Use the *x*-intercepts and the sign of the output value over each interval to sketch the graph. The new function will cross the *x*-axis at each of the *x*-intercepts as the factors. The graph will increase or decrease depending on whether the output is positive or negative as it moves from one interval to the next.

Example

$h(x) = -x^2 + 1$

$g(x) = x - 3$

$m(x) = h(x) \cdot g(x)$

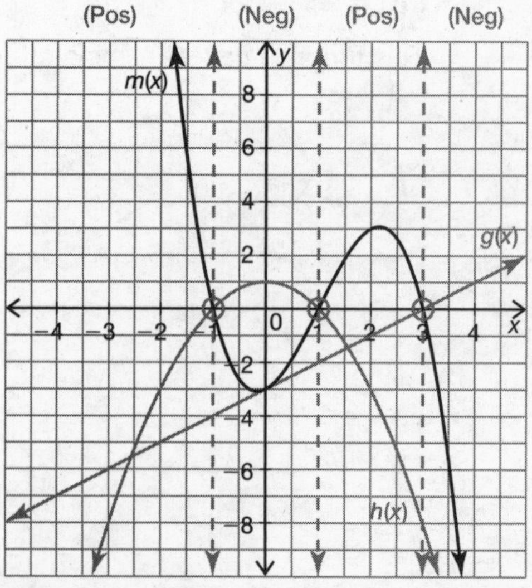

5

5.5 Graphing Linear and Quadratic Functions That Would Construct a Quartic Function With Key Characteristics

Quartic functions can be built by multiplying two quadratic functions, four linear functions, or a linear function and a cubic function. Key characteristics of quartic functions, such as zeros and *y*-intercepts can be used to determine the linear and quadratic functions whose product builds that quartic function.

Example

zeros are $x = 0$, $x = 1$, and $x = 2$ (multiplicity 2)

The graphs can be 4 linear functions, 1 quadratic and 2 linear functions, 1 linear and 1 cubic, or two quadratics. The following functions represent one possible solution.

$f(x) = (x^2 - x)$

$g(x) = (x - 2)^2$

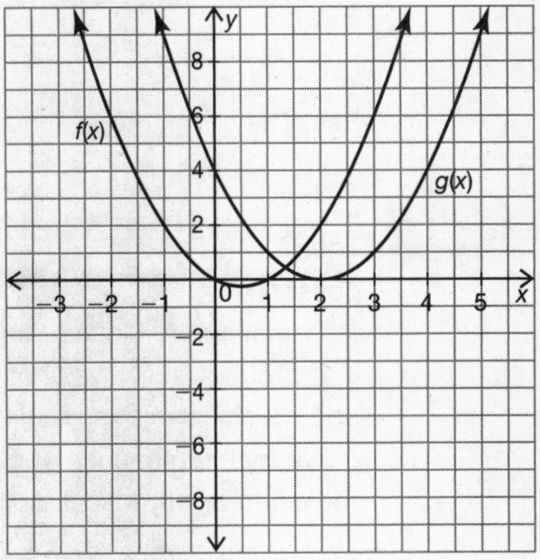

5.6 Determining Whether a Graph Represents a Polynomial or Not

The graph of a polynomial function is smooth, continuous, and increases or decreases to infinity as *x* approaches positive or negative infinity.

Example

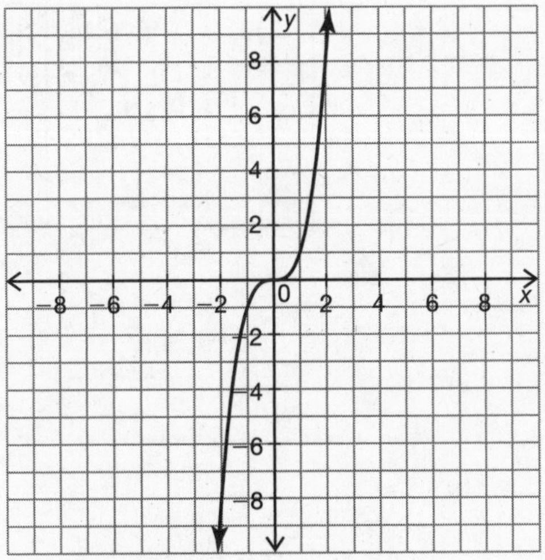

The graph is a polynomial function because it is continuous and increases as *x* approaches positive infinity and decreases as *x* approaches negative infinity.

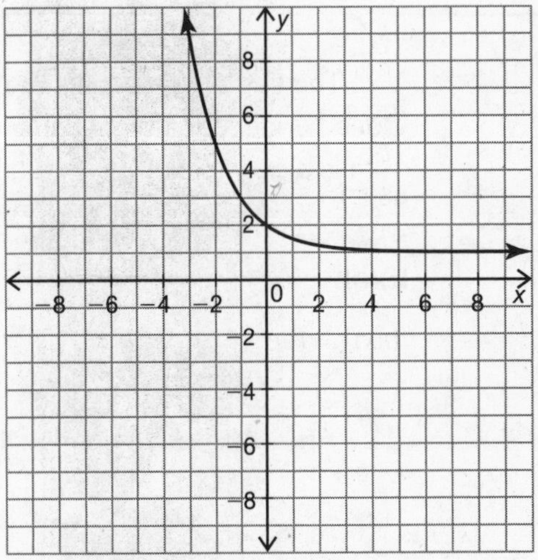

The graph is not of a polynomial function because as *x* approaches positive infinity, the graph approaches 0 instead of positive or negative infinity.

5

5.6 Determining Whether a Set Is Closed or Not Under Multiple Operations

When an operation is performed on any number or expression in a set and the result is in the same set, it is said to be closed under that operation.

Example

Is the set of integers closed under subtraction?

$-4 - 8 = -12$

Yes. The set of integers is closed under subtraction.

5.6 Determining Whether Polynomials Are Closed or Not Under Multiple Operations

Polynomials are closed under addition, subtraction, and multiplication. The sum, difference, and product is always another polynomial. They are not closed under division: the algebraic and graphical representations are not polynomials, the graph is not a smooth, continuous curve that approaches positive or negative infinity as x increases or decreases to infinity, and the algebraic representation is not in the correct form.

Example

Is the set of polynomials closed under addition?

$y_1 = -4x^3 + 2x^2 - x + 3$
$y_2 = 5x^3 - 2x^2 - 4$

$$\begin{array}{r} -4x^3 + 2x^2 - x + 3 \\ +5x^3 - 2x^2 \qquad - 4 \\ \hline x^3 \qquad\quad - x - 1 \end{array}$$

Yes. The set is polynomials are closed under addition because the sum is a polynomial.

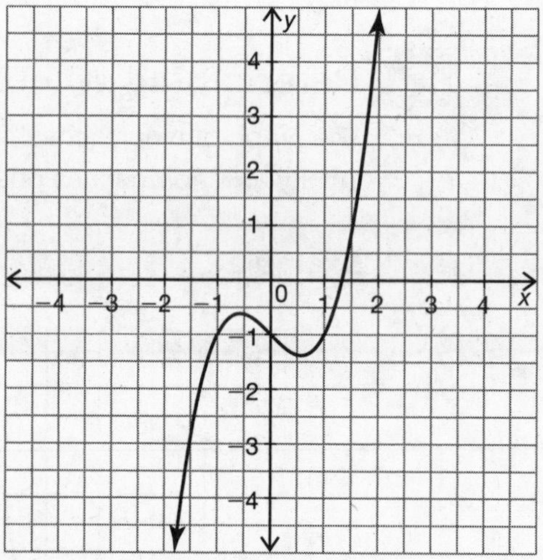

5

© Carnegie Learning

Polynomial Expressions and Equations

6

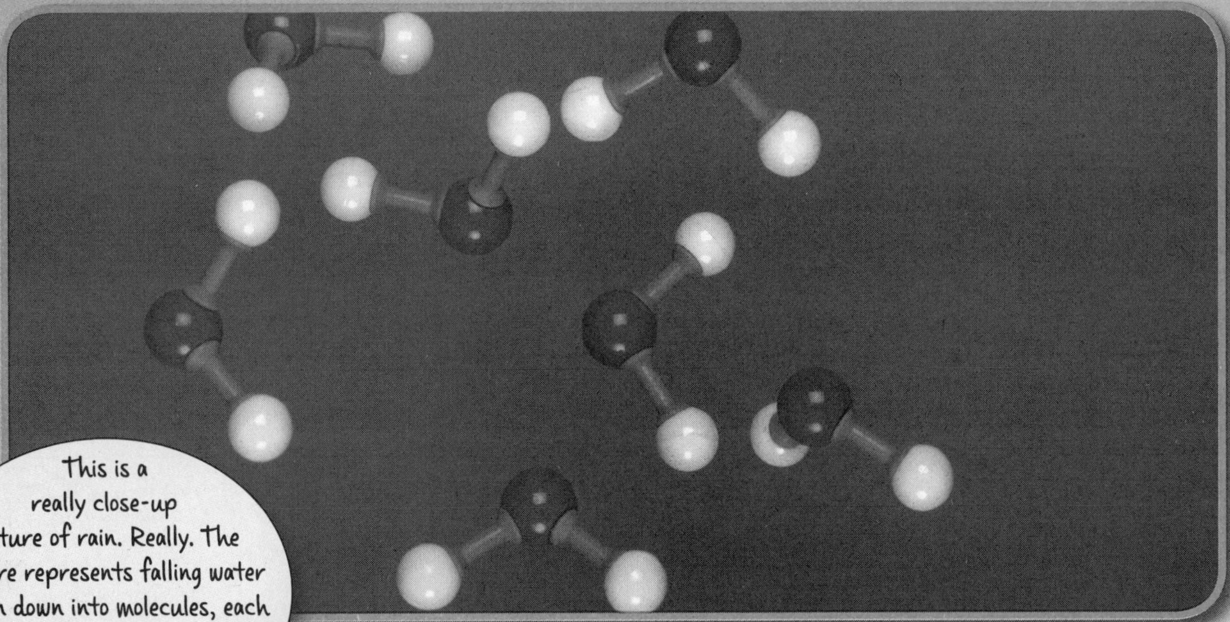

This is a really close-up picture of rain. Really. The picture represents falling water broken down into molecules, each with two hydrogen atoms connected to one oxygen atom: H_2O!

6.1

Don't Take This Out of Context

Analyzing Polynomial Functions

LEARNING GOALS

In this lesson, you will:

- Analyze the key characteristics of polynomial functions in a problem situation.
- Determine the average rate of change of a polynomial function.
- Solve equations and inequalities graphically.

KEY TERM

- average rate of change

The *kill screen* is a term for a stage in a video game where the game stops or acts oddly for no apparent reason. More common in classic video games, the cause may be a software bug, a mistake in the program, or an error in the game design. A well-known kill screen example occurs in the classic game *Donkey Kong*. When a skilled player reaches level 22, the game stops just seconds into Mario's quest to rescue the princess. Game over even though the player did not do anything to end the game!

Video game technology has advanced dramatically over the last several decades, so these types of errors are no longer common. Games have evolved from simple movements of basic shapes to real-time adventures involving multiple players from all over the globe.

How do you think video games will change over the next decade?

PROBLEM 1 Play Is Our Work

The polynomial function $p(x)$ models the profits of Zorzansa, a video game company, from its original business plan through its first few years in business.

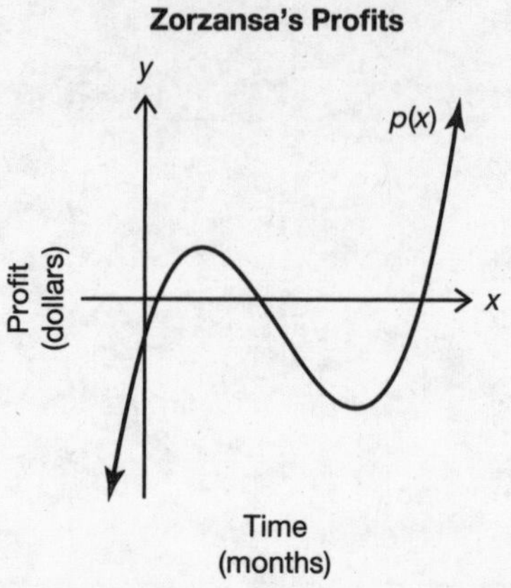

1. Label the portion(s) of the graph that model each of the memorable events in the company's history by writing the letter directly on the graph. Explain your reasoning.

Several answers may be correct as long as you can defend your reasoning. The events are not necessarily written in chronological order.

a. The Chief Executive Officer anxiously meets with her accountant.

b. The highly anticipated game, *Rage of Destructive Fury II*, is released.

c. The company opens its doors for business for the first time.

d. The company reaches its first short-term sales goal just as the holiday shopping season ends.

e. The company breaks even.

f. Members of the Board of Directors get in a heated debate over the next move the company should make.

g. The game design team is fired after their 2 game releases, *Leisurely Sunday Drive* and *Peaceful Resolution*, delight many parents but sell poorly.

h. A large conglomerate buys the company.

No model is perfect for real data, though some are more appropriate than others. In what ways does this cubic model make sense? In what ways does it not make sense?

2. Do you think this cubic function is an appropriate model for this scenario? Explain your reasoning.

PROBLEM 2 There's Nothing "Average" About This Rate of Change

The cubic function $p(x)$ models Zorzansa's total profits over the first five years of business.

Zorzansa's Profits Over Years 0 – 5

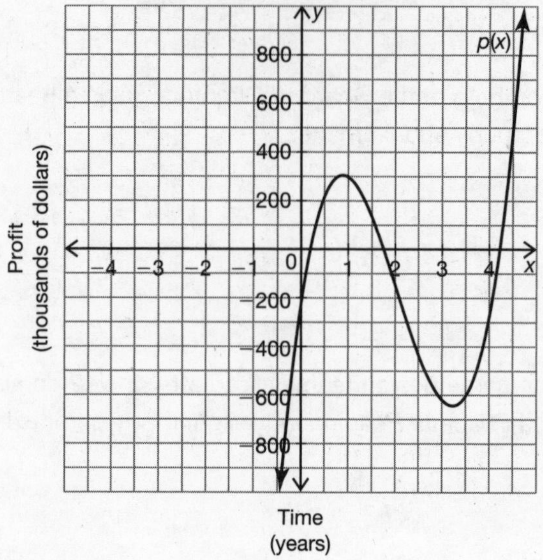

1. Use the graph to estimate when Zorzansa's achieved each profit. Then explain how you determined your estimate.

   a. \$800,000

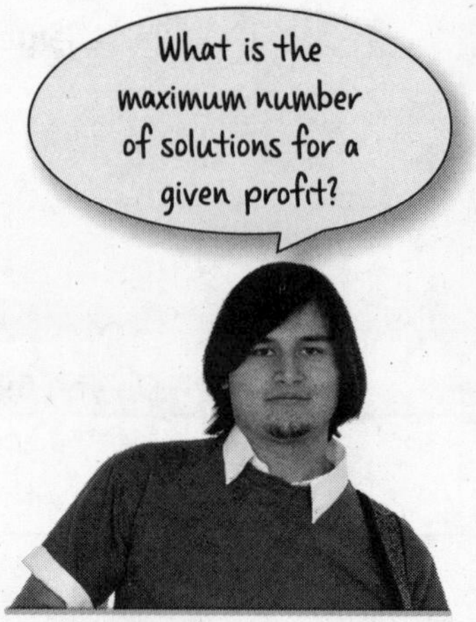

What is the maximum number of solutions for a given profit?

   b. \$200,000

   c. greater than \$200,000

   d. the company is losing money

   e. the company is making a profit.

6

2. Avi and Ariella disagree about the end behavior of the function.

Avi

The end behavior is incorrect. As time increases, profit approaches infinity. It doesn't make sense that the profits are increasing before the company even opens.

Ariella

The end behavior is correct. The function is cubic with a positive a-value. This means as x approaches infinity, y approaches infinity. As x approaches negative infinity, y also approaches negative infinity.

Who is correct? Explain your reasoning.

6

The **average rate of change** of a function is the ratio of the change in the dependent variable to the change in the independent variable over a specific interval. The formula for average rate of change is $\frac{f(b) - f(a)}{b - a}$ for the interval (a, b). The expression $b - a$ represents the change in the input values of the function f. The expression $f(b) - f(a)$ represents the change in the output values of the function f as the input values change from a to b.

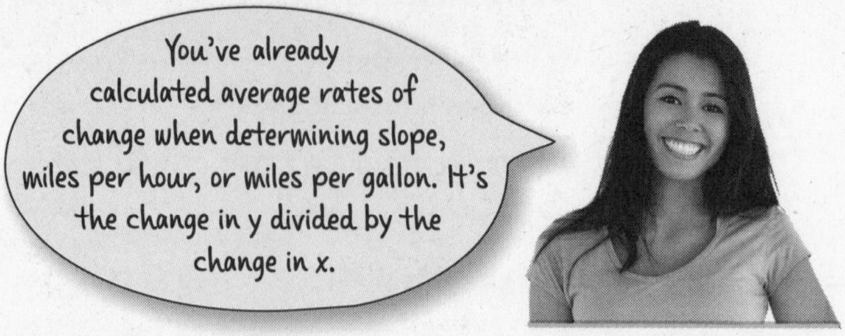
You've already calculated average rates of change when determining slope, miles per hour, or miles per gallon. It's the change in y divided by the change in x.

You can determine the average rate of change of Zorzansa's profit for the time interval (3.25, 4.25).

Zorzansa's Profits Over Years 0 – 5

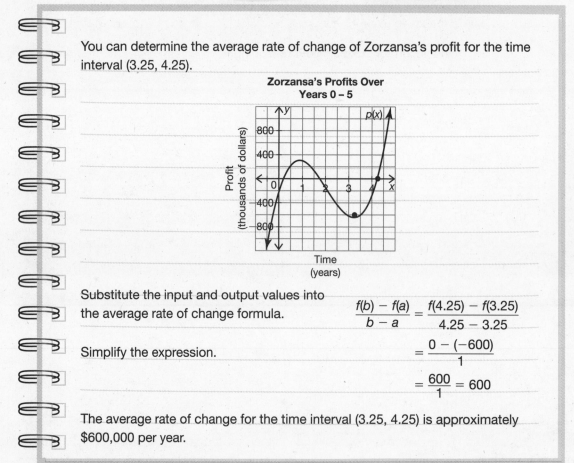

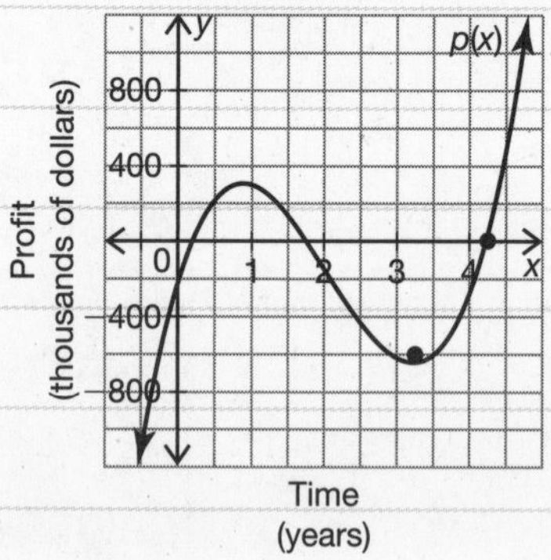

Substitute the input and output values into the average rate of change formula.

$$\frac{f(b) - f(a)}{b - a} = \frac{f(4.25) - f(3.25)}{4.25 - 3.25}$$

Simplify the expression.

$$= \frac{0 - (-600)}{1}$$

$$= \frac{600}{1} = 600$$

The average rate of change for the time interval (3.25, 4.25) is approximately \$600,000 per year.

6

3. Analyze the worked example.

a. Explain why the average rate of change is $600,000 per year, and not $600 per year.

b. Explain why the average rate of change is positive over this interval.

c. What does the average rate of change represent in this problem situation?

4. Determine the average rate of change of Zorzansa's profits for the time interval (1, 3).

5. Sam has a theory about the average rate of change.

> **Sam**
>
> *I can quickly estimate the average rate of change for intervals that are above and below the x-axis because they add to zero. For example, at year 1, the profit is about \$300,000 and at year 2.25 the profit is about −\$300,000. Therefore, the average rate of change for the time interval (1, 2.25) is approximately \$0.*

Describe the error in Sam's reasoning.

6. After 4.5 years, would you consider Zorzansa a successful business? Explain your reasoning.

6

Be prepared to share your solutions and methods.

The Great Polynomial Divide

6.2

Polynomial Division

LEARNING GOALS

In this lesson, you will:

- Describe similarities between polynomials and integers.
- Determine factors of a polynomial using one or more roots of the polynomial.
- Determine factors through polynomial long division.
- Compare polynomial long division to integer long division.

KEY TERMS

- polynomial long division
- synthetic division

Did you ever notice how little things can sometimes add up to make a huge difference? Consider something as small and seemingly insignificant as a light bulb. For example, a compact fluorescent lamp (CFL) uses less energy than "regular" bulbs. Converting to CFLs seems like a good idea, but you might wonder: how much good can occur from changing one little light bulb? The answer is a lot—especially if you convince others to do it as well. According to the U.S. Department of Energy, if each home in the United States replaced one light bulb with a CFL, it would have the same positive environmental effect as taking 1 million cars off the road!

If a new product such as the CFL can have such a dramatic impact on the environment, imagine the effect that other new products can have. A group of Canadian students designed a car that gets over 2,500 miles per gallon, only to be topped by a group of French students whose car gets nearly 7,000 miles per gallon! What impacts on the environment can you describe if just 10% of the driving population used energy efficient cars? Can all of these impacts be seen as positive?

PROBLEM 1 A Polynomial Divided . . .

The previous function-building lessons showed how the factors of a polynomial determine its key characteristics. From the factors, you can determine the type and location of a polynomial's zeros. Algebraic reasoning often allows you to reverse processes and work backwards. Specifically in this problem, you will determine the factors from one or more zeros of a polynomial from a graph.

1. Analyze the graph of the function $h(x) = x^3 + x^2 + 3x + 3$.

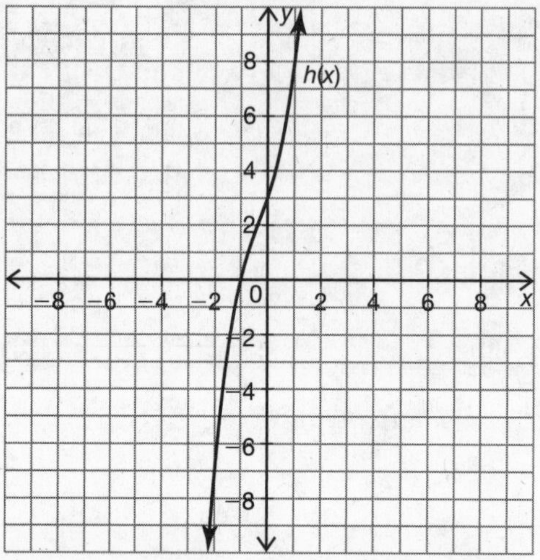

Recall the habit of mind comparing polynomials to real numbers. What does it mean to be a factor of a real number?

a. Describe the number and types of zeros of $h(x)$.

b. Write the factor of $h(x)$ that corresponds to the zero at $x = -1$.

c. What does it mean to be a factor of $h(x) = x^3 + x^2 + 3x + 3$?

d. How can you write any zero, r, of a function as a factor?

In Question 1 you determined that $(x + 1)$ is a factor of $h(x)$. One way to determine another factor of $h(x)$ is to analyze the problem algebraically through a table of values.

2. Analyze the table of values for $d(x) \cdot q(x) = h(x)$.

x	$d(x) = (x + 1)$	$q(x)$	$h(x) = x^3 + x^2 + 3x + 3$
−3	−2		−24
−2	−1		−7
−1	0		0
0	1		3
1	2		8
2	3		21

a. Complete the table of values for $q(x)$. Explain your process to determine the values for $q(x)$.

b. Two students, Tyler and McCall, disagree about the output $q(-1)$.

Tyler

The output value $q(-1)$ can be any integer. I know this because $d(-1) = 0$. Zero times any number is 0, so I can complete the table with any value for $q(-1)$.

McCall

I know $q(x)$ is a function so only one output value exists for $q(-1)$. I have to use the key characteristics of the function to determine that exact output value.

Who is correct? Explain your reasoning, including the correct output value(s) for $q(-1)$.

c. How can you tell from the table of values that $d(x)$ is a factor of $h(x)$?

3. Describe the key characteristics of $q(x)$. Explain your reasoning.

Recall that key characteristics include: vertex, line of symmetry, end behavior, and zeros. How do these key characteristics help you determine the algebraic representation?

4. What is the algebraic representation for $q(x)$? Verify algebraically that $d(x) \cdot q(x)$ is equivalent to $h(x)$.

You can use a graphing calculator to determine the quadratic, cubic, or quartic regression of a set of data.

Step 1: Press **ENTER** to return to the Plot Menu. Scroll down to **7:QUIT**. Press **ENTER**.

Step 2: You will see on the screen Lists 1 through 4 (**L1-L4**). The data needed to determine the quadratic, cubic, or quartic regression is located in Lists 1 and 2 which measures time and distance.

Step 3: Press **STAT**. Scroll right to **CALC**. Choose **5:QuadReg**. Press **ENTER**.

Step 4: Select **L1**, **L2**. Press **ENTER**.

Step 5: The information shows you the standard form of a quadratic, cubic, or quartic equation and the values of a, b, c, and r2.

5. Determine the zeros of $q(x)$. Then rewrite $h(x)$ as a product of its factors.

6

The Fundamental Theorem of Algebra states that every polynomial equation of degree n must have n roots. This means that every polynomial can be written as the product of n factors of the form $(ax + b)$. For example, $2x^2 - 3x - 9 = (2x + 3)(x - 3)$.

You know that a factor of an integer divides into that integer with a remainder of zero. This process can also help determine other factors. For example, knowing 5 is a factor of 115, you can determine that 23 is also a factor since $\frac{115}{5} = 23$. In the same manner, factors of polynomials also divide into a polynomial without a remainder. Recall that $a \div b$ is $\frac{a}{b}$, where $b \neq 0$.

Polynomial long division is an algorithm for dividing one polynomial by another of equal or lesser degree. The process is similar to integer long division.

> Notice in the dividend of the polynomial example, there is a gap in the degrees of the terms; every power must have a placeholder. The polynomial $8x^3 - 12x - 7$ does not have an x^2 term.

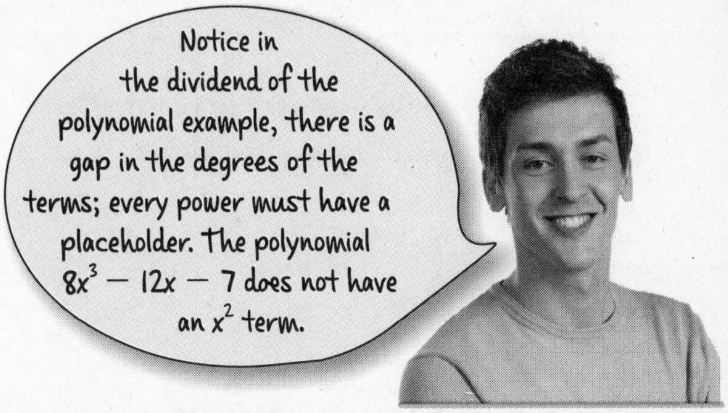

Integer Long Division	Polynomial Long Division	Description
$4027 \div 12$ or $\dfrac{4027}{12}$	$(8x^3 - 12x - 7) \div (2x + 3)$ or $\dfrac{8x^3 - 12x - 7}{2x + 3}$	
$\begin{array}{r} 335 \\ 12\overline{)4027} \\ -36 \\ \hline 42 \\ -36 \\ \hline 67 \\ -60 \\ \hline ⑦ \text{ Remainder} \end{array}$	$2x + 3\overline{)8x^3 + 0x^2 - 12x - 7}$ gives quotient $4x^2 - 6x + 3$ $-(8x^3 + 12x^2)$ $-12x^2 - 12x$ $-(-12x^2 - 18x)$ $6x - 7$ $-(6x + 9)$ Remainder -16	A. Rewrite the dividend so that each power is represented. Insert $0x^2$. B. Divide $\dfrac{8x^3}{2x} = 4x^2$. C. Multiply $4x^2(2x + 3)$, and then subtract. D. Bring down $-12x$. E. Divide $\dfrac{-12x^2}{2x} = -6x$. F. Multiply $-6x(2x + 3)$, and then subtract. G. Bring down -7. H. Divide $\dfrac{6x}{2x} = 3$. I. Multiply $3(2x + 3)$, and then subtract.
$\dfrac{4027}{12} = 335 \text{ R } 7$	$\dfrac{8x^3 - 12x - 7}{2x + 3} =$ $4x^2 - 6x + 3 \text{ R } -16$	Rewrite
$4027 = (12)(335) + 7$	$8x^3 - 12x - 7 =$ $(2x + 3)(4x^2 - 6x + 3) - 16$	Check

1. Analyze the worked example that shows integer long division and polynomial long division.

   a. In what ways are the integer and polynomial long division algorithms similar?

To determine another factor of $x^3 + x^2 + 3x + 3$ in Problem 1, you completed a table, divided output values, and then determined the algebraic expression of the result. Polynomial Long Division is a more efficient way to calculate.

   b. Is $2x + 3$ a factor of $f(x) = 8x^3 - 12x - 7$? Explain your reasoning.

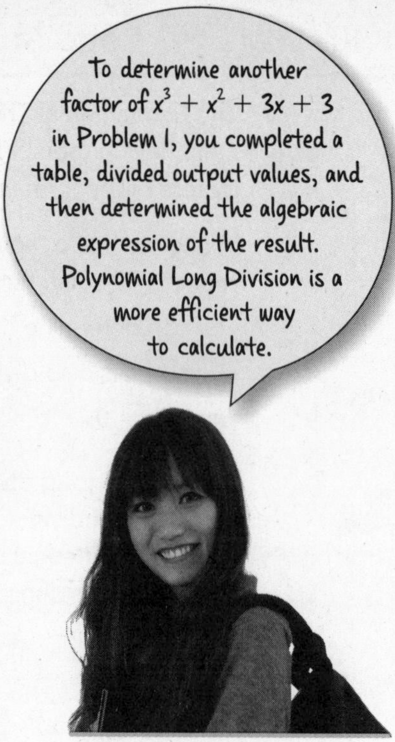

2. Determine the quotient for each. Show all of your work.

   a. $x \overline{)4x^3 - 0x^2 + 7x}$

   b. $x - 4 \overline{)x^3 + 2x^2 - 5x + 16}$

   c. $(4x^4 + 5x^2 - 7x + 9) \div (2x - 3)$

   d. $(9x^4 + 3x^3 + 4x^2 + 7x + 2) \div (3x + 2)$

6

3. Consider Question 2 parts (a) through (d) to answer each.

a. Why was the term $0x^2$ included in the dividend in part (a)? Why was this necessary?

b. When there was a remainder, was the divisor a factor of the dividend? Explain your reasoning.

c. Describe the remainder when you divide a polynomial by a factor.

4. Determine whether $m(x) = 2x + 1$ is a factor of each function. Explain your reasoning.

a. $j(x) = 2x^3 + 3x^2 + 7x + 5$

b.

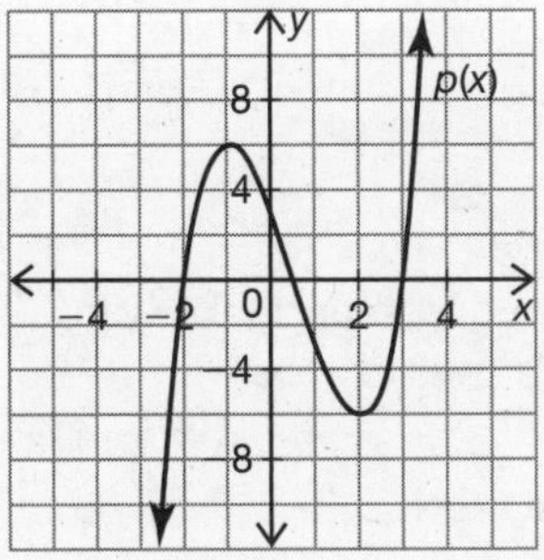

6

c.

x	$k(x)$
−2	−9
−1	−4
0	5
1	18
2	35

5. Determine the unknown in each.

a. $\frac{x}{7} = 18$ R 2. Determine x.

b. $\frac{p(x)}{x + 3} = 3x^2 + 14x + 15$ R 3. Determine the function $p(x)$.

c. Describe the similarities and differences in your solution strategies.

d. Use a graphing calculator to analyze the graph and table of $\frac{p(x)}{x + 3}$ over the interval (−10, 10). What do you notice?

6

6. Calculate the quotient using long division. Then write the dividend as the product of the divisor and the quotient plus the remainder.

Don't forget
every power in the dividend
must have a placeholder.

a. $f(x) = x^2 - 1$

$g(x) = x - 1$

Calculate $\frac{f(x)}{g(x)}$.

b. $f(x) = x^3 - 1$

$g(x) = x - 1$

Calculate $\frac{f(x)}{g(x)}$.

6

c. $f(x) = x^4 - 1$

$g(x) = x - 1$

Calculate $\frac{f(x)}{g(x)}$.

d. $f(x) = x^5 - 1$

$g(x) = x - 1$

Calculate $\frac{f(x)}{g(x)}$.

Do you see a pattern? Can you determine the quotient in part (d) without using long division?

6

7. Analyze the table of values. Then determine if $q(x)$ is a factor of $p(x)$. If so, explain your reasoning. If not, determine the remainder of $\frac{p(x)}{q(x)}$. Use the last column of the table to show your work.

x	$q(x)$	$p(x)$	
0	1	5	
1	2	7	
2	3	9	
3	4	11	
4	5	13	

8. Look back at the various polynomial division problems you have seen so far. Do you think polynomials are closed under division? Explain your reasoning.

PROBLEM 3 Improve Your Efficiency Rating

Although dividing polynomials through long division is analogous to integer long division, it can still be inefficient and time consuming. **Synthetic division** is a shortcut method for dividing a polynomial by a linear factor of the form $(x - r)$. This method requires fewer calculations and less writing by representing the polynomial and the linear factor as a set of numeric values. After the values are processed, you can then use the numeric outputs to construct the quotient and the remainder.

Notice in the form of the linear factor (x − r), the x has a coefficient of 1. Also, just as in long division, when you use synthetic division, every power of the dividend must have a placeholder.

6

To use synthetic division to divide a polynomial $ax^2 + bx + c$ by a linear factor $x - r$, follow this pattern.

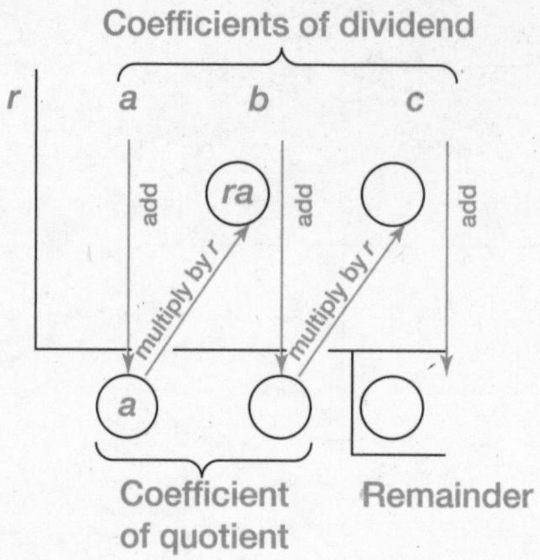

You can use synthetic division in place of the standard long division algorithm to determine the quotient for $(2x^2 - 3x - 9) \div (x - 3)$.

Long Division	Synthetic Division
$\begin{array}{r} 2x + 3 \\ x - 3\overline{)2x^2 - 3x - 9} \\ \underline{2x^2 - 6x} \\ 3x - 9 \\ \underline{3x - 9} \\ 0 \end{array}$	$r = 3$ $\begin{array}{r\|rrr} 3 & 2 & -3 & -9 \\ & & 6 & 9 \\ \hline & 2 & 3 & 0 \end{array}$ (add; multiply by r; add; multiply by r; add)
$(2x^2 - 3x - 9) \div (x - 3) = 2x + 3$	

1. Analyze the worked example.

   a. Write the dividend as the product of its factors.

   b. Why does the synthetic division algorithm work?

Notice when you use synthetic division, you are multiplying and adding, as opposed to multiplying and subtracting when you use long division.

6

2. Two examples of synthetic division are provided. Perform the steps outlined for each problem:

  i. Write the dividend.

  ii. Write the divisor.

  iii. Write the quotient.

  iv. Write the dividend as the product of the divisor and the quotient plus the remainder.

a.

2	1	0	−4	−3	6
		2	4	0	−6
	1	2	0	−3	0

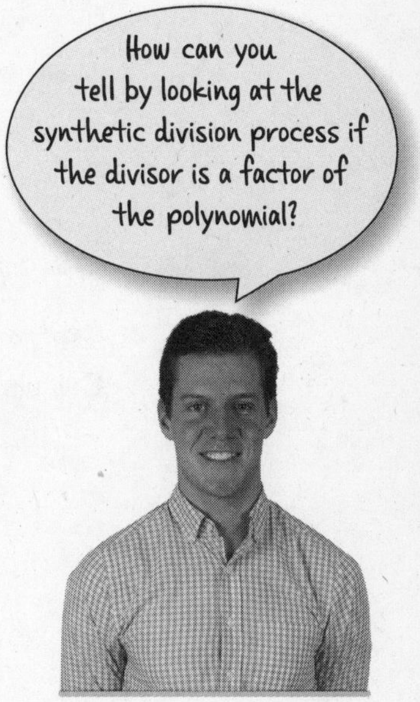

How can you tell by looking at the synthetic division process if the divisor is a factor of the polynomial?

i.

ii.

iii.

iv.

b.

−3	2	−4	−4	−3	6
		−6	30	−78	243
	2	−10	26	−81	249

i.

ii.

iii.

iv.

6

3. Calculate each quotient using synthetic division. Then write the dividend as the product of the divisor and the quotient plus the remainder.

a. $g(x) = x^3 + 1$

$r(x) = x + 1$

Calculate $\frac{g(x)}{r(x)}$.

b. $g(x) = x^3 + 8$

$r(x) = x + 2$

Calculate $\frac{g(x)}{r(x)}$.

c. $g(x) = x^3 + 27$

$r(x) = x + 3$

Calculate $\frac{g(x)}{r(x)}$.

Do you see a pattern? Can you determine the quotient in part (d) without using synthetic division?

d. $g(x) = x^3 + 64$

$r(x) = x + 4$

Calculate $\frac{g(x)}{r(x)}$.

6

4. Use a graphing calculator to compare the graphs and table of values for each pair of functions.

Group 1: $g(x) = \dfrac{x^3 + 1}{x + 1}$ and $j(x) = x^2 - x + 1$

Group 2: $g(x) = \dfrac{x^3 + 8}{x + 2}$ and $j(x) = x^2 - 2x + 4$

Group 3: $g(x) = \dfrac{x^3 + 27}{x + 3}$ and $j(x) = x^2 - 3x + 9$

Remember to use parenthesis when entering the functions in your graphing calculator.

a. Describe the similarities and differences in the graphs and tables of values within each pair of functions.

b. Are the functions within each pair equivalent? Explain your reasoning.

6

Synthetic division works only for linear divisors in the form $x - r$. If the divisor has a leading coefficient other than 1, you may need to factor out a constant in order to rewrite the divisor in the form $x - r$.

You can use synthetic division to determine the quotient of $\frac{2x^3 - 6x^2 + 4x + 2}{2x - 3}$. Since the divisor is not in the form $x - r$, you can rewrite $2x - 3$ as $2\left(x - \frac{3}{2}\right)$.

$r = \frac{3}{2}$

$$\begin{array}{c|cccc} \frac{3}{2} & 2 & -6 & 4 & 2 \\ & & 3 & -\frac{9}{2} & -\frac{3}{4} \\ \hline & 2 & -3 & -\frac{1}{2} & \boxed{\frac{5}{4}} \end{array}$$

The numbers in the last row become the coefficients of the quotient.

$2x^2 - 3x - \frac{1}{2}$ R $\frac{5}{4}$

You can write the dividend as the product of the divisor and the quotient plus the remainder.

$2x^3 - 6x^2 + 4x + 2 = \left(x - \frac{3}{2}\right)\left(2x^2 - 3x - \frac{1}{2}\right) + \frac{5}{4}$

5. Verify $(3x - 2)(x^2 + x + 1) = 3x^3 + x^2 + x - 2$ using synthetic division. Show all work and explain your reasoning.

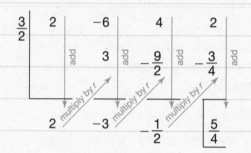

6. Analyze each division problem given $f(x) = x^3 - 3x^2 - x + 3$.

$$g(x) = \frac{f(x)}{x - 1} \qquad h(x) = \frac{f(x)}{2x - 2} \qquad j(x) = \frac{f(x)}{3x - 3}$$

a. Determine the quotient of each function.

b. Use function notation to write $h(x)$ and $j(x)$ in terms of $g(x)$.

6

c. Use a graphing calculator to compare the graphical representations of $g(x)$, $h(x)$, and $j(x)$. What are the similarities and differences in the key characteristics? Explain your reasoning.

Before you start calculating, think about the structure of the three functions and how they are similar or different.

d. Given the function $g(x)$, describe the transformation(s) that occurred to produce $h(x)$ and $j(x)$.

7. Is the function $q(x) = (x + 2)$ a factor of the function $p(x) = (x + 2)(x - 4)(x + 3) + 1$? Show all work and explain your reasoning.

8. The lesson opener discussed efficiency. Describe patterns and algorithms learned in this lesson that made your mathematical work more efficient.

6

Be prepared to share your solutions and methods.

The Factors of Life

The Factor Theorem and Remainder Theorem

6.3

LEARNING GOALS

In this lesson, you will:

- Use the Remainder Theorem to evaluate polynomial equations and functions.
- Use the Factor Theorem to determine if a polynomial is a factor of another polynomial.
- Use the Factor Theorem to calculate factors of polynomial equations and functions.

KEY TERMS

- Remainder Theorem
- Factor Theorem

When you hear the word *remainder*, what do you think of? Leftovers? Fragments? Remnants?

The United States, as a country, produces a great deal of its own "leftovers." The amount of paper product leftovers per year is enough to heat 50,000,000 homes for 20 years. The average household disposes of over 13,000 pieces of paper each year, most coming from the mail. Some studies show that 2,500,000 plastic bottles are used every hour, most being thrown away, while 80,000,000,000 aluminum soda cans are used every year. Aluminum cans that have been disposed of and not recycled will still be cans 500 years from now.

There are certain things you can do to help minimize the amount of leftovers you produce. For example, recycling one aluminum can save enough energy to watch TV for three hours. Used cans can be recycled into "new" cans in as little as 60 days from when they are recycled. If just $\frac{1}{10}$ of the daily newspapers were recycled, 25,000,000 trees could be saved per year. Recycling plastic uses half the amount of energy it would take to burn it.

PROBLEM 1 You Have the Right to the Remainder Theorem

You learned that the process of dividing polynomials is similar to the process of dividing integers. Sometimes when you divide two integers there is a remainder, and sometimes there is not a remainder. What does each case mean? In this lesson, you will investigate what the remainder means in terms of polynomial division.

Remember from your experiences with division that:

$$\frac{\text{dividend}}{\text{divisor}} = \text{quotient} + \frac{\text{remainder}}{\text{divisor}}$$

or

$$\text{dividend} = (\text{divisor})\,(\text{quotient}) + \text{remainder}.$$

It follows that any polynomial, $p(x)$, can be written in the form:

$$\frac{p(x)}{\text{linear factor}} = \text{quotient} + \frac{\text{remainder}}{\text{linear factor}}$$

or

$$p(x) = (\text{linear factor})\,(\text{quotient}) + \text{remainder}.$$

Generally, the linear factor is written in the form $(x - r)$, the quotient is represented by $q(x)$, and the remainder is represented by R, meaning:

$$p(x) = (x - r)q(x) + \text{R}.$$

1. Given $p(x) = x^3 + 8x - 2$ and $\frac{p(x)}{(x - 3)} = x^2 + 3x + 17$ R 49.

 a. Verify $p(x) = (x - r)q(x) + \text{R}$.

 b. Given $x - 3$ is a linear factor of $p(x)$, evaluate $p(3)$.

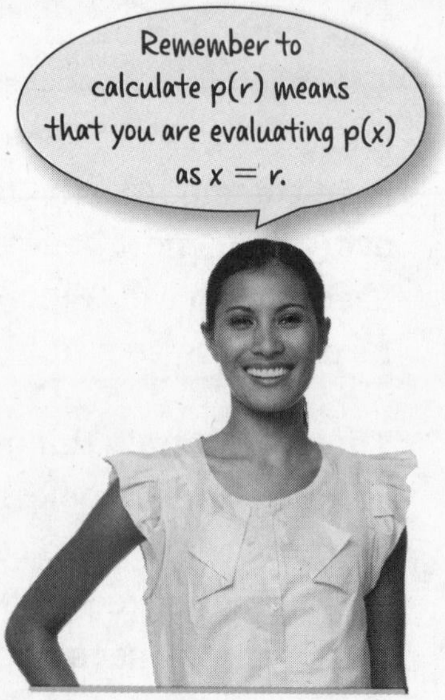
Remember to calculate p(r) means that you are evaluating p(x) as x = r.

2. Given $p(x) = (x - r)q(x) + \text{R}$, calculate $p(r)$.

3. Explain why $p(r)$, where $(x - r)$ is a linear factor, will always equal the remainder R, regardless of the quotient.

4. What conclusion can you make about any polynomial evaluated at r?

The **Remainder Theorem** states that when any polynomial equation or function, $f(x)$, is divided by a linear factor $(x - r)$, the remainder is $R = f(r)$, or the value of the equation or function when $x = r$.

5. Given $p(x) = x^3 + 6x^2 + 5x - 12$ and $\frac{p(x)}{(x - 2)} = x^2 + 8x + 21$ R 30,
Rico says that $p(-2) = 30$ and Paloma says that $p(2) = 30$.
Without performing any calculations, who is correct? Explain your reasoning.

6. The function, $f(x) = 4x^2 + 2x + 9$ generates the same remainder when divided by $(x - r)$ and $(x - 2r)$, where r is not equal to 0. Calculate the value(s) of r.

6

PROBLEM 2 Factors to Consider

Consider the factors of 24: 1, 2, 3, 4, 6, 8, 12, 24.

Notice that when you divide 24 by any of its factors the remainder is 0. This same principle holds true for polynomial division.

The **Factor Theorem** states that a polynomial has a linear polynomial as a factor if and only if the remainder is zero; or, in other words, $f(x)$ has $(x - r)$ as a factor if and only if $f(r) = 0$.

1. Haley and Lillian each prove that $(x - 7)$ is a factor of the polynomial $f(x) = x^3 - 10x^2 + 11x + 70$.

Haley

$(x^3 - 10x^2 + 11x + 70) \div (x - 7)$

$$\begin{array}{r|l} & x^2 - 3x - 10 \\ x - 7 & x^3 - 10x^2 + 11x + 70 \\ & \underline{x^3 - 7x^2} \\ & -3x^2 + 11x \\ & \underline{-3x^2 + 21x} \\ & -10x + 70 \\ & \underline{-10x + 70} \\ & 0 \end{array}$$

Lillian

$f(x) = x^3 - 10x^2 + 11x + 70$

$f(7) = 7^3 - 10(7)^2 + 11(7) + 70$

$f(7) = 343 - 490 + 77 + 70$

$f(7) = 0$

Explain why each student's method is correct.

6

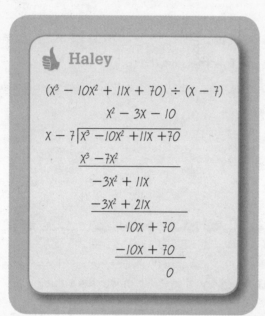

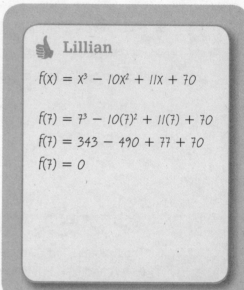

You can continue to factor the polynomial $f(x) = x^3 - 10x^2 + 11x + 70$.

From Haley and Lillian's work, you know that $f(x) = (x - 7)(x^2 - 3x - 10)$.

The quadratic factor can also be factored.

$$f(x) = (x - 7)(x^2 - 3x - 10)$$

$$f(x) = (x - 7)(x + 2)(x - 5)$$

2. Use the Factor Theorem to prove each factor shown in the worked example is correct.

3. What other method(s) could you use to verify that the factors shown in the worked example are correct?

4. Use the Factor Theorem to prove that $f(x) = (x + 1 - 3i)(x + 1 + 3i)$ is the factored form of $f(x) = x^2 + 2x + 10$.

5. Determine the unknown coefficient, a, in each function.

a. $f(x) = 2x^4 + x^3 - 14x^2 - ax - 6$ if $(x - 3)$ is a linear factor.

b. $f(x) = ax^4 + 25x^3 + 21x^2 - x - 3$ if $(x + 1)$ is a linear factor.

6

Talk the Talk

Given the information:

$$p(x) = x^3 + 6x^2 + 11x + 6, \text{ and}$$
$$p(x) \div (x + 4) = x^2 + 2x + 3 \text{ R } -6$$

Determine whether each statement is true or false. Explain your reasoning.

1. $p(-4) = 6$

2. $p(x) = (x + 4)(x^2 + 2x + 3) - 6$

3. -4 is not a zero of $p(x)$

4. -2 is a zero of $p(x)$

Be prepared to share your solutions and methods.

6

6

6.4

Break It Down

Factoring Higher Order Polynomials

LEARNING GOAL

In this lesson, you will:

- Factor higher order polynomials using a variety of factoring methods.

Factoring in mathematics is similar to the breakdown of physical and chemical properties in chemistry.

For example, the chemical formula of water is H_2O. This formula means that 2 molecules of hydrogen (H) combined with one molecule of oxygen (O) creates water. The formula for water gives us insight into its individual parts or factors.

Although the general idea is the same between factoring in mathematics, and the breakdown of chemicals, there are some big differences. When factoring polynomials, the factored form does not change any of the characteristics of the polynomial; they are two equivalent expressions. The decomposition of chemicals, however, can sometimes cause an unwanted reaction.

If you have ever taken prescription medication, you might have read the warning labels giving specific directions on how to store the medication, including temperature and humidity. The reason for these directions: if the temperature is too hot or too cold, or if the air is too humid or too dry, the chemicals in the medication may begin to decompose, thus changing its properties.

What other reasons might people want to break down the chemical and physical components of things? How else can these breakdowns be beneficial to people?

In this lesson, you will explore different methods of factoring. To begin factoring any polynomial, always look for a greatest common factor (GCF). You can factor out the greatest common factor of the polynomial, and then factor what remains.

Remember, a greatest common factor can be a variable, constant, or both.

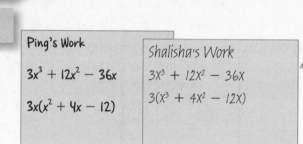

1. Ping and Shalisha each attempt to factor $3x^3 + 12x^2 - 36x$ by factoring out the greatest common factor.

Ping's Work

$3x^3 + 12x^2 - 36x$

$3x(x^2 + 4x - 12)$

Shalisha's Work

$3x^3 + 12x^2 - 36x$

$3(x^3 + 4x^2 - 12x)$

Analyze each student's work. Determine which student is correct and explain the inaccuracy in the other student's work.

2. If possible, completely factor the expression that Ping and Shalisha started.

© Carnegie Learning

6

3. Factor each expression over the set of real numbers. Remember to look for a greatest common factor first. Then, use the factors to sketch the graph of each polynomial.

Remember to think of the end behavior when sketching the function.

a. $3x^3 - 3x^2 - 6x$

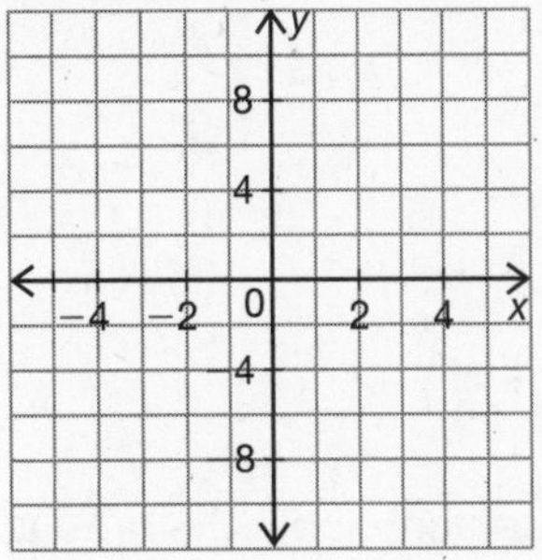

b. $x^3 - x^2 - 20x$

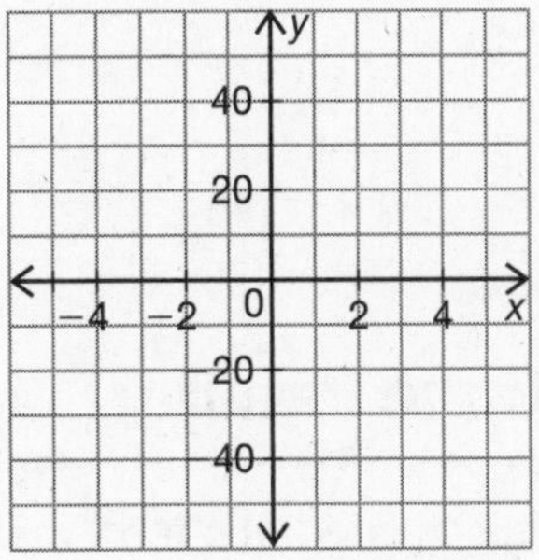

c. $2x^2 + 6x$

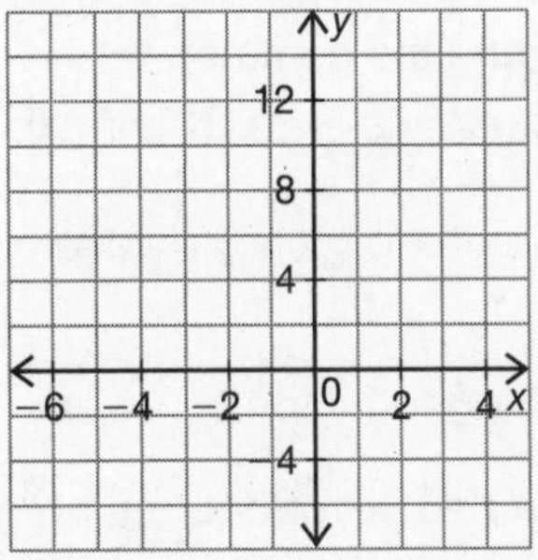

d. $3x^2 - 3x - 6$

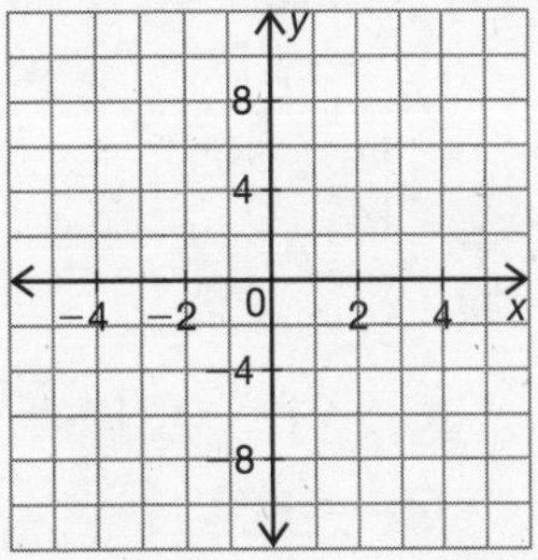

e. $10x^2 - 50x - 60$

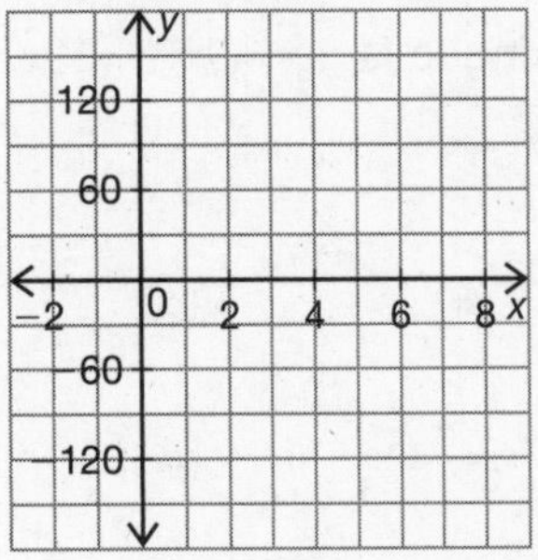

6

4. Analyze the factored form and the corresponding graphs in Question 3. What do the graphs in part (a) through part (c) have in common that the graphs of part (d) and part (e) do not? Explain your reasoning.

5. Write a statement about the graphs of all polynomials that have a monomial GCF that contains a variable.

PROBLEM 2 Continue Parsing

Some polynomials in quadratic form may have common factors in some of the terms, but not all terms. In this case, it may be helpful to write the terms as a product of 2 terms. You can then substitute the common term with a variable, z, and factor as you would any polynomial in quadratic form. This method of factoring is called *chunking*.

You can use chunking to factor $9x^2 + 21x + 10$.

Notice that the first and second terms both contain the common factor, $3x$.

$9x^2 + 21x + 10 = (3x)^2 + 7(3x) + 10$	Rewrite terms as a product of common factors.
$= z^2 + 7z + 10$	Let $z = 3x$.
$= (z + 5)(z + 2)$	Factor the quadratic.
$= (3x + 5)(3x + 2)$	Substitute $3x$ for z.

The factored form of $9x^2 + 21x + 10$ is $(3x + 5)(3x + 2)$.

6

1. Use chunking to factor $49x^2 + 35x + 6$.

2. Given $z^2 + 2z - 15 = (z - 3)(z + 5)$, write another polynomial in standard form that has a factored form of $(z - 3)(z + 5)$ with different values for z.

Using a similar method of factoring, you may notice, in polynomials with 4 terms, that although not all terms share a common factor, pairs of terms might share a common factor. In this situation, you can *factor by grouping*.

3. Colt factors the polynomial expression $x^3 + 3x^2 - x - 3$.

> **Colt**
>
> $x^3 + 3x^2 - x - 3$
>
> $x^2(x + 3) - 1(x + 3)$
>
> $(x + 3)(x^2 - 1)$
>
> $(x + 3)(x + 1)(x - 1)$

Explain the steps Colt took to factor the polynomial expression.

$x^3 + 3x^2 - x - 3$

$x^2(x + 3) - 1(x + 3)$ Step 1: ______________________________

____

$(x + 3)(x^2 - 1)$ Step 2: ______________________________

____

$(x + 3)(x + 1)(x - 1)$ Step 3: ______________________________

____

4. Use factor by grouping to factor the polynomial expression $x^3 + 7x^2 - 4x - 28$.

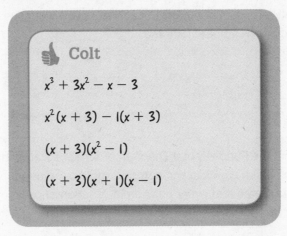

5. Braxton and Kenny both factor the polynomial expression $x^3 + 2x^2 + 4x + 8$.

Braxton

$x^3 + 2x^2 + 4x + 8$

$x^2(x + 2) + 4(x + 2)$

$(x^2 + 4)(x + 2)$

Kenny

$x^3 + 2x^2 + 4x + 8$

$x^2(x + 2) + 4(x + 2)$

$(x^2 + 4)(x + 2)$

$(x + 2i)(x - 2i)(x + 2)$

Analyze the set of factors in each student's work. Describe the set of numbers over which each student factored.

Recall that the Fundamental Theorem of Algebra states that any polynomial equation of degree n must have exactly n complex roots or solutions. Also, the Fundamental Theorem of Algebra states that every polynomial function of degree n must have exactly n complex zeros.

This implies that any polynomial function of degree n must have exactly n complex factors:

$f(x) = (x - r_1)(x - r_2) \ldots (x - r_n)$ where $r \in$ {*complex numbers*}.

Some 4th degree polynomials, written as a trinomial, look very similar to quadratics as they have the same form, $ax^4 + bx^2 + c$. When this is the case, the polynomial may be factored using the same methods you would use to factor a quadratic. This is called *factoring by using quadratic form*.

Factor the quartic polynomial by using quadratic form.

$x^4 - 29x^2 + 100$

- Determine whether you can factor the given trinomial into 2 factors.

$(x^2 - 4)(x^2 - 25)$

- Determine if you can continue to factor each binomial.

$(x - 2)(x + 2)(x - 5)(x + 5)$

6

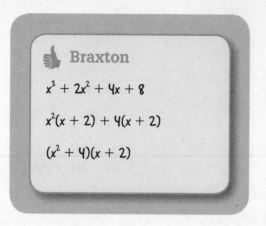

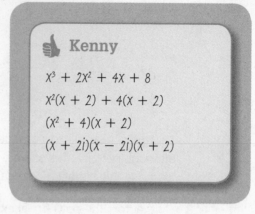

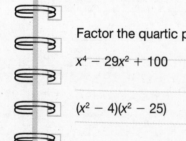

6. Factor each polynomial expression over the set of complex numbers.

a. $x^4 - 4x^3 - x^2 + 4x$

b. $x^4 - 10x^2 + 9$

PROBLEM 3 Still Parsing

1. Factor each polynomial function over the set of real numbers.

a. $f(x) = x^3 - 8$

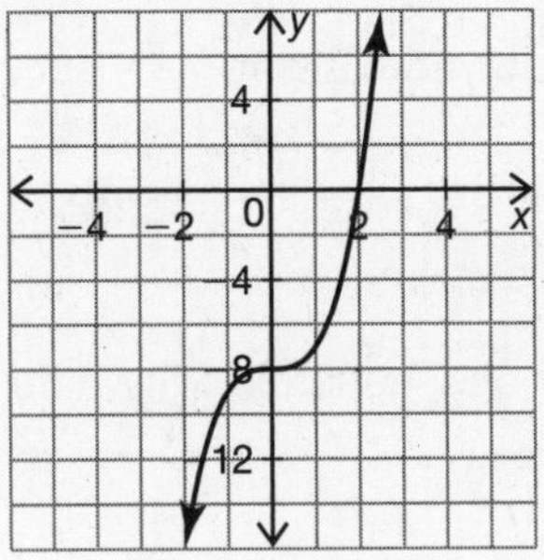

6

b.

x	$f(x) = x^3 + 27$
−4	−37
−3	0
−2	19
−1	26
0	27
1	28

You may have noticed that all the terms in the polynomials from Question 1 are perfect cubes. You can rewrite the expression $x^3 - 8$ as $(x)^3 - (2)^3$, and $x^3 + 27$ as $(x)^3 + (3)^3$. When you factor sums and differences of cubes, there is a special factoring formula you can use, which is similar to the difference of squares for quadratics.

To determine the formula for the difference of cubes, generalize the difference of cubes as $a^3 - b^3$.

To determine the factor formula for the difference of cubes, factor out $(a - b)$ by considering $(a^3 - b^3) \div (a - b)$.

$$
\begin{array}{r|l}
 & a^2 + ab + b^2 \\
\hline
a - b & a^3 + 0 + 0 - b^3 \\
 & \underline{a^3 - a^2b} \\
 & \quad a^2b + 0 \\
 & \quad \underline{a^2b - ab^2} \\
 & \qquad ab^2 - b^3 \\
 & \qquad \underline{ab^2 - b^3} \\
 & \qquad\qquad 0
\end{array}
$$

Therefore, the difference of cubes can be rewritten in factored form:
$a^3 - b^3 = (a - b)(a^2 + ab + b^2)$.

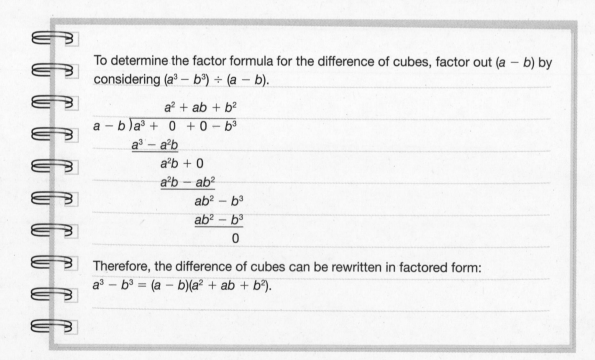

2. Determine the formula for the sum of cubes by dividing $a^3 + b^3$ by $(a + b)$.

Remember that you can factor a binomial that has perfect square *a*- and *c*-values and no middle value using the difference of squares.

You can use the difference of squares when you have a binomial of the form $a^2 - b^2$.

The binomial $a^2 - b^2 = (a + b)(a - b)$.

3. Use the difference of squares to factor each binomial over the set of real numbers.

   a. $x^2 - 64$

   b. $x^4 - 16$

   c. $x^8 - 1$

   d. $x^4 - y^4$

6

Another special form of polynomial is the perfect square trinomials. Perfect square trinomials occur when the polynomial is a trinomial, and where the first and last terms are perfect squares and the middle term is equivalent to 2 times the product of the first and last term's square root.

Factoring a perfect square trinomial can occur in two forms:

$$a^2 - 2ab + b^2 = (a - b)^2$$
$$a^2 + 2ab + b^2 = (a + b)^2$$

4. Determine which of the polynomial expression(s) is a perfect square trinomial and write it as a sum or difference of squares. If it is not a perfect square trinomial, explain why.

a. $x^4 + 14x^2 - 49$

b. $16x^2 - 40x + 100$

c. $64x^2 - 32x + 4$

d. $9x^4 + 6x^2 + 1$

Talk the Talk

You have used many different methods of factoring:

- Factoring Out the Greatest Common Factor
- Chunking
- Factoring by Grouping
- Factoring in Quadratic Form
- Sum or Difference of Cubes
- Difference of Squares
- Perfect Square Trinomials

Depending on the polynomial, some methods of factoring will prove to be more efficient than others.

6

1. Based on the form and characteristics, match each polynomial with the method of factoring you would use from the bulleted list given. Every method from the bulleted list should be used only once. Explain why you choose the factoring method for each polynomial. Finally, write the polynomial in factored form over the set of real numbers.

Polynomial	Method of Factoring	Reason	Factored Form
$3x^4 + 2x^2 - 8$			
$9x^2 - 16$			
$x^2 - 12x + 36$			
$x^3 - 64$			
$x^3 + 2x^2 + 7x + 14$			
$25x^2 - 30x - 7$			
$2x^4 + 10x^3 + 12x^2$			

Be prepared to share your solutions and methods.

6

6

6.5

Getting to the Root of It All

Rational Root Theorem

LEARNING GOALS

In this lesson, you will:

- Use the Rational Root Theorem to determine possible roots of a polynomial.
- Use the Rational Root Theorem to factor higher order polynomials.
- Solve higher order polynomials.

KEY TERM

- Rational Root Theorem

Out of the many vegetables there are to eat, root vegetables are unique. Root vegetables are distinguishable because the root is the actual vegetable that is edible, not the part that grows above ground. These roots would provide the plant above ground the nourishment they need to survive, just like the roots of daisies, roses, or trees; however, we pull up the roots of particular plants from the ground to provide our own bodies with nourishment and vitamins. Although root vegetables should only pertain to those edible parts below the ground, the category of root vegetables includes corms, rhizomes, tubers, and any vegetable that grows underground. Some of the most common root vegetables are carrots, potatoes, and onions.

Root vegetables were a very important food source many years ago before people had the ability to freeze and store food at particular temperatures. Root vegetables, when stored between 32 and 40 degrees Fahrenheit, will last a very long time. In fact, people had root cellars to house these vegetable types through cold harsh winters. In fact, some experts believe people have been eating turnips for over 5000 years! Now that's one popular root vegetable! So, what other root vegetables can you name? What root vegetables do you like to eat?

PROBLEM 1 Ideas Taking Root

Consider the product and sum of each set of roots.

Polynomial	Roots	Product of Roots	Sum of Roots
$x^2 + 4x - 1 = 0$	$-2 \pm \sqrt{5}$	-1	-4
$x^3 + 2x^2 - 5x - 6 = 0$	$-1, 2, -3$	6	-2
$2x^3 + 5x^2 - 8x - 20 = 0$	$\pm 2, -\frac{5}{2}$	10	$-\frac{5}{2}$
$4x^3 - 3x^2 + 4x - 3 = 0$	$\pm i, \frac{3}{4}$	$\frac{3}{4}$	$\frac{3}{4}$
$36x^3 + 24x^2 - 43x + 86 = 0$	$\frac{2}{3} \pm \frac{\sqrt{3}}{2}i, -2$	$-\frac{43}{18}$	$-\frac{2}{3}$
$4x^4 - 12x^3 + 13x^2 - 2x - 6 = 0$	$1 \pm i, -\frac{1}{2}, \frac{3}{2}$	$-\frac{3}{2}$	3

1. Compare the sums of the roots to the first two coefficients of each polynomial equation. What conclusion can you draw?

2. Compare the products of the roots to the first and last coefficients of each odd degree polynomial equation. What conclusion can you draw?

3. Compare the products of the roots to the first and last coefficients of each even degree polynomial equation. What conclusion can you draw?

These patterns will help you factor higher-order polynomials.

Up until this point, in order to completely factor a polynomial with a degree higher than 2, you needed to know one of the factors or roots. Whether that was given to you, taken from a table, or graph and verified by the Factor Theorem, you started out with one factor or root. What if you are not given any factors or roots? Should you start randomly choosing numbers and testing them to see if they divide evenly into the polynomial? This is a situation when the *Rational Root Theorem* becomes useful.

The **Rational Root Theorem** states that a rational root of a polynomial equation $a_nx^n + a_{n-1}x^{n-1} + \cdots + a_2x^2 + a_1x + a_0x^0 = 0$ with integer coefficients is of the form $\frac{p}{q}$, where p is a factor of the constant term, a_0, and q is a factor of the leading coefficient, a_n.

Go back and check out your answers to Questions 2 and 3. Did you identify the ratio $\frac{p}{q}$?

4. Beyonce and Ivy each list all possible rational roots for the polynomial equation they are given.

Beyonce

$4x^4 - 2x^3 + 5x^2 + x - 10 = 0$

p could equal any factors of -10, so $\pm 1, \pm 2, \pm 5, \pm 10$

q could equal any factors of 4, so $\pm 1, \pm 2, \pm 4$

Therefore, possible zeros are

$\frac{p}{q} = \pm 1, \pm 2, \pm 5, \pm 10, \pm\frac{1}{2}, \pm\frac{5}{2}, \pm\frac{1}{4}, \pm\frac{5}{4}.$

Ivy

$6x^5 - 2x^3 + x^2 - 3x - 15 = 0$

p could equal any factors of -15, so $\pm 1, \pm 3, \pm 5, \pm 15$

q could equal any factors of 6, so $\pm 2, \pm 3, \pm 6$

Therefore, possible zeros are

$\frac{p}{q} = \pm\frac{1}{2}, \pm\frac{3}{2}, \pm\frac{5}{2}, \pm\frac{15}{2}, \pm\frac{1}{3}, \pm 1, \pm\frac{5}{3}, \pm 5, \pm\frac{1}{6}, \pm\frac{5}{6}.$

Explain why Ivy is incorrect and correct her work.

6

5. Complete each step to factor and solve $x^4 + x^3 - 7x^2 - x + 6 = 0$.

a. Determine all the possible rational roots.

b. Use synthetic division to determine which of the possible roots are actual roots.

c. Rewrite the polynomial as a product of its quotient and linear factor.

d. Repeat steps *a*–*c* for the cubic expression.

e. Factor completely and solve.

6. Determine all roots for $x^4 - 7x^2 - 18 = 0$.

a. Determine the possible roots.

b. Use synthetic division to determine one of the roots.

c. Rewrite the original polynomial as a product.

d. Determine the possible rational roots of the quotient.

e. Use synthetic division to determine one of the roots.

f. Rewrite the original polynomial as a product.

g. Determine the possible rational roots of the quotient.

h. Determine the remaining roots.

i. Rewrite the original polynomial as a product.

PROBLEM 2   What Bulbs are in Your Garden?

You have learned many different ways to solve higher order polynomials. To determine all the roots or solutions of a polynomial equation:

- Determine the possible rational roots.
- Use synthetic division to determine one of the roots.
- Rewrite the original polynomial as a product.
- Determine the possible rational roots of the quotient.
- Repeat the process until all the rational roots are determined.
- Factor the remaining polynomial to determine any irrational or complex roots.
- Recall that some roots may have a multiplicity.

1. Solve each equation over the set of complex numbers.

   a. $x^3 + 1 = 0$

If a quadratic is not factorable, you might want to use the quadratic formula: $x = \dfrac{-b \pm \sqrt{b^2 - 4ac}}{2a}$.

b. $x^4 + 3x^2 - 28 = 0$

c. $x^4 - 5x^2 - 6x - 2 = 0$

6

2. Determine the zeros of each function.

a. $f(x) = x^3 + 11x^2 + 37x + 42$

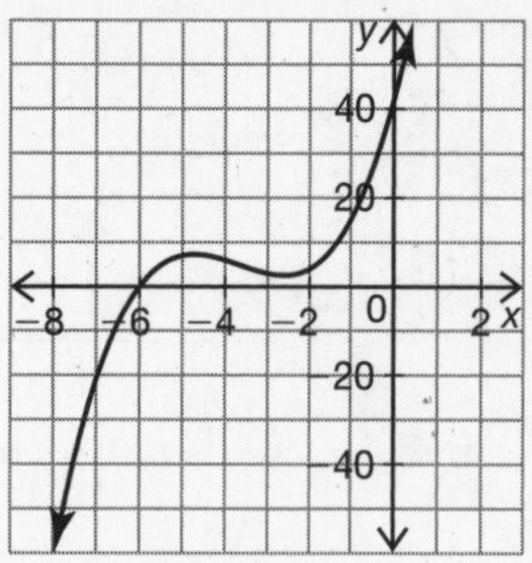

b. $f(x) = x^3 - 4.75x^2 + 3.125x - 0.50$

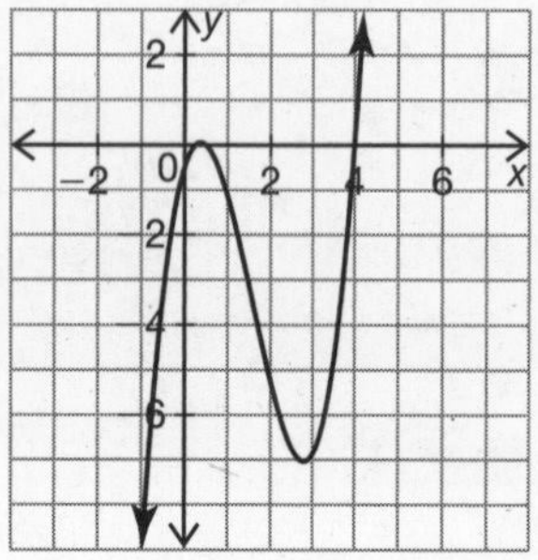

Be prepared to share your solutions and methods.

6.6

Identity Theft

Exploring Polynomial Identities

LEARNING GOALS

In this lesson, you will:

- Use polynomial identities to rewrite numeric expressions.
- Use polynomial identities to generate Pythagorean triples.
- Identify patterns in numbers generated from polynomial identities.
- Prove statements involving polynomials.

KEY TERM

- Euclid's Formula

Have you or someone you know ever been the victim of identity theft? With more and more tasks being performed through the use of technology, identity theft is a growing problem throughout the world. Identity theft occurs when someone steals another person's name or social security number in hopes of accessing that person's money or to make fraudulent purchases.

There are many different ways a person can steal another person's identity. Just a few of these methods are:

- rummaging through a person's trash to obtain personal information and bank statements,
- computer hacking to gain access to personal data,
- pickpocketing to acquire credit cards and personal identification, such as passports or drivers' licenses,
- browsing social networking sites to obtain personal details and photographs.

How important is it to you to secure your identity? What actions would you take to ensure that your identity is not stolen?

PROBLEM 1 Check Your Calculator at the Door

You have learned about many different equivalent polynomial relationships. These relationships are also referred to as polynomial identities.

Some of the polynomial identities that you have used so far are shown.

- $(a + b)^2 = a^2 + 2ab + b^2$
- $(a - b)^2 = a^2 - 2ab + b^2$
- $a^2 - b^2 = (a + b)(a - b)$
- $(a + b)^3 = (a + b)(a^2 + 2ab + b^2)$
- $(a - b)^3 = (a - b)(a^2 - 2ab + b^2)$
- $a^3 + b^3 = (a + b)(a^2 - ab + b^2)$
- $a^3 - b^3 = (a - b)(a^2 + ab + b^2)$

Polynomial identities can help you perform calculations. For instance, consider the expression 46^2. Most people cannot calculate this value without the use of a calculator. However, you can use a polynomial identity to write an equivalent expression that is less difficult to calculate.

You can use the polynomial identity $(a + b)^2 = a^2 + 2ab + b^2$ to calculate 46^2.

$46^2 = (40 + 6)^2$	Write 46 as the sum of 40 and 6.
$= 40^2 + 2(40)(6) + 6^2$	Apply the polynomial identity $(a + b)^2 = a^2 + 2ab + b^2$.
$= 1600 + 2(40)(6) + 36$	Apply exponents.
$= 1600 + 480 + 36$	Perform multiplication.
$= 2116$	Perform addition.

The value of 46^2 is 2116.

1. Calculate 46^2 in a different way by writing 46 as the difference of two integers squared.

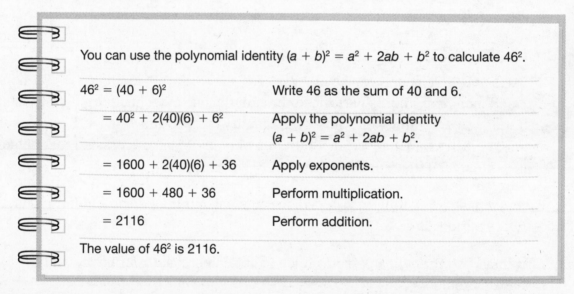

2. Use polynomial identities and number properties to perform each calculation. Show your work.

a. 112^2

b. 27^3

c. 55^3

6

PROBLEM 2 It's Triplets!

Remember that a Pythagorean triple is a set of three positive integers, a, b, and c, such that $a^2 + b^2 = c^2$.

1. Determine whether each set of numbers is a Pythagorean triple. Explain your reasoning.

   a. 4, 5, 9

   b. 0.4, 0.5, 0.3

   c. 89, 80, 39

You have just determined whether three positive numbers make up a Pythagorean triple, but suppose that you wanted to *generate* integers that are Pythagorean triples.

2. Describe a process you could use to calculate integers that are Pythagorean triples.

6

There is an efficient method to generate Pythagorean triples that involves a polynomial identity called *Euclid's Formula*.

Euclid's Formula is a formula used to generate Pythagorean triples given any two positive integers. Given positive integers r and s, where $r > s$, Euclid's Formula is shown.

$$(r^2 + s^2)^2 = (r^2 - s^2)^2 + (2rs)^2$$

The expressions in Euclid's Formula represent the side lengths of a right triangle, a, b, and c, as shown.

$$c^2 = a^2 + b^2$$

$$(r^2 + s^2)^2 = (r^2 - s^2)^2 + (2rs)^2$$

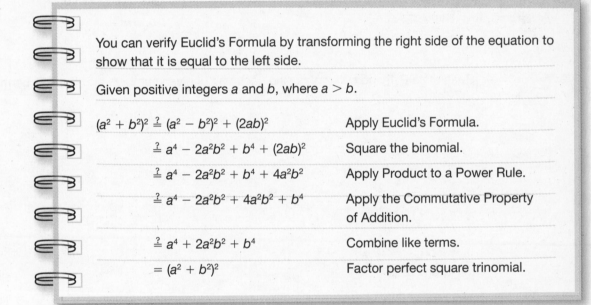

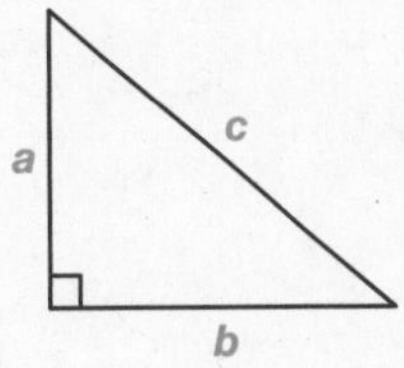

You can verify Euclid's Formula by transforming the right side of the equation to show that it is equal to the left side.

Given positive integers a and b, where $a > b$.

$(a^2 + b^2)^2 \stackrel{?}{=} (a^2 - b^2)^2 + (2ab)^2$	Apply Euclid's Formula.
$\stackrel{?}{=} a^4 - 2a^2b^2 + b^4 + (2ab)^2$	Square the binomial.
$\stackrel{?}{=} a^4 - 2a^2b^2 + b^4 + 4a^2b^2$	Apply Product to a Power Rule.
$\stackrel{?}{=} a^4 - 2a^2b^2 + 4a^2b^2 + b^4$	Apply the Commutative Property of Addition.
$\stackrel{?}{=} a^4 + 2a^2b^2 + b^4$	Combine like terms.
$= (a^2 + b^2)^2$	Factor perfect square trinomial.

3. Use Euclid's Formula to generate a Pythagorean triple.

   a. Choose two integers and use them to generate a Pythagorean triple. Explain your choice in integers.

   b. Compare your Pythagorean triple to others in your class. Did everyone get the same triple?

4. Generate a Pythagorean triple using each pair of given numbers and Euclid's Formula.

   a. 4 and 7

   b. 11 and 5

   c. 15 and 20

5. Did any of the Pythagorean triples you generated have a common factor? If so, identify them, and explain why you think this happened.

Do you think that there is only one r-value and only one s-value that will generate each Pythagorean triple?

6. The integers 5, 12, 13 make up a fairly well-known Pythagorean triple. What two integers generate this triple? Show your work.

PROBLEM 3 Is This Your Special Number?

After learning that Euclid's Formula generates numbers that are Pythagorean triples, Danielle and Mike wonder what other formulas they could use to generate interesting patterns. Each came up with their own sets of numbers.

Danielle named her numbers the "Danielle numbers." She defined them as shown.

> The Danielle numbers are any numbers that can be generated using the formula $a^2 + b^2$, where a and b are positive integers and $a > b$.

Following suit, Mike named his numbers the "Mike numbers," and he defined his numbers as shown.

> The Mike numbers are any numbers that can be generated using the formula $a^2 - b^2$, where a and b are positive integers and $a > b$.

1. Complete each table to determine the first few Danielle numbers and the first few Mike numbers. Shade the corresponding cell if a is not greater than b.

Danielle Numbers: $a^2 + b^2$

		b				
		1	2	3	4	5
a	1					
	2					
	3					
	4					
	5					

Mike Numbers: $a^2 - b^2$

		b				
		1	2	3	4	5
a	1					
	2					
	3					
	4					
	5					

6

2. Describe any and all patterns you see in each table in Question 1.

3. Determine whether each number is a Danielle number, a Mike number, both, or neither. Explain your reasoning.

a. 13

b. 3

c. 2

After hearing about Danielle and Mike's numbers, Dave and Sandy decide to create their own numbers as well. Their definitions are shown.

The Dave numbers are any numbers that can be generated using the formula $a^3 + b^3$, where a and b are positive integers and $a > b$.

The Sandy numbers are any numbers that can be generated using the formula $a^3 - b^3$, where a and b are positive integers and $a > b$.

4. Complete the tables to determine the first few Dave numbers, and the first few Sandy numbers. Shade the corresponding cell if a is not greater than b.

Dave Numbers: $a^3 + b^3$

		b				
		1	2	3	4	5
a	1					
	2					
	3					
	4					
	5					

Sandy Numbers: $a^3 - b^3$

		b				
		1	2	3	4	5
a	1					
	2					
	3					
	4					
	5					

6

5. Describe any and all patterns you see in each table in Question 4.

6. Determine whether each number is a Dave number, a Sandy number, both, or neither. Explain your reasoning.

a. 35

b. 5

7. Write a rule that defines your own set of numbers. What interesting patterns do you see with your numbers?

PROBLEM 4 Okay, Now Prove It!

Verify each algebraic statement by transforming one side of the equation to show that it is equivalent to the other side of the equation.

1. $v^6 - w^6 = (v^2 - w^2)(v^2 - vw + w^2)(v^2 + vw + w^2)$

2. $(p^4 + q^4)^2 = (p^4 - q^4)^2 + (2p^2q^2)^2$

6

3. $m^9 + n^9 = (m + n)(m^2 - mn + n^2)(m^6 - m^3n^3 + n^6)$

6

Be prepared to share your solutions and methods.

6.7

The Curious Case of Pascal's Triangle

Pascal's Triangle and the Binomial Theorem

LEARNING GOALS

In this lesson, you will:

- Identify patterns in Pascal's Triangle.
- Use Pascal's Triangle to expand powers of binomials.
- Use the Binomial Theorem to expand powers of binomials.
- Extend the Binomial Theorem to expand binomials of the form $(ax + by)^n$.

KEY TERM

- Binomial Theorem

Some sets of numbers are given special names because of the interesting patterns they create. A *polygonal number* is a number that can be represented as a set of dots that make up a regular polygon. For example, the number 3 is considered a polygonal number because it can be represented as a set of dots that make up an equilateral triangle, as shown.

More specifically, the polygonal numbers that form equilateral triangles are called the *triangular numbers*. The first four triangular numbers are shown. (Note that polygonal numbers always begin with the number 1.)

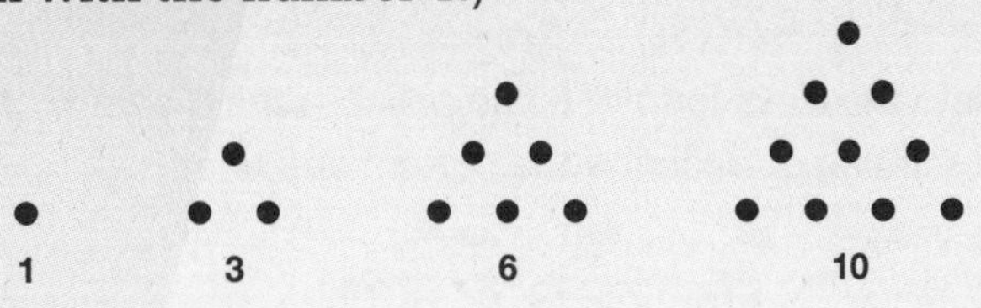

The *square numbers* are polygonal numbers that form squares. The first four square numbers are shown.

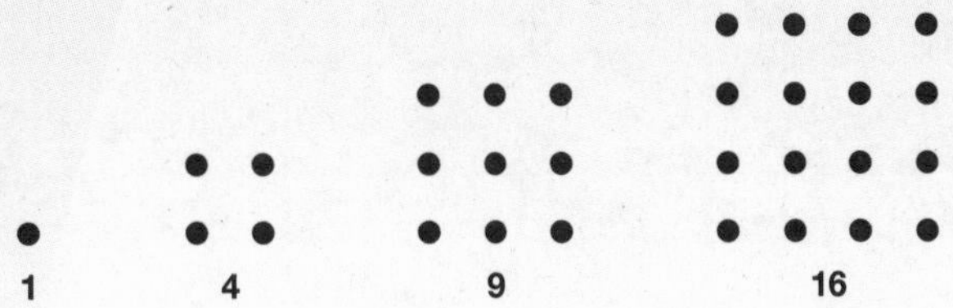

Can you determine the first four pentagonal numbers? How about the first four hexagonal numbers?

PROBLEM 1 So Many Patterns, So Little Time

There is an interesting pattern of numbers that makes up what is referred to as Pascal's Triangle.

The first six rows of Pascal's Triangle are shown, where $n = 0$ represents the first row, $n = 1$ represents the second row, and so on.

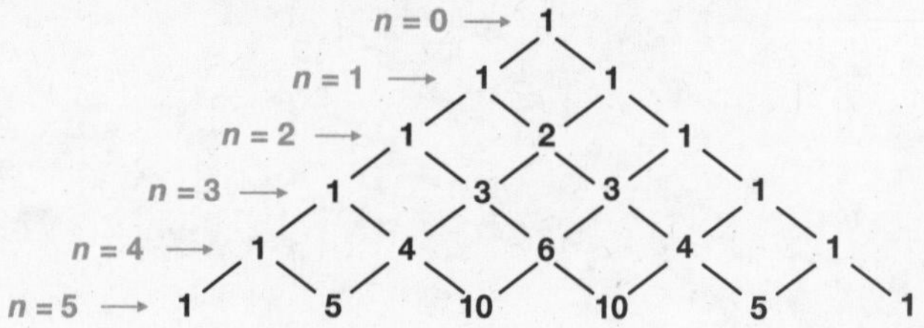

1. Analyze the patterns in Pascal's Triangle.

   a. Describe all the patterns you see in Pascal's Triangle.

Remember the types of numbers discussed in the lesson opener? Maybe you can see some of those patterns here!

   b. Complete the rows for $n = 6$ and $n = 7$ in the diagram of Pascal's Triangle. Describe the pattern you used.

2. Brianna loves hockey. In fact, Brianna is so obsessed with hockey that she drew "hockey sticks" around the numbers in Pascal's Triangle. Lo and behold, she found a pattern! Her work is shown.

Brianna

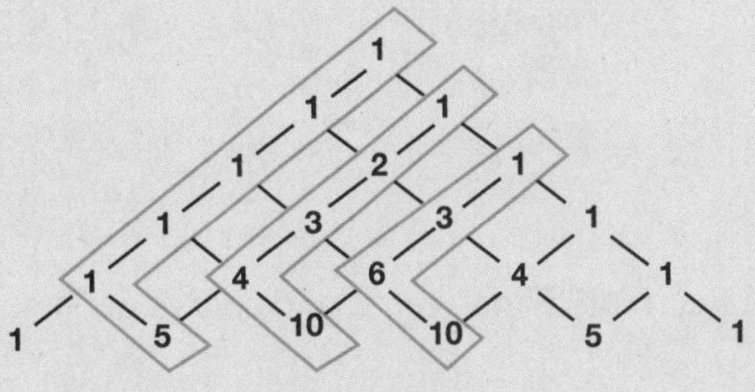

a. Describe the pattern shown by the numbers inside the hockey sticks that Brianna drew.

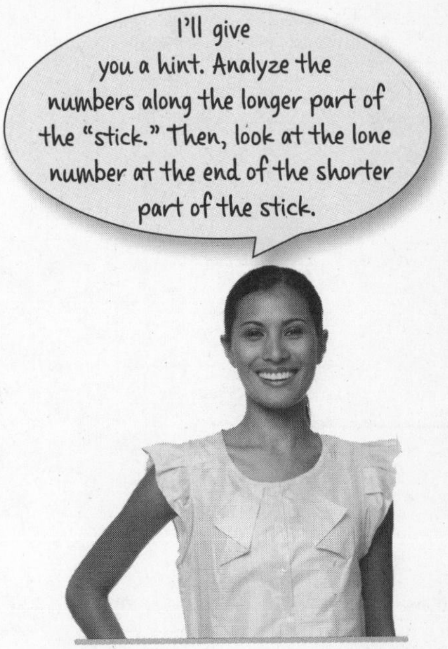
I'll give you a hint. Analyze the numbers along the longer part of the "stick." Then, look at the lone number at the end of the shorter part of the stick.

b. Sketch two more hockey sticks that include numbers that have the same pattern described in part (a).

3. Drew and Latasha analyzed Pascal's Triangle, and each described a pattern.

Drew

The sum of the numbers in each row is equal to 2^n, where $n = 0$ represents the first row.

Latasha

If I alternate the signs of the numbers in any row after the first row and then add them together, their sum is 0.

Who's correct? Either verify or disprove each student's work.

6

4. Consider the numbers along the dashed lines shown.

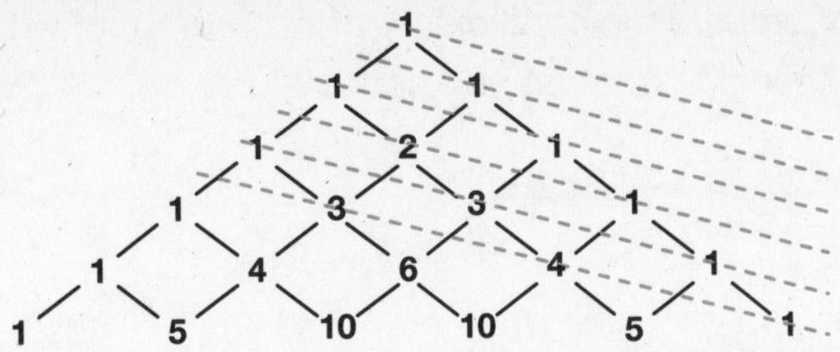

a. Write the sequence for the sum of numbers along each dashed line.

b. Explain how the sums of numbers along the dashed lines in Pascal's Triangle can be linked to a well-known sequence of numbers.

The patterns shown in Pascal's Triangle have many uses. For instance, you may have used Pascal's Triangle to calculate probabilities. Let's explore how you can use Pascal's Triangle to raise a binomial to a positive integer.

5. Multiply to expand each binomial. Write your final answer so that the powers of *a* are in descending order.

a. $(a + b)^0 =$

b. $(a + b)^1 =$

c. $(a + b)^2 =$

d. $(a + b)^3 =$

e. $(a + b)^4 =$

6. Analyze your answers to Question 5.

a. Compare the coefficients of each product with the numbers shown in Pascal's Triangle. What do you notice?

b. What do you notice about the exponents of the a- and b-variables in each expansion?

c. What do you notice about the sum of the exponents of the a- and b-variables in each expansion?

7. Use Pascal's Triangle to expand each binomial.

a. $(a + b)^5 =$

b. $(a + b)^6 =$

c. $(a + b)^7 =$

The directions say to use Pascal's Triangle. So, do not perform multiplication!

PROBLEM 2 Binomial Theorem Delirium!

What if you want to expand a binomial such as $(a + b)^{15}$? You could take the time to draw that many rows of Pascal's Triangle, but there is a more efficient way.

Recall that the factorial of a whole number n, represented as $n!$, is the product of all numbers from 1 to n.

You are going to see another method for expanding binomials. But, let's get some notation out of the way first.

1. Perform each calculation and simplify.

   a. $5! =$

   b. $2!3! =$

   c. $\frac{5!}{3!} =$

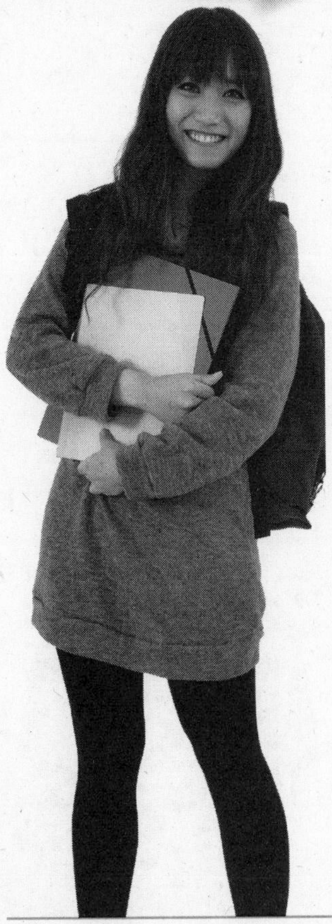
You may remember that the value of 0! is 1. This is because the product of zero numbers is equal to the multiplicative identity, which is 1.

You may have seen the notation $\binom{n}{k}$ or ${}_nC_k$ when calculating probabilities in another course. Both notations represent the formula for a *combination*. Recall that a combination is a selection of objects from a collection in which order does not matter. The formula for a combination of k objects from a set of n objects for $n \geq k$ is shown.

$$\binom{n}{k} = {}_nC_k = \frac{n!}{k!(n-k)!}$$

Calculate $\binom{4}{2}$, or $_4C_2$.

$\binom{n}{k} = {_nC_k} = \dfrac{n!}{k!(n-k)!}$	Write the formula for a combination.
$n = 4$ and $k = 2$	Identify n and k.
$\binom{4}{2} = \dfrac{4!}{2!(4-2)!}$	Substitute the values for n and k into the formula.
$= \dfrac{4 \cdot 3 \cdot 2 \cdot 1}{(2 \cdot 1)\,(2 \cdot 1)}$	Write each factorial as a product.
$= \dfrac{4 \cdot 3 \cdot \cancel{2 \cdot 1}}{(2 \cdot 1)\,(\cancel{2 \cdot 1})}$	Divide out common factors.
$= \dfrac{12}{2} = 6$	Simplify.

2. Explain why n must be greater than or equal to k in the formula for a combination.

3. Perform each calculation and simplify.

   a. $\binom{5}{1} =$

   b. $_7C_4 =$

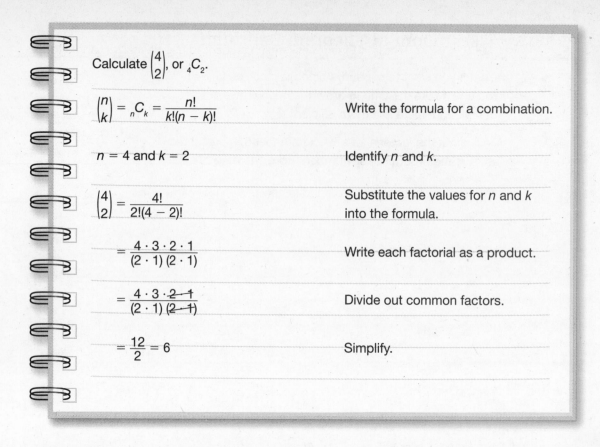

Check it out – your graphing calculator can compute factorials and combinations.

6

4. Sarah and Montel's teacher asks each student to use Pascal's Triangle to calculate ${}_6C_3$. Their answers and explanations are shown.

Sarah

I can calculate ${}_nC_k$ by looking at the kth number (from left to right) in the nth row of Pascal's Triangle. So, ${}_6C_3$ is equal to 20.

Montel

I can calculate ${}_nC_k$ by looking at the $(k + 1)$th number (from left to right) in the $(n + 1)$th row of Pascal's Triangle. So, ${}_6C_3$ is equal to 35.

Who is correct? Explain your reasoning.

The **Binomial Theorem** states that it is possible to extend any power of $(a + b)$ into a sum of the form shown.

$$(a + b)^n = \binom{n}{0}a^nb^0 + \binom{n}{1}a^{n-1}b^1 + \binom{n}{2}a^{n-2}b^2 + \cdots + \binom{n}{n-1}a^1b^{n-1} + \binom{n}{n}a^0b^n$$

5. Use the Binomial Theorem to expand $(a + b)^{15}$. You can use your calculator to determine the coefficients.

$(a + b)^{15} =$

6

Suppose you have a binomial with coefficients other than one, such as $(2x + 3y)^5$. You can use substitution along with the Binomial Theorem to expand the binomial.

You can use the Binomial Theorem to expand $(a + b)^5$, as shown.

$$(a + b)^5 = \binom{5}{0}a^5b^0 + \binom{5}{1}a^4b^1 + \binom{5}{2}a^3b^2 + \binom{5}{3}a^2b^3 + \binom{5}{4}a^1b^4 + \binom{5}{5}a^0b^5$$

$$= a^5 + 5a^4b^1 + 10a^3b^2 + 10a^2b^3 + 5a^1b^4 + b^5$$

Now consider $(2x + 3y)^5$.

Let $2x = a$ and let $3y = b$.

You can substitute $2x$ for a and $3y$ for b into the expansion for $(a + b)^5$.

$$(2x + 3y)^5 = (2x)^5 + 5(2x)^4(3y)^1 + 10(2x)^3(3y)^2 + 10(2x)^2(3y)^3 + 5(2x)^1(3y)^4 + (3y)^5$$

$$= 32x^5 + 5(16x^4)(3y) + 10(8x^3)(9y^2) + 10(4x^2)(27y^3) + 5(2x)(81y^4) + 243y^5$$

$$= 32x^5 + 240x^4y + 720x^3y^2 + 1080x^2y^3 + 810xy^4 + 243y^5$$

6. Use the Binomial Theorem and substitution to expand each binomial.

a. $(3x + y)^4$

b. $(x - 2y)^6$

Be prepared to share your solutions and methods.

Chapter 6 Summary

KEY TERMS

- average rate of change (6.1)
- polynomial long division (6.2)
- synthetic division (6.2)
- Euclid's Formula (6.6)

THEOREMS

- Remainder Theorem (6.3)
- Factor Theorem (6.3)
- Rational Root Theorem (6.5)
- Binomial Theorem (6.7)

6.1 Analyzing Graphs

A graph can be analyzed over certain intervals or at certain points.

Example

- From point C to point A the graph is increasing.
- From point A to point B the graph is decreasing.
- From point B to point F the graph is increasing.
- Points C, D, and E have a y-value of 0.
- Point A has a local maximum value of about 15.
- Point B has a local minimum value of about -5.

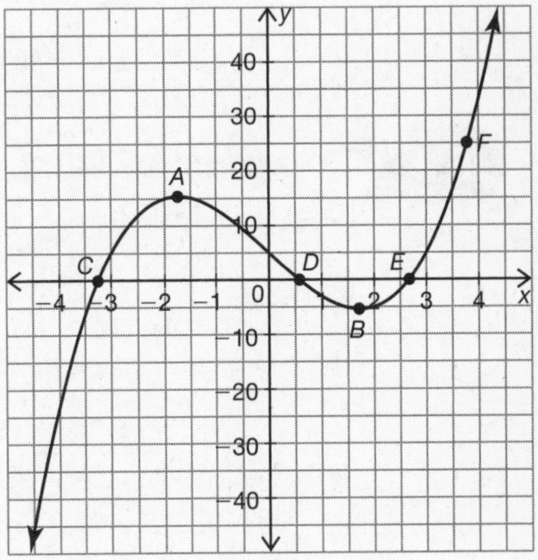

6.1 Determining the Average Rate of Change

The formula for average rate of change is $\frac{f(b) - f(a)}{b - a}$ for an interval (a, b).

Example

The average rate of change over the interval $(-1, 4)$ is

$f(4) \approx 100,\ f(-1) \approx -200$

$$= \frac{f(b) - f(a)}{b - a}$$

$$= \frac{f(4) - f(-1)}{4 - (-1)}$$

$$= \frac{100 - (-200)}{5}$$

$$= \frac{300}{5}$$

$$= 60$$

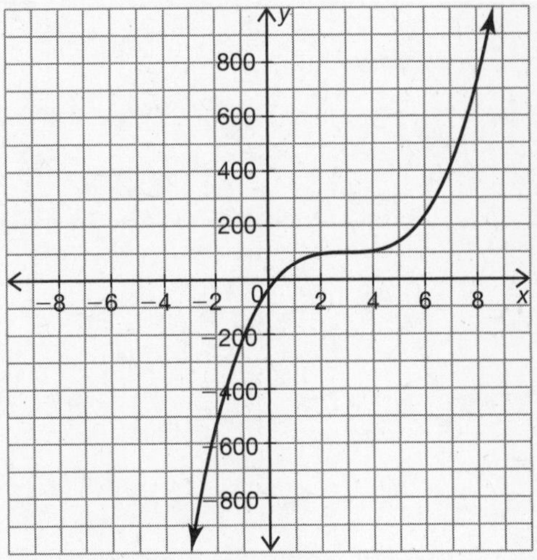

6

Using Polynomial Long Division

One polynomial can be divided by another of equal or lesser degree using a process similar to integer division. This process is called polynomial long division. To perform polynomial long division, every power in the dividend must have a placeholder. If there is a gap in the degrees of the dividend, rewrite it so that each power is represented.

Example

The quotient of $3x^3 - 4x^2 + 5x - 3$ divided by $3x + 2$ is $x^2 - 2x + 3$ R -9.

$$
\begin{array}{r}
x^2 - 2x + 3 \\
3x + 2\overline{)3x^3 - 4x^2 + 5x - 3} \\
\underline{3x^3 + 2x^2} \\
-6x^2 + 5x \\
\underline{-6x^2 - 4x} \\
9x - 3 \\
\underline{9x + 6} \\
-9
\end{array}
$$

Determining Factors Using Long Division

When the remainder of polynomial long division is 0, the divisor is a factor of the dividend.

Example

The binomial $2x - 1$ is a factor of $2x^4 + 5x^3 - x^2 + x - 1$ since the remainder is 0.

$$
\begin{array}{r}
x^3 + 3x^2 + x + 1 \\
2x - 1\overline{)2x^4 + 5x^3 - x^2 + x - 1} \\
\underline{2x^4 - x^3} \\
6x^3 - x^2 \\
\underline{6x^3 - 3x^2} \\
2x^2 + x \\
\underline{2x^2 - x} \\
2x - 1 \\
\underline{2x - 1} \\
0
\end{array}
$$

6.3 Using Synthetic Division

Synthetic division is a shortcut method for dividing a polynomial by a binomial $x - r$. To use synthetic division, follow the pattern:

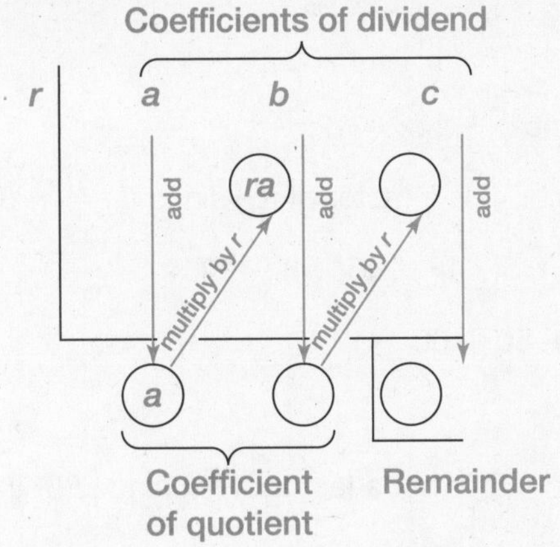

Example

$4x^3 + 3x^2 - 2x + 1$ divided by $x + 3$ is $4x^2 - 9x + 25 \text{ R } \frac{-74}{x+3}$.

−3	4	3	−2	1
		−12	27	−75
	4	−9	25	−74

6.3 Using the Remainder Theorem

The Remainder Theorem states that when any polynomial equation or function, $f(x)$, is divided by a linear factor $(x - r)$, the remainder is $R = f(r)$, or the value of the equation or function when $x = r$.

Example

Let $f(x) = 6x^3 - 2x^2 - x + 1$. When $f(x)$ is divided by $x - 3$, the remainder is 142 since $f(3) = 142$.

$$\begin{aligned} f(3) &= 6(3)^3 - 2(3)^2 - 3 + 1 \\ &= 162 - 18 - 3 + 1 \\ &= 142 \end{aligned}$$

6

6.3 Using the Factor Theorem

The Factor Theorem states that a polynomial has a linear polynomial as a factor if and only if the remainder is 0; $f(x)$ has $(x - r)$ as a factor if and only if $f(r) = 0$.

Examples

Let $f(x) = 2x^3 + 5x^2 - 15x - 12$.

The binomial $(x + 4)$ is a factor of $f(x)$ since $f(-4) = 0$.

$$\begin{aligned} f(-4) &= 2(-4)^3 + 5(-4)^2 - 15(-4) - 12 \\ &= -128 + 80 + 60 - 12 \\ &= 0 \end{aligned}$$

The binomial $(x - 5)$ is not a factor of $f(x)$ since $f(5) \neq 0$.

$$\begin{aligned} f(5) &= 2(5)^3 + 5(5)^2 - 15(5) - 12 \\ &= 250 + 125 - 75 - 12 \\ &= 288 \end{aligned}$$

6

6.4 Factoring Polynomials

There are different methods to factor a polynomial. Depending on the polynomial, some methods of factoring are more efficient than others.

Examples

Factoring out the Greatest Common Factor:

$6x^2 - 36x$

$6x(x - 6)$

Chunking:

$64x^2 + 24x - 10$

$(8x)^2 + 3(8x) - 10$

Let $z = 8x$.

$z^2 + 3z - 10$

$(z - 2)(z + 5)$

$(8x - 2)(8x + 5)$

Factoring by Grouping

$x^3 + 3x^2 + 2x + 6$

$x^2(x + 3) + 2(x + 3)$

$(x^2 + 2)(x + 3)$

Sum or Difference of Cubes

$x^3 - 27$

$(x - 3)(x^2 + 3x + 9)$

$x^3 + 8$

$(x + 2)(x^2 - 2x + 4)$

Difference of Squares

$x^2 - 25$

$(x + 5)(x - 5)$

Perfect Square Trinomials

$9x^2 - 12x + 4$

$(3x - 2)(3x - 2)$

6.5 Using the Rational Root Theorem

The Rational Root Theorem states that a rational root of a polynomial $a_nx^n + a_{n-1}x^{n-1} + \cdots + a_1x^1 + a_0x^0$ with integer coefficients will be of the form $\frac{p}{q}$ where p is a factor of the constant term a_0 and q is a factor of the leading coefficient a_n.

6

Example

Given the polynomial: $3x^2 + 2x - 6$

$p = \pm 1, \pm 2, \pm 3, \pm 6$

$q = \pm 1, \pm 3$

The possible rational roots are $\pm 1, \pm 2, \pm 3, \pm 6, \pm\frac{1}{3}$, and $\pm\frac{2}{3}$.

6.5 Solving Polynomials Equations

To determine all roots of a polynomial:

- Determine the possible rational roots.
- Use synthetic division to determine one of the roots.
- Rewrite the original polynomial as a product.
- Determine the possible rational roots of the quotient.
- Repeat the process until all the rational roots are determined.
- Factor the remaining polynomial to determine any irrational or complex roots.
- Recall that some roots may have a multiplicity.

Example

Solve $2x^3 - 9x^2 + 7x + 6 = 0$.

The possible rational roots of $2x^3 - 9x^2 + 7x + 6$ are $\pm\frac{1}{2}$, ±1, $\pm\frac{3}{2}$, ±2, ±3, and ±6 since $p = 6$ and $q = 2$.

Use synthetic division to divide the polynomial by $(x - 3)$.

3	2	−9	7	6
		6	−9	−6
	2	−3	−2	0

$2x^3 - 9x^2 + 7x + 6 = 0$

$(x - 3)(2x^2 - 3x - 2) = 0$

$(x - 3)(2x + 1)(x - 2) = 0$

$x - 3 = 0 \qquad 2x + 1 = 0 \qquad x - 2 = 0$

$x = 3 \qquad x = -\frac{1}{2} \qquad x = 2$

6

© Carnegie Learning

6.6 Using Polynomial Identities for Numerical Calculations

Some of the polynomial identities are shown. Polynomial identities can be used to perform calculations.

- $(a + b)^2 = a^2 + 2ab + b^2$
- $(a - b)^2 = a^2 - 2ab + b^2$
- $a^2 - b^2 = (a + b)(a - b)$
- $(a + b)^3 = (a + b)(a^2 + 2ab + b^2)$
- $(a - b)^3 = (a - b)(a^2 - 2ab + b^2)$
- $a^3 + b^3 = (a + b)(a^2 - ab + b^2)$
- $a^3 - b^3 = (a - b)(a^2 + ab + b^2)$

Example

To calculate 13^3, use the identity $(a + b)^3 = (a + b)(a^2 + 2ab + b^2)$.

$$13^3 = (10 + 3)^3$$
$$= (10 + 3)(10^2 + 2(10)(3) + 3^2)$$
$$= 13(100 + 60 + 9)$$
$$= 13(100) + 13(60) + 13(9)$$
$$= 1{,}300 + 780 + 117$$
$$= 2{,}197$$

6.6 Using Euclid's Formula to Generate Pythagorean Triples

Euclid's Formula is a formula used to generate Pythagorean triples given any two positive integers.

Given positive integers r and s, where $r > s$, Euclid's Formula is $(r^2 + s^2)^2 = (r^2 - s^2)^2 + (2rs)^2$.

Example

Generate a Pythagorean Triple using the numbers 6 and 13.

Let $r = 13$ and $s = 6$.

$$(13^2 + 6^2) = (13^2 - 6^2) + (2(13)(6))^2$$
$$(205)^2 = (133)^2 + (156)^2$$
$$42{,}025 = 42{,}025$$

So 133, 156, 205 is a Pythagorean triple.

6

6.7 Using Pascal's Triangle to Expand Binomials

The coefficients for the expansion of $(a + b)^n$ are the same as the numbers in the row of Pascal's Triangle where n is equal to the power of the original binomial.

$n = 0$ → 1
$n = 1$ → 1 1
$n = 2$ → 1 2 1
$n = 3$ → 1 3 3 1
$n = 4$ → 1 4 6 4 1
$n = 5$ → 1 5 10 10 5 1
$n = 6$ → 1 6 15 20 15 6 1
$n = 7$ → 1 7 21 35 35 21 7 1

Example

$(a + b)^5 = a^5 + 5a^4b + 10a^3b^2 + 10a^2b^3 + 5ab^4 + b^5$

6.7 Using the Binomial Theorem to Expand Binomials

The Binomial Theorem states that it is possible to expand any power of $(a + b)$ into a sum in the following form:

$$(a + b)^n = \binom{n}{0}a^nb^0 + \binom{n}{1}a^{n-1}b^1 + \binom{n}{2}a^{n-2}b^2 + \cdots + \binom{n}{n-1}a^1b^{n-1} + \binom{n}{n}a^0b^n.$$

Example

Expand $(2x - y)^6$.

$$\begin{aligned}(a + b)^6 &= \binom{6}{0}a^6b^0 + \binom{6}{1}a^5b^1 + \binom{6}{2}a^4b^2 + \binom{6}{3}a^3b^3 + \binom{6}{4}a^2b^4 + \binom{6}{5}a^1b^5 + \binom{6}{6}a^0b^6 \\ &= a^6 + 6a^5b + 15a^4b^2 + 20a^3b^3 + 15a^2b^4 + 6ab^5 + b^6\end{aligned}$$

Let $a = 2x$ and $b = -y$.

$$\begin{aligned}(2x - y)^6 &= (2x)^6 + 6(2x)^5(-y) + 15(2x)^4(-y)^2 + 20(2x)^3(-y)^3 + 15(2x)^2(-y)^4 + 6(2x)(-y)^5 + (-y)^6 \\ &= 64x^6 - 6(32)x^5y + 15(16)x^4y^2 - 20(8)x^3y^3 + 15(4)x^2y^4 - 12xy^5 + y^6 \\ &= 64x^6 - 192x^5y + 240x^4y^2 - 160x^3y^3 + 60x^2y^4 - 12xy^5 + y^6\end{aligned}$$

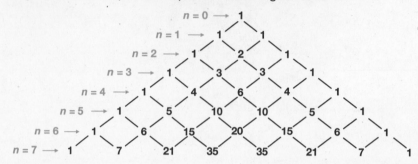

Polynomial Functions

7

Price changes for unleaded and diesel gas are difficult to model with simple functions from year to year. But no matter what year it is, a lot of people would agree that they pay a lot of money to fill up their tanks!

7.1

Unequal Equals

Solving Polynomial Inequalities

LEARNING GOALS

In this lesson, you will:

- Determine all roots of polynomial equations.
- Determine solutions to polynomial inequalities algebraically and graphically.

Income Inequality is a term used to describe the gap or difference between the amount of money that wealthy people possess as compared to the amount people without wealth possess. From the 1950s through the 1970s, the trend in the United States was toward *more* income equality. In other words, non-wealthy people earned money at a faster rate than the wealthiest segment of the population, creating a smaller gap between these two social classes. Many economists attribute this trend towards equality to the industrial boom leading up to and following World War II. Millions of soldiers returning from active war duty after World War II received low interest loans for housing, and money for college and career-training. This helped non-wealthy people earn a greater share of the country's wealth. In the 1970s the wealthiest 1% of the population owned approximately 9% of America's total wealth.

Since the 1970s, the United States has become a nation with much more income inequality. Wages in the middle and lower classes have remained fairly stagnant while the wealth of the top 1% has increased from 9% in the 1970s to nearly 25% today.

Why do you think the income inequality changed after the 1970s? Do you think this trend will continue for the foreseeable future? What factors play a part in determining wealthy and non-wealthy classes?

PROBLEM 1 **Analyzing Profits**

Lawn Enforcement is a small landscaping company. It has a profit model that can be represented by the function,

$$p(x) = -x^4 + 19.75x^3 - 133.25x^2 + 351.25x - 280.75$$

where profit, in thousands of dollars, is a function of time, in years, the company has been in business. Let's analyze $p(x)$ represented on a graph.

The graph shown represents the change in profit as a function of the number of years that Lawn Enforcement has been in business.

Years in Business

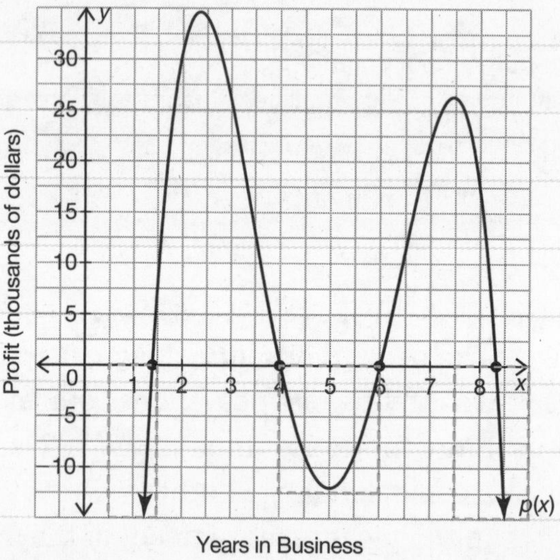

The points identified on the graph represent the zeros of the function where Lawn Enforcement's profit was 0.

Each point on the number line represents the years in business when Lawn Enforcement's profit was 0.

Years in Business

The function $p(x) = 0$ when $x = 1.4, 4, 6, 8.3$.

The regions enclosed in dashed boxes on the coordinate plane represent Lawn Enforcement's profit less than 0.

The regions on the number line enclosed in dashed boxes represent the years in business when Lawn Enforcement's profit was less than 0.

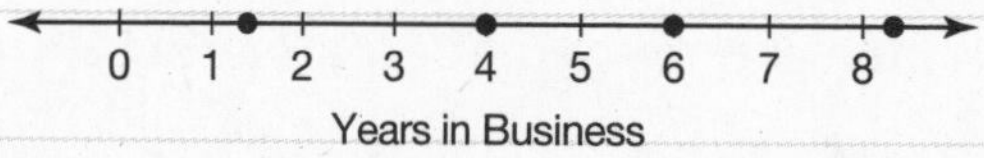

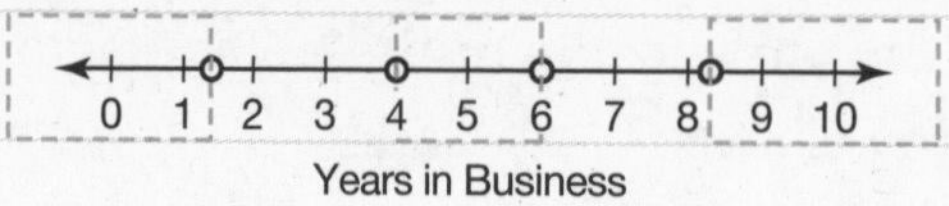

Years in Business

The function $p(x) < 0$ when $\begin{cases} x < 1.4 \\ 4 < x < 6 \\ x > 8.3 \end{cases}$.

7

1. Analyze the worked example.

 a. Why were the points changed to open circles on the number line to represent the years in business when $p(x) < 0$.

 b. Circle the parts of the graph on the coordinate plane that represent where $p(x) > 0$. Then circle the intervals on the number line that represent the years in business where $p(x) > 0$. Finally identify the set of x-values to complete the sentence and explain your answer in terms of this problem situation.

 The function $p(x) > 0$ when ____________________.

 c. Draw a solid box around the segment(s) where $p(x) > 35,000$. Then identify the set of x-values to complete the sentence. Finally, explain your answer in terms of this problem situation.

 The function $p(x) > 35,000$ when ______________________.

7

PROBLEM 2 Analyzing Methods for Solving Polynomial Inequalities

In this lesson, you will solve polynomial inequalities, which are very similar to solving linear inequalities. Recall from your experience of solving linear inequalities graphically, that $<$ or $>$ is represented with a dotted line, and $\leq$ or $\geq$ is represented with a solid line. Also remember that when you are determining which region(s) to shade, look at *y*-values above or below the boundary line depending on the inequality sign. It is always a good idea to check your work by selecting test points as well.

1. Samson, Kaley, Paco, and Sal each solved the quadratic inequality $-24 > 2x^2 + 14x$.

Samson

I graphed both sides of the inequality.

$y_1 = -24$

$y_2 = 2x^2 + 14x$

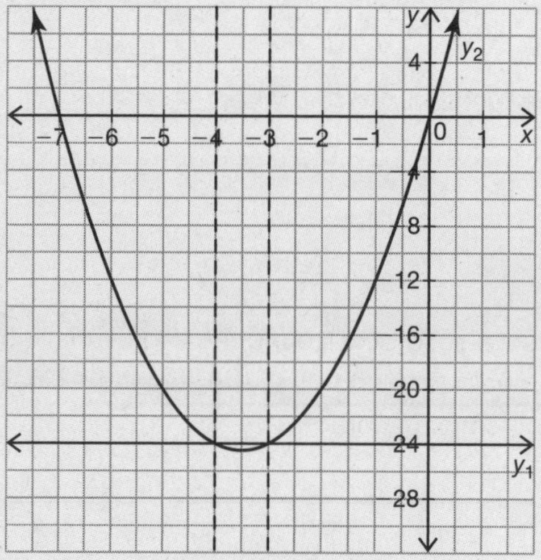

I drew vertical dashed lines at the two points where the graphs intersect.

I can then determine from the graph that the x-values of $2x^2 + 14x$ that generate values less than -24 are between -4 and -3.

Therefore the solution to the inequality is $-4 < x < -3$.

Paco

I added 24 to both sides of the inequality because I wanted one side to be equal to 0. Then, I graphed that inequality.

$y_1 = 2x^2 + 14x + 24$

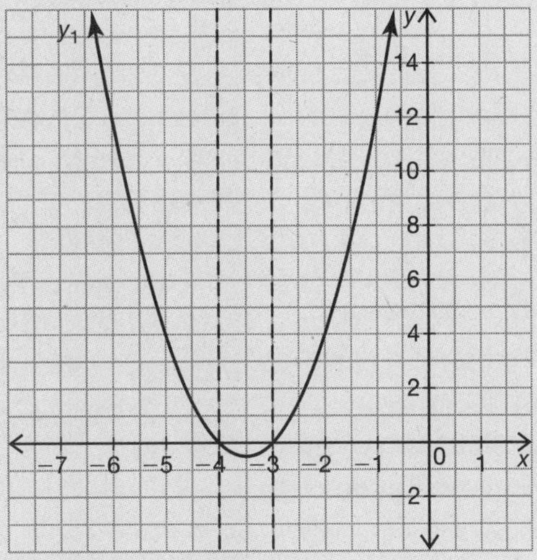

I drew vertical dashed lines where the graph crosses the x-axis.

I can then determine from the graph that the x-values of $2x^2 + 14x$ that generate values less than 0 are between −4 and −3.

Therefore the solution to the inequality is $-4 < x < -3$.

a. Explain why the graphs of Samson and Paco are different, yet generate the same answers.

b. Explain the error in Sal's work.

Kaley

I remember from solving linear inequalities that I can first treat the inequality as an equation and solve:

$0 = 2x^2 + 14x + 24$

$0 = 2(x^2 + 7x + 12)$

$0 = 2(x + 3)(x + 4)$

$x = -4, -3$

This means that the x-intercepts are -4 and -3. Breaking up the number line into 3 parts and testing each section in the original inequality $-24 > 2x^2 + 14x$, I can determine the solution:

Test $x = -3.5$

$-24 > 2(-3.5)^2 + 14(-3.5)$

$-24 > -24.5$

✓

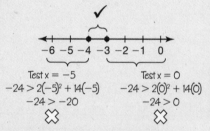

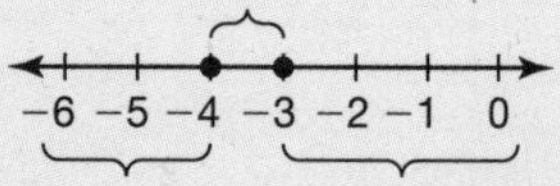

Test $x = -5$

$-24 > 2(-5)^2 + 14(-5)$

$-24 > -20$

✗

Test $x = 0$

$-24 > 2(0)^2 + 14(0)$

$-24 > 0$

✗

The only section that satisfies the original inequality is when x is between -4 and -3 so the solution to the inequality is $-4 < x < -3$.

Sal

I remember from solving linear inequalities that I can treat the inequality as an equation and solve:

$2x^2 + 14x = -24$

$2x(x + 7) = -24$

$2x = -24 \qquad (x + 7) = -24$

$x = -12 \qquad x = -31$

This means that the x-intercepts are -12 and -31, so the solution to the inequality is $-31 < x < -12$.

c. Compare Samson's method to Kaley's method. List advantages and disadvantages of each method.

2. Solve $18 \leq 3x^2 + x$ using any method. Explain why you chose the method.

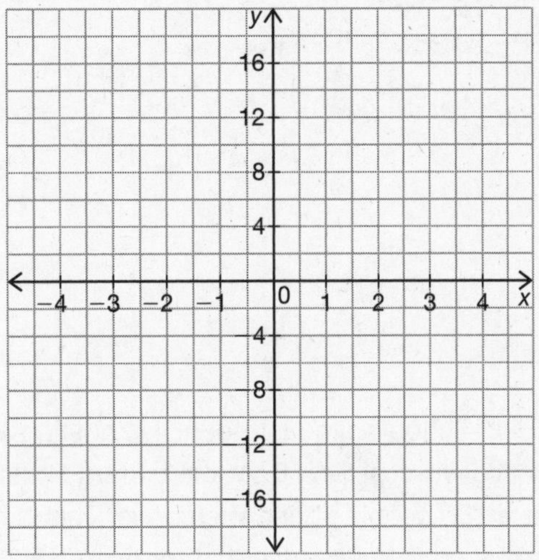

Polynomial inequalities can be used to represent everyday situations. Write and solve each real-world inequality.

1. Get Your Kicks is an indoor soccer complex. The roof's height at the facility is 80 feet. If a soccer ball is kicked and touches the ceiling during a game, the team that kicked the ball must have a player sit out for two minutes. Michael kicks a ball straight up in the air with an initial velocity of 73 feet per second.

   a. Write an inequality to represent this problem situation.

Remember the formula for initial velocity is
$$h(t) = -16t^2 + V_0t + h_0$$
where v_0 represents initial velocity and h_0 represents initial height.

   b. Use your inequality to determine whether Michael's team will be penalized for hitting the ceiling. Explain your reasoning.

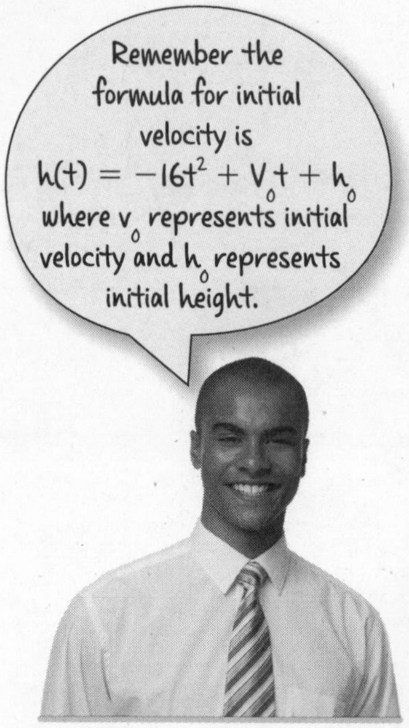

2. Glen High School's student council is hosting a dance to raise money for panda bears. The dance will cost $2250. At the current ticket price of $10, the council knows that they will have 185 people attend the dance. This is not enough people to cover the cost of the dance, so they estimate that for every $0.25 decrease in ticket price, 15 more people will attend the dance.

   a. Write an equation that will represent the profit that the dance will make.

   b. Write an inequality to represent the dance making a profit.

c. Determine the maximum price the council can charge for tickets and still make a profit.

d. Determine the price of the ticket that will maximize profit. What is the maximum profit?

3. Use a graphing calculator to solve each inequality.

a. $-5 \geq x^3 - 9x$

b. $0 < 2x^3 - 3x^2 - 3x + 2$

4. The average blood sugar (also known as glucose) levels in a person's blood should be between 70 and 100 mg/dL (milligrams per deciliter) one hour after eating. A person with Type 2 diabetes strives to keep glucose levels under 120 mg/dL with diet and exercise in order to avoid insulin injections. Glucose levels of one individual over the span of 72 hours can be represented with the polynomial function,

$$b(t) = 0.000139x^4 - 0.0188x^3 + 0.8379x^2 - 13.55x + 176.51$$

where glucose levels is a function of the number of hours.

a. For what hours were the glucose levels greater than 120 mg/dL?

b. For what hours were the glucose levels less than 120 mg/dL?

5. Solve each inequality by factoring and sketching. Use the coordinate plane to sketch the general graph of the polynomial in order to determine which values satisfy the inequality.

a. $2x^3 - 8x^2 - 8x + 32 > 0$

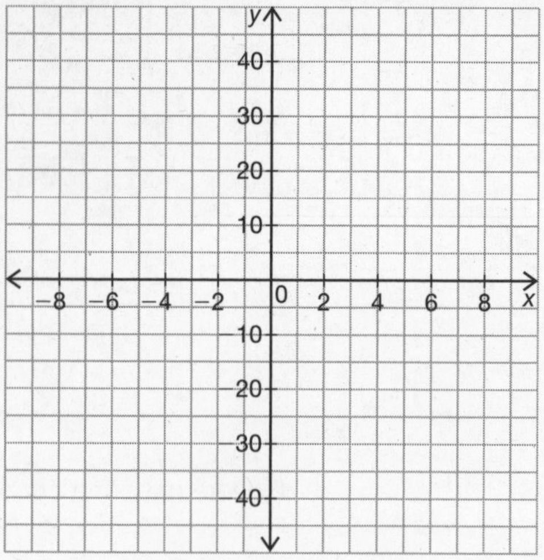

b. $6x^3 - 21x^2 - 12x > 0$

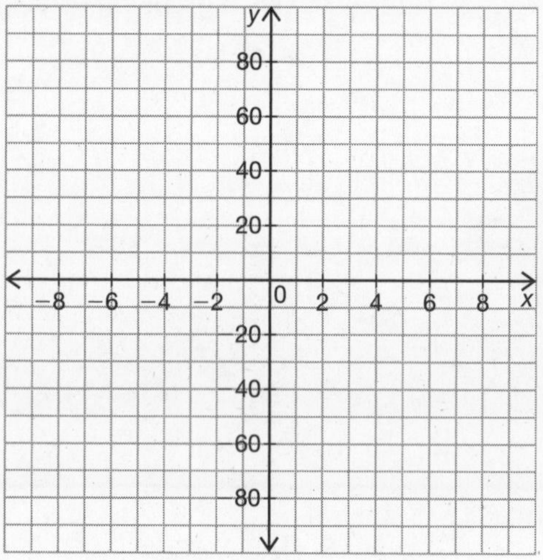

c. $x^4 - 13x^2 + 36 \leq 0$

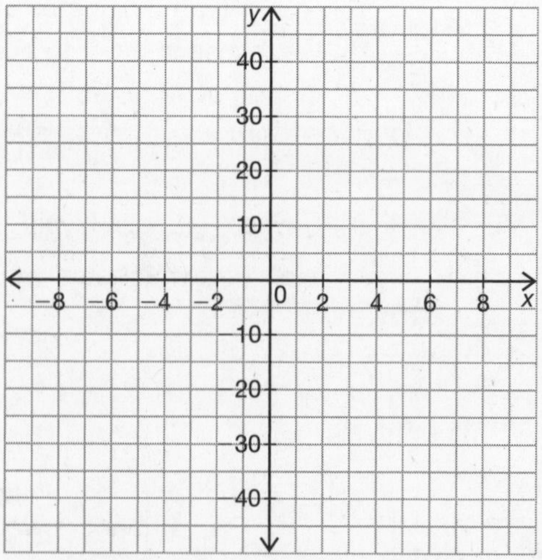

Be prepared to share your solutions and methods.

7.2

America's Next Top Polynomial Model

Modeling with Polynomials

LEARNING GOALS

In this lesson, you will:

- Determine the appropriate regression equation to model a problem situation.
- Predict outcomes using a regression equation.
- Sketch polynomial functions that appropriately model a problem situation.

KEY TERMS

- regression equation
- coefficient of determination

Transportation plans are an essential part of any large urban development project. Whether designing residential blocks, shopping districts, or stadiums, part of the planning process is determining how to move large groups of people in and out of an area quickly. Building new highways, bus stations, bike lanes, or railways may be necessary for some large-scale developments.

Part of urban development projects is monitoring existing conditions in a specific area. Planners must determine how well the current traffic infrastructure meets the community's needs before modeling and predicting what transportation processes may work best for a future project.

What things do you consider when planning projects? What type of predictions or considerations do you make when planning projects?

PROBLEM 1 Feeling a Little Congested

City planners consider building a new stadium on several acres of land close to the downtown of a large city. They monitored the number of cars entering and exiting downtown from a major highway between 1:00 PM and 7:00 PM to determine current traffic conditions.

1. Analyze the table of values that represent the average number of cars entering and exiting downtown during the given hours of a typical weekday. The value for time represents the start-time for the full hour over which the vehicles were monitored.

Time (PM)	Average Number of Vehicles on a Typical Weekday (thousands)
1:00	7.0
2:00	10.8
3:00	14.5
4:00	21.1
5:00	23.9
6:00	19.0
7:00	10.0

When entering the data into your calculator, enter 1:00 as 1, 2:00 as 2, 3:00 as 3, etc.

a. Describe any patterns you notice. Explain the patterns in the context of this problem situation.

b. Predict the type of polynomial that best fits the data. Explain your reasoning.

2. Create a scatter plot of the data.

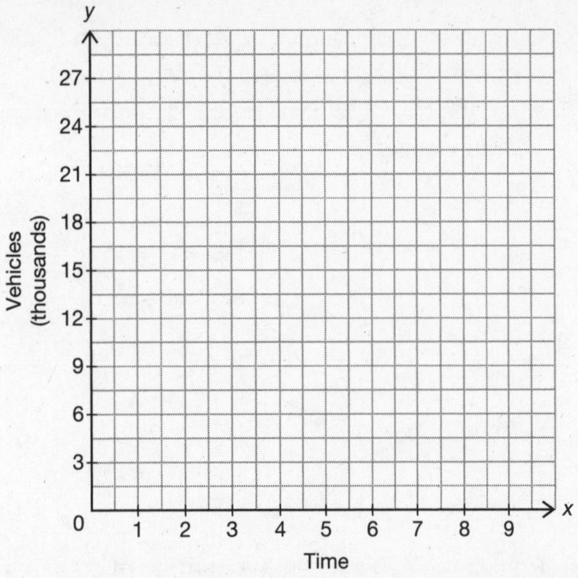

Recall that a **regression equation** is a function that models the relationship between two variables in a scatter plot. The regression equation can be used to make predictions about future events. Any degree polynomial can model a scatter plot, but data generally has one curve that best fits the data. You may also recall that the **coefficient of determination** (R^2) measures the "strength" of the relationship between the original data and its regression equation. The value ranges from 0 to 1 with a value of 1 indicating a perfect fit between the regression equation and the original data.

3. Use a graphing calculator to determine the regression equation for the average number of cars entering and exiting downtown on a typical weekday. Sketch the regression equation on the coordinate plane in Question 2. How well does the regression equation model the data? Was your prediction about the type of polynomial that best fits the data correct? Explain your reasoning.

4. Use the regression equation that best models the data to make predictions.

Use what you know about polynomials to work efficiently. Predict which degree function is the best fit first, then check to see if it has an R^2 value close to 1.

a. Downtown is congested when more than 20,000 cars are on the streets and highway. Predict when the downtown will be congested. Explain your reasoning.

b. Predict the hours when the number of cars that enter and exit downtown is less than 10,000. Explain your reasoning.

c. Predict the number of vehicles that enter or exit downtown during the hour starting at noon.

d. Predict the number of vehicles that enter or exit downtown during the hour starting at 9 PM.

e. Predict the number of cars that enter or exit downtown during the hour starting at midnight the previous evening.

5. Consider the data and your regression equation.

a. For what intervals is the model appropriate for this problem situation? For what intervals is the model inappropriate? Explain your reasoning.

b. Sketch a curve that you believe accurately predicts the number of vehicles on the road over a 2-day period. Explain your reasoning.

When are more drivers on the road? When are fewer drivers on the road? Will the graph follow any patterns?

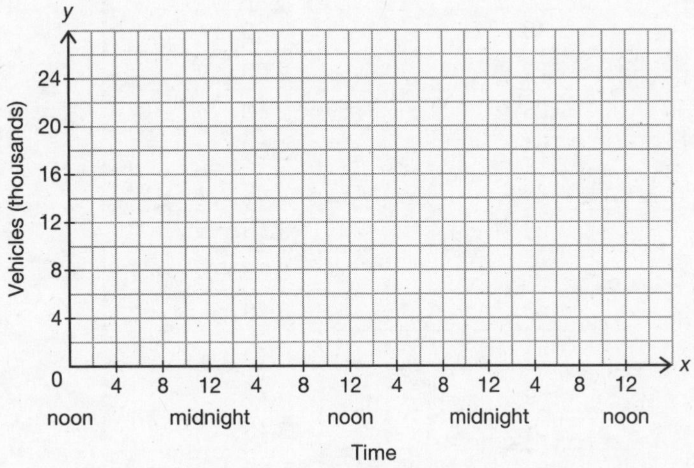

6. Do you think a polynomial function could accurately model this problem situation over the next 2 months before the next planning phase? Explain your reasoning.

PROBLEM 2 Keep It to a Minimum

Although the minimum wage may vary from state to state, the U.S. federal government sets an absolute minimum wage for the nation every few years.

1. Analyze the table of values that shows the absolute minimum wage, and the years they were enacted by Congress.

Time Since 1950 (years)	Absolute Minimum Wage (dollars)
5	0.75
6	1.00
11	1.15
13	1.25
17	1.40
18	1.60
24	2.00
25	2.10
28	2.65
29	2.90
30	3.10
31	3.35
40	3.80
41	4.25
46	4.75
47	5.15
57	5.85
58	6.55
59	7.25

Make sure you are comfortable with the data before analyzing the problem. How would you represent 1975? 1950? 1945?

a. Describe any patterns you notice.

b. Predict the type of polynomial that best fits this data. Explain your reasoning.

7

2. Analyze the data graphically.

a. Use a graphing calculator to determine the best regression function $f(x)$ to model the changes in the minimum wage over the years since 1950. Sketch the regression equation on the coordinate plane.

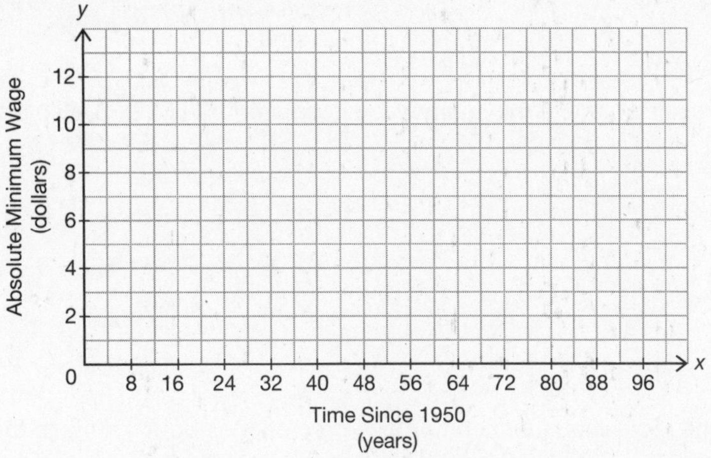

b. How well does the regression function model this data? Explain your reasoning.

All of the decimal places are important in your regression equation, so don't round your answer when entering it into your graphing calculator.

3. Use the regression equation that best models the data to make predictions.

a. Predict the absolute minimum wage in 2020. Explain your reasoning.

b. Predict the minimum wage in 1945. Explain your reasoning.

c. Predict when the minimum wage is greater than $12.50. Explain your reasoning.

4. Use the regression function to make predictions about events in the distant past and distant future.

a. According to the regression equation, what was the minimum wage when the Civil War ended in 1865? Explain your reasoning.

b. Predict the years when the minimum wage will be greater than $15.00. Explain your reasoning.

c. Do you think that a cubic model is appropriate to predict minimum wages in the distant past and future? Explain your reasoning.

Let's take a closer look at the minimum wage in the early part of the 20th Century. A minimum wage did not exist until 1938 under the Fair Labor Standards Act. Before this time, employers could pay employees any hourly wage that employees were willing to accept. The initial hourly minimum wage in 1938 was $0.25 per hour. The wage increased steadily before reaching $0.75 in 1955.

5. Consider the minimum wage from 1900 to 1955.

a. Sketch a graph that you believe accurately models the minimum wage for the time interval (1900, 1955). Explain your reasoning.

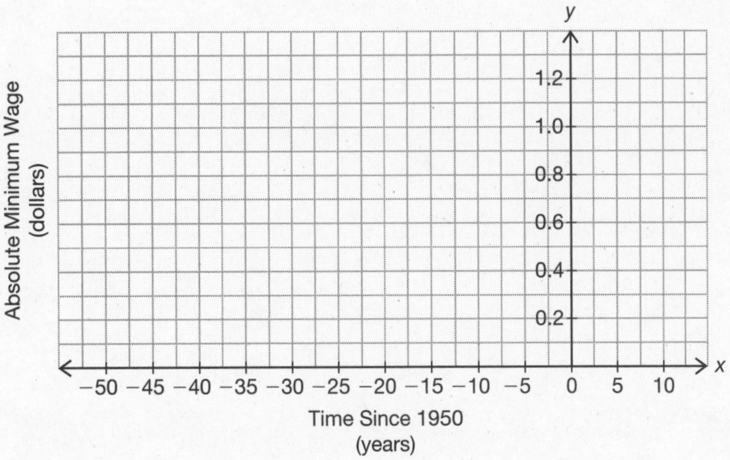

b. Do you think a polynomial function can accurately model the changes in minimum wage in the 20th Century? Explain your reasoning.

Be prepared to share your solutions and methods.

7.3

Connecting Pieces

Piecewise Functions

LEARNING GOALS

In this lesson, you will:

- Write a piecewise function to model data.
- Graph a piecewise function.
- Determine intervals for a piecewise function to best model data.

KEY TERM

- piecewise function

Some of the most popular children's books from the 1980s and 1990s had an interesting format: the reader controlled the action of the story! At various key moments throughout the text, the reader was given an opportunity to make a decision about the main character's next move. Each choice led to a different outcome.

For example, in a dragon adventure, the reader may have to decide whether the knight should run and hide from a dragon, or grab a sword and try to slay the beast. One set of conditions led to one outcome, while another set of conditions led to a different outcome.

This idea is fairly common today, but at the time it was revolutionary for the same book to have multiple story lines and endings.

Have you ever read a book like this? If so, what did you like or dislike about it?

PROBLEM 1 Keep It to a Minimum, Revisited

Recall the minimum wage problem from the previous lesson.

The table shows the absolute minimum wage during various years. A scatter plot of this data is also shown.

Time Since 1950 (years)	Absolute Minimum Wage (dollars)
5	0.75
6	1.00
11	1.15
13	1.25
17	1.40
18	1.60
24	2.00
25	2.10
28	2.65
29	2.90
30	3.10
31	3.35
33	3.35
35	3.35
38	3.35
39	3.35
40	3.80
41	4.25
46	4.75
47	5.15
48	5.15
50	5.15
53	5.15
56	5.15
57	5.85
58	6.55
59	7.25

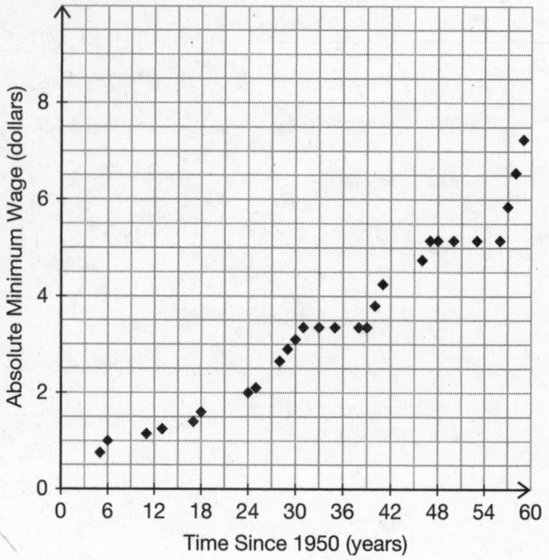

Sometimes, a single polynomial function is not the best model for a set of data. Analyze the graph of the minimum wage data. Instead of using a single polynomial function to model this data, consider separating the data into "pieces," where each piece is modeled by a single polynomial function.

To determine the pieces, look for breaks in the patterns that you see in the data. For example, the data in one part of the graph may appear to be linear, but then it may appear to be cubic in another part of the graph. Therefore, you can model these two parts of the graph with two different polynomial functions.

The number of pieces, or functions, that model the data can vary. For example, one person may look at the data and determine that it can be represented with two polynomial functions, while another person may see three, four, or even more functions.

Let's model the absolute minimum wage data by dividing it into five pieces, where each piece is modeled by a different polynomial function.

1. How do you think the data should be divided so that there are five pieces? Circle each piece on the given graph.

2. Consider the data from the years 1955 through 1981.

   a. Describe the type of polynomial function that best models the data over this interval. Explain your reasoning.

Your graphing calculator is limited in that it can only calculate linear, quadratic, cubic, and quartic polynomial regressions. So, choose one of these for each regression equation.

   b. Write the regression equation that best models the data over this interval.

   c. What is the coefficient of determination for the regression equation? Is the model you chose a good fit for the data over this interval? Explain why or why not.

3. Consider the data after the year 1981 and before the year 1989.

   a. Describe the type of polynomial function that best models the data over this interval. Explain your reasoning.

   b. Determine a regression equation for this data over this interval.

   c. What is the coefficient of determination for the regression equation? Is the model you chose a good fit for the data over this interval? Explain why or why not.

4. Consider the data from the years 1989 through 1997.

   a. Describe the type of polynomial function that best models the data over this interval. Explain your reasoning.

   b. Determine a regression equation for this data over this interval.

   c. What is the coefficient of determination for the regression equation? Is the model you chose a good fit for the data over this interval? Explain why or why not.

5. Consider the data after the year 1997 and before the year 2006.

   a. Describe the type of polynomial function that best models the data over this interval. Explain your reasoning.

   b. Determine a regression equation for this data over this interval.

   c. What is the coefficient of determination for the regression equation? Is the model you chose a good fit for the data over this interval? Explain why or why not.

6. Consider the data from the years 2006 through 2009.

   a. Describe the type of polynomial function that best models the data over this interval. Explain your reasoning.

b. Determine a regression equation for this data over this interval.

c. What is the coefficient of determination for the regression equation? Is the model you chose a good fit for the data over this interval? Explain why or why not.

The year 1955 is represented by x = 5, not x = 1955. Remember this when you write each domain.

7. Write the equation of the function $f(x)$, where $f(x)$ includes each regression equation you used to model the absolute minimum wage data from the years 1955 through 2009. Write each equation on the line before the comma and write its corresponding domain on the line after the comma. Then, use a graphing calculator to sketch the graph of this function on the scatter plot at the beginning of the problem.

$$f(x) = \begin{cases} \underline{\hspace{5cm}}, & \underline{\hspace{2cm}} \\ \underline{\hspace{5cm}}, & \underline{\hspace{2cm}} \\ \underline{\hspace{5cm}}, & \underline{\hspace{2cm}} \\ \underline{\hspace{5cm}}, & \underline{\hspace{2cm}} \\ \underline{\hspace{5cm}}, & \underline{\hspace{2cm}} \end{cases}$$

8. Explain why the function you wrote in Question 7 is a better fit for the data than a single linear, quadratic, cubic, or quartic function.

You have just written the equation for a *piecewise function*. A **piecewise function** includes different functions that represent different parts of the domain.

A piecewise function and its graph are shown.

$$f(x) = \begin{cases} x, & x < 0 \\ x^2, & 0 \le x < 3 \\ -(x-5)^3 + 1, & x \ge 3 \end{cases}$$

Notice the domain is the set of real numbers broken into three different parts.

$y = -(x-5)^3 + 1$

$y = x^2$

$y = x$

$x < 0$ $0 \le x < 3$ $x \ge 3$

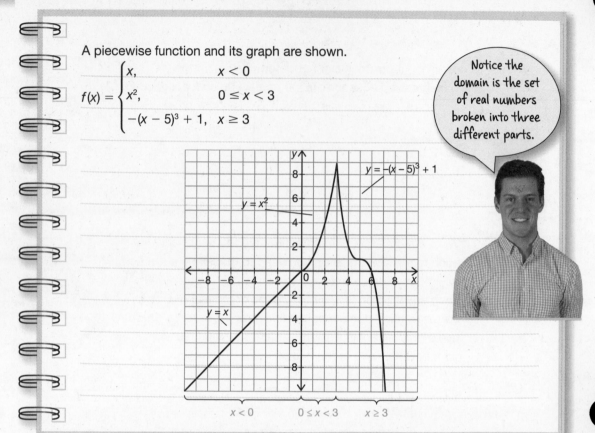

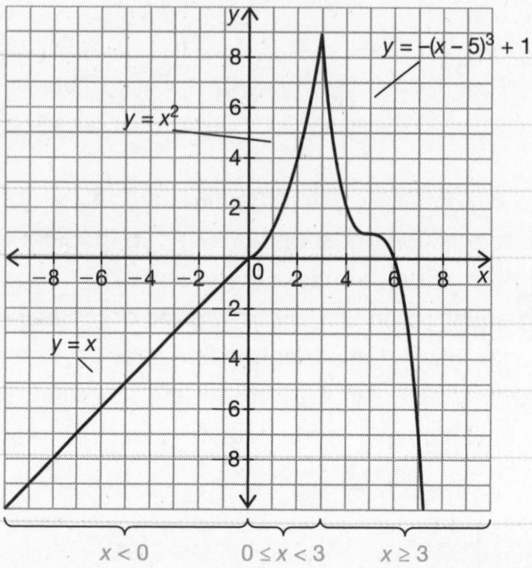

9. Sketch each piecewise function.

Pay attention to whether the endpoints are included or not included for each part of the piecewise function.

a. $g(x) = \begin{cases} \frac{1}{2}x + 1, & x < 4 \\ -(x - 4)^2 + 3, & x \geq 4 \end{cases}$

b. $t(x) = \begin{cases} x, & x < -2 \\ x^4 - 25x^2, & -2 \leq x \leq 2 \\ 2, & x > 2 \end{cases}$

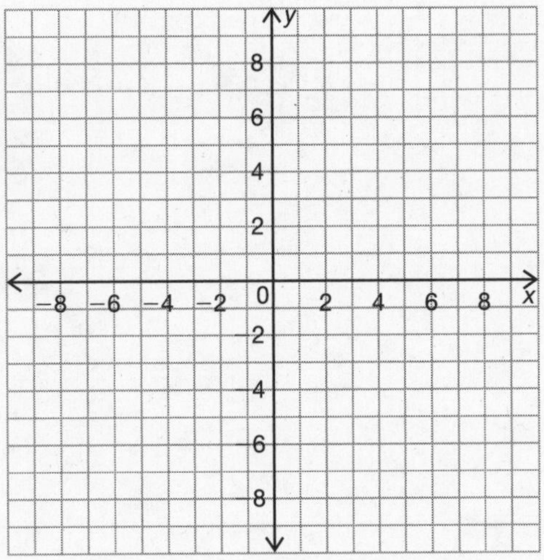

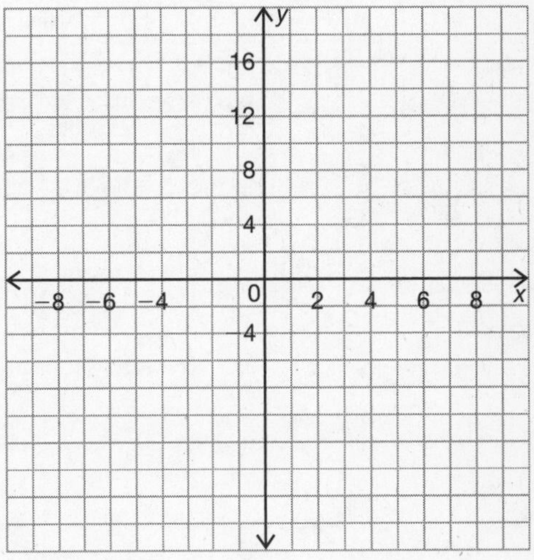

10. Billie, Kyle, and Avery were each asked to write the piecewise function to represent the graph shown.

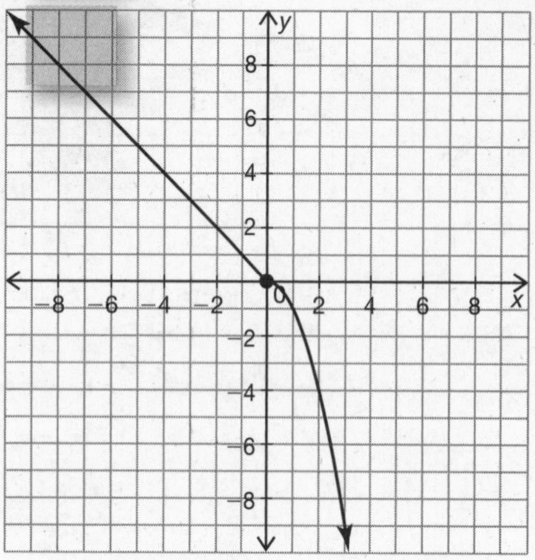

Kyle

$f(x) = \begin{cases} -x, & x < 0 \\ -x^2, & x \geq 0 \end{cases}$

Avery

$f(x) = \begin{cases} -x, & x \leq 0 \\ -x^2, & x > 0 \end{cases}$

Billie

$f(x) = \begin{cases} -x, & x \leq 0 \\ -x^2, & x \geq 0 \end{cases}$

Does analyzing a graph without a scenario change the way you write the function?

Who's correct? Explain your reasoning.

11. Write the equation for each piecewise function given its graph.

a. $h(x) =$

b. $b(x) =$

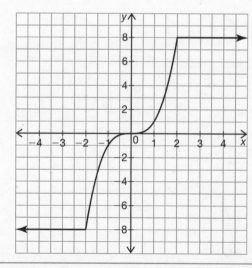

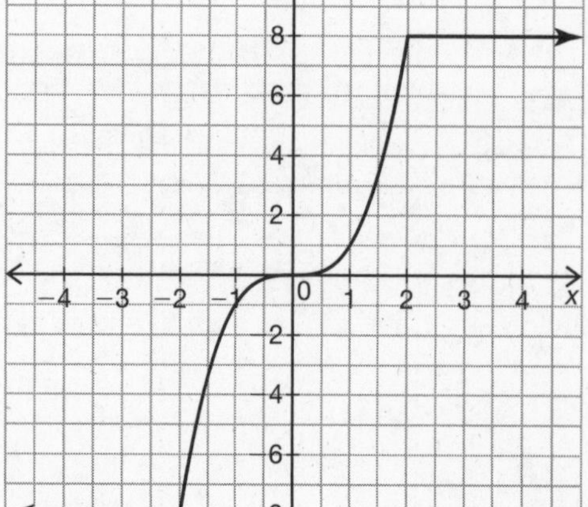

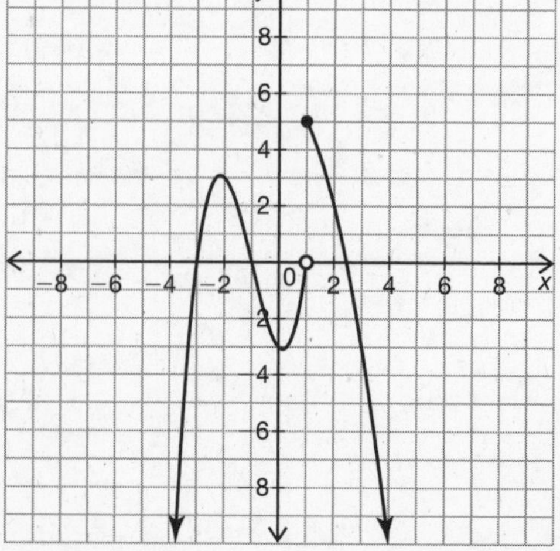

PROBLEM 2 Salinity Now! Salinity Now!

Salinity is the measure of saltiness, or dissolved salt content in water. Salinity in an estuary changes due to location, tidal functions, seasonal weather changes, and volume of freshwater runoff. Ecologists routinely measure salinity in estuaries because of its impact on plants, animals, and people. Too much salinity can reduce vegetation in surrounding areas.

The table shows the salinity levels in an estuary in North Carolina over a period of 24 days. A scatter plot of this data is also shown.

Time (days)	1	2	3	4	5	6	7	8
Salinity (parts per thousand)	27.9	27.9	28.2	30.5	29.6	28.3	27.9	27.9

Time (days)	9	10	11	12	13	14	15	16
Salinity (parts per thousand)	28.6	30.1	29.9	30	29.5	29.5	29.5	29.4

Time (days)	17	18	19	20	21	22	23	24
Salinity (parts per thousand)	29.2	29.1	29.0	29.0	28.9	28.8	28.8	28.7

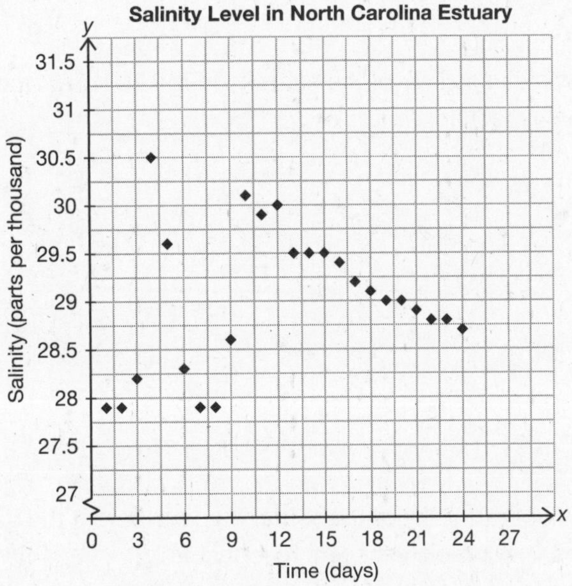

1. Consider the data for the first ten days. Determine the regression equation that is the best fit for the data over this interval. Explain your reasoning.

2. Consider the data after the tenth day. Determine the regression equation that is the best fit for the data over this interval. Explain your reasoning.

3. Use your answers to Questions 1 and 2 to write a piecewise function that models the salinity over the 24-day period. Then, graph the function on the scatter plot.

4. Predict the salinity of the estuary on the 30th day. Does your prediction seem reasonable?

5. Predict the salinity of the estuary 5 days before the data in the table was recorded. Does your prediction seem reasonable?

PROBLEM 3 Fill It Up!

The table shows the average price of a gallon of regular unleaded gas from the years 1980 through 2008.

Years Since 1980	0	1	2	3	4	5	6	7	8	9
Average Gas Price (dollars)	1.25	1.38	1.30	1.24	1.21	1.20	0.93	0.95	0.95	1.02

Years Since 1980	10	11	12	13	14	15	16	17	18	19
Average Gas Price (dollars)	1.16	1.14	1.13	1.11	1.11	1.15	1.23	1.23	1.06	1.17

Years Since 1980	20	21	22	23	24	25	26	27	28
Average Gas Price (dollars)	1.51	1.46	1.36	1.59	1.88	2.30	2.59	2.80	3.27

1. Create a scatter plot of the data on the grid shown.

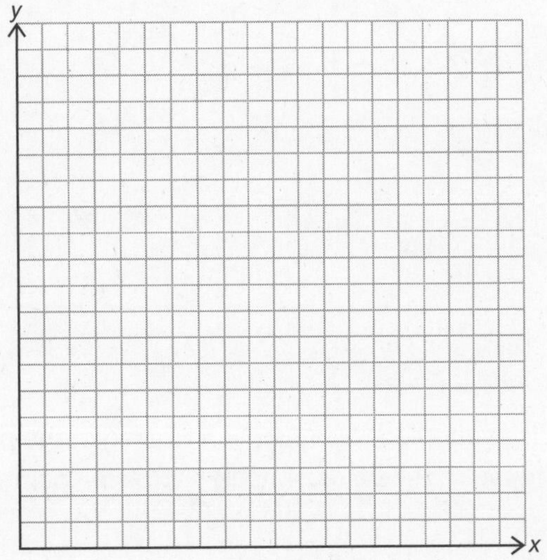

2. Describe the type of function(s) that best models this data. Explain your reasoning.

3. Consider using a piecewise function to model this data. Determine the intervals for the domain, and the type of polynomial function for each interval. Explain your reasoning.

4. Write a piecewise function to model the data. Then, graph the piecewise function on the grid in Question 1.

5. Use your piecewise function to predict the price of gas in the year 2020. Does your prediction seem reasonable? Explain your reasoning.

PROBLEM 4 Live Long and Strong

Life expectancy is a prediction of the number of years that a person will live. Life expectancies often vary significantly over time and across different groups such as country, gender, and race.

The table shows the average life expectancy of a person from the years 1910 through 1920.

Years Since 1910	0	1	2	3	4	5
Life Expectancy (years)	50.6	52.7	53.7	52.7	54.4	54.7

Years Since 1910	6	7	8	9	10
Life Expectancy (years)	52.0	51.2	39.4	54.8	54.1

1. Create a scatter plot of this data on the grid shown.

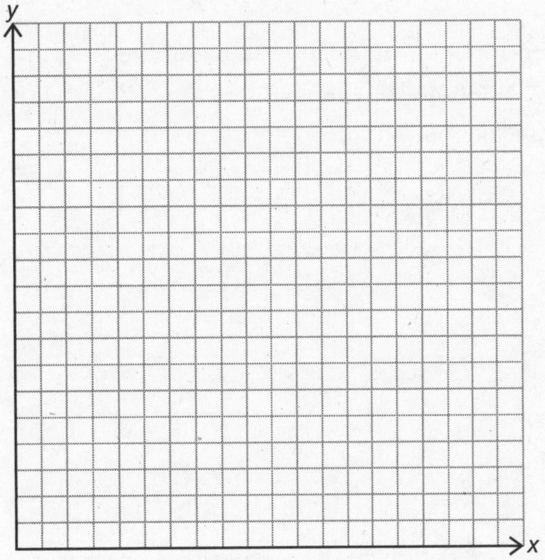

2. Write a piecewise function to model the data. Then, graph the piecewise function on the grid. Explain your reasoning.

3. Write a brief report that explains the patterns shown by the data in terms of life expectancy from 1910 through 1920. Do some research and use facts to support your claims.

Talk the Talk

Write a brief summary about what you've learned about using piecewise functions to model real-world data. Include advantages and disadvantages of using a piecewise function instead of a single function type to model data.

Be prepared to share your solutions and methods.

7.4

Modeling Gig

Modeling Polynomial Data

LEARNING GOALS

In this lesson, you will:

- Model a problem situation with a polynomial function.
- Solve problems using a regression equation.

Americans watch a lot of movies. The first ever movie was made in the 1870s, but it wasn't until the early 20th century that movie theaters were invented. Americans lined up to pay a quarter to see black and white productions with no sound. As audio-visual technology advanced, so did the quality of movie productions. Changes in technology not only improved the quality of movies, they also led to changes in the entire industry.

The Video Home System (also known as VHS), developed in the 1970s, allowed consumers to rent or purchase movies and watch them on their TVs at home. With the invention of the remote control, people could even fast forward to their favorite parts, without even getting off the couch! Video stores were a huge business, leading way to newer technology that allowed customers to stream movies from their computers at home.

How do you think movies will change throughout the 21st Century? Do you think people will still go to "old-fashioned" movie theaters to watch movies?

PROBLEM 1 Strut Down the Statwalk

The CALC_U-Now Company sells a variety of calculators. The table shows the relationship between the price of various models of graphing calculators and the monthly profit earned from the sale of the calculators.

1. Analyze the data in the table of values.

Price of Calculators (dollars)	Monthly Profit (dollars)
65	15,950
70	17,600
75	19,060
80	19,300
85	19,290
90	19,240
95	18,000
100	17,150
105	15,300

a. What patterns do you notice in the data?

b. Describe the polynomial function that best models this data. Explain your reasoning.

2. Use a graphing calculator to determine the regression function that best models this data.

3. Write inequalities to represent the prices for which CALC-U-Now would lose money? Explain your reasoning.

4. CALC-U-Now must make budget cuts! As a financial contractor, you must determine which calculator price will generate the most profit. Write a statement to support your decision including all relevant mathematics.

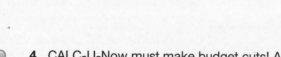

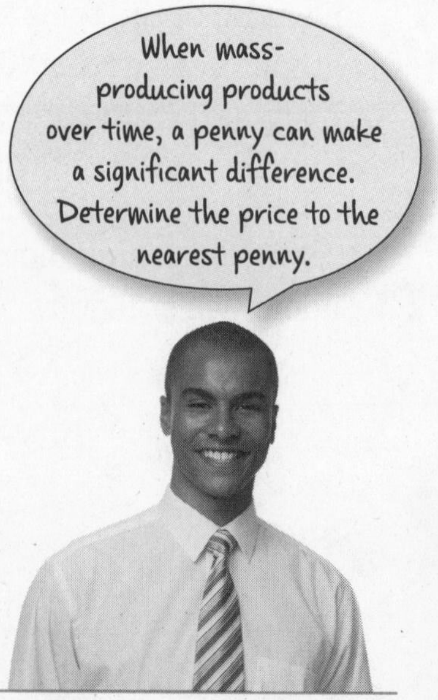

When mass-producing products over time, a penny can make a significant difference. Determine the price to the nearest penny.

PROBLEM 2 3,2,1.... Polynomial Modeling Action!

Inflation has influenced the price of a movie ticket over the years. The first movie theater opened in the year 1900, charging $.05 per ticket. The data provided shows how the average price of a movie ticket has increased over the years.

Years	Average Price of a Movie Ticket (dollars)
1900	0.05
1948	0.36
1958	0.68
1971	1.65
1983	3.15
1995	4.35
2003	6.03
2007	6.88
2009	7.50

Remember the function that best models the data has a coefficient of determination closest to 1.

1. Determine a regression function that best models this data.

2. Use your regression equation to predict when the average price of a movie ticket will reach $15.00. Explain your reasoning.

3. Use your regression equation to predict the cost of a movie ticket in the year 2100. Explain your reasoning.

7

4. Jessica and Lindsay disagree over how to model this situation with a polynomial function.

Jessica

A cubic function is the most appropriate model. The coefficient of determination is closest to 1.

Lindsay

A piece-wise function is most appropriate for this situation.

Who's correct? Explain your reasoning.

PROBLEM 3 "Polynomial Models" for $500, Please!

The Math Club sponsors an event each year to raise money for their trip to the Quiz Bowl. As the president of the Math Club, you propose having a movie night fundraiser. You survey the students to see how many students will attend. The number of students varies depending on the ticket price.

Ticket Price (dollars)	Students Who Will Attend
1.25	120
1.75	105
2.25	95
2.75	83
3.25	77
3.75	64
4.25	58
4.75	40
5.25	30

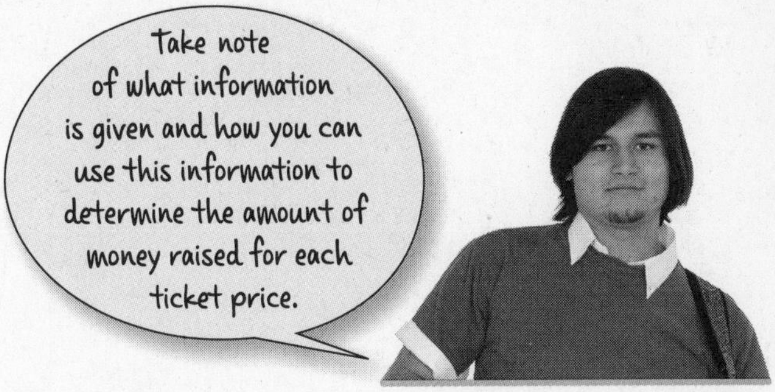
Take note of what information is given and how you can use this information to determine the amount of money raised for each ticket price.

Write a short letter to your principal about your findings. Include details about the exact ticket price that raises the most money as well as the approximate number of students who will attend.

Be prepared to share your solutions and methods.

7.5

The Choice Is Yours

Comparing Polynomials in Different Representations

LEARNING GOALS

In this lesson, you will:

- Compare polynomials using different representations.
- Analyze key characteristics of polynomials.

Infinity refers to something that goes on without end. The set of natural numbers {1, 2, 3, . . .} and the set of integers {. . . −2, −1, 0, 1, 2 . . .} are examples of infinite sets because they continue without end. Another example of an infinite set is the set of rational numbers between 0 and 1.

Seeing different infinite sets of numbers begs the question: do all infinite sets have the same quantity of numbers in them? The set of natural numbers are only positive, while the set of integers are positive and negative. Does this mean that the set of natural numbers has fewer numbers than the set of integers?

How do you compare the size of these sets of numbers? Is it possible for one infinite set to be greater than another infinite set?

PROBLEM 1 The Best of Both Representations

Recall that you can represent a polynomial using a graph, table of values, equation, or description of its key characteristics. The ability to compare functions using different representations is an important mathematical habit. This skill allows you to model problems in different ways, solve problems using a variety of methods, and more easily identify patterns. At times you may need to compare functions when they are in different representations.

When comparing two functions in different forms, it may be helpful to ask yourself a series of questions. Examples include:

- *What information is given?*
- *What is the degree of each function?*
- *What do I know about all functions of this degree?*
- *What key characteristics do I need to know?*
- *How do the functions compare?*

Consider two polynomial functions $f(x)$ and $g(x)$. Which polynomial has a greater number of real zeros? Justify your choice.

$f(x) = -2(x - 1)^3$

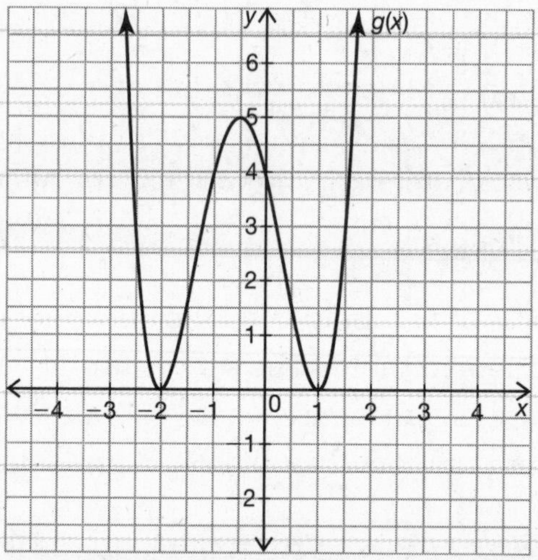

Metacognition is an important mathematical habit that involves mentally asking yourself a series of questions to determine what you know about a problem and how you can reason your way to a solution.

- The Fundamental Theorem of Algebra states that the number of zeros must be equal to the degree of the function. Therefore, $f(x)$ has 3 zeros.
- The function $f(x)$ has a real zero at 1 (multiplicity 3), so all zeros are real.
- The graph of $g(x)$ shows each zero has multiplicity 2, for a total of 4 real zeros.

The function $g(x)$ has 4 real zeros while $f(x)$ has 3. Therefore the correct choice is $g(x)$.

7

1. Toby compared the table of values for $f(x)$ and the graph of $g(x)$ to determine which polynomial function has the greater number of real zeros.

x	$f(x)$
−2	3
−1	−2
0	−5
1	−6
2	−5
3	−2
4	3

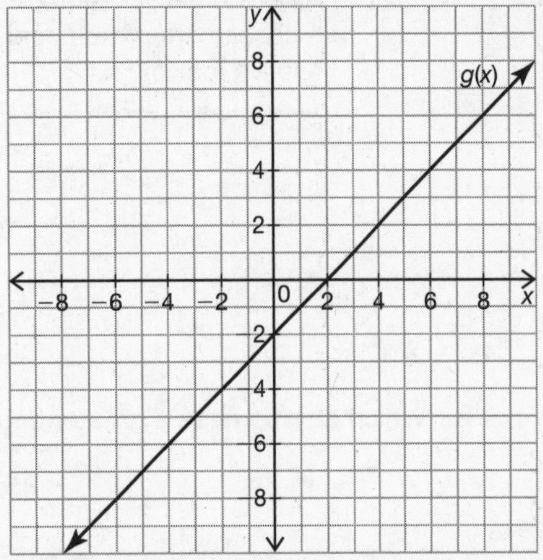

Toby

Function $g(x)$ has the greater number of real zeros. The graph has 1 zero at $x = 2$ while the table of values has no output value of 0, and therefore no zeros.

Is Toby correct? Explain your reasoning.

2. Analyze each pair of representations. Then, answer each question and justify your reasoning.

a. Which function has a greater degree?

A polynomial function $h(x)$ has 1 absolute maximum and 1 relative maximum.	$j(x) = -40(x - 7)^2 + 30x^2 - 17x + 1$

b. Which function has a greater degree?

x	$m(x)$
−2	9
−1	3
0	1
1	3
2	9

A polynomial function $n(x)$ has a real zero and an imaginary zero.

c. Which function has a degree divisible by 2?

x	$p(x)$
−2	2
−1	4
0	6
1	8
2	10

The function $q(x)$ has only imaginary solutions.

d. Determine which function has the greater output as x approaches infinity.

An odd function $r(x)$ with $a < 0$.	$k(x) = x^6 + x^4 + 3x^2 + 5x - 10{,}000$

e. Determine which function has the greater output as x approaches negative infinity.

$t(x) = -3(x - 4)^8 + 130$	A quartic function $s(x)$ with y-intercept (0, 5) and all imaginary roots.

3. Sam and Otis disagree when they compared the two functions shown to determine which one has an odd degree.

The function $f(x)$ has an absolute maximum value.	$g(x) = x^4(3 - x)(2x^2 + 3)(x^4 + 4)$

Sam

The function f(x) has an odd degree because odd functions approach positive infinity as x either increases or decreases. This means f(x) has a maximum value.

Otis

The function g(x) has an odd degree. When I multiplied the factors, I got a term with a highest exponent of 11: $x^4(-x)(2x^2)(x^4) = -2x^{11}$.

Therefore, g(x) is odd.

Who is correct? Justify your reasoning.

Two Representations Are Better Than One

Many problems in mathematics are unique, without specific step-by-step algorithms that lead to an answer. In Problem 1, *The Best of Both Representations*, you mentally asked yourself a series of metacognitive questions to compare functions in different representations. As you consider additional questions in this lesson, it may be helpful to compare the problems to ones that you have already completed.

Ask yourself:

- *How is this problem the same or different than the previous ones that I have already solved?*
- *What do I know about the function that is given? What can I conclude that is not directly stated?*

Consider the representations shown. Which function has a greater *y*-intercept? Justify your reasoning.

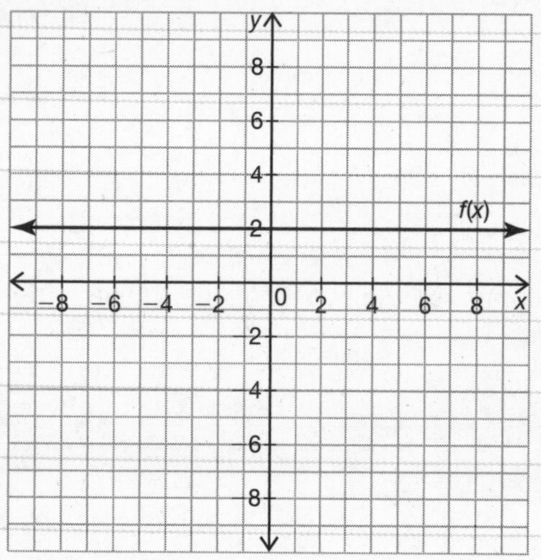

A function *g*(*x*) has an *a*-value less than zero and all roots have a multiplicity of 2.

Remember that the *a*-value is the coefficient of the leading term. For example, in the function $f(x) = 5x^2 + 3x + 4$, the *a*-value is 5.

Solution:

This problem is similar to previous problems in that you must consider functions with restrictions on the *a*-value and functions with multiple roots. The problem is also similar in that you must consider an output value for a given input. In this case, the input is 0.

In function *f*(*x*), the output value is 2 for any given input. Analyzing function *g*(*x*), the multiplicity 2 tells you that the function is even, and the negative *a*-value indicates that the function opens downward. The multiplicity of the roots also tells you that the function does not cross the *x*-axis. Instead, it reflects at a given point where the double root occurs.

Comparing the two functions, you know that function *g*(*x*) is always below the *x*-axis and function *f*(*x*) is above the *x*-axis. Therefore, *f*(*x*) has a greater *y*-intercept.

1. Isaac and Tina disagree over which function has a greater y-intercept.

$g(x) = 2(x - 2)(x + 2)(x - 3) - 4$

x	$h(x)$
−2	−2
−1	0
0	4
1	10
2	18

Isaac

Function g(x) has a greater y-intercept. I calculated the y-intercept by substituting 0 for x. This value is greater than (0, 4) shown in the table for the function h(x).

Tina

Function h(x) has a greater y-intercept. The y-intercept of h(x) is (0, 4) and the y-intercept of g(x) is (0, −4).

Who is correct? Justify your reasoning.

7

2. Analyze each pair of representations. Then, answer each question and justify your reasoning.

a. Which function has a greater average rate of change for the interval (−4, 4)?

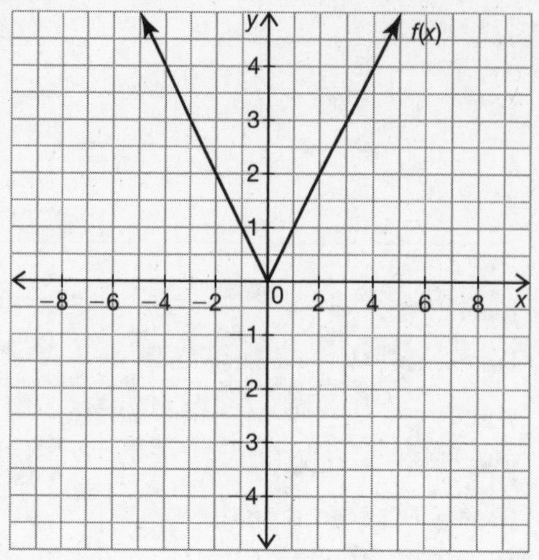

$g(x) = x$

b. Which function has a greater average rate of change for the interval (−1, 1)?

x	$j(x)$
−2	4
−1	1
0	0
1	1
2	4

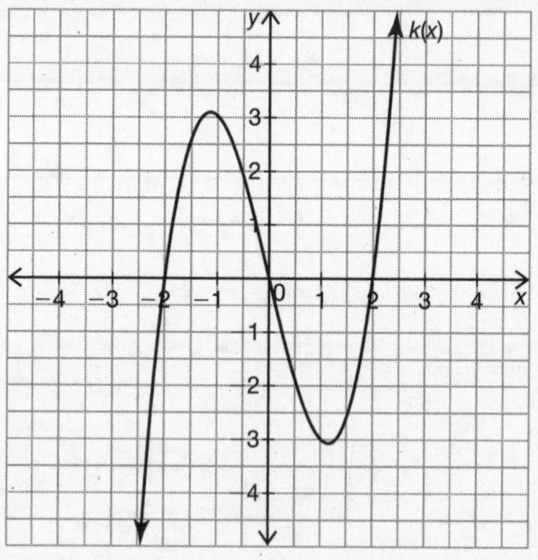

7

c. Which function has a greater relative minimum?

A cubic function $a(x)$ with $a > 0$ and 3 distinct real roots.	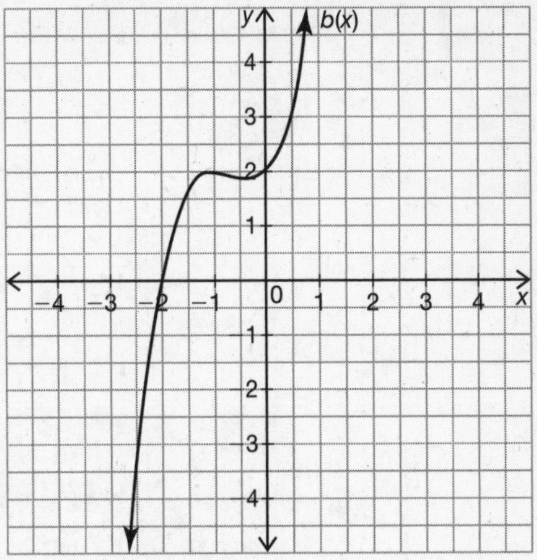

d. Which function's axis of symmetry has a greater x-value?

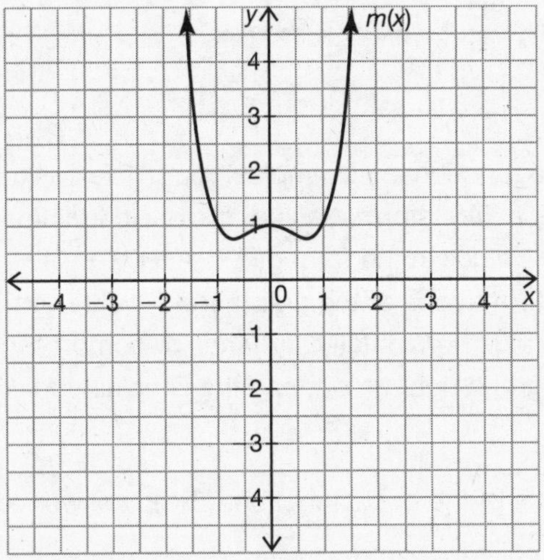	$n(x) = x^2 - 3x + 1$

3. Emilio studied the table of values and description of the key characteristics to determine which function has a greater minimum.

x	$d(x)$	
−2	5	A quartic function $m(x)$ has $a < 0$ and 2 pairs of real zeros (multiplicity 2).
−1	2	
0	1	
1	2	
2	5	

Emilio

Function $d(x)$ has a greater minimum. This function is a parabola opening up, with its vertex at (0, 1). Function $m(x)$ opens down because $a < 0$. Since the real zeros have multiplicity 2, I know any real zeros occur when the function reflects off the x-axis. Therefore, the output values of $m(x)$ never reach a point greater than $y = 0$.

Is Emilio correct? Justify your reasoning.

Recall that a basic function is a function in its simplest form. The basic function of *a* is $f(x) = x^n$ for any natural number n. Transformations of the basic functions are performed by changing the A-, B-, C-, and D-values in the form $g(x) = Af(B(x) - C) + D$. Remember, each value describes different transformations of the graph: the A-value vertically stretches or compresses the graph, the B-value horizontally stretches or compresses the graph, the C-value horizontally shifts the graph right or left, and the D-value vertically shifts the graph up or down.

4. Analyze the transformations of the basic functions. Then answer each question and justify your reasoning.

   a. Which function has a greater output for a given input?

The basic quadratic function $f(x) = x^2$.	$g(x) = f(x - 2) + 1$

7

b. Which function has a lower minimum?

x	$j(x)$
−2	16
−1	1
0	0
1	1
2	16

$k(x) = 5f(x - 4) + 2$

c. Which function has the greater input for a given output value?

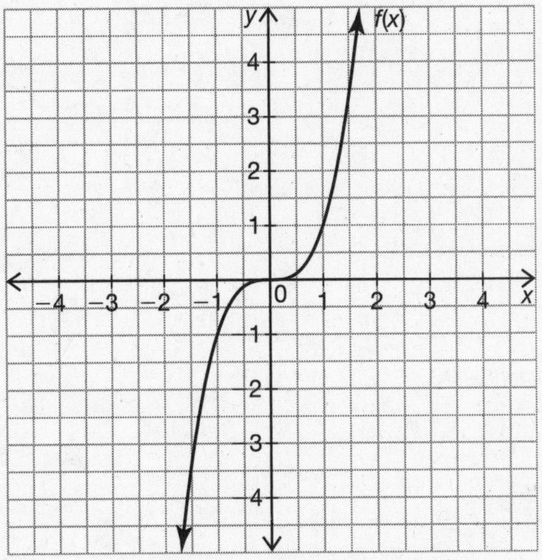

$g(x) = 3f(x - 5) + 1$

Be prepared to share your solutions and methods.

- regression equation (7.2)
- coefficient of determination (7.2)
- piecewise function (7.3)

7.1 Determining When a Polynomial Function is Greater Than and When it is Less Than 0 Using Its Roots

To determine when a polynomial function is greater than or less than 0, first determine the zeros of the function or where the function equals 0. Then use the graph to determine whether the function is greater than or less than 0 for the intervals between the zeros.

Example

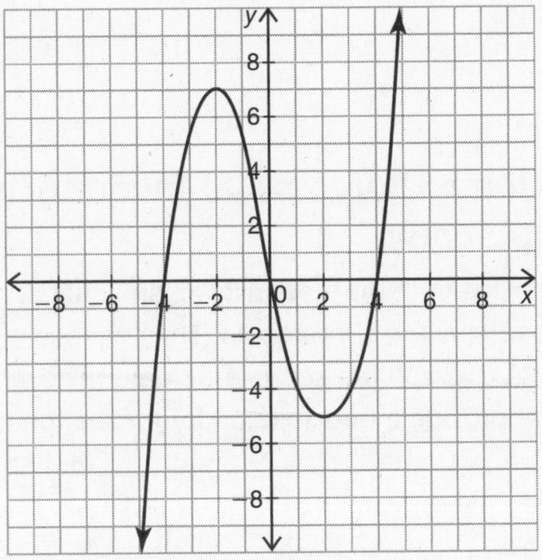

$$f(x) < 0 \text{ when } \begin{Bmatrix} x < -4 \\ 0 < x < 4 \end{Bmatrix}$$

$$f(x) > 0 \text{ when } \begin{Bmatrix} -4 < x < 0 \\ x > 4 \end{Bmatrix}$$

Determining the Solution to Polynomial Inequalities Using a Graphing Calculator

You can use a graphing calculator to solve higher order polynomials that are not easily factorable.

Step 1: Press **Y** = and input the expression.

Step 2: Scroll to the left of the Y_1, when your cursor is blinking over the diagonal line, press **ENTER** 2 times, you will see the area above the diagonal shaded (this represents $y \geq$ expression). If you Press **ENTER** 1 more time, you will see the area below the diagonal line shaded (this represents $y \leq$ expression).

Step 3: Make sure your viewing window is appropriate and press **GRAPH**.

Step 4: To determine the particular values of x that makes the inequality true, press 2nd, **CALC, 2:ZERO**. Scroll to the appropriate bounds to determine the zeros.

Step 5: Determine if x must be greater than or less than the roots depending on the inequality sign for your solution.

Example

$12 < x^2 - 2x + 3$

$x < -2.16$ or $x > 4.16$

Determining the Solution to Polynomial Inequalities Algebraically and Graphically

When solving polynomial inequalities treat the inequality as an equation and solve. Factor or use the quadratic formula to determine the x-intercepts. Then choose a test point between each interval created by the roots or graph the equation to determine which values satisfy the inequality. The section(s) that provide a true solution for the test point is the solution to the inequality.

Example

$x^2 - x - 12 < 0$

$(x + 3)(x - 4) = 0$

$x = -3, 4$

$x^2 - x - 12 < 0$ when $-3 < x < 4$

© Carnegie Learning

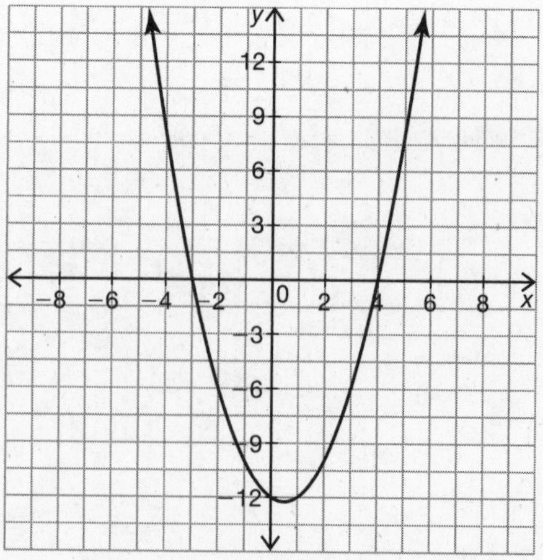

7.2 Determining the Appropriate Regression Equation to Model a Problem

Analyze data as a scatter plot to identify any patterns in the data. Based on how the data increases or decreases, determine the type of polynomial that best fits the data. Then, use a graphing calculator to determine the regression equation. A regression equation is a function that models the relationship between 2 variables in a scatter plot. Generally, there is 1 curve or degree of polynomial that will best fit the data. The coefficient of determination measures the strength of the relationship between the original data and the regression equation. The value ranges from 0 to 1 with a value of 1 indicating a perfect fit between the curve and the original data.

Example

The table shows the concentration of medication in a patient's blood as time passes.

Time (hours)	Concentration (mg/l)
0	0
0.5	78
1	100
1.5	84
2	50
2.5	15

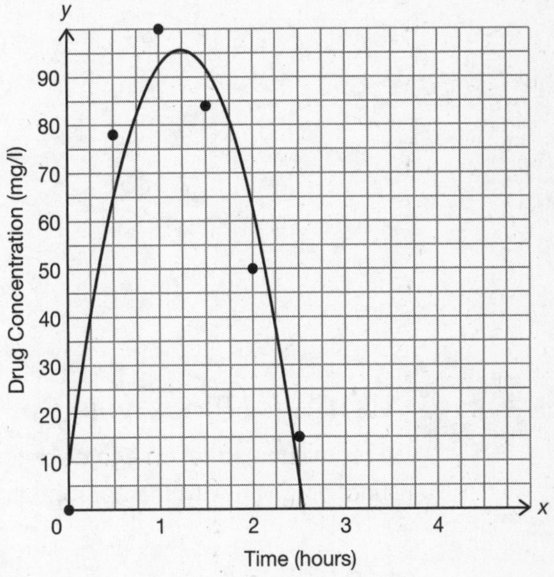

The data could be represented by a quadratic equation.

Regression equation:
$y = -56.357x^2 + 139.464x + 9.321$

Coefficient of determination: 0.924

The curve is a pretty good fit for the data.

7.2 Predicting Outcomes Using a Regression Equation

The regression equation is often used to make predictions about past and future events. Substitute various inputs into the regression equation to determine the likely outputs. Or, use intersecting lines to determine inputs.

Example

The medicine is considered at its most effective when the concentration in the blood is at least 60 mg/l. About for how long after administering is the medicine most effective? Use the regression equation: $g(x) = -56.357x^2 + 139.464x + 9.321$ where x is time in hours and $g(x)$ is the concentration of the medicine in the blood in mg/l.

The drug is most effective between 0.44 hour after administering and 2.03 hours after administering.

7.3 Graphing a Piecewise Function

A piecewise function includes different functions that represent different parts of the domain. Sometimes a single polynomial function is not the best model for a set of data. Data with breaks in the patterns can be better modeled by separating the data into pieces where each piece is modeled by a different polynomial function. Each equation can be graphed for its domain. Open points are associated with $<$ and $>$ and closed points are associated with $\leq$ and $\geq$.

Example

$$d(x) = \begin{cases} x^2 - 3x + 5, & x < 3 \\ 4x - 1, & x \geq 3 \end{cases}$$

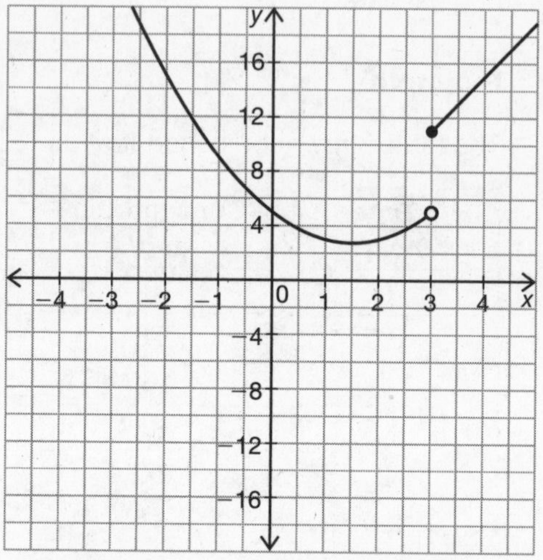

7.3 Writing a Piecewise Function Based on Its Graph

A regression equation can be determined for each interval on the graph of a piecewise function given with the appropriate domain.

Example

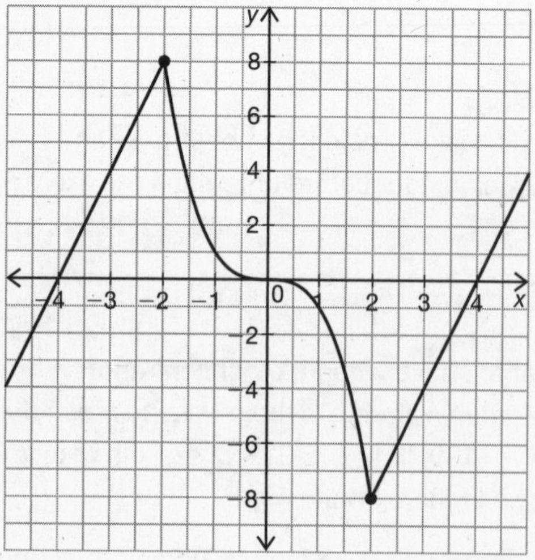

$$c(x) = \begin{cases} 4x + 16, & x \leq -2 \\ -x^3, & -2 < x < 2 \\ 4x - 16, & x \geq 2 \end{cases}$$

7.4 Modeling a Problem Situation with a Polynomial Function

Examine data in a table or scatter plot for patterns to determine what type of polynomial would best match the data. Use a graphing calculator to determine a regression equation to best model the data.

Example

Day	Attendance
1	40
2	70
3	50
4	60
5	75
6	45
7	0

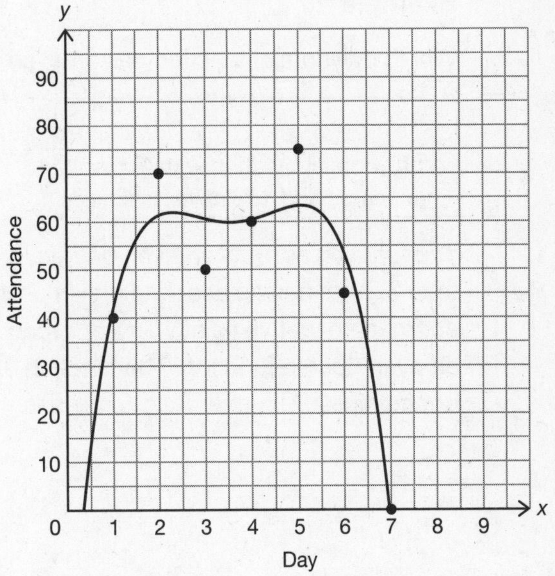

The data increases, decreases, increases, and decreases. A quartic function would best model the data.

Regression equation: $y = -0.758x^4 + 11.01x^3 - 57.083x^2 + 124.72x - 35.714$

7.4 Solving Problems Using Polynomial Regression Equations

Use the regression equation for the data to answer questions and make predictions about the data. The vertex, intersection of lines, or table of values can each be useful for solving problems about the data.

Example

Attendance at a local museum fluctuates throughout the week according to the regression equation $f(x) = -0.758x^4 + 11.01x^3 - 57.083x^2 + 124.72x - 35.714$, where x is the day and $f(x)$ is attendance. If the days 1–7 correspond to days of the week Monday through Sunday, how many people should the museum plan to expect on a typical Wednesday?

The museum can expect about 60–61 people on a typical Wednesday.

7.5 Comparing Polynomials Using Different Representations

Polynomials can be represented using a graph, table of values, equation, or description of key characteristics. When comparing 2 functions in different forms, important information to look for includes the degree of each function, the shape of the graph, the number and type of zeros, transformations of a basic function, etc.

Example

Which polynomial function has an even degree?

$a(x)$	$b(x)$
A polynomial function with 2 absolute maximums and 1 relative minimum.	$b(x) = 4(3 - 2x) + 3(x + 6)$

The function $a(x)$ has an even degree. A function with 3 turns must have a degree greater than 3. And, having absolute maximums means the end behavior of the function is to approach negative infinity as x approaches both negative and positive infinity. This indicates an even degree function. The function $b(x)$ is a linear function—the x-values are added, not multiplied.

Sequences and Series

8

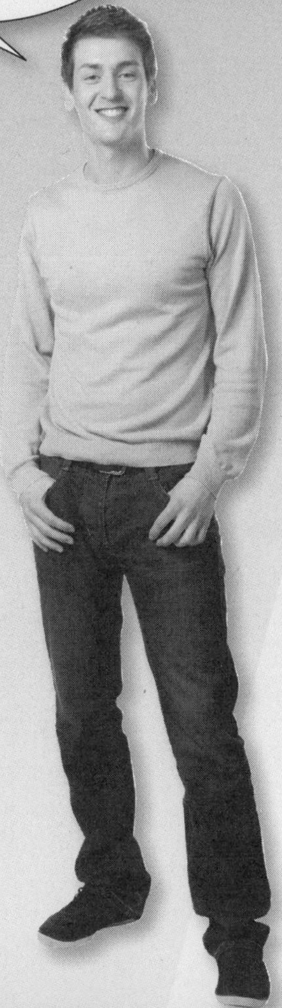
Covered in bees!
Bees build honeycombs
to hold larvae, pollen, and of
course honey. Honeycombs are
constructed of hexagonal cells
that tile a surface with no
overlaps or gaps.

Sequence—Not Just Another Glittery Accessory

8.1

Arithmetic and Geometric Sequences

LEARNING GOALS

In this lesson, you will:

- Recognize patterns as sequences.
- Determine the next term in a sequence.
- Write explicit and recursive formulas for arithmetic and geometric sequences.
- Use formulas to determine unknown terms of a sequence.

KEY TERMS

- arithmetic sequence
- geometric sequence
- finite sequence
- infinite sequence

"Ostinato" is a musical term that indicates a repeating pattern of notes. A word that you might be familiar with that is related to "ostinato" is "obstinate," meaning "stubborn".

An ostinato is indeed a stubborn pattern. Musicians commonly use ostinati (the plural of ostinato) to underlay a particular feeling they want a certain song to portray. They may also use it to stabilize a variety of pitches to provide uniformity within a song.

A basso ostinato is a type of ostinato that is used to form a harmonic pattern and is repeated throughout a song. Some argue that the basso ostinato should be thought of more as a device than a form of music.

The term "riff" is the modern day ostinato for popular music. A riff is defined as a short series of notes that create a melody within a melody of a song. Unlike an ostinato, a riff does not need to be repeated throughout the whole song.

You may be familiar with Pachelbel's Canon in D, which features one of the most famous repeating patterns of all time.

Just as with ostinati, when dealing with sequences, you look to identify an underlying pattern. You try to identify what it is that is moving the pattern along, so that you may be able to determine what is coming next.

PROBLEM 1 I Spy With My Little Eye, A Pattern!

Patterns, both numerical and physical, can be defined as sequences. Recall, a sequence is a pattern involving an ordered arrangement of numbers, geometric figures, letters, or other objects called terms. An **arithmetic sequence** is a sequence of terms in which the difference between any two consecutive terms is a constant. A **geometric sequence** is a sequence of terms in which the ratio between any two consecutive terms is a constant. A sequence that is neither arithmetic or geometric has a pattern, but there is no common difference or ratio.

An ellipsis is 3 periods which means "and so on." Ellipses are used to represent infinite sequences.

Sequences can have a fixed number of terms, or they can continue forever. If a sequence terminates it is called a **finite sequence**. If a sequence continues forever it is called an **infinite sequence**.

1. Lisa and Ray give the next few terms in the sequence: 1, 1, 1, . . .

Lisa

2, 2, 2, 3, 3, 3

The sequence is writing each natural number three times.

Ray

1, 1, 1, 1, 1, 1, . . .

The sequence just repeats 1 forever.

Who is correct? Explain your reasoning.

It is important to recognize that when you are only given the first few terms in a sequence, you may not have enough information to determine the next term.

8

2. Analyze each sequence and then circle the appropriate type of sequence. If the sequence is arithmetic, identify the common difference. If the sequence is geometric, identify the common ratio. Finally, circle whether the sequence is finite or infinite.

a. number of tiles

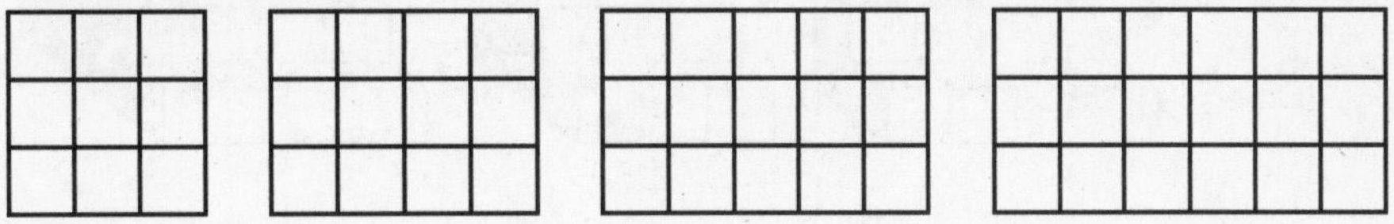

Arithmetic Sequence ________ Geometric Sequence ________ Neither

Infinite Sequence Finite Sequence

b. number of toothpicks

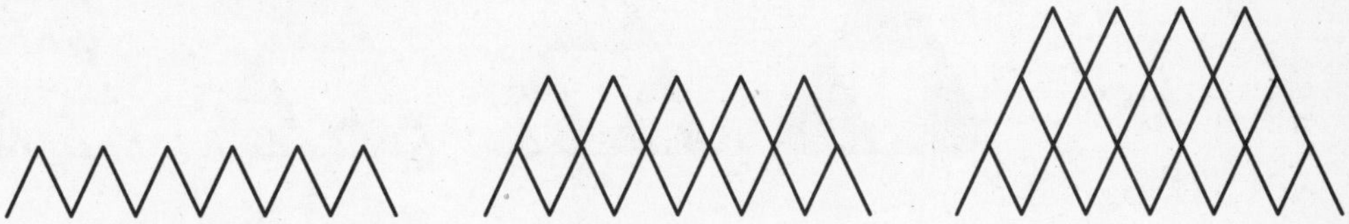

Arithmetic Sequence ________ Geometric Sequence ________ Neither

Infinite Sequence Finite Sequence

c. number of rows

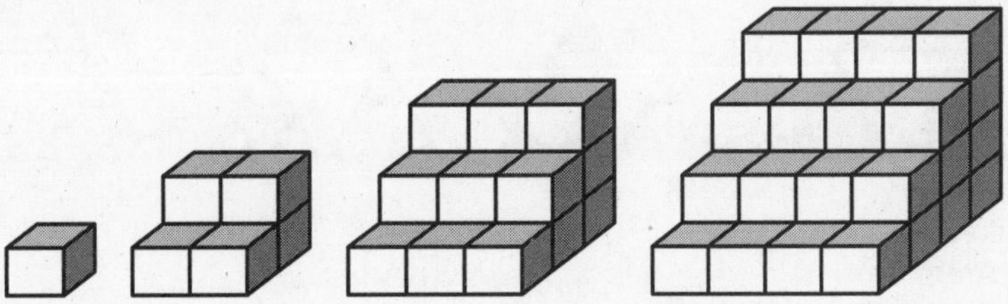

Arithmetic Sequence ________ Geometric Sequence ________ Neither

Infinite Sequence Finite Sequence

d. number of cubes

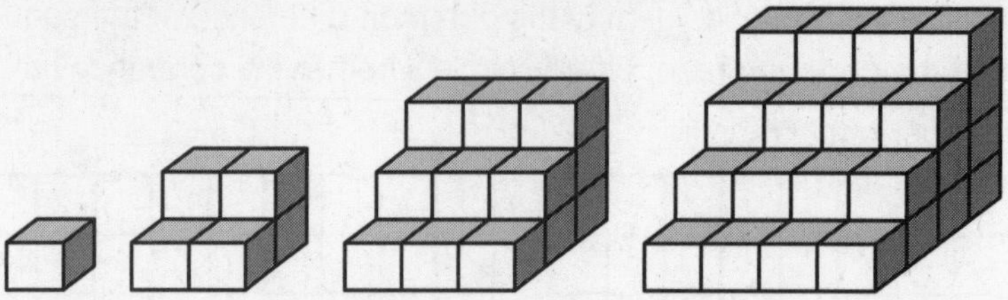

Arithmetic Sequence ________ Geometric Sequence ________ Neither

Infinite Sequence Finite Sequence

e. number of black triangles

Arithmetic Sequence ________ Geometric Sequence ________ Neither

Infinite Sequence Finite Sequence

f. number of white triangles

Arithmetic Sequence ________ Geometric Sequence ________ Neither

Infinite Sequence Finite Sequence

g. Side length of smallest shaded square within the unit square

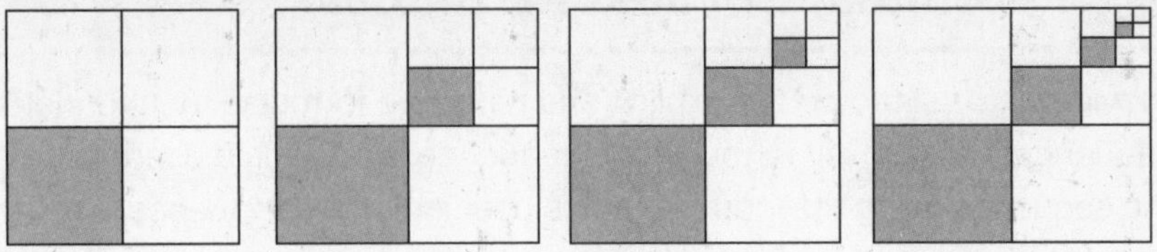

Arithmetic Sequence ______ Geometric Sequence ______ Neither

Infinite Sequence Finite Sequence

h. Number of shaded squares

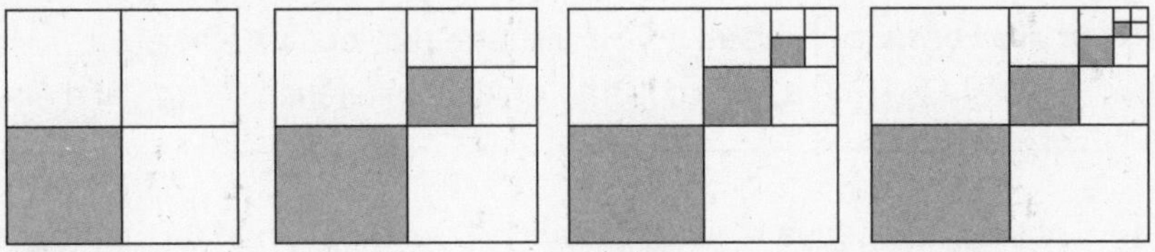

Arithmetic Sequence ______ Geometric Sequence ______ Neither

Infinite Sequence Finite Sequence

3. Create your own sequence given the type indicated. Include the first three terms.

a. Arithmetic Sequence

b. Geometric Sequence

c. Neither Arithmetic or Geometric Sequence

8

PROBLEM 2 Formula: Not Just for Babies

Previously, you learned the explicit and recursive formulas for arithmetic and geometric sequences. An explicit formula for a sequence is a formula used for calculating each term of the sequence using the index, a term's position in the sequence. A recursive formula generates each new term of a sequence based on a preceding term of the sequence.

	Arithmetic Sequence	Geometric Sequence
Explicit Formula	$a_n = a_1 + d(n - 1)$ where a_1 is the first term, d is the common difference, and n is the nth term in the sequence.	$g_n = g_1 \cdot r^{n-1}$ where g_1 is the first term, and r is the common ratio.
Recursive Formula	$a_n = a_{n-1} + d$ where a_{n-1} is the term previous to a_n, and d is the common difference.	$g_n = g_{n-1} \cdot r$ where g_{n-1} is the term previous to g_n, and r is the common ratio.

1. Consider the sequence in Problem 1, Question 1, part (a), *number of tiles*.

a. Use the recursive formula to determine the 5th term.

b. Use the explicit formula to determine the 5th term.

2. Consider the sequence in Problem 1, Question 1, part (e), *number of black triangles*.

a. Use the recursive formula to determine the 5th term.

b. Use the explicit formula to determine the 5th term.

3. Which formula would you use if you wanted to determine the 95th term of either sequence? Explain your reasoning.

8

4. Identify each sequence as arithmetic, geometric, or neither. If possible, determine the 50th term of each sequence.

a. $-5, -1, 3, 7, 11, 15, 19, 23 \ldots$

Type of Sequence: ____________________

50th term: ________________

b. $0, 1, 1, 2, 3, 5, 8, 13 \ldots$

Type of Sequence: ____________________

50th term: ____________________________

c. $27, 9, 3, 1, \frac{1}{3}, \frac{1}{9}, \frac{1}{27}, \frac{1}{81}$

Type of Sequence: ____________________

50th term: ________________

5. Use either the recursive or explicit formula to determine each answer.

a. The sum of the interior angles in a triangle is 180°, in a quadrilateral is 360°, and in a pentagon is 540°. How many degrees are in a decagon?

b. The employees at Franco's Pizza Shack turn the pizza ovens down to 200° overnight. When the workers open the shop in the morning, they turn the ovens up to 550°. The temperature of each oven increases by 40% every 30 minutes. Will the ovens reach the required 550° in 1.5 hours?

Talk the Talk

Complete each row in the table using the given information in that row.

	Sequences	Type of Sequence	Recursive Formula	Explicit Formula
A			$g_n = 3(g_{n-1})$ $g_1 = 4$	
B	320, 80, 20, 5, . . .			
C			$a_n = a_{n-1} + 10$ $a_1 = 20$	
D				$g_n = 10 \cdot 5^{n-1}$ $n = 1, 2, 3 \ldots$
E	3, 11, 19, 27 . . .			
F				$a_n = 5 + 20(n - 1)$ $n = 1, 2, 3 \ldots$

Be prepared to share your solutions and methods.

This Is Series(ous) Business

8.2

Finite Arithmetic Series

LEARNING GOALS

In this lesson, you will:

- Compute a finite series.
- Use sigma notation to represent a sum of a finite series.
- Use Gauss's method to compute finite arithmetic series.
- Write a function to represent the sum of a finite arithmetic series.
- Use finite arithmetic series to solve real-world problems.

KEY TERMS

- tessellation
- series
- finite series
- infinite series
- arithmetic series

Honey bees are fascinating little creatures. Did you know that honey bees are the only insects that produce food that humans eat? They also identify members of their colony by a unique smell.

Another amazing aspect of the honey bee is how they build their hive. Honey bees build hexagonal honey cells from a single cell. Layers of honey cells are then built around the edges, as shown.

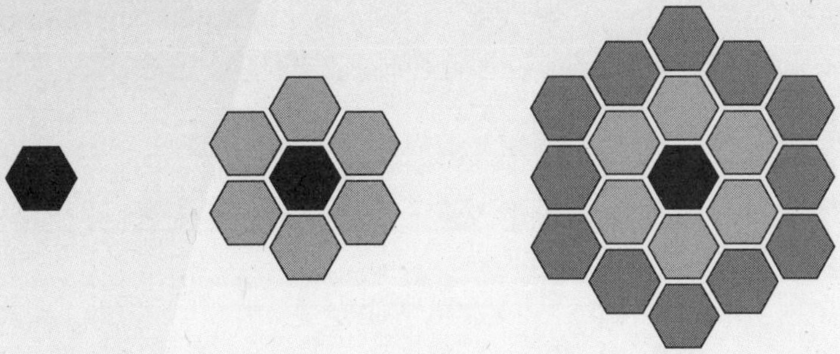

Could you sketch the next figure in the sequence? Could you predict how many total hexagons would be in the next term of the sequence? How does this pattern translate to an arithmetic sequence?

PROBLEM 1 Project: Toothpick Tessellation

Josephine is helping her little brother Pauley with his latest art project. He is using toothpicks to create a *tessellation*. A **tessellation** is created when a geometric shape is repeated over a two-dimensional plane such that there are no overlaps and no gaps.

Pauley starts his tessellation project by gluing toothpicks to a large piece of poster board to make a single diamond shape. This is the first row.

Then, he places additional toothpicks parallel to the first row to create the second row. The second row consists of two diamond shapes.

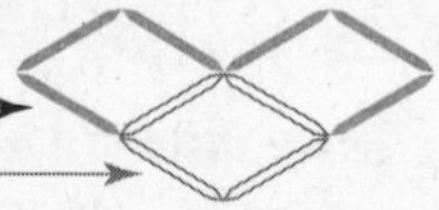

He continues to place toothpicks in this manner, so that each row has one more diamond shape than the previous row. The first three rows of Pauley's tessellation are shown.

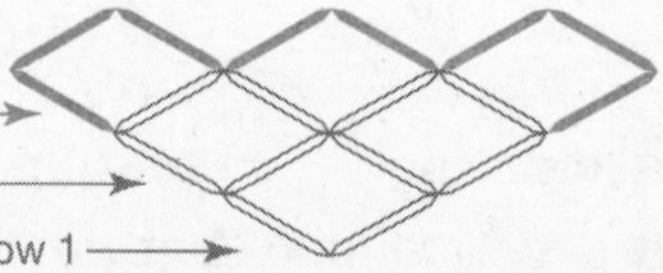

1. Sketch the next two rows of the tessellation on the previous diagram.

2. Complete the table to show the number of additional toothpicks used to create each row.

Row	Number of Additional Toothpicks Used to Create the Row
1	
2	
3	
4	
5	

3. Can this tessellation be represented by an arithmetic or geometric sequence? Explain how you know.

4. Write an explicit formula for this sequence. Let n represent the row number, and let a_n represent the number of additional toothpicks used to create that row.

5. Suppose that Pauley knows that he wants his tessellation to include 18 rows. How many additional toothpicks will he need for the 18th row? Explain how you determined your answer.

6. Describe how to calculate the total number of toothpicks that Pauley needs for a tessellation that includes 18 rows. (Do not actually perform the calculation.)

You know how to determine the *n*th term of a sequence. However, sometimes it is necessary to determine the *sum* of the terms in a sequence.

A **series** is the sum of terms in a given sequence. The sum of the first *n* terms of a sequence is denoted by S_n. For example, S_3 is the sum of the first three terms of a sequence.

There is a special notation for the summation of terms using a capital sigma, Σ:

$$S_n = \sum_{i=1}^{n} a_i$$

- upper bound of summation: n
- an indexed variable representing each successive term in the series: a_i
- index of summation: i
- lower bound of summation: 1

This expression means sum the values of *a*, starting at a_1 and ending with a_n.

In other words, $S_n = \sum_{i=1}^{n} a_i = a_1 + a_2 + a_3 + \cdots + a_{n-1} + a_n$.

A series can be *finite* or *infinite*. A **finite series** is the sum of a finite number of terms. An **infinite series** is the sum of an infinite number of terms. For example, the sum of all of the even integers from 1 to 100 is a finite series, and the sum of all of the even whole numbers is an infinite series.

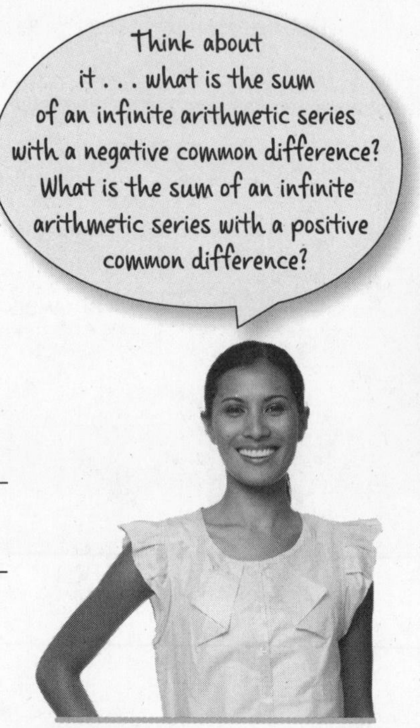
Think about it . . . what is the sum of an infinite arithmetic series with a negative common difference? What is the sum of an infinite arithmetic series with a positive common difference?

7. Use sigma notation to rewrite each finite series, and then compute.

   a. 5 + 9 + 13 + 17 + 21

   S_2 = ______________________

   S_5 = ______________________

   b. 3 + 6 + 12 + 24 + 48 + 96 + 192

   S_1 = ______________________

   S_7 = ______________________

8. Use sigma notation to represent the total number of toothpicks Pauley needs to complete 5 rows of his tessellation. Then, use your table in Question 2 to calculate this amount.

PROBLEM 2 Gauss's Method to the Rescue!

Remember that an arithmetic sequence is a sequence of numbers in which the difference between any two consecutive terms is a constant. An **arithmetic series** is the sum of an arithmetic sequence.

You can compute a finite arithmetic series by adding each individual term, but this can take a lot of time. A famous mathematician named Carl Friedrich Gauss developed another way to compute a finite arithmetic series.

As the story goes, when Gauss was in elementary school, his teacher asked the class to calculate the sum of the first 100 positive integers. Apparently, Gauss determined the answer in a matter of seconds! How did Gauss determine his answer so quickly?

1. Complete the steps and answer the questions to see how Gauss was able to calculate the sum of the first 100 positive integers so quickly.

a. The series S_{100} is shown. The same series in descending order is shown beneath it. Add the series by computing the sum of each pair of vertical, or partial sums.

$$S_{100} = 1 + 2 + 3 + \cdots + 98 + 99 + 100$$
$$+S_{100} = 100 + 99 + 98 + \cdots + 3 + 2 + 1$$

$$2S_{100} = \_\_\_\_ + \_\_\_\_ + \_\_\_\_ + \cdots + \_\_\_\_ + \_\_\_\_ + \_\_\_\_$$

b. What do you notice about each partial sum?

c. How many partial sums are there in this series?

d. Write the sum of the partial sums.

$2S_{100} =$ ____________________

e. To arrive at the total in part (d), you actually added each term of the series twice. How could you calculate the correct total from the sum of the partial sums, or S_{100}?

f. What is S_{100}?

$S_{100} =$ ____________________

Gauss's method can be generalized for any finite arithmetic series.

2. Consider a finite arithmetic series S_n written as a sum of its terms.

$$S_n = a_1 + a_2 + a_3 + \cdots + a_{n-2} + a_{n-1} + a_n$$

Complete the steps shown to determine Gauss's formula to compute any finite arithmetic series.

a. First, write S_n in terms of a_1, a_n, and the common difference d. Remember that for an arithmetic sequence, $a_n = a_1 + d(n - 1)$.

$$S_n = a_1 + (\underline{\hspace{1cm}}) + (a_1 + 2d) + \cdots + (a_n - 2d) + (\underline{\hspace{1cm}}) + \underline{\hspace{1cm}}$$

b. Then, write S_n in reverse order.

$$S_n = \underline{\hspace{1cm}} + (a_n - d) + (\underline{\hspace{1cm}}) + \cdots + (a_1 + 2d) + (\underline{\hspace{1cm}}) + a_1$$

c. Add the series, keeping the "+" and "=" signs vertically aligned.

$$S_n = \quad a_1 \quad + (\underline{\hspace{0.5cm}}) + (\underline{\hspace{0.5cm}}) + \cdots + (\underline{\hspace{0.5cm}}) + (\underline{\hspace{0.5cm}}) + \quad a_n$$
$$+S_n = \quad a_n \quad + (\underline{\hspace{0.5cm}}) + (\underline{\hspace{0.5cm}}) + \cdots + (\underline{\hspace{0.5cm}}) + (\underline{\hspace{0.5cm}}) + \quad a_1$$
$$\overline{2S_n = (\underline{\hspace{0.5cm}}) + (\underline{\hspace{0.5cm}}) + (\underline{\hspace{0.5cm}}) + \cdots + (\underline{\hspace{0.5cm}}) + (\underline{\hspace{0.5cm}}) + (\underline{\hspace{0.5cm}})}$$

d. Identify each partial sum.

e. Fill in the blanks to show the sum of the partial sums.

$$2S_n = \underline{\hspace{1cm}}(a_1 + \underline{\hspace{1cm}})$$

f. Fill in the blanks to write the formula for S_n.

$$S_n = \frac{\underline{\hspace{0.5cm}}(a_1 + \underline{\hspace{1cm}})}{2}$$

g. Describe Gauss' rule to compute any finite arithmetic series by completing the sentence.

Add the _____ term and the _____ term of the series,

multiply the sum by the number of _____ of the series, and divide by

_____.

So, Gauss's formula to compute the first n terms of an arithmetic series is shown.

$$S_n = \frac{n(a_1 + a_n)}{2}$$

3. Use the *Toothpick Tessellation* problem situation to answer each question.

   a. Use Gauss's formula to calculate the total number of toothpicks Pauley needs to complete 5 rows of his tessellation. Show your work.

   b. Remember that Pauley wanted his tessellation to include a total of 18 rows. If he has a box of 350 toothpicks, does he have enough? Explain why or why not.

PROBLEM 3 Human Calculator, or Inspiration from Gauss?

In the previous problem, you learned a way to compute the first n-terms of any finite arithmetic series. Now, you will take a closer look at some special series of numbers.

1. Consider a sequence of odd whole numbers.

   a. Write an explicit formula to determine any term of the sequence.

If possible, use the distributive property and combine like terms when you write your answers. This way, you can be more efficient!

8

b. Use Gauss's formula to calculate the sum of the first 20 odd whole numbers. What information did you need to use Gauss's formula?

Emma claims that she can calculate the sum of the first 20 odd whole numbers using a different method. Emma's method does not require her to calculate the last term of the series.

2. Let's determine how Emma can perform this calculation.

a. Substitute the known value of a_1 and the algebraic expression for a_n into Gauss's formula.

b. Write your answer from part (a) using function notation. Describe the function.

c. Use your function from part (b) to calculate the sum of the first 20 odd whole numbers. Verify that your result the same as your result in Question 1.

3. Calculate the sum of the first 100 odd whole numbers. Then, verify your result using Gauss's formula.

What about even numbers? You can use a similar process to compute the series of even whole numbers.

8

4. Follow the given steps to calculate the sum of the first 100 even whole numbers.

   a. Write an explicit formula to calculate any term of the sequence of even whole numbers.

   b. Substitute the known value of a_1 and the algebraic expression for a_n into Gauss's formula.

   c. Write your answer from part (b) using function notation.

   d. Use your function from part (c) to calculate the first 100 even whole numbers. Then, verify using Gauss's formula.

5. Compare the function for the series of even whole numbers with the function for the series of odd whole numbers. What makes them different? Explain why you think the difference exists.

8

PROBLEM 4 "Chair"-ity Case

You are in charge of setting up for your high school band's annual Spring concert. The concert will be held outdoors on the school soccer field, and one of your duties is to arrange the seating for the show.

You have gathered the following information.

- The stage is 20 feet wide.
- The first row of chairs will be about the same width as the stage.
- Each successive row of chairs will have three more chairs than the previous row. This way, the chairs are offset so that each person does not have a chair directly in front of them for better viewing.
- Each chair is 1.5 feet wide and 1.5 feet deep.
- There needs to be 0.5 foot of spacing in between the chairs within a row so that the audience can sit comfortably.
- In order to have enough room for people to walk through the rows, there needs to be 4 feet of space in between each row, from the back of one chair to the back of the other chair.

Use the given information to answer each question.

1. What factors do you need to consider when determining how many rows of chairs there could be?

2. How many chairs are in the first row? Explain your reasoning.

3. Sketch a seating chart that includes the given information and dimensions.

Answer each question based on the additional given information. Show all your work.

4. Suppose that the first 5 rows of chairs make up the "gold circle" section.

a. How many chairs are in the gold circle section?

b. How many feet deep is the gold circle section?

8

5. Suppose that you need a total of 500 chairs for the concert.

   a. How many rows will you need with this number of chairs?

   b. How deep is the seating area with this number of chairs?

6. Suppose that no row can have more than 40 chairs.

   a. What is the maximum number of rows possible?

   b. What is the maximum number of people that can be seated?

Be prepared to share your solutions and methods.

8

8.3

I Am Having a Series Craving (For Some Math)!

Geometric Series

LEARNING GOALS

In this lesson, you will:

- Generalize patterns to derive the formula for the sum of a finite geometric series.
- Compute a finite geometric series.

KEY TERM

- geometric series

The art that is produced in a culture often reflects the peoples' social values, struggles, and important events over a given time period. While it is generally not considered one of the great art forms of our time, television drama is an art that regularly reflects current events and social issues.

Consider *Mission Impossible*, a spy series which brought millions of viewers the secret assignments of a group of government agents battling dictators around the globe. It's no accident that this series was hugely popular in the 1960's, a time of heightened Cold War anxieties. During the 1980s, a time when more women entered the work force, *Cagney and Lacey* featured a career-focused, single mother battling crime. During the 2000s, *West Wing* focused on political scandals, terrorism, and other foreign affairs issues that were in the news during that period.

What are some of the pressing current events right now? Are they reflected in any popular television series you watch?

PROBLEM 1 Geometric Series Episode 1: The Rise of Euclid

A **geometric series** is the sum of the terms of a geometric sequence. Recall, that the sequence 1, 3, 9, 27, 81 is a geometric sequence because the ratio of any two consecutive terms is constant. Adding the terms creates the geometric series $1 + 3 + 9 + 27 + 81$.

The constant ratio of this geometric sequence is 3 because
$$\frac{3}{1} = \frac{9}{3} = \frac{27}{9} = \frac{81}{27} = 3$$
Recall all geometric sequences have a constant ratio between successive terms.

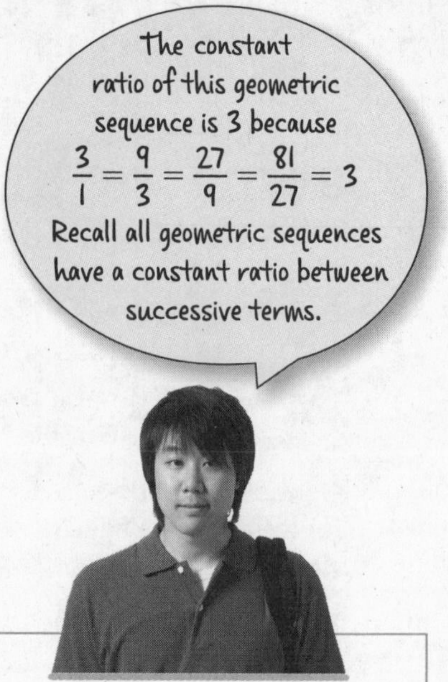

Theresa raises her hand and claims that she has a "trick" for quickly calculating the sum of any geometric series. She asks members of the class to write any geometric series on the board. She boasts that she can quickly tell them how to determine the sum without adding all of the terms. Several examples are shown.

Paul:	Theresa:
"OK, so prove it! What is the sum of $1 + 3 + 9 + 27 + 81 + 243 + 729$?"	"Multiply 729(3) and subtract 1. Then divide by 2."
Stella:	**Theresa:**
"What is $5 + 20 + 80 + 320 + 1280 + 5120$?"	"I will have the answer if I multiply 5120(4), subtract 5, and then divide by 3."
Julian:	**Theresa:**
"Let me see . . . How about $10 + 50 + 250 + 1250$?"	"No problem. Multiply 1250(5), subtract 10, and then divide by 4."
Henry:	**Theresa:**
"Hmmm . . . I bet I can stump you with $10 + (-20) + 40 + (-80) + 160$."	"Pretty sneaky with the negatives, Henry, but the method still works. Multiply 160(-2) and subtract 10. This time divide by -3."

1. Verify that Theresa is correct for each series.

How can you tell all of the series are geometric?

2. What is Theresa's "trick"? Describe in words how to calculate the sum of any geometric sequence.

3. Use Theresa's "trick" to calculate 1 + 2 + 4 + 8 + 16 + 32 + 64 + 128. Show all work and explain your reasoning.

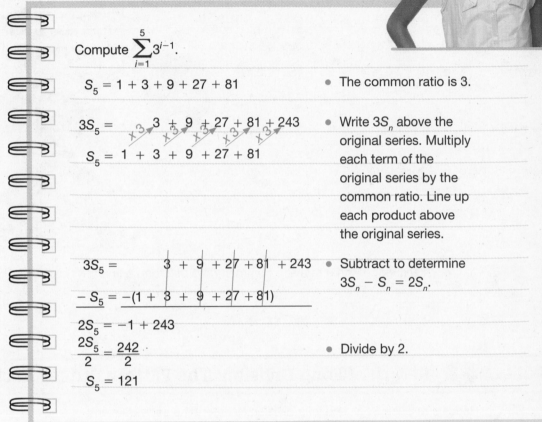

Theresa's "trick" really isn't a trick. It is known as Euclid's Method. An example of this method, along with a justification for each step, is shown.

Compute $\sum_{i=1}^{5} 3^{i-1}$.

$S_5 = 1 + 3 + 9 + 27 + 81$	• The common ratio is 3.
$3S_5 = \quad 3 + 9 + 27 + 81 + 243$ (×3 ×3 ×3 ×3 ×3) $S_5 = 1 + 3 + 9 + 27 + 81$	• Write $3S_n$ above the original series. Multiply each term of the original series by the common ratio. Line up each product above the original series.
$3S_5 = \quad 3 + 9 + 27 + 81 + 243$ $-S_5 = -(1 + 3 + 9 + 27 + 81)$	• Subtract to determine $3S_n - S_n = 2S_n$.
$2S_5 = -1 + 243$	
$\frac{2S_5}{2} = \frac{242}{2}$	• Divide by 2.
$S_5 = 121$	

In all of the examples, Theresa knew that she could calculate each sum by first multiplying the last term by the common ratio and subtracting the first term. Then she could divide that quantity by one less than the common ratio.

In other words, $S_n = \frac{\text{(Last Term)(Common Ratio)} - \text{(First Term)}}{\text{(Common Ratio} - 1)}$.

4. Analyze the worked example.

a. In the worked example, why multiply both sides of the equation by 3? Does the algorithm still work if you multiply by a different number? Explain your reasoning.

b. Why do you always divide by one less than the common ratio?

The formula to compute any geometric series becomes $S_n = \dfrac{g_n(r) - g_1}{r - 1}$, where g_n is the last term, r is the common ratio, and g_1 is the first term.

5. Apply Euclid's Method to compute each.

a. $1 + 10 + 100 + \cdots + 1{,}000{,}000$

Do you need to know all of the terms? How can you determine just the terms that you need? Remember to work efficiently, looking for patterns and applying formulas that you already know.

b. $10 + 20 + 40 + 80 + 160 + 320$

c. $\sum_{k=1}^{8} 5^{k-1}$

d. A sequence with 9 terms, a common ratio of 2, and a first term of 3.

PROBLEM 2 Return of Long Division: The Pattern Strikes Back

Recall previously you used long division to determine each quotient:

Polynomial Long Division	→	**Rewritten Using the Reflexive and Commutative Properties of Equality**
Example 1 $\dfrac{r^3 - 1}{r - 1} = r^2 + r + 1$	→	$1 + r + r^2 = \dfrac{r^3 - 1}{r - 1}$
Example 2 $\dfrac{r^4 - 1}{r - 1} = r^3 + r^2 + r + 1$	→	$1 + r + r^2 + r^3 = \dfrac{r^4 - 1}{r - 1}$
Example 3 $\dfrac{r^5 - 1}{r - 1} = r^4 + r^3 + r^2 + r + 1$	→	$1 + r + r^2 + r^3 + r^4 = \dfrac{r^5 - 1}{r - 1}$

Each Example represents a geometric series, where r is the common ratio and $g_1 = 1$. Each geometric series can be written in summation notation.

Example 1: $n = 3$ $\sum_{i=1}^{3} r^{i-1}$ or $\sum_{i=0}^{2} r^{i}$

Example 2: $n = 4$ $\sum_{i=1}^{4} r^{i-1}$ or $\sum_{i=0}^{3} r^{i}$

1. For each Example, explain why the power of the common ratio in the summation notation is different, yet still represents the series.

2. Identify the number of terms in the series in Example 3, and then write the series in summation notation.

3. Use the pattern generated from repeated polynomial long division to write a formula to compute any geometric series $1 + r + r^2 + r^3 + \cdots + r^{n-1}$ where n is the number of terms in the series, r is the common ratio, and $g_1 = 1$.

$$\sum_{i=0}^{n} r^i = \underline{\qquad\qquad}$$

You can show a proof of $S_n = \frac{r^n - 1}{r - 1}$ where S_n is a series in the form $r^0 + r^1 + r^2 + r^3 + \cdots + r^{n-1}$ with n-terms and a common ratio r.

$$S_n = r^0 + r^1 + r^2 + r^3 + \cdots + r^{n-1}$$

$$rS_n = \qquad r^1 + r^2 + r^3 + \cdots + r^{n-1} + r^n$$

$$S_n = r^0 + r^1 + r^2 + \cdots + r^{n-2} + r^{n-1}$$

(×r arrows from each term to the term above)

- Write rS_n above the original series. Multiply each term by r. Line up each product above the original series.

$$rS_n = \qquad r^1 + r^2 + r^3 + \cdots + r^{n-1} + r^n$$

$$- \quad S_n = -(1 + r^1 + r^2 + r^3 + \cdots + r^{n-1})$$

$$rS_n - S_n = -1 + r^n$$

$$S_n(r - 1) = r^n - 1$$

- Subtract $rS_n - S_n$. Eliminate terms that subtract to 0.

$$\frac{S_n(r-1)}{(r-1)} = \frac{(r^n - 1)}{(r - 1)}$$

- Divide by $(r - 1)$.

$$S_n = \frac{r^n - 1}{r - 1}$$

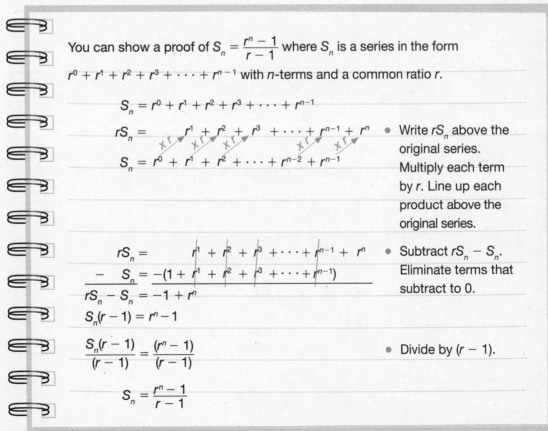

4. Identify the number of terms, the common ratio, and g_1 for each series. Then compute each.

a. $1 + 2^1 + 2^2 + 2^3 + 2^4$

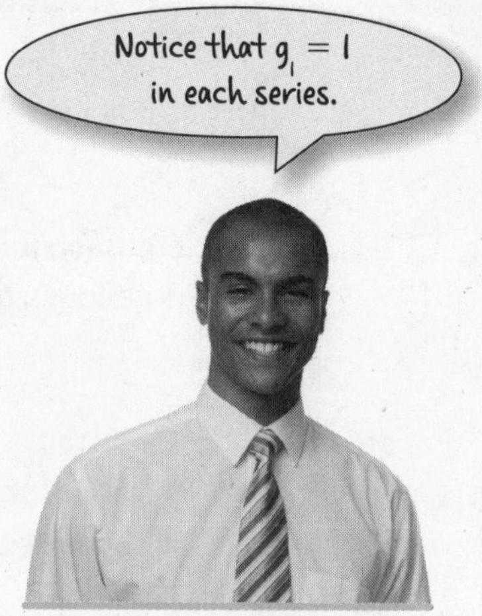
Notice that $g_1 = 1$ in each series.

b. $1 + 5 + 25 + 125 + 625$

c. $1 + (-2) + 4 + (-8) + 16 + (-32)$

5. Angus and Perry each wrote the geometric series 7 + 14 + 28 + 56 + 112 + 224 + 448 + 896 in summation notation and then computed the sum.

Angus

I know that $g_n = g_1 r^{n-1}$. The number of terms is 8, the common ratio is 2, and the first term is 7, so I can write the series as $\sum_{i=1}^{8} 7 \cdot 2^{i-1}$.

I know the last term is 896, so I can use Euclid's Method to compute the sum.

$\frac{896 \cdot 2 - 7}{2 - 1}$

Perry

I can rewrite the series as $7(1 + 2 + 4 + 8 + 16 + 32 + 64 + 128)$.

I know the common ratio is 2, so I can rewrite the series using powers as $7(2^0 + 2^1 + 2^2 + 2^3 + 2^4 + 2^5 + 2^6 + 2^7)$.

The number of terms is 8, so I can write the series in summation notation as $7\sum_{i=1}^{8} 2^{i-1}$.

Then, I can compute the series as $7\left(\frac{2^8 - 1}{2 - 1}\right)$.

Verify that both methods produce the same sum.

The formula to compute a geometric series that Perry used is $S_n = \frac{g_1(r^n - 1)}{r - 1}$.

Recall Euclid's Method to compute a geometric series is $S_n = \frac{g_n(r) - g_1}{r - 1}$.

You can use the fact that $g_n = g_1r^{n-1}$ to verify that these two formulas are equivalent.

$S_n = \frac{g_n(r) - g_1}{r - 1}$	• Given Euclid's Method.
$= \frac{g_1r^{n-1}(r) - g_1}{r - 1}$	• Substitute $g_n = g_1r^{n-1}$.
$= \frac{g_1r^n - g_1}{r - 1}$	• Perform multiplication.
$= \frac{g_1(r^n - 1)}{r - 1}$	• Factor out g_1.

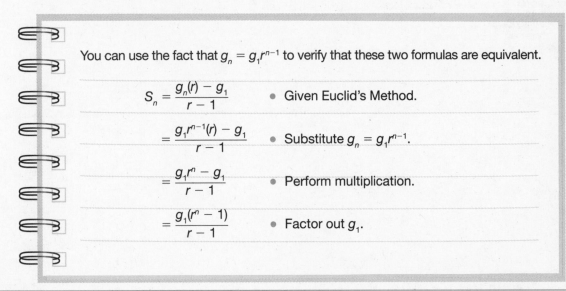

8

6. When is it appropriate to use each formula?

7. Rewrite each series using summation notation.

a. $4 + 12 + 36 + 108 + 324$

b. $64 + 32 + 16 + 8 + 4 + 2 + 1$

8. Compute each geometric series.

a. $\sum_{i=1}^{4} 6^{i-1}$

b. $10\sum_{i=0}^{4} 3^i$

c. $6\sum_{i=0}^{4}\left(\frac{1}{3}\right)^i$

9. Analyze the table of values.

x	$f(x)$	$\frac{f(x+1)}{f(x)}$
0	3	
1	4.5	
2	6.75	
3	10.125	
4	15.1875	
5		

a. Complete the table.

b. Describe any patterns that you notice.

c. Assume the geometric sequence continues, determine $f(0) + f(1) + \cdots + f(9)$. Show all work and explain your reasoning

d. Explain why the ratio of any two consecutive terms in a geometric sequence is always a constant.

PROBLEM 3 Making Choices

1. Jane analyzes the salary schedule for the same position at two different electrical engineering companies, Nothing's Shocking and High Voltage. The salary schedules for the first 5 years are provided with promises from each company that the rate of salary increase will be the same over time.

Time (years)	Nothing's Shocking Salary ($)	High Voltage Salary ($)
1	40,000	46,000
2	42,400	47,840
3	44,944	49,754
4	47,641	51,744
5	50,499	53,814

   a. What is the salary in year 10 for each company? Show all work and explain your reasoning.

b. Assuming all other factors are equal, which company offers the better salary over a 10-year period? Show all work and explain your reasoning.

You're not determining who pays more on year 10, but who pays more over the entire 10-year period.

c. What would be the difference in total career salary if you choose one company over the other? Assume a 30-year career. Show all work and explain your reasoning.

2. A single elimination basketball tournament begins with 128 games in the first round. Each round eliminates half of the teams until an overall winner is decided. The tournament sponsor needs to purchase a new ball for every game that will be played throughout the tournament. How many basketballs must the sponsor purchase? Explain your reasoning.

Be prepared to share your solutions and methods.

8.4

These Series Just Go On . . . And On . . . And On . . .

Infinite Geometric Series

LEARNING GOALS

In this lesson, you will:

- Write a formula for an infinite geometric series.
- Compute an infinite geometric series.
- Draw diagrams to model infinite geometric series.
- Determine whether series are convergent or divergent.
- Use a formula to compute a convergent infinite geometric series.

KEY TERMS

- convergent series
- divergent series

Infinity is a concept that philosophers and mathematicians have struggled with for centuries. Infinity is a very abstract idea. How can something be limitless? What does it mean for something to go on forever?

The following quote is from an Indian philosophical text dating back to the 4th or 3rd century B.C.

If you remove a part from infinity or add a part to infinity, still what remains is infinity.

How can this be so?

What does infinity mean to you?

8

PROBLEM 1 Hang On Bessie, We're Almost There

Previously, you calculated sums of finite series. What if a series was infinite? Let's see if there is a way to calculate the sum of an infinite series.

The first three terms of an infinite sequence are represented by the figures shown. In this sequence, each square represents a unit square, and the shaded part represents area.

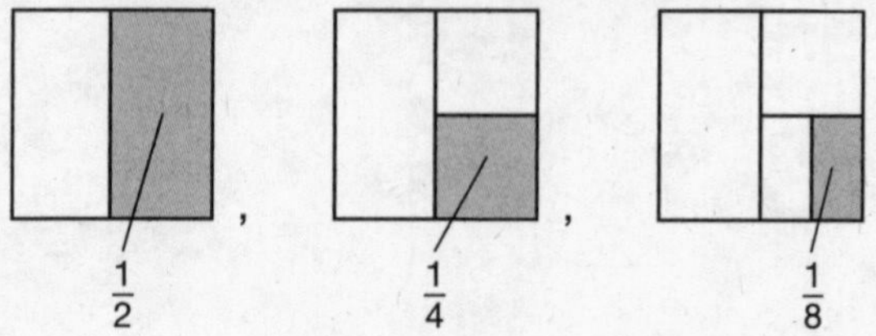

1. Sketch the next two figures to model this sequence, and write the numbers that correspond to each term.

2. Is this sequence arithmetic, geometric, or neither? Explain how you know. If possible, write an explicit formula for the sequence.

3. Consider the series, or sum, of the first two terms of this infinite sequence. The sum of the first two terms can be modeled with a diagram, as shown.

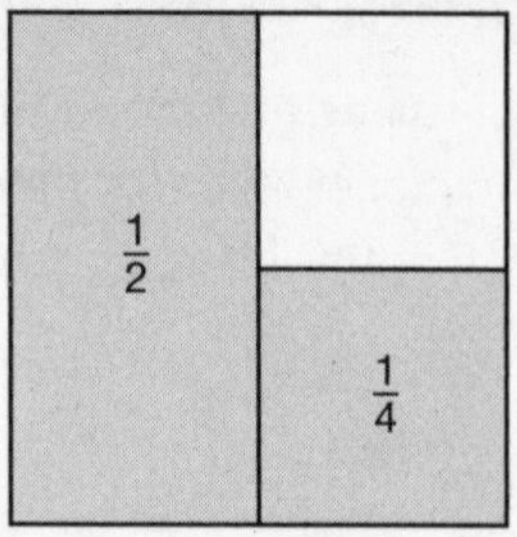

Continue shading the diagram to represent the sum of the first five terms of the series. What happens to the total area that is shaded every time you shade another piece of the unit square?

4. In the table shown, n represents the term number of the series, and S_n represents the sum of the first n terms of the series. Use the sequence from the unit square in Question 3 to answer each question.

n	1	2	3	4	5	10	25
S_n as a Fraction							
S_n as a Decimal							

a. Complete the table for $n = 1$ through $n = 5$ to show the sum of the series that corresponds to the previous diagram. Write each sum as a fraction and as a decimal.

b. Describe the pattern you see in the table.

c. Use the pattern to complete the table for the final two columns.

5. What value does the series approach as n gets greater?

8

In the figure that models this series, each additional part of the unit square is one half of the previous part. If you could continue to add these parts forever, the unit square would eventually be filled.

Likewise, in the table of values that models this series, the sums get closer and closer to 1 as n gets greater. Therefore, you can say that this infinite geometric series is equal to 1.

So, an infinite series can have a finite sum . . . it sounds crazy, but it's true!

6. Miley and Damian determined formulas they could use to compute the first n-terms of the series.

Miley

I noticed that when each sum is written as a fraction, the denominator is equal to 2^n and the numerator is one less than the denominator.

So, I can calculate the first n-terms of the series by using the formula shown.

$$S_n = \frac{2^n - 1}{2^n}$$

Damian

I know that $S_n = \frac{g_n \cdot r - g_1}{r - 1}$ can be used to compute the first n-terms of any geometric series.

For this series, $g_n = \left(\frac{1}{2}\right)^n$, $g_1 = \frac{1}{2}$, and $r = \frac{1}{2}$.

Substituting these values gives:

$$S_n = \frac{\left(\frac{1}{2}\right)^n \left(\frac{1}{2}\right) - \frac{1}{2}}{\frac{1}{2} - 1}$$

Show that both representations for S_n are equivalent.

PROBLEM 2 To Infinity, and Beyond!

In the previous problem, you saw how an infinite geometric series can have a finite sum. Let's see if this is the case for *any* infinite geometric series.

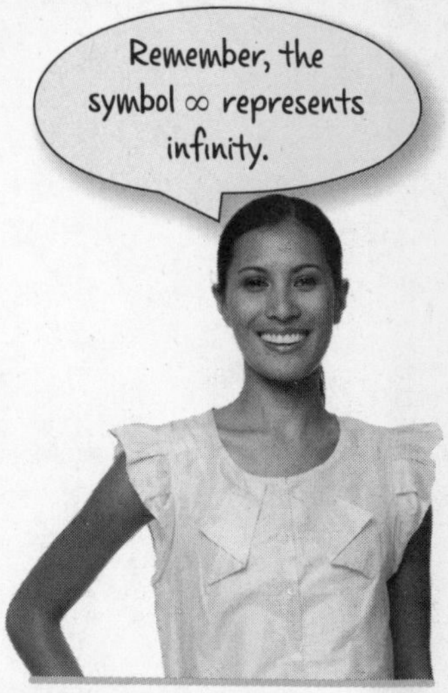

1. Examine the given formula and accompanying diagram for each infinite geometric series. Identify both r and g_1 for each series. Then, determine if the sum is infinite or finite. If the sum is finite, estimate it.

   a. $\frac{1}{3} + \frac{1}{9} + \frac{1}{27} + \cdots = \sum_{i=1}^{\infty} \left(\frac{1}{3}\right)^i$

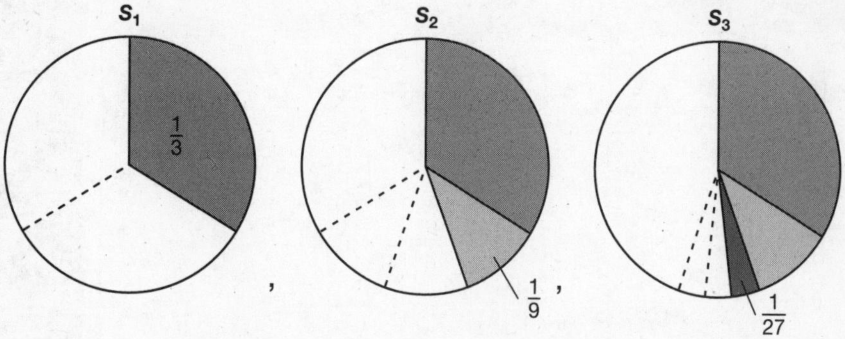

$r =$ ______________________

$g_1 =$ ______________________

$S =$ ______________________

b. $1 + 3 + 9 + 27 + \cdots = \sum_{i=1}^{\infty} \frac{1}{3}(3)^i$

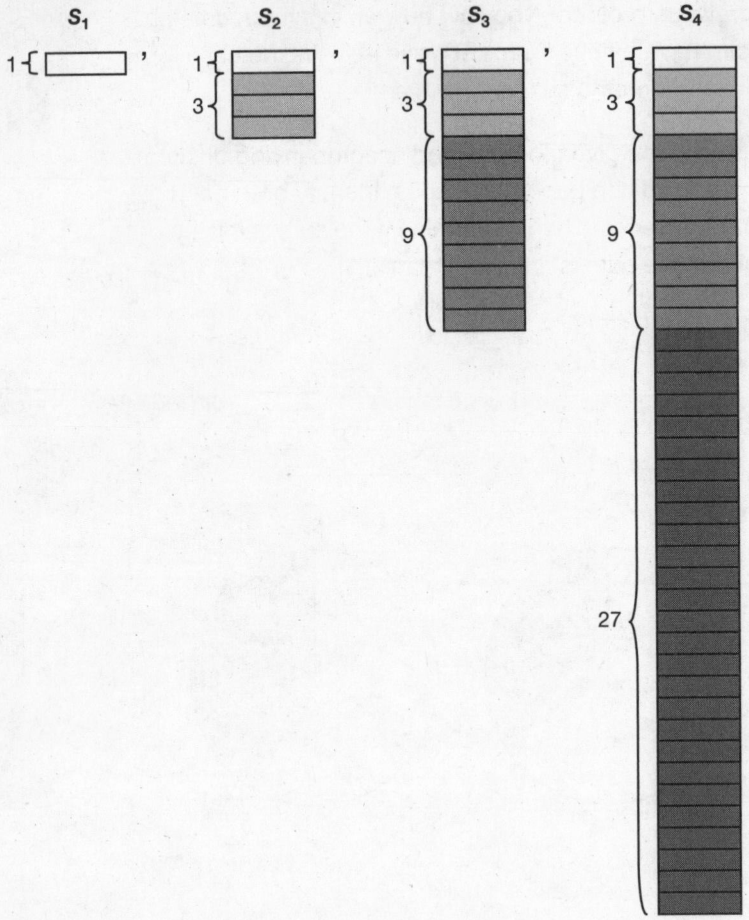

$r =$ ______________________________

$g_1 =$ ______________________________

$S =$ ______________________________

c. $1 + \frac{3}{4} + \frac{9}{16} + \frac{27}{64} + \frac{81}{256} + \frac{243}{1024} + \frac{729}{4096} + \cdots = \sum_{i=1}^{\infty} \frac{4}{3}\left(\frac{3}{4}\right)^i$

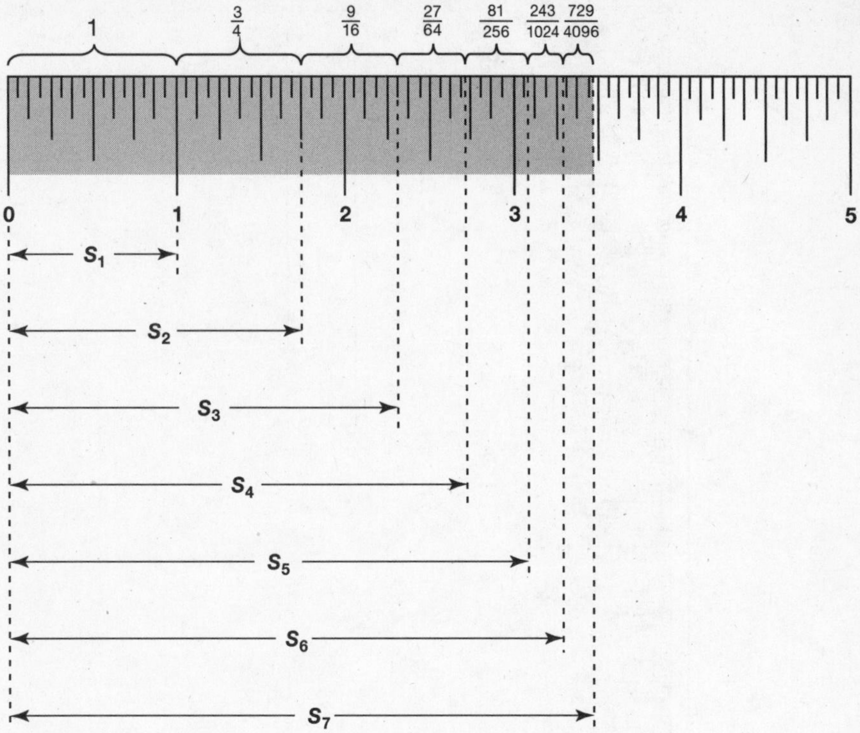

$r =$ ____________________

$g_1 =$ ____________________

$S =$ ____________________

d. $\frac{1}{4} + \frac{1}{16} + \frac{1}{64} + \cdots = \sum_{i=1}^{\infty} \left(\frac{1}{4}\right)^i$

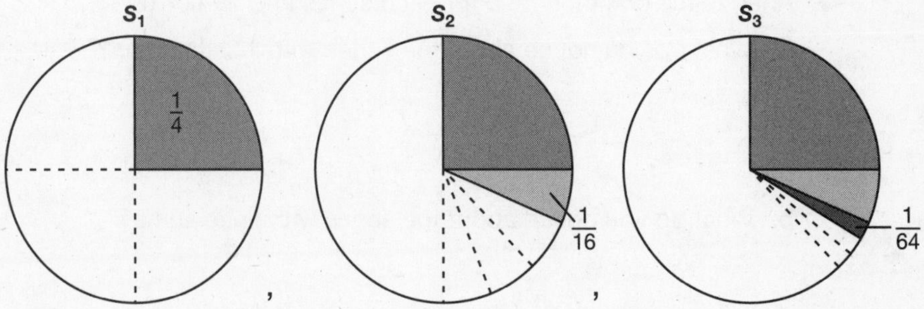

$r =$ ____________________

$g_1 =$ ____________________

$S =$ ____________________

8

e. $1 + \frac{3}{2} + \frac{9}{4} + \frac{27}{8} + \cdots = \sum_{i=1}^{\infty} \frac{2}{3}\left(\frac{3}{2}\right)^i$

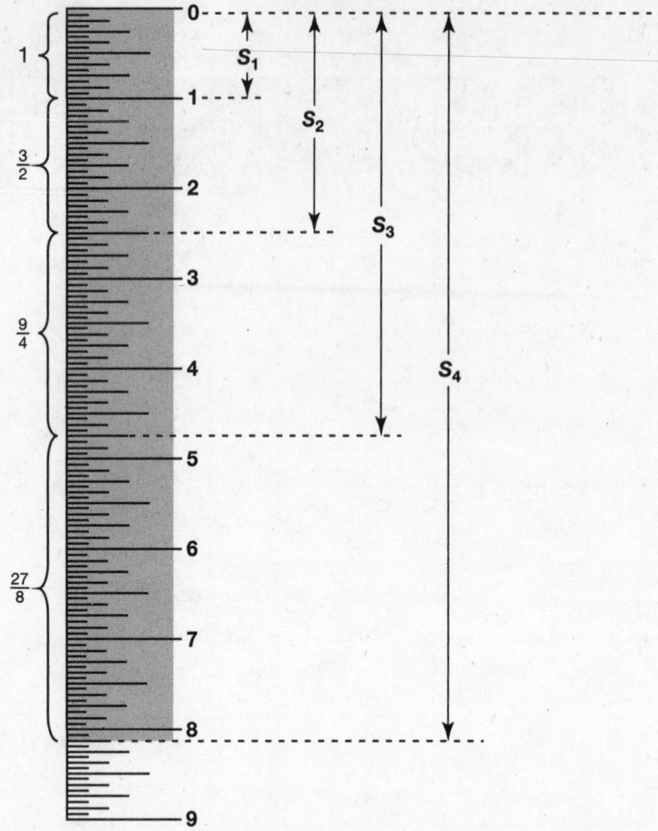

$r =$ ______________________________

$g_1 =$ ______________________________

$S =$ ______________________________

2. Analyze the common ratio for each series in Question 1.

a. What do you notice about the series with infinite sums?

b. What do you notice about the series with finite sums?

A **convergent series** is an infinite series that has a finite sum. A **divergent series** is an infinite series that does not have a finite sum. If a series is divergent, the sum is infinity.

8

The formula to compute a convergent geometric series S is shown.

$$S = \frac{g_1}{1 - r}$$

Notice that S denotes the sum of an *infinite* series. This notation should not be confused with S_n, which represents the sum of the nth term of a series.

Keep in mind
that you cannot use
this formula unless you know
that you are working with a
convergent geometric
series.

3. Consider each infinite geometric series from Question 1. Determine whether each series is convergent or divergent, and explain how you know. If a series is convergent, use the formula to compute the sum. If a series is divergent, write infinity.

a. $\frac{1}{3} + \frac{1}{9} + \frac{1}{27} + \cdots = \sum_{i=1}^{\infty} \left(\frac{1}{3}\right)^i$

Convergent or divergent? ____________________

Explanation:

$S =$ ____________________________

b. $1 + 3 + 9 + 27 + \cdots = \sum_{i=1}^{\infty} \frac{1}{3}(3)^i$

Convergent or divergent? ____________________

Explanation:

$S =$ ____________________

c. $1 + \frac{3}{4} + \frac{9}{16} + \frac{27}{64} + \frac{81}{256} + \frac{243}{1024} + \frac{729}{4096} + \cdots = \sum_{i=1}^{\infty} \frac{4}{3}\left(\frac{3}{4}\right)^i$

Convergent or divergent? ____________________

Explanation:

$S =$ ____________________________

d. $\frac{1}{4} + \frac{1}{16} + \frac{1}{64} + \cdots = \sum_{i=1}^{\infty} \left(\frac{1}{4}\right)^i$

Convergent or divergent? ____________________

Explanation:

$S =$ ____________________________

e. $1 + \frac{3}{2} + \frac{9}{4} + \frac{27}{8} + \cdots = \sum_{i=1}^{\infty} \frac{2}{3}\left(\frac{3}{2}\right)^i$

Convergent or divergent? ____________________

Explanation:

$S =$ ____________________

4. Zoe computed the infinite geometric series.

$$\frac{5}{8}+\frac{25}{32}+\frac{125}{128}+\frac{625}{512}+\cdots=\sum_{i=1}^{\infty}\frac{1}{2}\left(\frac{5}{4}\right)^{i}$$

Zoe

The formula to compute the series is $S=\frac{g_1}{1-r}$.
In this series, $g_1=\frac{5}{8}$ and $r=\frac{5}{4}$.

So, $S=\frac{\frac{5}{8}}{1-\frac{5}{4}}=\frac{\frac{5}{8}}{-\frac{1}{4}}=\frac{5}{8}\left(-\frac{4}{1}\right)=-\frac{5}{2}$.

Explain why Zoe is incorrect, and then determine the correct sum.

5. Compute each infinite geometric series, if possible.

a. $\frac{9}{10}+\frac{9}{100}+\frac{9}{1000}+\frac{9}{10{,}000}+\frac{9}{100{,}000}+\cdots$

b. $0.9+0.09+0.009+0.0009+\cdots$

c. 0.9999999 . . .

So far in this lesson, you have only seen infinite *geometric* series. What about infinite *arithmetic* series?

6. Consider the statements made by Ronald and Jeremiah about the infinite arithmetic series.

Ronald

Some infinite arithmetic series are convergent, and some are divergent; it all depends on the common difference.

Jeremiah

All infinite arithmetic series are divergent.

Who is correct? Explain your reasoning.

Talk the Talk

Write the formula to compute each type of series.

The First n-Terms of an Arithmetic Series:

$S_n =$

The First n-Terms of a Geometric Series:

$S_n =$

A Convergent Geometric Series:

$S =$

A Divergent Geometric Series:

$S =$

Be prepared to share your solutions and methods.

The Power of Interest (It's a Curious Thing)

8.5

Geometric Series Applications

LEARNING GOALS

In this lesson you will:

- Apply your understanding of series to problem situations.
- Write the formula for a geometric series representing a problem situation.

Imagine walking up to the counter of a major electronics store to purchase a new flat screen television for $999. When the salesperson rings up your purchase, she says: "After fees and interest charges, your total is $1950!" Would you still buy the television?

In another scenario, imagine walking into the tuition office at a local university. You are interested in taking 2 classes this fall while working part-time. The cost of the 6 credits is supposed to be $5000, but after discussing a particular payment option with the financial aid officer, you realize that the classes will cost more than $10,000 over the next 12 years. Would you still accept that payment option?

It may surprise you, but many people accept these terms for their purchases every day and don't even realize it. You may wonder how this could happen. The answer lies in the mathematics behind credit cards. When used wisely, credit cards can be convenient and flexible. They allow consumers to purchase expensive or necessary items and pay for them at a later date. On the other hand, if used unwisely, consumers waste a lot of money on interest charges.

How do credit cards work? How could you end up paying twice the amount for a television, or make monthly payments and still carry a balance on two college classes that you took over a decade ago?

PROBLEM 1 I Don't Want Credit For This

Vince wants to purchase a laptop with high screen resolution for his gaming hobby. He charges the $1000 purchase to a credit card with 19% interest.

The credit card company requires a minimum monthly payment of the greater of:

- 2% of the balance on the card, or
- $15.00.

To determine how long it will take to pay off the credit card when paying the minimum balance, Vince calls the company. He learns that when making a monthly payment, 75% of the minimum payment goes toward interest and the remaining portion of the minimum monthly payment goes toward the principal.

1. Determine the percent of the payment that is paid toward interest and principal for each monthly payment.

   a. Monthly payment is 2% of balance.

Calculating finance charges is a very complex endeavor. The calculations in this lesson closely approximate what happens in real life.

   b. Monthly payment is 10% of balance.

   c. Monthly payment is 25% of balance.

Let's consider Vince's monthly payment.

In order to calculate the minimum monthly payment, you will need to calculate 2% of the balance.

$$\begin{aligned} \text{minimum payment} &= (0.02)(\text{balance}) \\ &= 0.02(1000) \\ &= 20 \end{aligned}$$

If the credit card balance is \$1000.00, the minimum monthly payment would be \$20.00.

The amount paid toward interest is 1.5% of the balance.

$$\begin{aligned} \text{amount paid toward interest} &= 0.015(\text{balance}) \\ &= (0.015)(1000) \\ &= 15 \end{aligned}$$

If the minimum monthly payment is \$20.00, the amount paid toward interest would be \$15.00.

The amount paid toward principal is 0.5% of the balance.

$$\begin{aligned} \text{amount paid toward principal} &= (0.005)(\text{balance}) \\ &= (0.005)(1000) \\ &= 5 \end{aligned}$$

If the minimum monthly payment is \$20.00, the amount paid toward principal would be \$5.00.

The remaining balance on the credit card will be the current balance minus the amount paid toward principal.

$$\begin{aligned} \text{remaining balance} &= (\text{current balance}) - (\text{amount paid toward principal}) \\ &= 1000 - 5 \\ &= 995 \end{aligned}$$

So, if Vince makes a monthly payment of \$20.00 on the \$1000.00 balance, the balance after the monthly payment is \$995.00.

2. Calculate the monthly payment details for the first 12 months of minimum payments. The first row of the table reflects the calculations from the worked example.

Number of Months (n)	Balance Before Monthly Payment ($)	Minimum Monthly Payment ($)	Amount Paid Toward Principal ($)	Amount Paid Toward Interest ($)	Balance After Monthly Payment ($)
1	1000.00	20.00	5.00	15.00	995.00
2					
3					
4					
5					
6					
7					
8					
9					
10					
11					
12					
n					

3. Consider the worked example and the answers to each part to complete the n-row of the table.

   a. Write the explicit formula for the geometric sequence represented in the "Balance Before Monthly Payment" column.

   b. Write the formula to calculate the minimum monthly payment.

To write the explicit formulas of each column in the n-row, consider the initial value and the rate of change.

c. Write the formula to calculate the amount paid toward interest.

d. Write the formula to calculate the amount paid toward principal.

e. Write the formula to calculate the balance after minimum payment.

Vince knows how much he is paying each month, but it would be helpful if he knew how much he had paid in both interest and principal over a certain amount of time instead of on any given month.

4. Calculate each.

a. the total monthly payment in the first 12 months

You developed two different formulas to compute a geometric series. Which one are you going to use in this situation?

b. the amount paid toward principal in the first 12 months

c. the amount paid toward interest in the first 12 months

5. Write a formula for the geometric series that represents:

a. the total monthly payment.

b. the total payment toward principal over time.

c. the total payment toward interest over time.

6. Use the formulas you created in Question 5 to complete the table.

	Total Amount Paid Toward Principal	Total Amount Paid Toward Interest
2 years		
5 years		

7. Assume the credit card company does not require a monthly payment of $15.00. Determine how long will it take to pay off the credit card completely.

8. Does your answer to Question 7 seem reasonable? Explain your reasoning.

Use a graphing calculator to help solve these problems.

8

9. Determine the amount of time it will take to pay off the credit card balance, taking into account the minimum payment of $15.00.

a. After how many months will the minimum monthly payment become $15.00?

b. What will be the balance on Vince's credit card when the minimum monthly payment becomes $15.00?

c. How much will Vince pay toward principal with every $15.00 payment?

d. How much will Vince pay toward interest with every $15.00 payment?

e. Suppose Vince continues to make $15.00 payments until the end of the loan. How many months will Vince have to make the $15.00 minimum payment to pay off the remaining balance?

f. How many years will it take Vince to pay off the entire balance?

10. How much money will Vince end up spending on his $1000.00 laptop?

Keep in mind, Vince paid 2% of the balance for awhile, and then he made $15 monthly payments until the balance was paid in full.

11. How much money will Vince spend in interest to pay for his $1000.00 laptop?

PROBLEM 2 A Little Less Interest-ing

After realizing how long it would take to pay his entire credit card bill when only paying the minimum amount, Vince decides that he should pay more than the minimum amount every month. Vince determines that he can pay 10% of the balance every month.

Remember, amount paid toward interest is still 75% of the monthly payment. You might want to use a spreadsheet to perform these calculations.

1. Complete the table to represent this information for 12 months.

Number of Months (n)	Balance Before Monthly Payment ($)	10% Monthly Payment ($)	Amount Paid Toward Principal ($)	Amount Paid Toward Interest ($)	Balance After Monthly Payment ($)
1	1000.00	0.10(1000) = 100	25.00	75.00	975.00
2					
3					
4					
5					
6					
7					
8					
9					
10					
11					
12					
n					

2. Write the formula for the geometric series that represents:

a. the total monthly payment.

Use the formulas from the table in Problem 1 to help you with the formulas for this table.

b. the total payment toward principal over time.

c. the total payment toward interest over time.

3. Use the formulas you created in Question 2 to complete the table.

	Total Money Spent in Principal	Total Money Spent in Interest
1.5 years		
2 years		

4. After how many months will the minimum monthly payment become $15.00?

5. What will the balance on his credit card, when the minimum payment becomes $15.00?

6. Vince decides that once he gets to the minimum payment, he will pay off the rest of the balance in one lump sum.

   a. How long will it take Vince to pay off the entire balance?

   b. How much money will Vince end up spending on his $1000.00 laptop?

   c. How much money will Vince spend in interest to pay for his $1000.00 laptop?

7. How much money will Vince save by paying 10% instead of the required 2% minimum payment?

PROBLEM 3 Enough of These Interest Payments

Vince is still concerned about paying so much money in interest on his credit card, and decides that he can afford to pay a flat amount of $100 each month.

1. Sean calculates how long it will take Vince to pay off his credit card this way.

> **Sean**
>
> $\frac{\$1000}{100} = 10$
>
> *It will take Vince 10 months to pay off his credit card bill.*

What is wrong with Sean's work? Explain your reasoning.

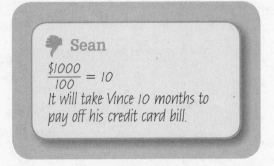

2. How long do you think it will take Vince to pay off his credit card this way? Explain your reasoning.

3. Complete the table to represent this information for 12 months.

Number of Months (n)	Balance Before Monthly Payment ($)	$100 Monthly Payment ($)	Amount Paid Toward Principal ($)	Amount Paid Toward Interest ($)	Balance After Monthly Payment ($)
1	1000.00	100.00	25.00	75.00	975.00
2					
3					
4					
5					
6					
7					
8					
9					
10					
11					
12					
n					

4. What pattern do you notice in this table that is different from the tables in Problems 1 and 2?

5. How long will it take Vince to pay off the entire balance?

6. How much money will Vince end up spending on his $1000.00 laptop?

7. How much money will Vince spend in interest to pay for his $1000.00 laptop?

PROBLEM 4 Interest Free? Whoopee!

Now that Vince has become more educated about credit card finances and proven that he can be responsible for paying off his debt, he applies for a new credit card that offers the first 6 months interest free for any purchases. Like his other credit card, this new credit card requires a minimum monthly payment of the greater of:

- 2% of the balance on the card, or
- $15.00.

How will
your calculations change
for month 7?

Vince is approved for the card, and charges $1000 for a flat screen TV. He still decides to pay 10% of the balance after noticing how much money that saved him the last time.

1. Complete the table to show 12 months of payments.

Number of Months (n)	Balance Before Monthly Payment ($)	10% Monthly Payment ($)	Amount Paid Toward Principal ($)	Amount Paid Toward Interest ($)	Balance After Monthly Payment ($)
1	1000.00	0.10(1000) = 100	100.00	0.00	900.00
2					
3					
4					
5					
6					
Interest begins on the 7th month.					
7					
8					
9					
10					
11					
12					
n					

2. Describe the change in Vince's balance in the first 6 months compared to the last 6 months.

3. Analyze the 12 months of payments. What recommendations would you give Vince about paying off his credit card? Include the number of months he would be paying on the balance, the total amount that he would pay for the flat screen TV, and the amount of total interest he would pay.

8

Talk the Talk

Consider the four credit card payment scenarios Vince explored:

a. Paying minimum payment

b. Paying 10% of balance until minimum payment and then paying off in one lump sum

c. Paying $100.00 a month

d. Paying 10% interest free for 6 months and then continuing to pay 10%

1. Why might payment method (c) not be an option for some people?

2. Which method of payment do you consider the best option? Explain your reasoning.

3. When considering applying for a credit card, what details should you look for? How would you plan to pay off your bill?

Be prepared to share your solutions and methods.

A Series of Fortunate Events

8.6

Applications of Arithmetic and Geometric Series

LEARNING GOALS

In this lesson, you will:

- Apply your understanding of series to problem situations.
- Determine whether a situation is best modeled by a geometric or arithmetic series.

Have you ever heard the expression "money can't buy happiness"? Do you think it's true? People spend a lot of time and mental energy dreaming about having a lot of money or material possessions. It's interesting to think about whether winning the lottery or suddenly acquiring a lot of fancy things would actually make you a happier person. Researchers at universities across the globe have studied this question, and some of the results of the studies may surprise you.

- Lottery winners often become less satisfied with life's simple pleasures over time.
- Once earnings surpass the ability to purchase essential items (food, clothing, shelter, etc.), additional money generally doesn't lead to an increase in happiness.
- Wealthy people tend to relish positive life experiences much less than people who aren't wealthy.

That isn't to say that money isn't important. Making sound financial decisions can save you a lot of headaches and put you in a position where you aren't worrying about money. However, research says that having a lot of money won't necessarily make you a happier person.

What financial decisions have you made so far in your life? What important financial decisions are coming up?

PROBLEM 1 A Time of Serious Financial Decisions

Some of the most important financial decisions often occur during the years following the completion of high school or college. This is a time when young adults usually face their first serious choices about things such as a career, buying a car, assuming a mortgage for a house, or investing money in the bank.

1. Benjamin is anxious. After finishing his undergraduate degree he must take the GRE in order to get into graduate school, but the amount of information that he needs to cover is overwhelming. “I only have a month to prepare!” he exclaims. Sally tells him to calm down and start slowly. She recommends studying just 15 minutes the first day, but adding 3 minutes every day to his study time.

   “But a friend told me that you have to study at least 20 hours to get ready for this thing! I think I need a different plan.”

   Will Sally’s plan lead to enough study time? Show all work and explain your reasoning.

Did Sally describe an arithmetic or geometric series?

2. Carlos meets up with Jake after a visit to the bank. He has a confused look.

Carlos said, "I wanted to determine the best way to invest my money, but everybody at the bank was busy. I found this graph showing how $50 increases over time from two of their investment options."

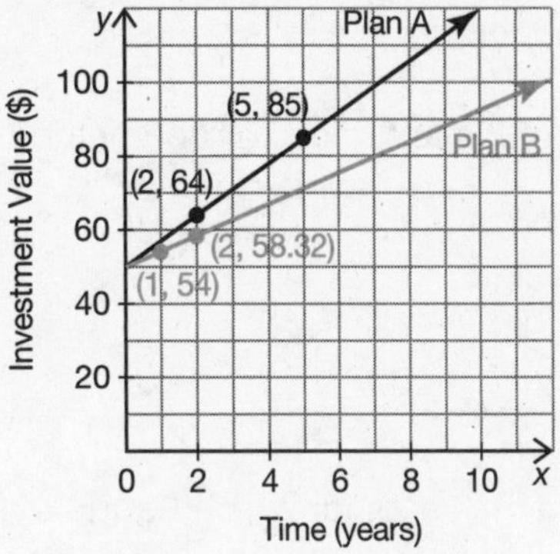

"So what's the problem?" Jake asks.

Carlos explains his dilemma: "I want to invest my money in a plan and keep it there for 20 years. This brochure was ripped and only shows the first few years. I need to know which plan is a better long-term investment.

a. Are the investment plans arithmetic or geometric? Explain your reasoning.

b. Determine the better investment for Carlos. Show all work and explain your reasoning.

3. Rhonda is considering two different physical therapist positions.

- Range of Motion offers an initial salary of $50,000 per year with annual increases of $1,500 per year.
- Mobility, Inc. offers an initial salary of $42,000 with a guaranteed 4% increase in salary every year.

a. Is this situation arithmetic or geometric? Explain your reasoning.

b. Determine the years for which Range of Motion pays more than Mobility, Inc. Show all work and explain your reasoning.

c. Determine which company pays more salary over a 30-year career. Show all work and explain your reasoning.

PROBLEM 2 If This Wordplay Doesn't End, I Might "Series-ly" Get Sick!

1. A stomach virus spreads rapidly through a town. Initially only 12 people were infected, but the virus spreads quickly, increasing the number of people infected by 15% every day.

   a. How many new people are infected on the 10th day? Show all work and explain your reasoning.

   b. How many total people were infected on the 10th day? Show all work and explain your reasoning.

2. A total of 123,000 cases of a different cold virus were reported throughout the country in a particular year. The production and distribution of a vaccine is projected to decrease the number of reported cases by 26% every year.

   a. Approximately how many new cases will be reported in 15 years? Show all work and explain your reasoning.

   b. A company reports that vaccine production will cost approximately $9 per person. Estimate the total cost of production for the next 15 years.

   c. Will the virus be eliminated? If so, when? Show all work and explain your reasoning.

Be prepared to share your solutions and methods.

8

Chapter 8 Summary

KEY TERMS

- arithmetic sequence (8.1)
- geometric sequence (8.1)
- finite sequence (8.1)
- infinite sequence (8.1)
- tessellation (8.2)
- series (8.2)
- finite series (8.2)
- infinite series 8.2)
- arithmetic series (8.2)
- geometric series (8.3)
- convergent series (8.4)
- divergent series (8.4)

8.1 Identifying Whether a Sequence is Arithmetic, Geometric, or Neither

An arithmetic sequence is a sequence of numbers in which the difference between two consecutive terms is a constant. A geometric sequence is a sequence of numbers in which the ratio between two consecutive terms is a constant. A sequence that is neither arithmetic nor geometric has no common difference or ratio between two consecutive terms.

Example

The sequence 5, 11, 17, 23, 29 is arithmetic because the difference between consecutive terms is 6.

The sequence $\frac{1}{2}, \frac{1}{6}, \frac{1}{18}, \frac{1}{54}$ is geometric because the ratio between two consecutive terms is $\frac{1}{3}$.

The sequence -2, 0, 4, 10 is neither arithmetic nor geometric because there is no common difference or ratio between two consecutive terms.

8.1 Writing an Explicit Formula and/or Recursive Formula for Determining a Term of an Arithmetic or Geometric Sequence

An explicit formula for a sequence is a formula for calculating each term of the sequence using the index, which is a term's position in the sequence. A recursive formula expresses each new term of a sequence based on a preceding term of the sequence.

	Arithmetic Sequence	Geometric Sequence
Explicit Formula	$a_n = a_1 + d(n - 1)$ where a_1 is the first term, d is the common difference, and n is the nth term in the sequence.	$g_n = g_1 \cdot r^{n-1}$ where g_1 is the first term and r is the common ratio.
Recursive Formula	$a_n = a_{n-1} + d$ where a_{n-1} is the term previous to a_n and d is the common difference.	$g_n = g_{n-1} \cdot r$ where g_{n-1} is the term previous to g_n and r is the common ratio.

Example

The Explicit Formula for the arithmetic sequence 3, 7, 11, 15, 19 where $a_1 = 3$ and $d = 4$ is as shown.

$$a_n = a_1 + d(n - 1)$$
$$= 3 + 4(n - 1)$$
$$= 3 + 4n - 4$$
$$a_n = 4n - 1$$

The Recursive Formula for the geometric sequence −2, −4, −8, −16 where $g_1 = -2$ and $r = 2$ is as shown.

$$g_n = g_{n-1} \cdot r$$
$$g_n = g_{n-1} \cdot 2$$

8.1 Using an Explicit Formula and/or Recursive Formula for Determining a Term of an Arithmetic or Geometric Sequence

Deciding whether to use an explicit formula or recursive formula to determine a term in a sequence depends on what information is known. To determine the nth term in an arithmetic sequence use an explicit formula if the first term and common difference are known or use a recursive formula if the $(n - 1)$th term and common difference are know. To determine the nth term in an geometric sequence use an explicit formula if the first term and common ratio are known or use a recursive formula if the $(n - 1)$th term and common ratio are know.

Example

To determine the term a_7 of an arithmetic sequence given $a_6 = 15$ and $d = 3$ use a recursive formula.

$a_n = a_{n-1} + d$

$a_7 = a_6 + 3$

$= 15 + 3$

$= 18$

To determine the term g_7 of a geometric sequence given $g_1 = 2$ and $r = 4$ use an explicit formula.

$g_n = g_1 \cdot r^{n-1}$

$g_7 = 2 \cdot 4^6$

$= 8192$

8.2 Using Sigma Notation to Rewrite the Sum of a Series

Sigma notation is a convenient way to write the sum, S_n, of the series $a_1 + a_2 + a_3 + \cdots + a_n$.

The notation is as follows: $S_n = \sum_{i=1}^{n} a_i = a_1 + a_2 + a_3 + \cdots + a_{n-1} + a_n$

Example

Series: $2 + 7 + 12 + 17$

$S_4 = \sum_{i=1}^{4} a_i$

$= 2 + 7 + 12 + 17$

8.2 Using Gauss's Formula to Compute the First *n* Terms of an Arithmetic Series

To compute S_n, of the first n terms of an arithmetic series Gauss's Formula,

$S_n = \frac{n(a_1 + a_n)}{2}$, can be used providing the first term, a_1, and the last term, a_n, are known.

Example

Series: $-\frac{1}{2} + 0 + \frac{1}{2} + 1 + \frac{3}{2}$

$n = 5, a_1 = -\frac{1}{2}, a_5 = \frac{3}{2}$

$$S_n = \frac{n(a_1 + a_n)}{2}$$

$$S_5 = \frac{5\left(-\frac{1}{2} + \frac{3}{2}\right)}{2}$$

$$= \frac{5}{2}$$

8.2 Determining a Function that Computes the First *n* Terms of an Arithmetic Series

The explicit formula, $a_n = a_1 + d(n - 1)$, together with Gauss's Formula, $S_n = \frac{n(a_1 + a_n)}{2}$, can be used to determine a function that computes the first n terms of an arithmetic series.

Example

Series: $-1 + (-3) + (-5) + (-7) + (-9) + \cdots$

$a_1 = -1, d = -2$

$a_n = a_1 + d(n - 1)$

$= -1 + (-2)(n - 1)$

$= -1 - 2n + 2$

$a_n = 1 - 2_n$

$$S_n = \frac{n(a_1 + a_n)}{2}$$

$$= \frac{n[-1 + (1 - 2n)]}{2}$$

$$= \frac{n[-2n]}{2}$$

$$= \frac{-2n^2}{2}$$

$$S_n = -n^2$$

Solving Real-World Problems Using Finite Arithmetic Series

Identify what the problem is asking. Then determine what information is provided so that the correct approach to the solution can be used. Choose the appropriate formula(s) need, make the correct substitution(s), and solve the problem. Check to see that the question asked has been answered.

Example

Barry planted sunflowers in his garden. In the first row he planted 4 plants, in the second row he planted 10 plants, and in the third row he planted 16 plants. If this pattern continued, how many plants did Barry place in the sixth row?

The problem asks how many sunflower plants are placed in the sixth row. The information provided is that $n = 6$, $a_1 = 4$, and $d = 6$.

$$a_n = a_1 + d(n - 1)$$

$$a_6 = 4 + 6(6 - 1)$$

$$= 34 \text{ sunflowers}$$

Barry placed 34 sunflower plants in the sixth row.

8.3 **Using Euclid's Method to Determine the Sum of a Finite Geometric Series**

Euclid's Method can be used to compute a finite geometric series provided the first term, g_1, the last term, g_n, and the common ratio, r, are known. In which case, the formula $S_n = \dfrac{g_n(r) - g_1}{r - 1}$ can be used.

Example

$$-5 + (-10) + (-20) + (-40)$$

$$g_1 = -5, n = 4, g_4 = -40, r = 2$$

$$S_n = \frac{g_n(r) - g_1}{r - 1}$$

$$S_4 = \frac{-40(2) - (-5)}{2 - 1}$$

$$= -75$$

8.3 Using the Formula $S_n = \frac{g_1(r^n - 1)}{r - 1}$ to Compute a Finite Geometric Series

The formula, $S_n = \frac{g_1(r^n - 1)}{r - 1}$, can be used to compute a finite geometric series provided the first term, g_1, the common ratio, r, and the number of terms, n, are known.

Example

$2 + 6 + 18 + 54 + 162$

$g_1 = 2, r = 3, n = 5$

$$S_n = \frac{g_1(r^n - 1)}{r - 1}$$

$$S_5 = \frac{2(3^5 - 1)}{3 - 1}$$

$$= 242$$

8.4 Determining Whether an Infinite Geometric Series Converges or Diverges

A convergent series is an infinite series that has a finite sum. A divergent series is an infinite series that does not have a finite sum. If a series is divergent, it is said that the sum is infinity. An infinite geometric series converges providing the common ratio, r, is greater than zero and less than 1.

Example

$$\frac{2}{3} + \frac{2}{9} + \frac{2}{27} + \frac{2}{81} + \cdots$$

The common ratio for the infinite geometric series is $\frac{1}{3}$ which is greater than zero and less than 1. The series converges.

8.4 Computing an Infinite Convergent Geometric Series

The formula to compute S of a convergent geometric series with a first term g_1 and common ratio r is $S = \frac{g_1}{1 - r}$ provided $0 < r < 1$.

Example

$5 + \frac{5}{2} + \frac{5}{4} + \frac{5}{8} + \cdots$

Observe that $g_1 = 5$ and $r = \frac{1}{2}$. Since r is greater than zero and less than 1, the infinite geometric series converges.

$$S = \frac{g_1}{1 - r}$$

$$S = \frac{5}{1 - \frac{1}{2}}$$

$$= 10$$

8.5 Solving Real-World Problems Involving Geometric Sequences or Series

Identify what the problem is asking. Then determine what information is provided so that the correct approach to the solution can be used. Choose the appropriate formula(s) need, make the correct substitution(s), and solve the problem. Check to see that the question asked has been answered.

Example

Every Saturday Chloe places money in her piggy bank. On the first Saturday she placed \$0.02 in the piggy bank, on the second Saturday she placed \$0.06 in the piggy bank, and on the third Saturday she place \$0.18 in the piggy bank. If Chloe continues to place money in her piggy bank using the same pattern, how much money will she place in her piggy bank on the seventh Saturday?

The problem is asking how much money Chloe places in her piggy bank on the seventh Saturday. The information indicates that Chloe is using a geometric pattern where the first term, g_1, is \$0.02 and the common ratio, r, is 3. The formula needed to answer the question is $g_n = g_1 \cdot r^{n-1}$ where $n = 7$.

$$g_n = g_1 \cdot r^{n-1}$$

$$g_7 = 0.02 \cdot 3^6$$

$$= \$14.58$$

The amount of money Chloe places in her piggy bank on the seventh Saturday is \$14.58.

8

8.6 Determining Whether a Situation Is Best Modeled by a Arithmetic or Geometric Series

When solving a problem involving a series it is important to determine whether the given situation is arithmetic or geometric. If consecutive terms of the series have a common difference then the series is arithmetic. If consecutive terms of the series have a common ratio then the series is geometric.

Example

Gia applied for a job that initially pays her \$13 per hour but she is guaranteed a yearly raise of \$1.50 per hour.

The progression in her yearly salary is arithmetic with a common difference of \$1.50.

8.6 Solving Real-World Problems Involving Arithmetic or Geometric Sequences or Series

Identify what the problem is asking. Then determine what information is provided so that the correct approach to the solution can be found. Choose the appropriate formula(s) need, make the correct substitution(s), and solve the problem. Check to see that the question asked has been answered.

Example

Belinda likes to write poetry. The table shows how many poems she wrote over the course of 5 weeks. Determine how many poems Belinda wrote.

Week	Number of Poems Written
1	4
2	8
3	16
4	32
5	64

The problem asks for the number of poems written by Belinda. The number of poems written forms a geometric series. Using Euclid's Method, $S_n = \frac{g_n(r) - g_1}{r - 1}$, where $n = 5$, $g_5 = 64$, $r = 2$, and $g_1 = 4$ the number of poems written by Belinda can be determined.

$$S_5 = \frac{g_5(r) - g_1}{r - 1}$$

$$= \frac{64(2) - 4}{2 - 1}$$

$$= 124 \text{ poems}$$

Belinda wrote 124 poems during the 5 week period.

A

absolute maximum

A function has an absolute maximum if there is a point that has a y-coordinate that is greater than the y-coordinates of every other point on the graph.

Example

The ordered pair (4, 2) is the absolute maximum of the graph of the function $f(x) = -\frac{1}{2}x^2 + 4x - 6$.

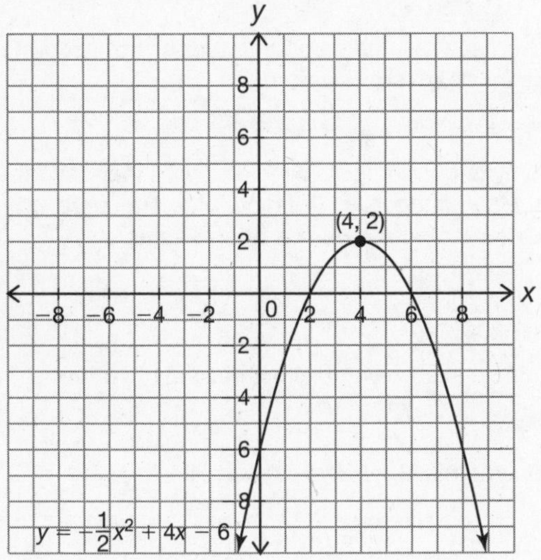

absolute minimum

A function has an absolute minimum if there is a point that has a y-coordinate that is less than the y-coordinates of every other point on the graph.

Example

The ordered pair (1, −4) is the absolute minimum of the graph of the function $y = \frac{2}{3}x^2 - \frac{4}{3}x - \frac{10}{3}$.

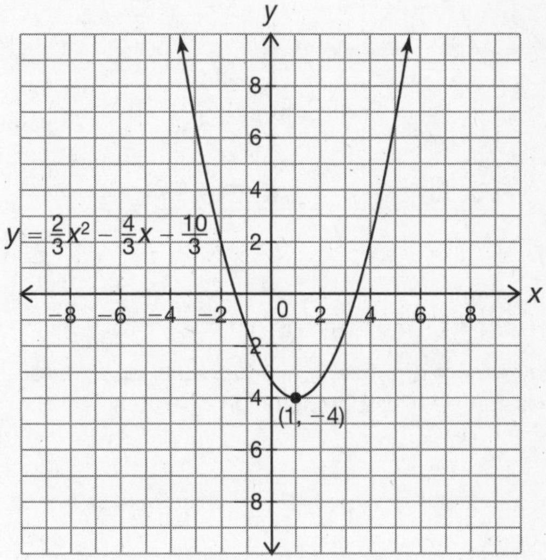

amplitude

The amplitude of a periodic function is one-half of the distance between the maximum and minimum values of the function.

Example

The function $y = \sin(x)$ has a maximum of 1 and a minimum of -1. The distance between the maximum and minimum is 2. So, the amplitude of $y = \sin(x)$ is 1.

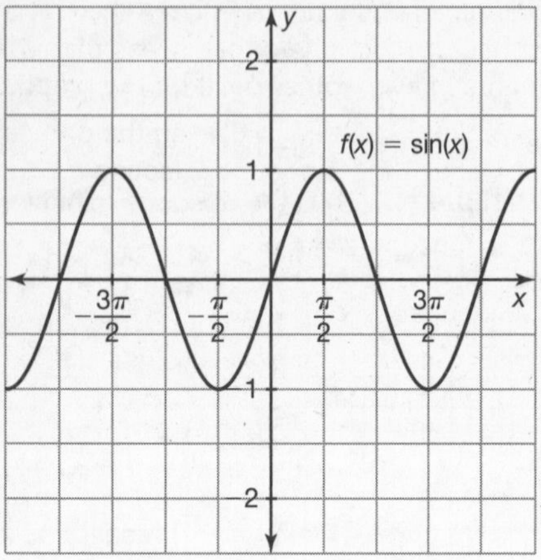

argument of a function

The argument of a function is the variable, term, or expression on which the function operates.

Example

In the function $f(x + 5) = 32$, the argument is $x + 5$.

arithmetic sequence

An arithmetic sequence is a sequence of numbers in which the difference between any two consecutive terms is a constant.

Example

The sequence 1, 3, 5, 7 is an arithmetic sequence with a common difference of 2.

arithmetic series

An arithmetic series is the sum of the terms of an arithmetic sequence.

Example

The arithmetic series corresponding to the arithmetic sequence 1, 3, 5, 7 is 1 + 3 + 5 + 7, or 16.

average rate of change

The average rate of change of a function is the ratio of the independent variable to the dependent variable over a specific interval. The formula for average rate of change is $\frac{f(b) - f(a)}{b - a}$ for an interval (a, b). The expression $a - b$ represents the change in the input of the function f. The expression $f(b) - f(a)$ represents the change in the function f as the input changes from a to b.

Example

Consider the function $f(x) = x^2$.

The average rate of change of the interval (1, 3) is $\frac{3^2 - 1^2}{3 - 1} = \frac{9 - 1}{3 - 1} = \frac{8}{2} = 4$.

B

biased sample

A biased sample is a sample that does not accurately represent all of a population.

Example

A survey is conducted asking students their favorite class. Only students in the math club are surveyed. The sample of students is a biased sample.

binomial

A binomial is a polynomial with exactly two terms.

Example

The polynomial $3x + 5$ is a binomial.

Binomial Theorem

The Binomial Theorem is used to calculate any term of any binomial expansion. It is written in the form:

$$\begin{aligned}(x + y)^k &= \sum_{r=0}^{k} \binom{k}{r} x^{k-r} y^r \\ &= \binom{k}{0} x^k y^0 + \binom{k}{1} x^{k-1} y^1 + \binom{k}{2} x^{k-2} y^2 + \cdots \\ &\quad + \binom{k}{k-2} x^2 y^{k-2} + \binom{k}{k-1} x^1 y^{k-1} \\ &\quad + \binom{k}{k} x^0 y^k\end{aligned}$$

where k is the degree of the binomial exponent. Note that a given term is the $(r + 1)$th term.

Example

Use the Binomial Theorem to find the third term of $(x + y)^{20}$.

$$\begin{aligned}(x + y)^{20} &= \binom{20}{2} x^{20-2} y^2 = \frac{20!}{18!2!} x^{18} y^2 \\ &= \frac{20 \cdot 19}{2 \cdot 1} x^{18} y^2 = 190 x^{18} y^2\end{aligned}$$

Glossary

C

carrying capacity

The carrying capacity of a species is the maximum population size of the species that the environment can sustain. In logistic functions $f(x) = \frac{C}{1 + Ae^{-Bx}}$, C is the carrying capacity.

Example

The number of fish in a small pond is modeled by the logistic growth function $f(x) = \frac{150}{1 + 7e^{-0.06x}}$. The carrying capacity of the pond is 150 fish.

Change of Base Formula

The Change of Base Formula allows you to calculate an exact value for a logarithm by rewriting it in terms of a different base. It is especially helpful when using a calculator.

The Change of Base Formula states: $\log_b (c) = \frac{\log_a (c)}{\log_a (b)}$, where $a, b, c > 0$ and $a, b \neq 1$.

Example

$$\log_4 (50) = \frac{\log 50}{\log 4}$$
$$\approx 2.821928095$$

characteristic of interest

A characteristic of interest is the specific question that you are trying to answer or specific information that a study is trying to gather.

Example

In a sample survey to determine teenagers' online habits, a characteristic of interest is the amount of time that a teenager spends online per day.

closed under an operation

A set is closed under an operation if the operation is performed on any of the numbers in the set and the result is a number that is also in the same set.

Example

The set of whole numbers is closed under addition. The sum of any two whole numbers is always another whole number.

clusters

Clusters are area of the graph where data are grouped close together.

Example

A city manager randomly selects one block in the city and surveys all of the residents of that block. Each block is considered a cluster.

cluster sample

A cluster sample is a sample obtained by creating clusters, with each cluster containing the characteristics of the population, and randomly selecting a cluster.

Example

If students in a high school are divided into clusters of 20 students based on their student I.D. number and then one cluster is randomly selected, this is a cluster sample.

coefficient of determination

The coefficient of determination (R^2) measures the "strength" of the relationship between the original data and its regression equation. The value of the coefficient of determination ranges from 0 to 1 with a value of 1 indicating a perfect fit between the regression equation and the original data.

common logarithm

A common logarithm is a logarithm with a base of 10. Common logarithms are usually written without a base.

Example

$\log (10x)$ or $\log x$ are examples of a common logarithm.

complex conjugates

Complex conjugates are pairs of numbers of the form $a + bi$ and $a - bi$. The product of a pair of complex conjugates is always a real number.

Example

The expressions $(1 + i)$ and $(1 - i)$ are complex conjugates. The product of $(1 + i)$ and $(1 - i)$ is a real number: $(1 + i)(1 - i) = 1 - i^2 = 1 - (-1) = 2$.

composition of functions

Composition of functions is the process of substituting one function for the variable in another function.

Example

If $f(x) = 3x - 5$ and $g(x) = x^2$, then the composition of the functions $f(g(x))$ can be written as $f(g(x)) = 3(x^2) - 5 = 3x^2 - 5$.

The composition of functions $g(f(x))$ can be written as $g(f(x)) = (3x + 5)^2$.

concavity of a parabola

The concavity of a parabola describes the orientation of the curvature of the parabola.

Example

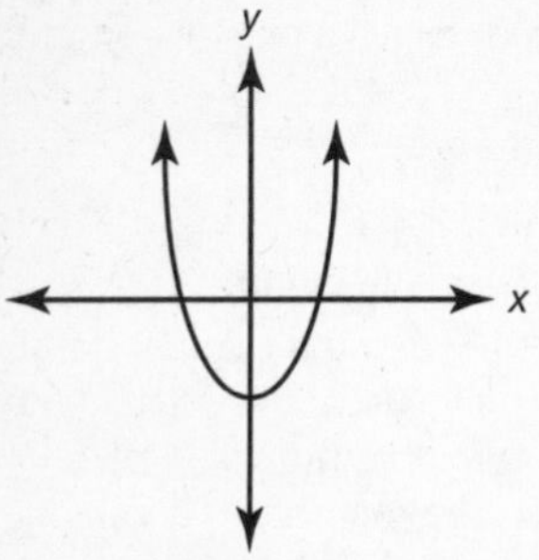

concave up

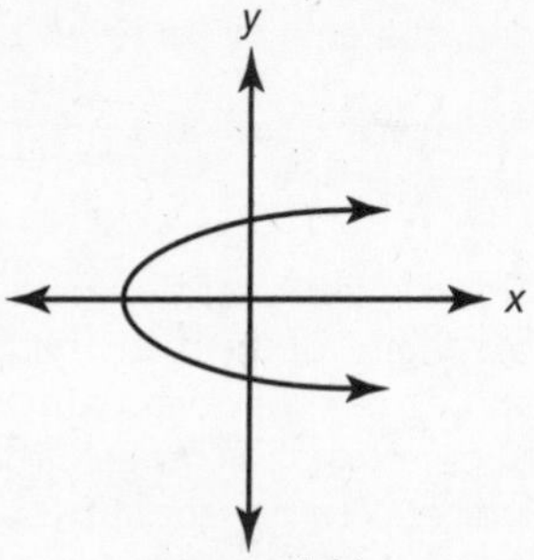

concave right

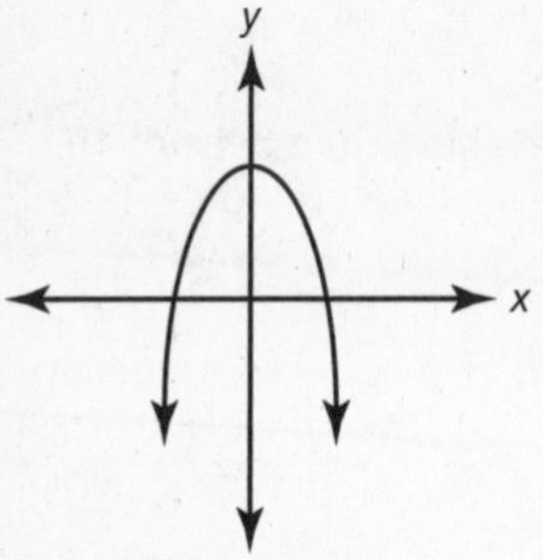

concave down

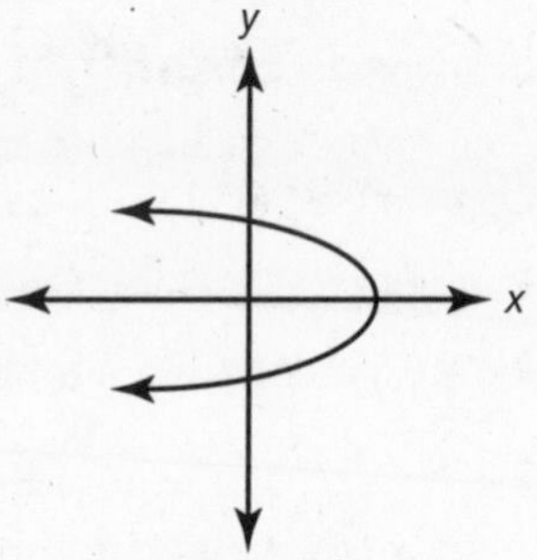

concave left

confidence interval

A confidence interval is an estimated range of values, based on the results of a sample survey, that will likely include the population proportion. Typically, a confidence interval of 95%, or 2 standard deviations from the mean, is used. The formula for calculating the confidence interval for proportions is $\sqrt{\frac{\hat{p}(1 - \hat{p})}{n}}$, where $\hat{p}$ is the sample population and n is the sample size. The formula $\frac{S}{\sqrt{n}}$, where S is the standard deviation of the sample and n is the sample size, is used for continuous data.

Example

A survey of 2000 teenagers reports that 42% have a part-time job.

$$\sqrt{\frac{0.42(1 - 0.42)}{2000}}$$

$$\sqrt{\frac{0.42(0.58)}{2000}}$$

$$\approx 0.011$$

The interval from 40.9% to 43.1% represents a 95% confidence interval for the population proportion.

confounding

Confounding is the process of overlooking factors and situations that distort the final results when seeking to gather information or data.

Example

Suppose that a study is conducted to determine if there is a link between a certain type of insulin that some diabetic patients use and cancer. Confounding can occur due to the fact that there are other potential causes of cancer that could be involved in the sample.

continuous data

Continuous data are data that have an infinite number of possible values.

Example

The heights of students is an example of continuous data.

convenience sample

A convenience sample is a sample whose data are based on what is convenient for the person choosing the sample.

Example

If you choose the students sitting closest to you in math class as your sample, you have a convenience sample.

convergent series

A convergent series is an infinite series that has a finite sum. The sum of a convergent series S can be calculated as $\frac{g_1}{1 - r}$ where g_1 is the first term of the series and r is the common ratio.

Example

The infinite geometric series $1 + \frac{1}{2} + \frac{1}{4} + \frac{1}{8} + \cdots$

can be calculated as $S = \dfrac{1}{1 - \frac{1}{2}} = \dfrac{1}{\frac{1}{2}} = 2$.

cosine function

The cosine function is a periodic function. It takes angle measures (θ values) as inputs and then outputs real number values which correspond to the coordinates of points on the unit circle.

Example

The function $h(\theta) = 4\cos(\theta + \pi)$ is a cosine function.

cube root function

The cube root function is the inverse of the power function $f(x) = x^3$.

Example

The cube root function is $g(x) = \sqrt[3]{x}$.

cubic function

A cubic function is a function that can be written in the standard form $f(x) = ax^3 + bx^2 + cx + d$ where $a \neq 0$.

Example

The function $f(x) = x^3 - 5x^2 + 3x + 1$ is a cubic function.

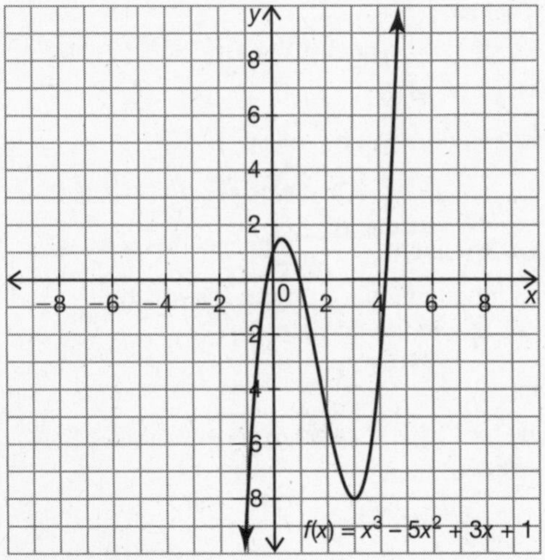

$f(x) = x^3 - 5x^2 + 3x + 1$

damping function

A damping function is a function that is multiplied to a periodic function to decrease its amplitude over time. It can be from a multitude of function families, including linear, quadratic, or exponential.

Example

In the function $f(x) = 2^x \cdot \sin(x) + 1$, the exponential function 2^x is the damping function.

degree of a polynomial

The degree of a polynomial is the greatest variable exponent in the expression.

Example

The polynomial $2x^3 + 5x^2 - 6x + 1$ has a degree of 3 because the greatest exponent is 3.

discrete data

Discrete data are data that have a finite number of possible values.

Example

If you roll a number cube 10 times and record the results, the results are discrete data.

discriminant

The radicand expression in the Quadratic Formula, $b^2 - 4ac$, is called the discriminant because it "discriminates" the number and type of roots of a quadratic equation.

Example

For the function $f(x) = 2x^2 - 5x + 1$, the discriminant is $(-5)^2 - 4(2)(1)$, or 17.

divergent series

A divergent series is an infinite series that does not have a finite sum.

Example

The infinite geometric series $1 + 2 + 4 + 8 + 16 + \cdots$ is a divergent series.

Glossary

double root

A double root of an equation is a root that appears twice.

Example

The equation $x^2 + 2x + 1 = 0$ has a double root at $x = -1$.

$x^2 + 2x + 1 = 0$

$(x + 1)(x + 1) = 0$

$x + 1 = 0$ or $x + 1 = 0$

$x = -1$ or $x = -1$

E

Empirical Rule for Normal Distributions

The Empirical Rule for Normal Distributions states that:

- Approximately 68% of the area under the normal curve is within one standard deviation of the mean.
- Approximately 95% of the area under the normal curve is within two standard deviations of the mean.
- Approximately 99.7% of the area under the normal curve is within three standard deviations of the mean.

Example

For a data set that is normally distributed with a mean of 10 and a standard deviation of 1, the following are true:

- Approximately 68% of the data values are between 9 and 11.
- Approximately 95% of the data values are between 8 and 12.
- Approximately 99.7% of the data values are between 7 and 13.

end behavior

The end behavior of the graph of a function is the behavior of the graph as x approaches infinity and as x approaches negative infinity.

Example

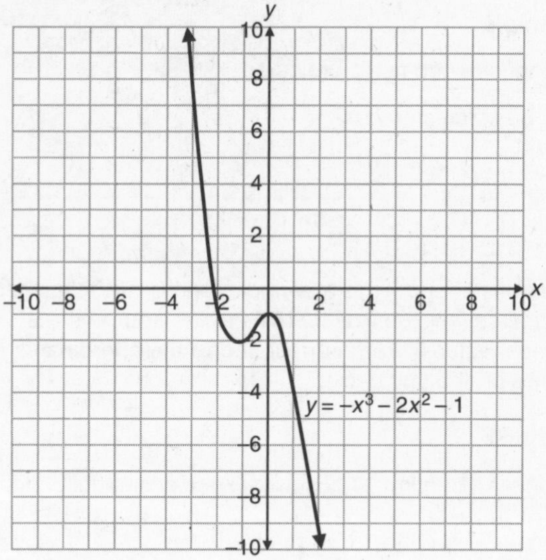

The end behavior of the graph shown can be described as follows:

As x approaches infinity, y approaches negative infinity.

As x approaches negative infinity, y approaches infinity.

Euclid's Formula

Euclid's Formula is a formula used to generate Pythagorean triples given any two positive integers. Given positive integers r and s, where $r > s$, Euclid's Formula is $(r^2 + s^2)^2 = (r^2 - s^2)^2 + (2rs)^2$.

Example

Let $r = 3$ and $s = 1$.

$(3^2 + 1^2)^2 = (3^2 - 1^2)^2 + (2 \cdot 3 \cdot 1)^2$

$10^2 = 8^2 + 6^2$

So, one Pythagorean triple is 6, 8, 10.

even function

An even function f is a function for which $f(-x) = f(x)$ for all values of x in the domain.

Example

The function $f(x) = x^2$ is an even function because $(-x)^2 = x^2$.

Glossary

experiment

An experiment gathers data on the effect of one or more treatments, or experimental conditions, on the characteristic of interest.

Example

The following is an example of an experiment.

A sample of 200 asthma patients participated in the clinical trial for a new asthma drug. One hundred of the patients received a placebo treatment along with an inhaler, while the remaining 100 patients received the new drug along with an inhaler. Monthly blood and breathing tests were performed on all 200 patients to determine if the new drug was effective.

experimental unit

An experimental unit is a member of a sample in an experiment.

Example

Suppose that an experiment is conducted to test the effects of a new drug on a sample of patients. Each patient is an experimental unit in the experiment.

extraneous solution

Extraneous solutions are solutions that result from the process of solving an equation; but are not valid solutions to the equation.

Example

$$\log_2(x) + \log_2(x + 7) = 3$$
$$\log_2(x^2 + 7x) = 3$$
$$x^2 + 7x = 2^3$$
$$x^2 + 7x = 8$$
$$x^2 + 7x - 8 = 0$$
$$(x + 8)(x - 1) = 0$$
$$x + 8 = 0 \quad \text{or} \quad x - 1 = 0$$
$$x = -8 \qquad\qquad x = 1$$

The solution $x = -8$ is an extraneous solution because the argument of a logarithm must be greater than zero.

extrema

Extrema are the set of all relative maxima and minima for a graph.

Example

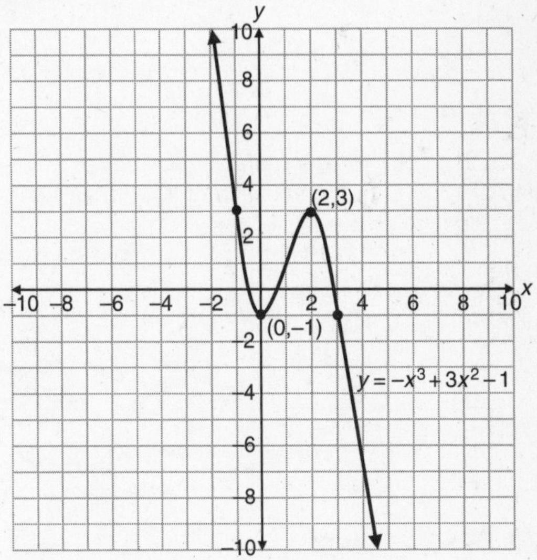

The graph shown has 2 extrema, a relative maximum at (2, 3) and a relative minimum at (0, −1).

F

Factor Theorem

The Factor Theorem states that a polynomial is divisible by $(x - r)$ if the value of the polynomial at r is zero.

Example

The polynomial $x^3 - 2x^2 + 2x - 1$ is divisible by $x - 1$ because $(1)^3 - 2(1)^2 + 2(1) - 1 = 0$.

factored form of a quadratic function

A quadratic function written in factored form is in the form $f(x) = a(x - r_1)(x - r_2)$, where $a \neq 0$.

Example

The function $h(x) = x^2 - 8x + 12$ written in factored form is $h(x) = (x - 6)(x - 2)$.

finite sequence

If a sequence terminates, it is called a finite sequence.

Example

The sequence 22, 26, 30 is a finite sequence.

Glossary

finite series

A finite series is the sum of a finite number of terms.

Example

The sum of all of the even integers from 1 to 100 is a finite series.

fractal

A fractal is a complex geometric shape that is constructed by a mathematical pattern. Fractals are infinite and self-similar.

Example

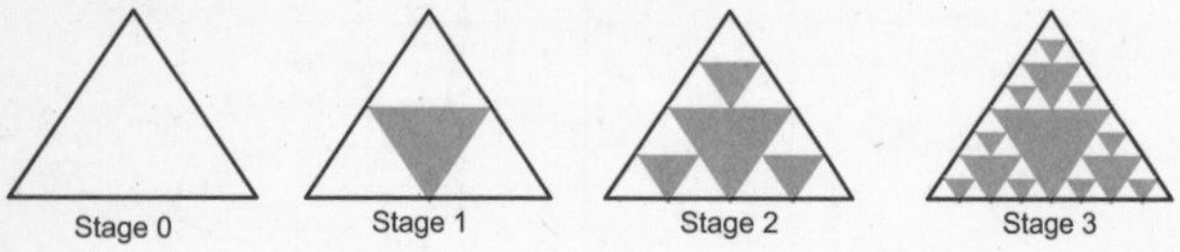

frequency

The frequency of a periodic function is the reciprocal of the period and specifies the number of repetitions of the graph of a periodic function per unit. It is calculated by the formula $\frac{|B|}{2\pi}$.

Example

The function $f(x) = 3 \cos (2x)$ has a B-value of 2, so the frequency is $\frac{|2|}{2\pi}$ or $\frac{1}{\pi}$ units.

function

A function is a relation such that for each element of the domain there exists exactly one element in the range.

Example

The equation $y = 2x$ is a function. Every x-value has exactly one corresponding y-value.

function notation

Function notation is a way of representing functions algebraically. The function $f(x)$ is read as "f of x" and indicates that x is the input and $f(x)$ is the output.

Example

The function $f(x) = 0.75x$ is written using function notation.

Fundamental Theorem of Algebra

The Fundamental Theorem of Algebra states that any polynomial equation of degree n must have exactly n complex roots or solutions; also, every polynomial function of degree n must have exactly n complex zeros. However, any root or zero may be a multiple root or zero.

Example

The polynomial equation $x^5 + x^2 - 6 = 0$ has 5 complex roots because the polynomial $x^5 + x^2 - 6$ has a degree of 5.

G

geometric sequence

A geometric sequence is a sequence of terms in which the ratio between any two consecutive terms is a constant.

Example

The sequence 2, 4, 8, 16 is a geometric sequence with a common ratio of 2.

geometric series

A geometric series is the sum of the terms of a geometric sequence.

Example

The geometric series corresponding to the geometric sequence 2, 4, 8, 16 is 2 + 4 + 8 + 16, or 30.

H

half-life

The half-life of a sample is the time it takes for half of the atoms in the sample to decay.

Example

The radioactive isotope strontium-90 has a half life of about 30 years. A 1000-gram sample of strontium-90 will decay to 500 grams in 30 years.

horizontal compression

Horizontal compression is the squeezing of a graph toward the y-axis.

Example

The graph of $g(x) = (2x)^2$ is a horizontal compression compared to the graph of $f(x) = x^2$.

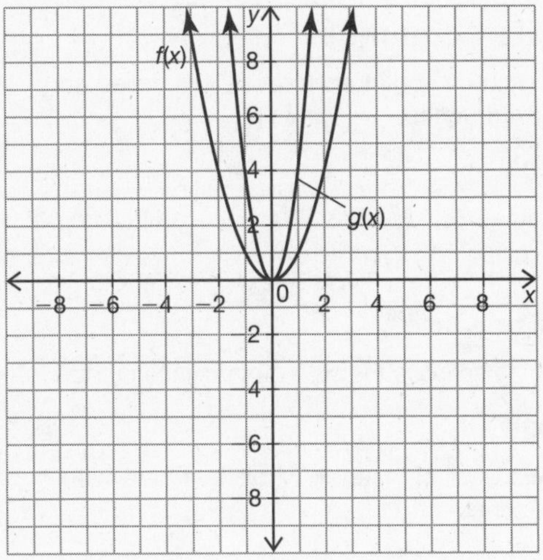

horizontal dilation

A horizontal dilation is a type of transformation that stretches or compresses the entire graph.

Example

The graphs of $g(x) = (2x)^2$ and $h(x) = \left(\frac{1}{2}x\right)^2$ are horizontal dilations of the graph of $f(x) = x^2$.

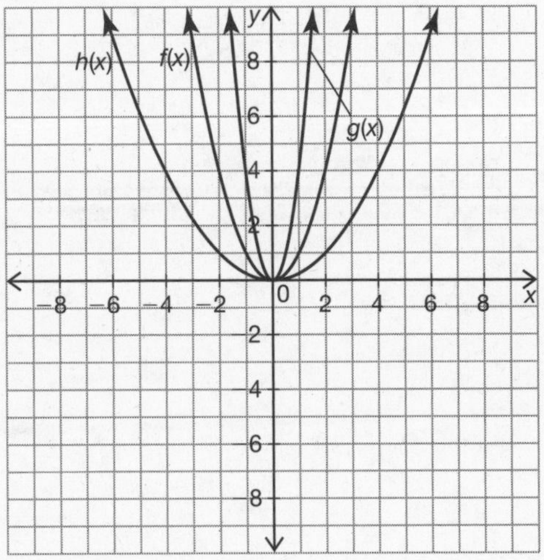

Horizontal Line Test

The Horizontal Line Test is a test to determine if a function is one to one. To use the test, imagine drawing every possible horizontal line on the coordinate plane. If no horizontal line intersects the graph of a function at more than one point, then the function is one to one.

Example

The function $y = x$ passes the Horizontal Line Test because no horizontal line can be drawn that intersects the graph at more than one point. So, the function is one to one.

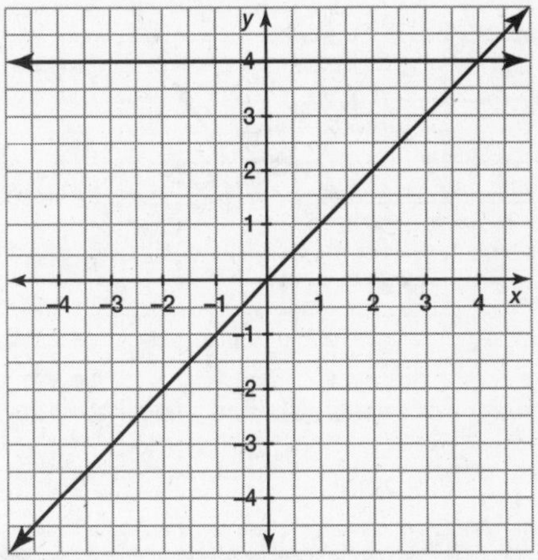

The function $y = x^2$ does not pass the Horizontal Line Test because a horizontal line can be drawn that intersects the graph at more than one point. So, the function is not one to one.

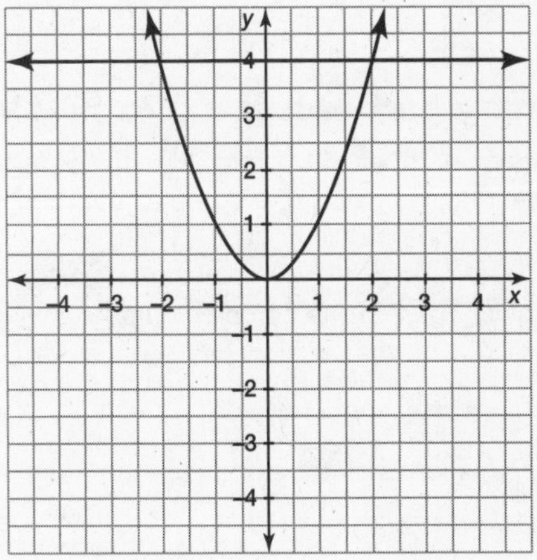

Glossary

horizontal stretching

Horizontal stretching is the stretching of a graph away from the *y*-axis.

Example

The graph of $g(x) = \left(\frac{1}{2}x\right)^2$ is a horizontal stretching compared to the graph of $f(x) = x^2$.

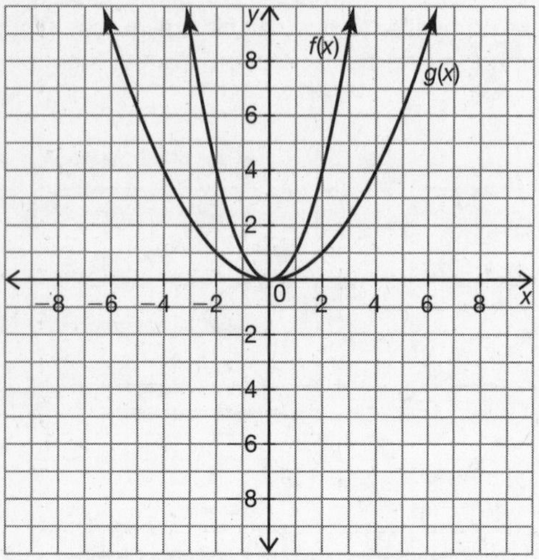

I

identity function

The identity function, also known as the composition identity, is defined as $f(x) = x$.

imaginary part of a complex number

In a complex number of the form $a + bi$, the term bi is called the imaginary part of a complex number.

Example

The imaginary part of the complex number $3 + 2i$ is $2i$.

imaginary roots

Imaginary roots are imaginary solutions to equations.

Example

The quadratic equation $x^2 - 2x + 2$ has two imaginary roots: $1 + i$ and $1 - i$.

infinite sequence

If a sequence continues forever, it is called an infinite sequence.

Example

The sequence 22, 26, 30, 34 . . . is an infinite sequence.

infinite series

An infinite series is the sum of an infinite number of terms.

Example

The sum of all of the even whole numbers is an infinite series.

initial ray of an angle

The initial ray of an angle in standard position is the ray with its endpoint at the origin and extending along the positive *x*-axis.

Example

The initial ray of the angle is labeled in the diagram.

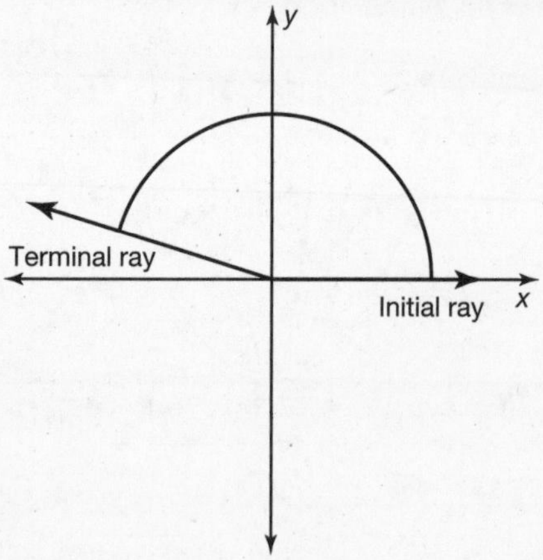

inverse cosine ($\cos^{-1}$)

The $\cos^{-1}$ function is the inverse of the cosine function. The inverse cosine function is written as arccos or $\cos^{-1}$.

Example

$\cos(60°) = \frac{1}{2}$ so $\cos^{-1}\left(\frac{1}{2}\right) = 60°$

inverse of a function

The inverse of a one-to-one function is a function that results from exchanging the independent and dependent variables. A function $f(x)$ with coordinates $(x, f(x))$ will have an inverse with coordinates $(f(x), x)$.

Example

The inverse of the function $y = 2x$ can be found by exchanging the variables x and y.

The inverse of $y = 2x$ is $x = 2y$.

inverse sine ($\sin^{-1}$)

The $\sin^{-1}$ function is the inverse of the sine function. The inverse sine function is written as arcsin or $\sin^{-1}$.

Example

$\sin(30°) = \frac{1}{2}$ so $\sin^{-1}\left(\frac{1}{2}\right) = 30°$

inverse tangent ($\tan^{-1}$)

The $\tan^{-1}$ function is the inverse of the tangent function. The inverse tangent function is written as arctan or $\tan^{-1}$.

Example

$\tan(45°) = 1$ so $\tan^{-1}(1) = 45°$

invertible function

An invertible function is a function whose inverse exists. It is one-to-one and passes the Horizontal Line Test, so its inverse will also be a function.

Example

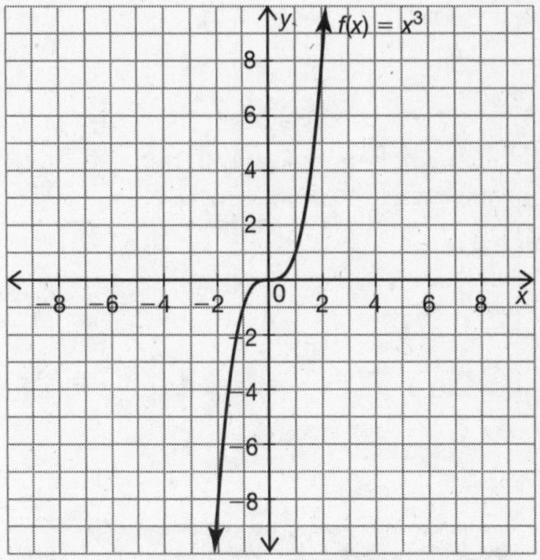

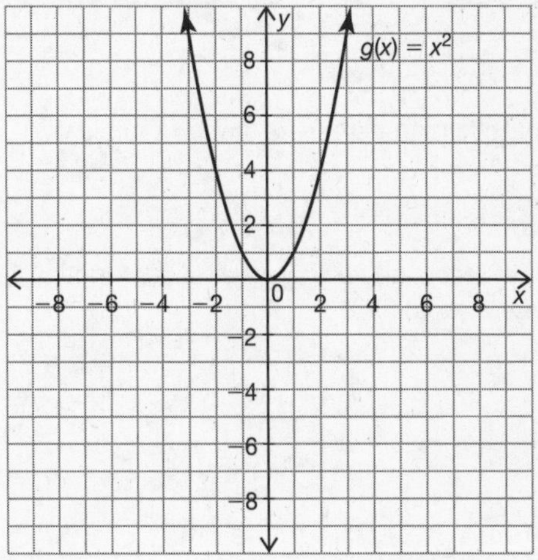

The graph of $f(x) = x^3$ is an invertible function because it is one-to-one and passes the Horizontal Line Test. Therefore its inverse will also be a function.

The graph of $g(x) = x^2$ is not an invertible function because it does not pass the Horizontal Line Test.

Glossary

iterative process

An iterative process is one in which the output from one iteration is used as the input for the next iteration.

Example

A recursive sequence uses an iterative process to generate its terms.

$a_n = 3a_{n-1} + 1$

$a_1 = 2$

Begin with the first term, which is 2, and substitute it into the sequence to get the next term.

$a_2 = 3a_1 + 1$

$= 3(2) + 1$

$= 7$

Then substitute a_2 into the sequence to produce a_3, and so on.

L

line of reflection

A line of reflection is the line that a graph is reflected about.

Example

The line of reflection for the graph of the function $f(x) = x^2$ is the y-axis, or the line $x = 0$.

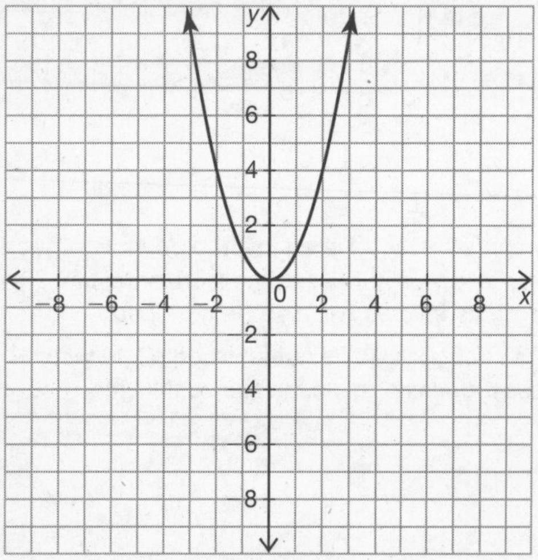

logarithm

The logarithm of a positive number is the exponent to which the base must be raised to result in that number.

Example

Because $10^2 = 100$, the logarithm of 100 to the base 10 is 2.

$\log 100 = 2$

Because $2^3 = 8$, the logarithm of 8 to the base 2 is 3.

$\log_2 (8) = 3$

logarithm with same base and argument

The logarithm of a number, with the base equal to the same number, is always equal to 1.

$$\log_b(b) = 1$$

Example

$\log_4(4) = 1$

logarithmic equation

A logarithmic equation is an equation that contains a logarithm.

Example

The equation $\log_2(x) = 4$ is a logarithmic equation.

logarithmic function

A logarithmic function is a function involving a logarithm.

Example

The function $f(x) = 3 \log x$ is a logarithmic function.

logistic functions

Logistic functions are functions that can be written in the form $f(x) = \dfrac{C}{1 + Ae^{-Bx}}$. It is used to model population growth. The graph of a logistic growth function is shaped like an S-curve. The function appears to grow exponentially during the initial growth stage, but as it approaches the carrying capacity C, the growth slows and then stops when it reaches equilibrium.

Example

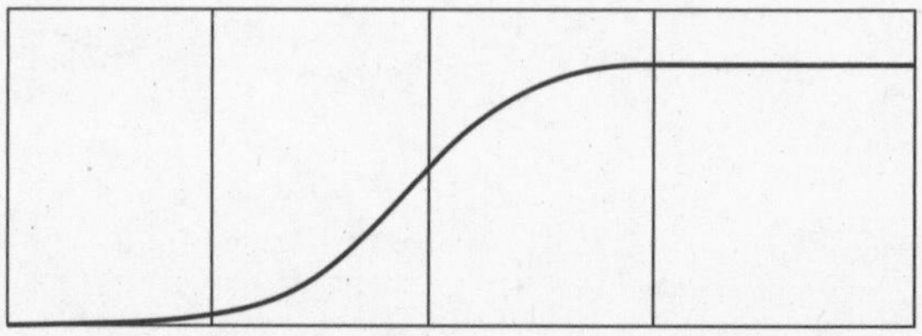

M

mean

The mean of a data set is the sum of all of the values of the data set divided by the number of values in the data set. With normal curves, the mean of a population is represented with the symbol μ, and the mean of a sample is represented with the symbol $\bar{x}$.

Example

The mean of the numbers 7, 9, 13, 4, and 7 is $\frac{7 + 9 + 13 + 4 + 7}{5}$, or 8.

The mean of a set of normally distributed data is aligned with the peak of the normal curve.

midline

The midline of a periodic function is a reference line whose equation is the average of the minimum and maximum values of the function.

Example

In the graph of $g(x) = -2\cos(x) + 3$ the midline occurs at $y = 3$ because the maximum value is 5 and the minimum value is 1.

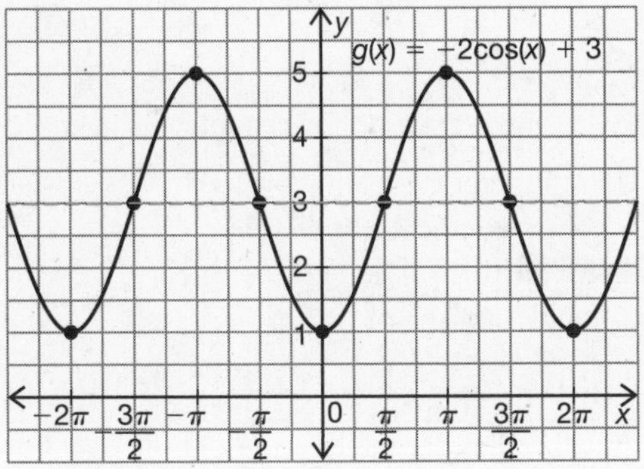

monomial

A monomial is a polynomial with exactly one term.

Example

The expressions $5x$, 7, $-2xy$, and $13x^3$ are monomials.

multiplicity

Multiplicity is how many times a particular number is a zero for a given function.

Example

The equation $x^2 + 2x + 1 = 0$ has a double root at $x = -1$. The root -1 has a multiplicity of 2.

$x^2 + 2x + 1 = 0$

$(x + 1)(x + 1) = 0$

$x + 1 = 0$ or $x + 1 = 0$

$x = -1$ or $x = -1$

N

natural base, *e*

The natural base *e* is an irrational number equal to approximately 2.71828.

Example

$e^2 \approx 2.7183^2 \approx 7.3892$

natural logarithm

A natural logarithm is a logarithm with a base of *e*. Natural logarithms are usually written as ln.

Example

$\log_e(x)$ or $\ln x$ is a natural logarithm.

normal curve

A normal curve is a curve that is bell-shaped and symmetric about the mean.

Example

A normal curve is shown.

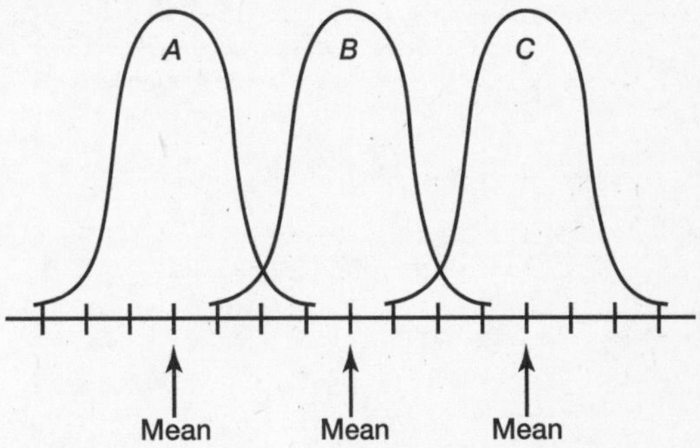

normal distribution

A normal distribution, or normal probability distribution, describes a continuous data set that can be modeled using a normal curve.

Example

Adult IQ scores, gas mileage of certain cars, and SAT scores are all continuous data that follow a normal distribution.

O

observational study

An observational study gathers data about a characteristic of the population without trying to influence the data.

Example

The following is an example of an observational study.

New research funded by a pediatric agency found that nearly 70% of in-house day care centers show as much as 2.5 hours of television to the children in the center per day. The study examined 132 day care programs in 2 Midwestern states.

odd function

An odd function f is a function for which $f(-x) = -f(x)$ for all values of x in the domain.

Example

The function $f(x) = x^3$ is an odd function because $(-x)^3 = -x^3$.

P

parameter

When data are gathered from a population, the characteristic used to describe the population is called a parameter.

Example

If you wanted to find out the average height of the students at your school, and you measured every student at the school, the characteristic "average height" would be a parameter.

percentile

A percentile divides a data set into 100 equal parts.

period

A period of a periodic function is the length of the smallest interval over which the function repeats.

Example

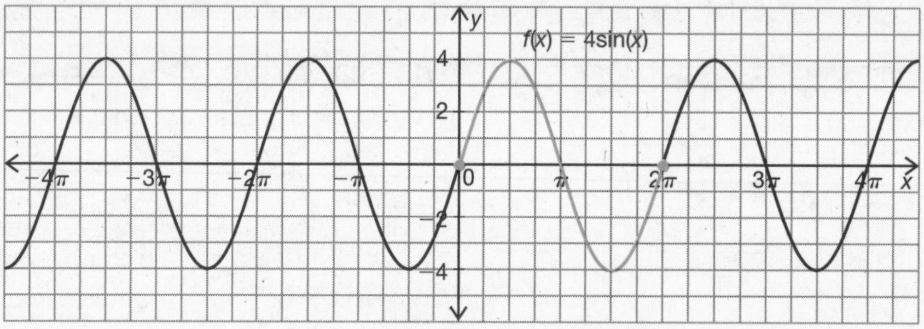

Glossary

periodic function

A periodic function is a function whose graph consists of repeated instances of a portion of the graph.

Example

The function $f(x) = \sin(x)$ is a periodic function. The portion of the graph between $x = 0$ and $x = 2\pi$ repeats.

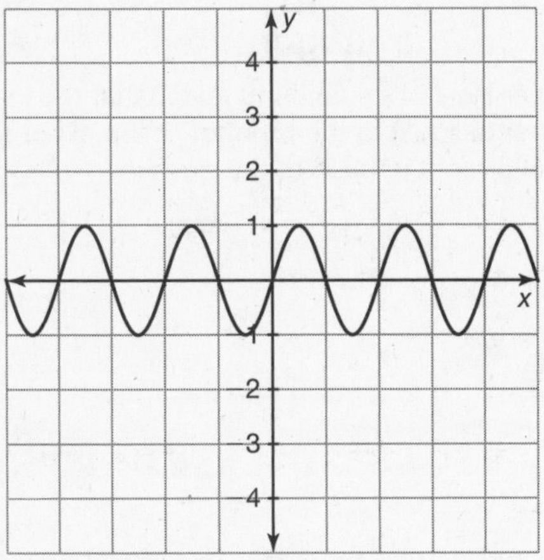

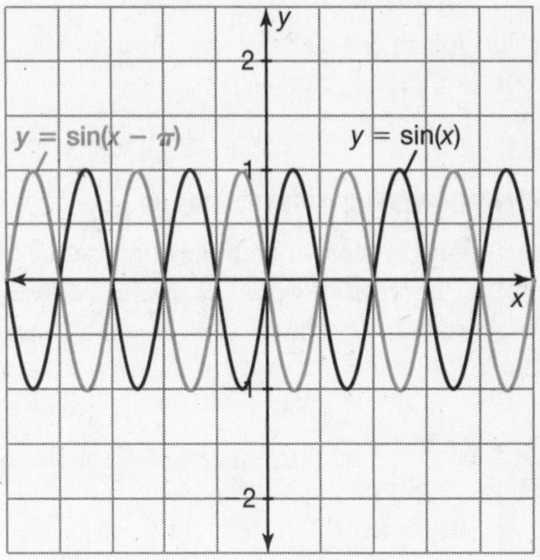

periodicity identity

A periodicity identity is a trigonometric identity based on the period of the trigonometric functions.

Example

The six periodicity identities are:
$\sin(x + 2\pi) = \sin(x)$; $\cos(x + 2\pi) = \cos(x)$
$\sec(x + 2\pi) = \sec(x)$; $\csc(x + 2\pi) = \csc(x)$
$\tan(x + \pi) = \tan(x)$; $\cot(x + \pi) = \cot(x)$

phase shift

A phase shift of a periodic function is a horizontal translation.

Example

The function $y = \sin(x - \pi)$ has a phase shift of π units from the basic function $y = \sin(x)$.

piecewise function

A piecewise function includes different functions that represent different parts of the domain.

Example

The function $f(x)$ is a piecewise function.

$$f(x) = \begin{cases} x + 5, & x \leq -2 \\ -2x + 1, & -2 < x \leq 2 \\ 2x - 9, & x > 2 \end{cases}$$

polynomial

A polynomial is a mathematical expression involving the sum of powers in one or more variables multiplied by coefficients.

Example

The expression $3x^3 + 5x^2 - 6x + 1$ is a polynomial.

Glossary

Glossary

polynomial function

A polynomial function is a function that can be written in the form
$p(x) = a_n x^n + a_{n-1}x^{n-1} + \cdots + a_2x^2 + a_1x + a_0$, where the coefficients $a_n, a_{n-1}, \ldots a_2, a_1, a_0$ are complex numbers and the exponents are nonnegative integers.

Example

The function $f(x) = 5x^3 + 3x^2 + x + 1$ is a polynomial function.

polynomial long division

Polynomial long division is an algorithm for dividing one polynomial by another of equal or lesser degree.

Example

$$
\begin{array}{r}
4x^2 - 6x + 3 \\
2x + 3 \overline{\smash{)}\, 8x^3 + 0x^2 - 12x - 7} \\
\underline{-(8x^3 + 12x^2)} \qquad\qquad \\
-12x^2 - 12x \qquad \\
\underline{-(-12x^2 - 18x)} \qquad \\
6x - 7 \\
\underline{-(6x + 9)} \\
\text{Remainder } -16
\end{array}
$$

population

The population is the entire set of items from which data can be selected. When you decide what you want to study, the population is the set of all elements in which you are interested. The elements of that population can be people or objects.

Example

If you wanted to find out the average height of the students at your school, the number of students at the school would be the population.

population proportion

A population proportion is the percentage of an entire population that yields a favorable outcome in an experiment.

Example

In an election, the population proportion represents the percentage of people in the entire town who vote to re-elect the mayor.

power function

A power function is a function of the form $P(x) = ax^n$ where n is a non-negative integer.

Example

The functions $f(x) = x$, $f(x) = x^2$, and $f(x) = x^3$ are power functions.

Power Rule of Logarithms

The Power Rule of Logarithms states that the logarithm of a power is equal to the product of the exponent and the logarithm of the base of the power.

$$\log_b (x)^n = n \cdot \log_b (x)$$

Example

$\ln (x)^2 = 2 \ln x$

principal square root of a negative number

For any positive real number n, the principal square root of a negative number, $-n$, is defined by $\sqrt{-n} = i\sqrt{n}$.

Example

The principal square root of -5 is $\sqrt{-5} = i\sqrt{5}$.

Product Rule of Logarithms

The Product Rule of Logarithms states that the logarithm of a product is equal to the sum of the logarithms of the factors.

$$\log_b (xy) = \log_b (x) + \log_b (y)$$

Example

$\log (5x) = \log (5) + \log (x)$

pure imaginary number

A pure imaginary number is a number of the form bi, where b is not equal to 0.

Example

The imaginary numbers $-4i$ and $15i$ are pure imaginary numbers.

Pythagorean identity

A Pythagorean identity is a trigonometric identity based on the Pythagorean Theorem.

Example

The three Pythagorean identities are:
$\sin^2(x) + \cos^2(x) = 1$
$1 + \tan^2(x) = \sec^2(x)$
$1 + \cot^2(x) = \csc^2(x)$

Q

quartic function

A quartic function is a polynomial function with a degree of four.

Example

The function $f(x) = 3x^4 - 2x + 5$ is a quartic function.

quintic function

A quintic function is a polynomial function with a degree of five.

Example

The function $f(x) = 5x^5 + 3x^4 + x^3$ is a quintic function

Quotient Rule of Logarithms

The Quotient Rule of Logarithms states that the logarithm of a quotient is equal to the difference of the logarithms of the dividend and the divisor.

$$\log_b\left(\frac{x}{y}\right) = \log_b(x) - \log_b(y)$$

Example

$\log\left(\frac{x}{2}\right) = \log x - \log 2$

R

radians

A radian is a unit of measurement for an angle in standard position. It is equal to the length of its intercepted arc in the unit circle.

Example

The angle shown has a radian measure of π radians.

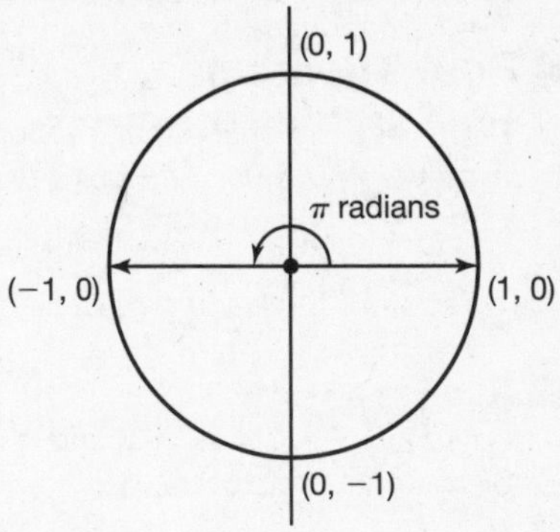

radical function

A radical function is a function that contains one or more radical expressions.

Example

The function $f(x) = \sqrt{3x + 5}$ is a radical function.

random sample

Random sample is a method of collecting data in which every member of a population has an equal chance of being selected.

Example

Choosing 100 fans at random to participate in a survey from crowd of 5000 people is an example of random sample.

rational equation

A rational equation is an equation that contains one or more rational expressions.

Example

The equation $\frac{1}{x - 1} + \frac{1}{x + 1} = 4$ is a rational equation.

Glossary

rational function

A rational function is any function that can be written as the ratio of two polynomial functions. A rational function can be written in the form $f(x) = \frac{P(x)}{Q(x)}$ where $P(x)$ and $Q(x)$ are polynomial functions, and $Q(x) \neq 0$.

Example

The function $f(x) = \frac{1}{x - 1} + \frac{1}{x + 1}$ is a rational function.

Rational Root Theorem

The Rational Root Theorem states that a rational root of a polynomial $a_n x^n + a_{n-1} x^{n-1} + \cdots + a_2 x^2 + a_1 x + a_0 x^0$ must be of the form $\frac{p}{q}$, where p is a factor of the constant term and q is a factor of the leading coefficient.

Example

For the polynomial $2x^2 - x + 4$, $p = 4$, and $q = 2$.
So, the possible rational roots of the polynomial are ± 4, ± 2, ± 1, $\pm \frac{1}{2}$.

real part of a complex number

In a complex number of the form $a + bi$, the term a is called the real part of a complex number.

Example

The real part of the complex number $3 + 2i$ is 3.

reference points

Reference points are a set of key points that help identify the basic form of any function.

Example

The reference points of the basic quadratic function are (0, 0), (1, 1), and (2, 4).

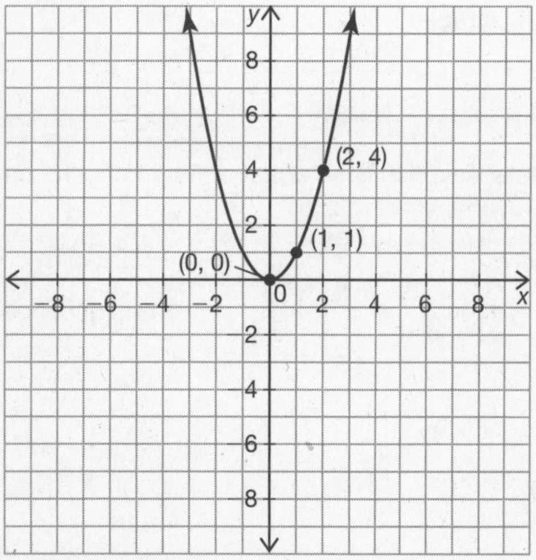

reflection

A reflection of a graph is a mirror image of the graph about a line of reflection.

Example

The triangle on the right is a reflection of the triangle on the left.

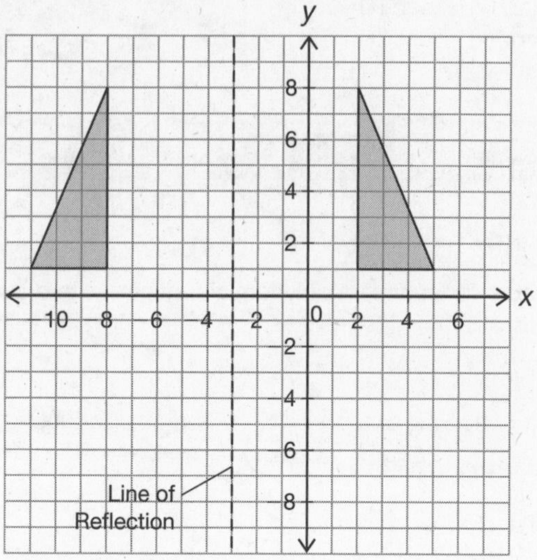

regression equation

A regression equation is a function that models the relationship between two variables in a scatter plot.

Example

The regression equation
$y = -0.41x^3 + 3.50x^2 - 4.47x + 8.44$ models the relationship between time and the number of vehicles.

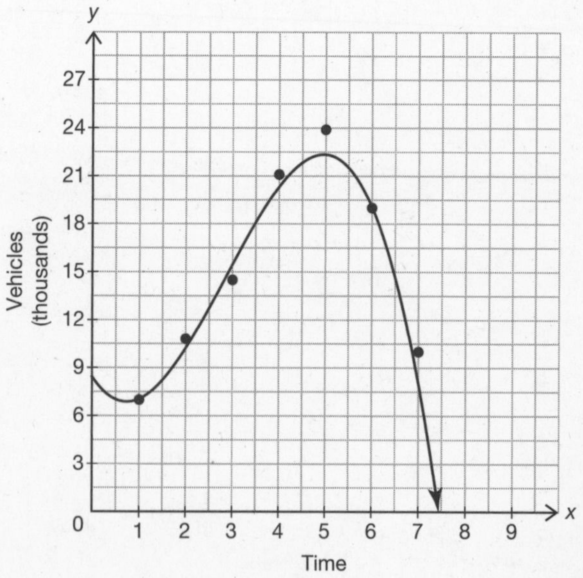

relation

A relation is the mapping between a set of input values called the domain and a set of output values called the range.

Example

The set of points {(0, 1), (1, 8), (2, 5), (3, 7)} is a relation.

relative maximum

A relative maximum is the highest point in a particular section of a graph.

Example

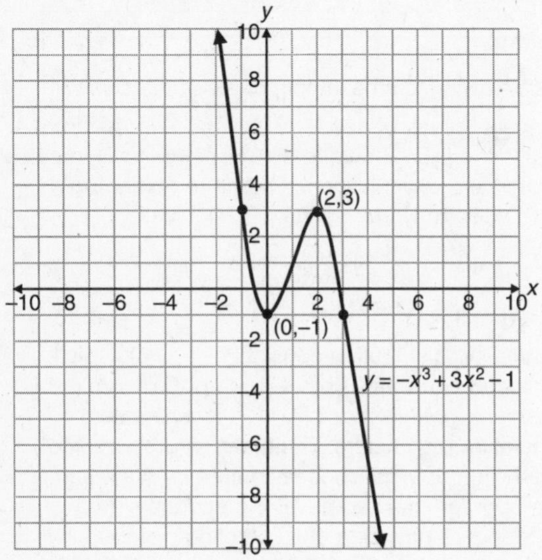

The graph shown has a relative maximum at (2, 3).

relative minimum

A relative minimum is the lowest point in a particular section of a graph.

Example

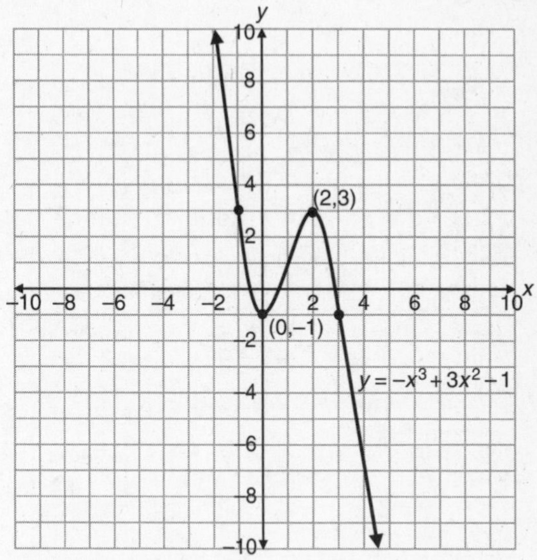

The graph shown has a relative minimum at (0, −1).

Remainder Theorem

The Remainder Theorem states that the remainder when dividing a polynomial by $(x - r)$ is the value of the polynomial at r.

Example

The value of the polynomial $x^2 + 5x + 2$ at 1 is $(1)^2 + 5(1) + 2 = 8$. So, the remainder when $x^2 + 5x + 2$ is divided by $x - 1$ is 8.

$$\begin{array}{r} x + 6 \\ x - 1 \overline{) x^2 + 5x + 2} \\ \underline{x^2 - x } \\ 6x + 2 \\ \underline{6x - 6} \\ 8 \end{array}$$

Glossary

removable discontinuity

A removable discontinuity is a single point at which the graph of a function is not defined.

Example

The graph of the function $f(x) = \frac{x^2}{x}$ has a removable discontinuity at $x = 0$.

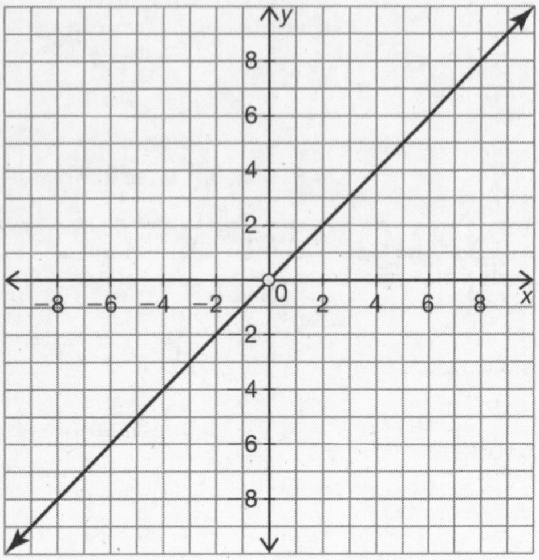

rigid motion

A rigid motion is a transformation that preserves size and shape.

Example

Reflections, rotations, and translations are examples of rigid motion.

S

sample

Where data are collected from a selection of the population, the data are called a sample.

Example

If you wanted to find out the average height of the students in your school, you could choose just a certain number of students and measure their heights. The heights of the students in this group would be the sample.

sample proportion

A sample proportion is the percentage of a sample that yields a favorable outcome in an experiment. This is often used to make predictions about a population.

Example

In an election, a sample of townspeople is surveyed. The sample proportion represents the percentage of the survey results that indicate that they will vote to re-elect the mayor.

sample survey

A sample survey poses a question of interest to a random sample of the targeted population.

Example

The following is an example of a sample survey.

A recent survey of nearly 1200 young people from across the U.S. shows that 40% of 16- to 20- year-olds who have a driver's license admit to texting on a regular basis while they are driving.

sampling distribution

A sampling distribution consists of every possible sample of equal size from a given population. A sampling distribution provides an estimate for population parameters. The mean or proportion of a sampling distribution is estimated by the mean or proportion of a sample. For categorical data, the standard deviation of a sampling distribution is estimated by calculating $\sqrt{\frac{\hat{p}(1 - \hat{p})}{n}}$ where $\hat{p}$ (p-hat) is the sample proportion and n is the sample size. For continuous data, the standard deviation of a sampling distribution is estimated by calculating $\frac{S}{\sqrt{n}}$ where S is the standard deviation of the original sample and n is the sample size.

Example

A sleep survey of 50 teens resulted in a sample mean of 7.7 hours and sample standard deviation of 0.8 hours.

The estimated mean of the sampling distribution is 7.7 hours. The estimated standard deviation of the sampling distribution is approximately 0.11 hours.

$\frac{S}{\sqrt{n}} = \frac{0.8}{\sqrt{50}} \approx 0.11$

self-similar

A self-similar object is exactly or approximately similar to a part of itself.

Example

A Koch snowflake is considered to be self-similar.

series

A series is the sum of the terms of a sequence. The sum of the first n terms of a sequence is denoted by S_n.

Example

The series corresponding to the sequence 1, 1, 2, 3, 5 is $1 + 1 + 2 + 3 + 5$, or 12.

set of complex numbers

The set of complex numbers is the set of all numbers written in the form $a + bi$, where a and b are real numbers. The set of complex numbers consists of the set of imaginary numbers and the set of real numbers.

Example

The numbers $1 + 2i$, 7, and $-3i$ are complex numbers.

set of imaginary numbers

The set of imaginary numbers is the set of all numbers written in the form $a + bi$, where a and b are real numbers and b is not equal to 0.

Example

The numbers $2 - 3i$ and $5i$ are imaginary numbers. The number 6 is not an imaginary number.

simple random sample

A simple random sample is a sample in which every member of the population has the same chance of being selected.

Example

Using a random number generator to select a sample is an example of simple random sampling.

sine function

The sine function is a periodic function. It takes angle measures (θ values) as inputs and then outputs real number values which correspond to the coordinates of points on the unit circle.

Example

The function $h(\theta) = -\sin(2\theta) + 1$ is a sine function.

square root function

The square root function is the inverse of the power function $f(x) = x^2$ when the domain is restricted to $x \geq 0$.

Example

The square root function is $g(x) = \sqrt{x}$.

standard deviation

Standard deviation is a measure of the variation of the values in a data set from the mean of the data. A lower standard deviation represents data that are more tightly clustered near the mean. A higher standard deviation represents data that are more spread out from the mean. Use the formula below to calculate standard deviation.

$$\text{standard deviation} = \sqrt{\frac{\sum_{i=1}^{n}(x_1 - \bar{x})^2}{n}}$$

where $\bar{x}$ is the mean and n is the number of data values in the data set $\{x_1, x_2, \ldots, x_n\}$.

Example

In the data set of test scores
60, 70, 80, 90, 100,
the mean $\bar{x}$ is 80 and the number of data elements n is 5. So, the standard deviation of the test scores is
standard deviation =

$$\sqrt{\frac{(60 - 80)^2 + (70 - 80)^2 + (80 - 80)^2 + (90 - 80)^2 + (100 - 80)^2}{5}}$$

$$= \sqrt{\frac{1000}{5}}$$

$$= \sqrt{200}$$

$$\approx 14.14.$$

standard form (general form) of a quadratic function

A quadratic function written in the form $f(x) = ax^2 + bx + c$, where $a \neq 0$, is in standard form, or general form.

Example

The function $f(x) = -5x^2 - 10x + 1$ is written in standard form.

Glossary

standard normal distribution

The standard normal distribution is a normal probability distribution with the following properties:

- The mean is equal to 0.
- The standard deviation is 1.
- The curve is bell-shaped and symmetric about the mean.

Example

A standard normal distribution curve is shown.

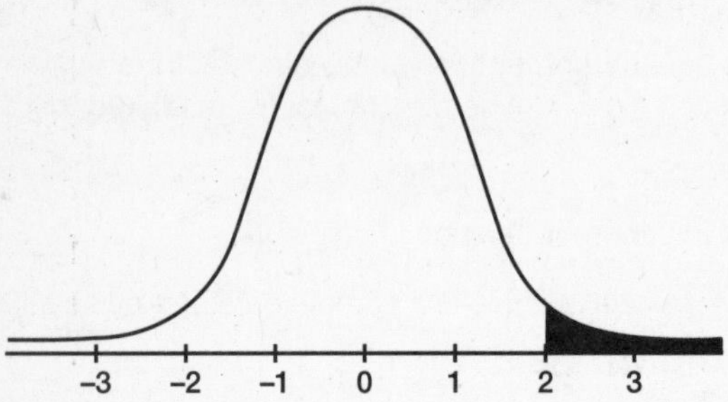

standard position of an angle

The standard position of an angle occurs when the vertex of the angle is at the origin and one ray of the angle is on the *x*-axis.

Example

The angle shown is in standard position.

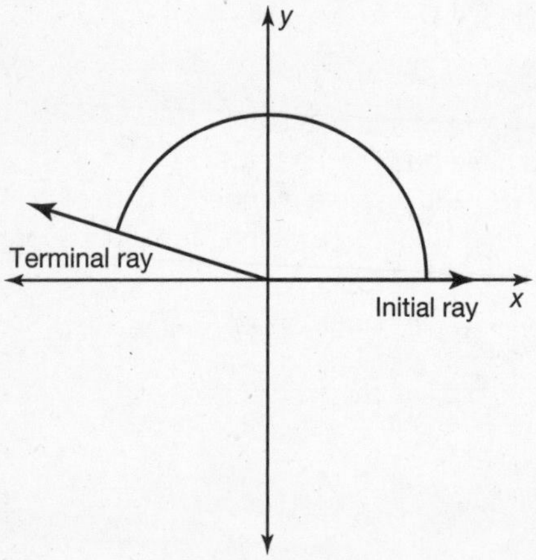

statistic

When data are gathered from a sample, the characteristic used to describe the sample is called a statistic.

Example

If you wanted to find out the average height of the students in your school, and you chose just a certain number of students randomly and measured their heights, the characteristic "average height" would be called a statistic.

statistically significant

A survey that has a result that is statistically significant indicates that the result did not likely occur by chance, but is likely linked to a specific cause. Typically, a result that is more than 2 standard deviations away from the mean is considered statistically significant.

Example

A survey of 2000 teenagers reports that 42% have a part-time job. The interval from 40.9% to 43.1% represents a 95% confidence interval for the population proportion. A survey that yields a report of 50% of teenager with a part-time job would be considered statistically significant.

stratified random sample

A stratified random sample is a sample obtained by dividing the population into different groups, or strata, according to a characteristic, and randomly selecting data from each group.

Example

If students in a high school are divided by class, and random samples are then taken from each class, the result is a stratified random sample.

subjective sample

A subjective sample is a sample that is chosen based on some criteria, rather than at random.

Example

From a set of students, "choosing five students you know" is a subjective sample. In contrast, "choosing five students at random" is a random sample.

symmetric about a line

If a graph is symmetric about a line, the line divides the graph into two identical parts.

Example

The graph of $f(x) = x^2$ is symmetric about the line $x = 0$.

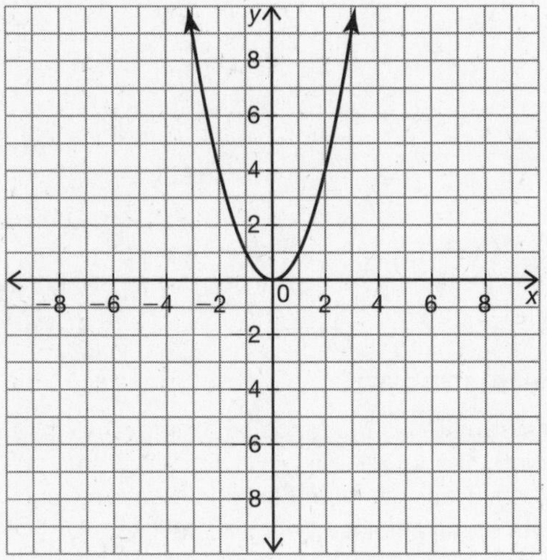

symmetric about a point

A function is symmetric about a point if each point on the graph has a point the same distance from the central point, but in the opposite direction.

Example

The graph of $f(x) = x^3$ is symmetric about the point (0, 0).

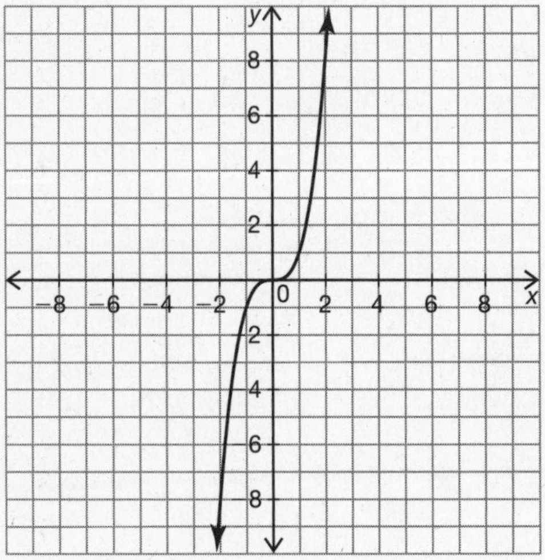

synthetic division

Synthetic division is a method for dividing a polynomial by a linear factor of the form $(x - r)$.

Example

The quotient of $2x^2 - 3x - 9$ and $x - 3$ can be calculated using synthetic division.

3	2	−3	−9
		6	9
	2	3	0

The quotient of $2x^2 - 3x - 9$ and $x - 3$ is $2x + 3$.

systematic sample

A systematic sample is a sample obtained by selecting every *n*th data in the population.

Example

If you choose every 12th student that walks into school, your sample is a systematic sample.

T

tangent function

The tangent function is a periodic function. It takes angle measures (θ values) as inputs and then outputs real number values which correspond to the coordinates of points on the unit circle.

Example

The function $f(\theta) = \tan\left(\frac{\theta}{2}\right)$ is a tangent function.

Glossary

terminal ray of an angle

The terminal ray of an angle in standard position is the ray with its endpoint at the origin that is not the initial ray.

Example

The terminal ray of the angle is labeled in the diagram.

theta (θ)

Theta is a symbol typically used to represent the measure of an angle in standard position.

Example

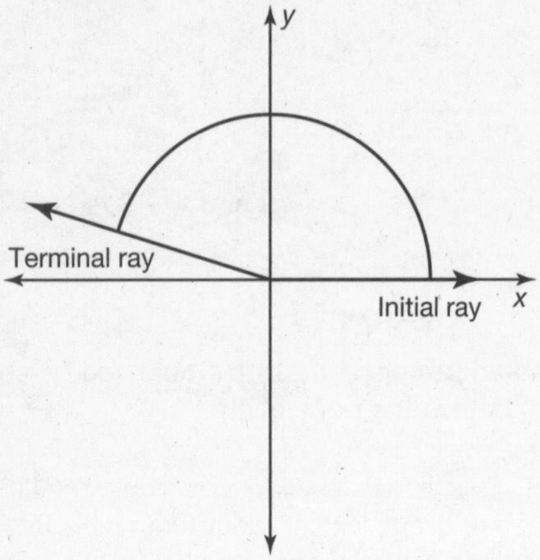

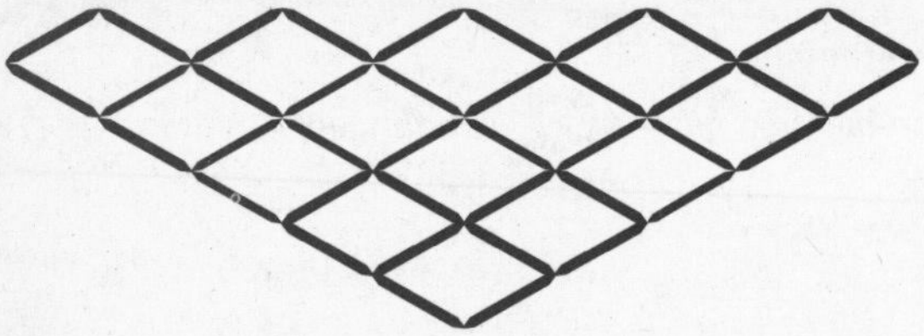

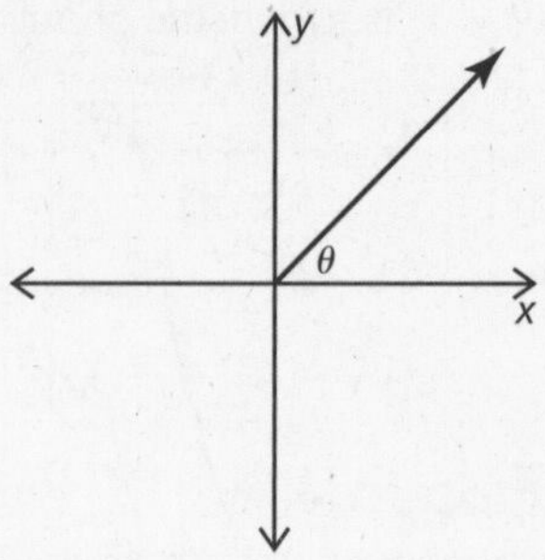

transformation

A transformation is the mapping, or movement, of all the points of a figure in a plane according to a common operation. Translations, reflections, rotations, and dilations are examples of transformations.

Example

reflection about a line   rotation about a point

tessellation

A tessellation is created when a geometric shape is repeated over a two-dimensional plane such that there are no overlaps among the shapes and no gaps.

Example

A tessellation of diamonds is shown.

the imaginary number *i*

The number i is a number such that $i^2 = -1$.

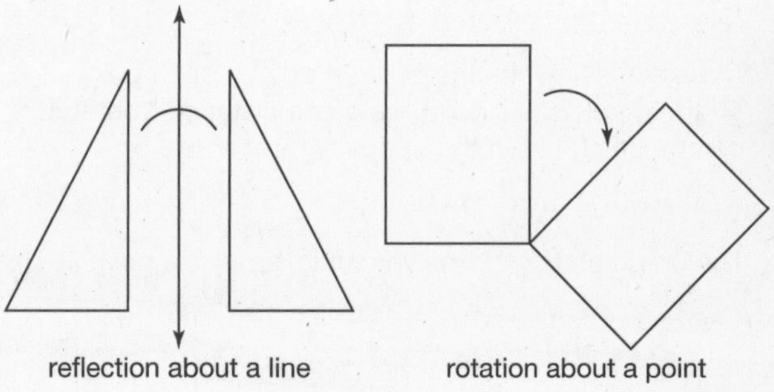

translation

A translation is a type of transformation that shifts an entire figure or graph the same distance and direction.

Example

The graph of $g(x) = (x - 2)^2$ is a translation of the graph of $f(x) = x^2$ right 2 units.

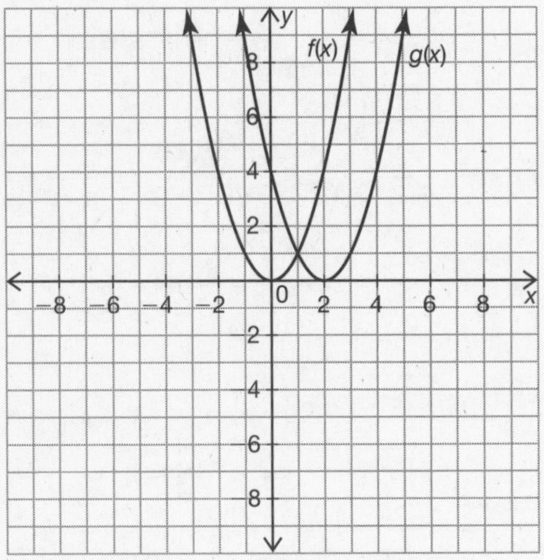

treatment

A treatment is a condition in an experiment.

Example

Suppose that an experiment is conducted to test the effects of a new drug on a sample of patients. The distribution of the drug to the patients is the treatment in the experiment.

trigonometric equation

A trigonometric equation is an equation that includes one or more trigonometric functions.

Example

The equation $\cos(x) = \frac{\sqrt{2}}{2}$ is a trigonometric equation.

trigonometric function

A trigonometric function is a periodic function that takes angle measures (θ values) as inputs and then outputs real number values which correspond to the coordinates of points on the unit circle.

Example

The function $g(x) = \sin(x)$ is a trigonometric function. The graph of the sine function $g(\theta) = \sin(\theta)$ is obtained by evaluating the θ values of the unit circle and graphing the coordinates.

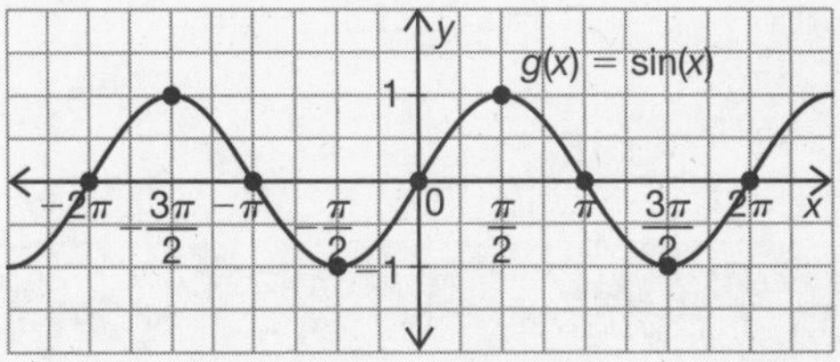

θ	$g(\theta) = \sin(\theta)$	$(\theta, g(\theta))$
0	$\sin(0) = 0$	(0, 0)
$\frac{\pi}{2}$	$\sin\left(\frac{\pi}{2}\right) = 1$	$\left(\frac{\pi}{2}, 1\right)$
π	$\sin(\pi) = 0$	$(\pi, 0)$
$\frac{3\pi}{2}$	$\sin\left(\frac{3\pi}{2}\right) = -1$	$\left(\frac{3\pi}{2}, -1\right)$
2π	$\sin(2\pi) = 0$	$(2\pi, 0)$

trinomial

A trinomial is a polynomial with exactly three terms.

Example

The polynomial $5x^2 - 6x + 9$ is a trinomial.

Glossary

U

unit circle

A unit circle is a circle whose radius is one unit of distance.

Example

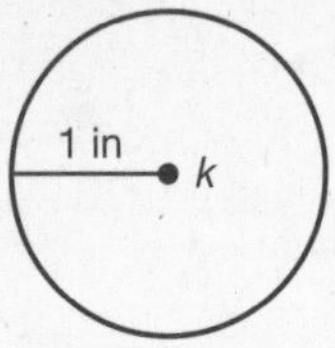

Circle *K* is a unit circle.

V

vertex form of a quadratic function

A quadratic function written in vertex form is in the form $f(x) = a(x - h)^2 + k$, where $a \neq 0$.

Example

The quadratic equation $y = 2(x - 5)^2 + 10$ is written in vertex form. The vertex of the graph is the point (5, 10).

vertical asymptote

A vertical asymptote is a vertical line that a function gets closer and closer to, but never intersects. The asymptote does not represent points on the graph of the function. It represents the output value that the graph approaches.

Example

The graph has two asymptotes: a vertical asymptote $x = 2$ and a horizontal asymptote $y = -1$.

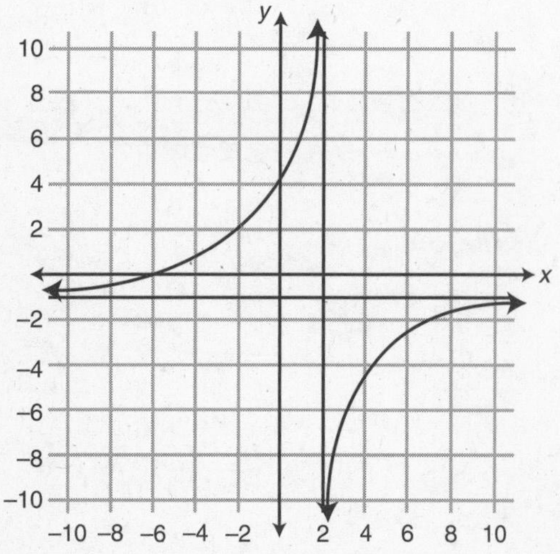

vertical compression

Vertical compression is the squeezing of a graph toward the *x*-axis.

Example

The graph of $g(x) = \frac{1}{2}x^2$ is a vertical compression compared to the graph of $f(x) = x^2$.

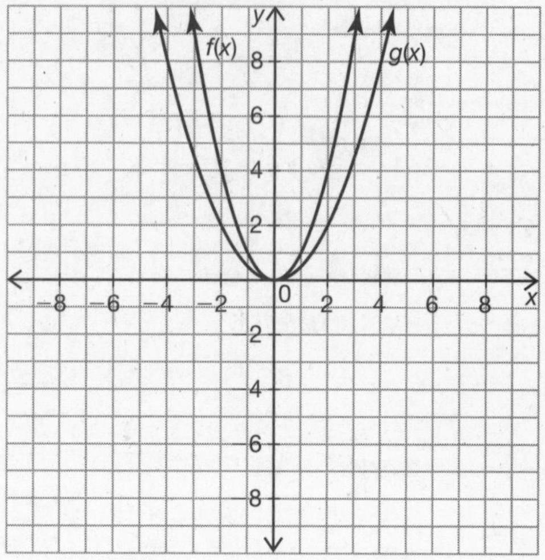

vertical dilation

A vertical dilation is a type of transformation that stretches or compresses an entire figure or graph. In a vertical dilation, notice that the *y*-coordinate of every point on the graph of a function is multiplied by a common factor, *A*.

Example

The graphs of $g(x) = 2x^2$ and $h(x) = \frac{1}{2}x^2$ are vertical dilations of the graph of $f(x) = x^2$.

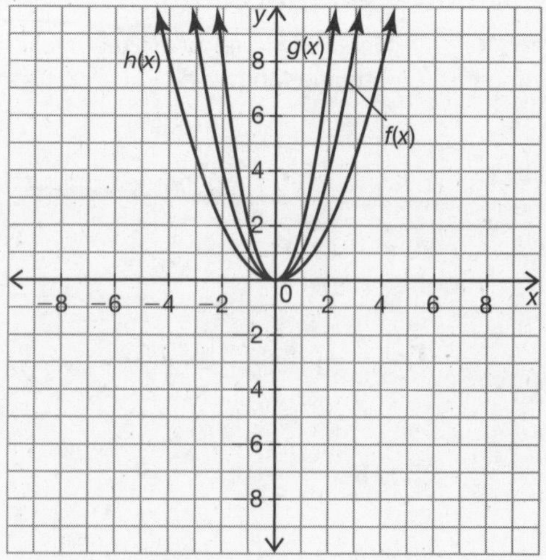

vertical stretching

Vertical stretching is the stretching of a graph away from the x-axis.

Example

The graph of $g(x) = 2x^2$ is a vertical stretching compared to the graph of $f(x) = x^2$.

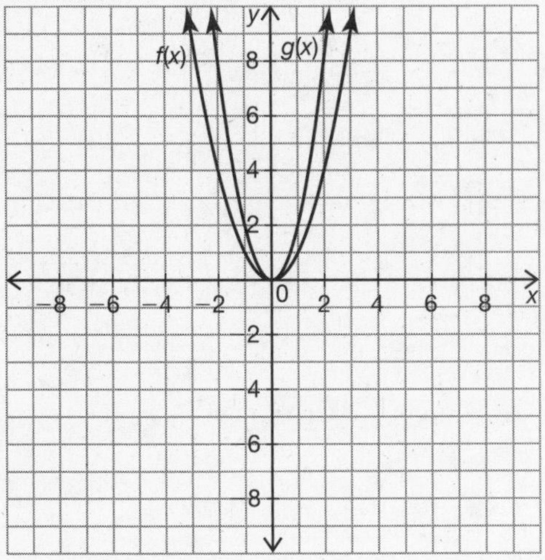

volunteer sample

A volunteer sample is a sample whose data consists of those who volunteer to be part of the sample.

Example

If you ask students in your school to complete and submit an optional survey so that you can collect data, your sample is a volunteer sample.

Z

z-score

A z-score is a number that describes how many standard deviations from the mean a particular value is. The following formula can be used to calculate a z-score for a particular value, where z represents the z-score, x represents the particular data value, μ represents the mean, and σ represents the standard deviation.

$$z = \frac{x - \mu}{\sigma}$$

Example

Suppose that a set of data follows a normal distribution with a mean of 22 and a standard deviation of 2.4.

The z-score for a data value of 25 is $z = \frac{25 - 22}{2.4} = 1.25$.

Zero Product Property

The Zero Product Property states that if the product of two or more factors is equal to zero, then at least one factor must be equal to zero. This is also called the Converse of Multiplication Property of Zero.

Example

According to the Zero Product Property, if $(x - 2)(x + 3) = 0$ then $x - 2 = 0$ or $x + 3 = 0$.

Zero Property of Logarithms

The Zero Property of Logarithms states that the logarithm of 1, with any base, is always equal to 0.

$$\log_b (1) = 0$$

Example

$\log_3 (1) = 0$

Glossary

Glossary

Index

Index

D

Index

E

F

Index

Index

K

L

Index

M

Index

N

O

P

Index

Q

R

Index

S

Index

T

Index

Y

Z

Index